Methods in Hormone Research

VOLUME II
Bioassay

METHODS IN HORMONE RESEARCH

Volume I: Chemical Determinations
Volume II: Bioassay

Methods in
Hormone Research

Edited by
RALPH I. DORFMAN

The Worcester Foundation for
Experimental Biology
Shrewsbury, Massachusetts

VOLUME II
Bioassay

1962

ACADEMIC PRESS · *New York and London*

Copyright © 1962, by
ACADEMIC PRESS INC.

ACADEMIC PRESS INC.
111 FIFTH AVENUE
NEW YORK 3, N. Y.

United Kingdom Edition
Published by
ACADEMIC PRESS INC. (LONDON) LTD.
BERKELEY SQUARE HOUSE
BERKELEY SQUARE, LONDON W. 1

Library of Congress Catalog Card Number 61–12275

PRINTED IN THE UNITED STATES OF AMERICA

CONTRIBUTORS TO VOLUME II

VIVIAN L. BEACH, *Warner-Lambert Research Institute, Department of Physiology, Morris Plains, New Jersey*

OTTO K. BEHRENS, *The Lilly Research Laboratories, Indianapolis, Indiana*

WILLIAM W. BROMER, *The Lilly Research Laboratories, Indianapolis, Indiana*

RALPH I. DORFMAN, *The Worcester Foundation for Experimental Biology, Shrewsbury, Massachusetts*

FRED ELMADJIAN, *The Worcester Foundation for Experimental Biology, Shrewsbury, Massachusetts*

C. W. EMMENS, *Department of Veterinary Physiology, University of Sydney, Sydney, Australia*

JOSEPH D. FISHER, *Armour Pharmaceutical Company, Kankakee, Illinois*

ROBERT L. KROC, *Warner-Lambert Research Institute, Department of Physiology, Morris Plains, New Jersey*

F. W. LANDGREBE, *Department of Materia Medica and Pharmacology, Welsh National School of Medicine, Cardiff, Wales*

CHOH HAO LI, *Hormone Research Laboratory, University of California, Berkeley, California*

TAMOTSU MIYAKE, *Shionogi Research Laboratory, Osaka, Japan*

HAROLD PAPKOFF, *Hormone Research Laboratory, University of California, Berkeley, California*

B. N. PREMACHANDRA, *Department of Dairy Husbandry, University of Missouri, Columbia, Missouri*[1]

ALBERT SEGALOFF, *Alton Ochsner Medical Foundation, New Orleans, Louisiana*

ELVA G. SHIPLEY, *The Endocrine Laboratories of Madison, Inc., Madison, Wisconsin*

K. L. SMITH, *Standards Department, Boots Pure Drug Co., Ltd., Nottingham, England*

[1] Present address: Institute of Experimental Pathology, The Jewish Hospital, St. Louis, Missouri.

BERNARD G. STEINETZ, *Warner-Lambert Research Institute, Morris Plains, New Jersey*

R. H. THORP, *Department of Pharmacology, University of Sydney, Sydney, Australia*

C. W. TURNER, *Department of Dairy Husbandry, University of Missouri, Columbia, Missouri*

H. WARING, *Department of Zoology, University of Western Australia, Nedlands, Western Australia*

PREFACE

Volume I of this series, Methods in Hormone Research, has considered the assay of hormones and related compounds by chemical and physical means. These relatively exact techniques, unfortunately, cannot be employed in the assay of all hormonal materials since frequently the problem is the assessment of a certain type of physiological activity which of course can only be evaluated in a physiological system or by a bioassay method. This volume is concerned with a detailed and critical account of these bioassay methods. It is over ten years since a similar volume was edited by Professor C. W. Emmens and published by Academic Press, and the abundance of new methods demands a new treatment of this subject. Some of the original contributors to the earlier volume have again contributed to this work, including Professor C. W. Emmens.

Since 1950 the field of bioassay of hormones and particularly bioassay of steroid hormones has grown rapidly and extensively. Perhaps the principal reason for this rapid development has been the recent extensive use of steroid hormones and related substances in clinical medicine. Whereas ten years ago steroid hormone therapy was limited essentially to replacement therapy such as estrogens in the menopause, androgens for hypogonadal and castrated men, and corticoid hormones for Addisonian patients, today these uses are insignificantly small compared to current pharmacological utility. Steroids are now used for the control of various collagen diseases, control of certain forms of cancer, as anabolic agents, for fertility control, for diseases involving the allergic state, and even as anesthetics as well as for their replacement value in the hypofunctional state. It is essential to have animal bioassay methods to predict usefulness of compounds in man and these newer subjects are considered critically and in detail in these pages.

This volume also crystallizes some ideas on the bioassay of compounds with anti-hormonal activity. In the case of anti-estrogens and anti-androgens, methods are presented even before practical application has been established. It is not unlikely that within a few years compounds with these types of biological activity will be highly regarded in the field of chemotherapy.

Statistical methods are the comforting and practical backbone of bioassay. Biostatistics are presented here in detail and this subject matter serves as a general guide to most of the material presented in this volume. The second part of the volume is a detailed consideration of bioassay procedures involving steroid hormones and related sub-stances, while bioassays of protein hormones and related hormones are discussed in Part Three. The final section, Part Four, presents some standard methods which have been evolved as a result of the efforts of the Staff of the Endocrinology Panel of the Cancer Chemotherapy National Service Center, Bethesda.

It is expected that students of the biological sciences from biology through medicine should find this compendium a valuable aid for their daily problems in research. A work of this type should also assist the pharmacologist, the organic chemist, and the biochemist to understand the problem of structure and activity relationships. In some instances bioassay procedures are of importance as an aid in diagnosis, and for this reason the clinician will often find the volume of great value.

The editor is grateful to all the contributors who cooperated on this volume and made it a successful reality. Sincere thanks to Mrs. Iola Graton and Miss Elaine Massad for their able assistance with the many details so necessary for the completion of this task.

RALPH I. DORFMAN

Shrewsbury, Massachusetts

CONTENTS

PART I

Statistical Methods

1. Statistical Methods

PART II

Steroid Hormones and Related Substances

2. Estrogens

3. Anti-Estrogenic Compounds

PART III

Protein Hormones and Related Hormones and Substances

9. Epinephrine and Norepinephrine

10. Thyroidal Substances

11. Insulin

12. Glucagon

PART IV

Standard Methods

CONTENTS OF VOLUME I
CHEMICAL DETERMINATIONS

PART I

Statistical Methods

Chapter 1

Statistical Methods

C. W. EMMENS

I. Introduction

A. THE BIOLOGICAL ASSAY

In a biological assay, animals are used as if they were test tubes, as a convenient way of observing a reaction usually called the response. This response may be the death of the animal, or changes in

3

its growth rate, blood constituents, or other tissues. Sometimes each animal can only be used once, sometimes it can be used in repeated assays. Whichever is possible, groups of animals are usually employed, and their mean responses are the basis of the subsequent calculations. This is because, unlike a set of test tubes treated alike, animals usually show considerable variation in response, and little reliance can be placed on individual observations.

A satisfactory assay must give an unbiased estimate of potency, and of the range of potencies within which the mean estimate lies, to a given degree of probability. It has become conventional to regard a probability of 1 in 20 as satisfactory for ordinary purposes, but sometimes 1 in 100 is demanded. These are usually referred to as the 95 and 99% limits, respectively (sometimes as the 5 and 1% limits), and imply that in repeated assays of the type under consideration, only in 5 or 1% of cases will the stated limits fail to include the true potency. It is also usual to center the range so presented on the mean estimate of potency, so that $2\frac{1}{2}$ or $\frac{1}{2}$% of each tail of the calculated distribution is cut off.

To perform a satisfactory assay, certain elements of design must be fulfilled, and a potency determination will only be valid if they are. The essential requirements are given in the following paragraphs.

1. The substances compared must have similar actions on the test material. This is usually checked to some extent by determining the parallel nature of the individual dose-response lines, and rejecting any assay not showing parallelism.

2. The assay must be balanced in time, all responses being obtained simultaneously or so balanced that secular variation may be discounted in analysis.

3. The living material is allotted to dosage groups in such a way that variation in response will not bias the result or the estimate of error.

4. An estimate of error must be available from the internal evidence of the assay itself.

These are restrictions which must be placed on any assay of whatever form, in addition there are other highly desirable points which should be adhered to if at all possible.

5. The assay should be completely balanced, with equal numbers per group and equal numbers and spacing of groups on whatever scale is used (often a log scale).

6. A standard preparation should be employed as a routine, either a substance carefully calibrated against an international standard, or a local standard if no international standard exists.

Many of these considerations have been ignored by investigators in the past, but it is fortunately becoming more frequent to pay careful attention to them. Perhaps the second requirement for a valid assay, simultaneity or temporal balance, has been the most often ignored, but it must be closely followed by the fifth. However, lack of attention to any of the first few points leads to invalidity; lack of attention to point 5 leads to tedious calculations and less precision than could otherwise have been gained.

Almost every assay in this volume is based on a log dose-response relationship, i.e., equal increments in response are produced, at least over the working part of the dose-response line, by equal increments in log dose, not in the dose itself. This relationship leads to straightforward methods of calculation, and since there is almost never any point in failing to keep the numbers of test objects per group and per substance constant, only this case will be treated in detail. In assays where some degree of mortality before the end of the test is likely, it is still possible to keep group numbers effectively constant either by replacing missing observations as described in standard texts or by reducing group numbers to the minimum encountered in any one group. This is done by random rejection of surplus observations in the other groups. Except when first investigating the characteristics of a dose-response line, it will usually also be pointless to do other than a 4- or 6-point assay, with two or three groups each on the standard and the unknown. A 6-point assay checks for linearity, while a 4-point assay is the least that gives any running check on similarity of action. In special circumstances, when a very limited amount of a preparation is available as in some clinical work, a 3-point assay with only one group on the unknown and two on the standard may be forced upon the investigator, but should never be regarded as really satisfactory.

B. BIOLOGICAL STANDARDS

The need for a standard has been mentioned above. It arises because of the great influence of changes in technique, in the animal material itself, and in time-to-time variation in response on the estimate of potency obtained. In a satisfactory assay a standard must be included so as to discount these effects, which are the cause of the failure of various types of animal unit so frequently used in the past in comparing activities. The same group of animals responds differently from time to time, and different animals within the group have different levels of response at any one time. Even stocks of animals kept under apparently constant conditions show these phenomena. Thus

Burn (1937) found that the frog unit for digitalis varied during a year from 1310 to 2940 units/g., and Emmens (1939) found that the mouse unit for estrone varied during a similar period from 0.064 to 0.150 μg.

Recognition of this source of error has led to the establishment of international and local standards, kept under conditions designed to preserve them unchanged and to enable their use as stable reference materials on which to base potency estimates. International standards are available for many hormones, and other widely circulated preparations exist, such as the purified pituitary preparations of the National Institute of Health at Bethesda, Maryland. These are distributed to various laboratories in which it will usually be desirable to establish carefully calibrated substandards for everyday use.

If the unknown and the standard preparations act in a similar manner, so that one may in fact be regarded merely as a dilution of the other, an estimate of relative potency should be independent of the particular test method employed. Very careful safeguards have been found necessary in practice to ensure that this is the case, and different assays will often be found to be extremely sensitive to different impurities or inhomogeneity in either preparation. Such difficulties led Emmens (1939) and Pedersen-Bjergaard (1939) to conclude that, in estrogen assays, only pure characterized substances could be meaningfully compared with the estrogen standards by biological assay of the types then available.

C. Design and Analysis

Emphasis has been placed on the design of valid assays, and minimum adequate types of design have been indicated. However, assays of a far more complex nature than this may be designed, sometimes with great advantage. In addition, in the exploration of new methods of assay, it is frequently advantageous to use factorial or other advanced types of design in order to gain as much information as possible in a limited time and with limited animal stocks. These methods will be treated in greater detail below. It is however usual, once an assay method has become established, to use it under rigid conditions, so as to help preserve continuity in results. This may not necessarily be wise; it depends on the findings from such more complex investigations as have just been mentioned. If it is found that wide variations in technique do not change relative potency estimates significantly, it may be best to arrange assays on a factorial basis and to gain all the added information available. The fact that this is almost never done in practice should not stop us from contemplating doing so, particularly since it is becoming apparent that animal material frequently gives few or no significant interactions in complex tests (Emmens, 1960). The stability of a potency estimate over a range of test conditions should add to the confidence placed in it.

Within certain limits, the design of an assay dictates how it must be analyzed if all the information is to be salvaged. Within these limits, however, we are free to make use of various so-called models upon which to base calculations. It is usual to assume log-normality in distribution or log-linearity in dose-response lines, and the fact that no dose-response line is log-linear over the whole range of doses, or that log-normality of distribution is rarely proved, should not worry us unduly. It is better to choose a log-linear segment and to work within that, than to try to cope with a wider range of dosage by adopting less convenient statistics, and better to assume log-normality than to try to make calculations on some less likely basis or on no such assumption to all—which may give very wide and almost useless estimates of error. It has been shown in several instances that various "reasonable" methods of calculation all give virtually the same answer, so that it is usually a question of choosing, from an infinity of possible functions, that which while giving an acceptable fit to the data is the easiest to use in computations. Thus Finney (1952a) showed that the same data analyzed by four different methods gave practically identical estimates of potency and limits of error (Table I). In discussing

TABLE I

RELATIVE POTENCY OF DIGITALIS IN FROGS[a]

Transform	Relative potency	Limits of error
Probit	2.09	1.70–2.65
Logit	2.09	1.69–2.67
Angular	2.08	1.70–2.62
$P = Y$	2.06	1.72–2.53

[a] Injected by two different routes, and calculated on different assumptions. Table adopted from Finney (1945).

in detail comparisons between these transformations of response, Finney (1952b) concluded that all but the rectangular $(P = Y)$ are very nearly the same between responses of 2 and 98%. Biggers (1951) came to exactly the same conclusions.

The importance of appreciating this position will be more apparent when quantal responses are discussed below, where it will be seen that some methods of calculation, notably those using such transforms as the probit or logit, lead to very tedious or impossibly complex calculations, while others which give the same answers are simple to handle and permit experimental designs of a much more complex nature. This may be important to the investigator who wishes to make the most of his material and to the routine worker who is faced with many assays to compute in a short period of time. The growing possibilities of using automatic computers in this field have served to emphasize the importance of alternatives to probits, for instance, since although a medium- to large-sized machine can handle the requirements for probit analysis on a considerable scale, it may not do so as rapidly as desirable and the costs are likely to be high.

Since an assay is not complete without an estimate of error, and approximate methods of calculation do not yield unbiased estimates, or yield none at all, these are to be avoided. If a rough idea of the results is to be obtained for immediate use, a simple graphical estimate is best, to be followed by the calculation of fiducial limits of error as soon as necessary. These were investigated by Irwin (1943) and take into account uncertainties in the slope of the dose-response line when small numbers of animals are used. If this slope does not exceed about eight times its standard error, the fiducial limits will appreciably exceed the approximate limits calculated prior to Irwin's work. If the slope is known with high precision, the approximate limits are good enough. These calculations do not affect the estimate of potency, only the limits of error.

II. Terminology and Procedure

A. Sampling and Randomizing

The statistical discussions in this chapter assume that the samples of test material used have been obtained and allotted to dosage groups by a process of randomization. This means that of all possible test objects that could have been selected for use, those taken represent a sample in which each individual object was independently chosen by a process which made it as equally likely to be selected as any other. It means additionally that in allotting test objects to dosage groups, each, independently, was as likely to fall into any one group as into any other. The word independently has been introduced into these definitions to ensure that it is clearly understood that allotment of groups of animals together by one act of selection is not permissible unless each group has been formed by the individual random selection of test objects.

Completely unbiased sampling from a population in an animal house or from other stocks is often impossible, but every attempt should be made to achieve it or to approximate it. Failure to take care in this direction may lead to inconsistent estimates of slope, of variability, and even of potency from one assay to another. Sometimes there is a very restricted choice, or no choice at all, of the test objects to be used, as when all of the animals of a certain age or weight available must be used. When this occurs, care must still be taken to see that random allocation occurs to the dosage groups, and notice should be taken of time-to-time differences in population characteristics and response.

Any bias in the allotment of test objects to dosage groups or to any other integral subdivision of the assay will invalidate conclusions. Bias in the selection of test objects to be used may not invalidate an individual assay, although it may invalidate the combination of a series of assays. The allotment to dosage groups must therefore be strictly at random, by a process analogous to writing the number of each object on a card, shuffling thoroughly, and then dealing into the various groups. In practice it is usually easier to use a table of random numbers such as those of Fisher and Yates (1957) or Snedecor (1956). Common errors in randomization are discussed by Emmens (1948) and include such procedures as taking animals from a large cage or run and allotting them by hand to dosage groups. Such a procedure will usually select the tamest or the largest first, and not, therefore, be random. Even more subtle errors may creep in if such a process is left to an assistant who does not understand the object of randomizing, and may try to balance out groups in a nonpermissible manner, thereby reducing the real error, if he is successful, but increasing the estimate of it.

However, random allocation to dosage groups is often practiced within various restrictions in design, examples of which are discussed below. Thus, several litters may be available for use in an assay, and we may wish to take advantage of the greater similarity in response usually exhibited by litter mates in comparison with the general population. If one member of each litter can be placed into each dosage group, again at random, then in the subsequent analysis appropriate steps are taken to segregate the variation attributable to differences between litters and to base the estimate of error on differences within litters. The same procedure may be used with any class of test objects which is believed to react alike to a greater extent than the population from which it is drawn. If the assumption is wrong, no harm is done unless an usually few degrees of freedom are available for the eventual estimate of error.

B. DISTRIBUTIONS

As in a previous volume dealing with hormone assay (Emmens, 1950) there is insufficient space for a full discussion of the appropriate statistical methods. These have been covered by various authors. Emmens (1948) and Finney (1952b) may be consulted for an elementary and more advanced and comprehensive treatment, respectively. The basic principles of bioassay do not change, although detailed methods are always changing. It is still felt, however, that a useful purpose is to be served by introducing the nonmathematical reader to the basic concepts and to the elements of statistical procedure, without which he will fail to realize the need for various measures in design and analysis. It is still true to say that the biologist's reading of statistical papers is often spoiled by his being plunged into unfamiliar concepts with little or no explanation, even when these papers are addressed to biologists. The usual cause is that it is not possible to include the elements of statistics with every paper published, and it is quite reasonable to expect the biologist to familiarize himself with at least the basic ideas and procedures involved.

There is an infinity of ways in which a set of observations may be distributed about their mean or average value. It has been shown, however, that the expected distribution of a series of estimates such as the height or weight of the same object is a bell-shaped curve, shown in Fig. 1. This was called the *curve of error*, or *normal distribution*, and has the equation

$$y = \frac{n}{\sigma\sqrt{2\pi}} \, e^{-x^2/\sigma^2}$$

with points of inflection at $x = \pm\sigma$. The same distribution has been encountered when measuring attributes of a population, such as heights or weights, with the proviso that so-called outliers, extreme individuals at one or either end of the scale, tend to be a little more frequent than expected. Note that the distribution of repeated measurements of the same object is to be distinguished from that of one measurement each (or a mean of several measurements) of a population of objects. Each may be normal, but the first arises from errors of measurement and the second from errors of measurement plus natural variation. Errors of measurement are often unimportant, as in weighing animals for a test or organs after it, and the distribution is then effectively that due to natural causes.

It is quite unusual to have sufficient observations in bioassay to confirm normality of distribution in the responses to drugs or hormones.

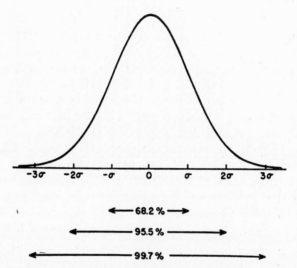

FIG. 1. The normal distribution. From Emmens (1948).

It is assumed that the distribution is normal unless evidence is presented to the contrary, and it may be shown that this assumption will cause no trouble unless it is rather widely wrong. It is also a useful property of any distribution that the distribution of means of samples tends rapidly to normality as sample size increases. As it is with means that the statistician is often primarily concerned in bioassay, any tendency to departure from normality in the basic data is often eliminated by using units derived from the combination of observations. This may not be so, however, and the assumption of normality may occasionally lead us astray. The small likelihood of this is demonstrated by Table I above.

Normality of distribution is nevertheless inherent in the assumptions of probit analysis, in that the individual responses are assumed lognormally distributed. This has again rarely been demonstrated, but Fig. 2 shows an example from Bliss (1944) in which individual cats were slowly injected with digitalis until death occurred. In a few other cases, it has been shown that the over-all distribution is not log-normal, but in the great majority no decision is possible, and in the absence of any definite contrary evidence, it is usually assumed that log-normality holds. The consequences of this in relation to advanced design of assay and other

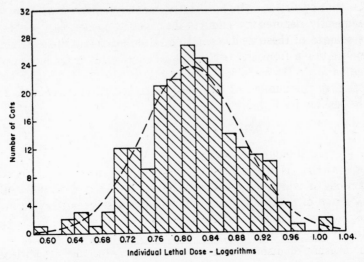

Fig. 2. A normal distribution of individual effective log lethal doses of digitalis in cats. From Bliss (1944).

investigations are discussed in more detail below, where it is shown that the log-normal distribution may lead to difficult or impossible analyses, and that substitutes for it are to be preferred.

C. Means, Variances, and Standard Errors

A *variate* is something that varies, like the response of a series of animals to a drug, which may assume a normal or other distribution. There are two variates which appear in all assays, the *independent variate,* or dose of drug, so-called because we determine what it shall be, and the *dependent variate,* or response to the drug, which has to be measured. Other *covariates,* such as body weight of animals may also be measured and entered into the analysis. The dose is usually denoted by X and the response by Y.

The *arithmetic mean* of a series of observations is indicated by placing a bar over the appropriate symbol; thus the mean of several responses is $\overline{Y}$, and

$$\overline{Y} = SY/n,$$

where S is an operative symbol implying the sum of all values of Y, and n is the number of values summed. The arithmetic mean of the logs of a series of doses (or anything else) is the log of the *geometric mean* of these doses, the geometric mean being defined as the nth root of the product of n numbers. This enters into calculations where response is related to log dose.

The sum of the deviations of all values of Y from $\overline{Y}$ is zero. These are frequently denoted by small italics, i.e., y, hence $Sy = 0$. The sum of the squares of these deviations from $\overline{Y}$ is less than that which results if they are taken from any other point, hence Sy^2 is minimal.

The *variance* (or *mean square*) is the sum of squares of y divided by one less than the number of observations in the group concerned, and is usually denoted by V, hence

$$V = s^2 = Sy^2/(n - 1),$$

where s is the *standard deviation,* the square root of the variance. The divisor, $(n - 1)$, is the number of *degrees of freedom* or independent comparisons on which the estimate is based. For each statistic calculated from a group of data, one degree of freedom must be subtracted in subsequent computation, thus having calculated the mean, the variance must be allotted $(n - 1)$ degrees of freedom. Another way of looking at it is that a measure of dispersion must be based on the $(n - 1)$ differences which exist between any observation and the rest. Any subsequent comparisons are not independent of these and can be derived from them.

The variance is a measure which is independent of sign, and includes all positive and negative deviations squared. The standard deviation, s, is not the average deviation, and about two thirds of all deviations fall into the range $\pm s$ in a normal distribution. It is more informative to think in terms of variances rather than the standard deviation when considering the sources and meaning of variation in experimental work. Thus, the inverse of a variance, or *invariance,* is a measure of the amount of information conveyed by members of a sample, relevant to the point at issue. A member of a group with unit variance supplies one unit of information; a member of a group with a variance of four supplies a quarter of a unit.

The *variance of a mean* is $1/n$ of the variance of the group supplying that mean, and thus the mean conveys n times the information that any one observation supplies.

$$V\overline{Y} = Sy^2/n(n - 1), \text{ where } V\overline{Y} \text{ is the variance of } \overline{Y}.$$

The *standard error* of a mean $s_{\overline{Y}}$, is the square root of the variance of the mean; thus $V\overline{Y} = s_{\overline{Y}}^2$. The term standard error distinguishes this quantity from the standard deviation of the individual observations.

D. ANALYSIS OF VARIANCE

The more completely balanced an assay or experiment, along the lines indicated above, the easier it is to analyze it, particularly in the form of an analysis of variance. As one of the simplest examples of such an analysis, consider the data in Table II, from Emmens (1948). This

TABLE II

BLOOD-SUGAR LEVELS IN MILLIGRAMS PER CENT OF FOUR BREEDS OF RABBIT

				Breed			
Y_p	$(Y_p - 100)^2$	Y_p	$(Y_p - 100)^2$	Y_p	$(Y_p - 100)^2$	Y_p	$(Y_p - 100)^2$
117	289	137	1369	135	1225	109	81
116	256	136	1296	122	484	108	64
128	784	121	441	135	1225	117	289
104	16	113	169	138	1444	118	324
121	441	145	2025	131	961	101	1
100	0	123	529	134	1156	134	1156
123	529	113	169	140	1600	113	169

SY_p 809		888		935		800	
$S(Y_p - 100)^2$	2315		5998		8095		2084
$n_p(\overline{Y}_p - 100)^2$	1697.29		5049.14		7889.29		1428.57
Sy_p^2	617.71		948.86		205.71		655.43

Total sum of squares, $SSy_p^2 = 2427.71$

table shows measurements of blood sugar in milligrams per cent in groups of seven examples each of four breeds of rabbit, as used in the biological assay of insulin. We wish to know, among other things, whether these breeds differ in mean blood-sugar level and thus to decide how assays using them should be planned. If the rabbits appear homogeneous in this respect, no advantage may be gained by keeping breeds separate.

Before performing an analysis, the following identities must be known:

$$Sy^2 = SY^2 - n\overline{Y}^2 = SY^2 - \overline{Y}T = SY^2 - T^2/n,$$

where T is the total of all observations (SY). Also:

$$Sy^2 = Sn_p\overline{y}_p^2 + SSy_p^2,$$

where n_p, y_p, and $\bar{y}_p$ refer to the observations in group p (any group). This means that the sum of the squares of the deviations from the grand mean, $\overline{Y}$, can be calculated readily without subtracting each from the mean; and, that this sum may be split into two portions. The portion $Sn_p\bar{y}_p^2$ represents the sum of squares attributable to the departures of the group means, $\overline{Y}_p$ (of which there are four in this instance) from $\overline{Y}$, while the portion SSy_p^2 represents the sum of squares attributable to the departure of the individual observations from the group means. These are the *between groups* and *within groups* sums of squares, respectively. The symbol SS means "the sum of the sums of."

Further, the variance of $\overline{Y}_p$ about $\overline{Y}$ is $Sn_p y_p{}^2/3$, and that of the individual observations from their own group means is $SSy_p{}^2/4 \times 6$, there being 6 degrees of freedom within each group available for the estimation of error.

These calculations are made in Table II. For convenience, in all but machine calculation, the actual observations have each had 100 subtracted from them before taking squares, a form of *coding* which does not alter the results.

We then determine $Sy_p{}^2$ separately for each group, and find that their added total is 2427.71. In addition, the value of $Sn_p \bar{y}_p{}^2$ is determined from the calculated means or, more easily, from the identity:

$$Sn_p \bar{y}_p{}^2 = Sn_p \overline{Y}_p{}^2 - n\overline{Y}^2,$$

and is found to be 1799.14. These quantities added together should equal the total sum of squares, Sy^2, or $SY^2 - n\overline{Y}^2$, which may be calculated as an independent check and is found to be 4,226.85. In practice, it is often more convenient to calculate this total and then to subtract from it $SSy_p{}^2$ in order to obtain $Sn_p \bar{y}_p{}^2$, but in hand calculations it is often a good idea to make the full check. The quantities $n_p \overline{Y}_p{}^2$ and $n\overline{Y}^2$ are often called the *correction factors* for the respective means.

If there are no differences in mean level of blood sugar for the different breeds of rabbit, the within-groups variance should, on a per item basis (per degree of freedom), equal the between-groups variance, since the only contribution to the latter is from the former. If, however, there is a difference between breeds, the between-groups variance will exceed that within groups by an amount determined by the difference that exists. The comparison of these data leads to an analysis of variance as in Table

TABLE III

ANALYSIS OF VARIANCE OF THE DATA IN TABLE II

Source of variation	Formula	Degrees of freedom	Sum of squares	Mean square
Between groups	$n_p S\bar{y}_p{}^2$	3	1799.14	599.7
Within groups	$SSy_p{}^2$	24	2427.71	101.2
	Sy^2	27	4226.85	

$$F = 5.93; \; P < 0.01$$

III, where the mean squares, or variances attributable to these factors, are compared. It is seen that the mean square between groups (599.7) is much greater than that within groups (101.2), but we have yet to discuss how to determine the significance of this. Note that on the basis of the variance of *means* we would estimate the expected variance of any individual mean as $101.2/7 = 14.46$ on the *null hypothesis*, that breed makes no difference, whereas that observed is $599.7/7 = 85.67$, quantities in the same ratio as above.

E. The Variance Ratio

To estimate the significance of such differences in variance as are discussed above, tables of a function, F, the variance ratio, have been prepared. F is equal to the larger variance divided by the smaller one, in the above case it is $599.7/101.2 = 5.93$. From F tables, it is seen that, with 3 and 24 degrees of freedom, respectively, a variance ratio as high as 4.72 would only be encountered once in a 100 trials and from this we conclude that the observed figure of 5.93 is highly significant and that breed differences exist. If the estimate of the within-groups variance had turned out to be the larger one, we should conclude immediately that no difference exists between breeds because the within-groups variance cannot in reality be the larger of the two, unless some undetected bias has entered the assay. A *significantly* larger within-groups variance should lead us to suspect the whole assay.

F is a general function of which two other common ones, t^2 and some types of χ^2 are particular cases. If it is desired to test only two groups, so that there is only 1 degree of freedom between them, tables of F are often replaced for convenience by tables of t, which is the square root of F with one degree of freedom associated with what is usually the larger variance. Tables of t itself cover cases where the single degree of freedom may be associated with the smaller variance and also include various levels of significance. The statistic χ^2 (Chi-squared) is used when the measurement of Y is discontinuous, particularly when it is quantal. If a percentage of reactors can, for example, be provided, the homogeneity of these is tested by χ^2, which in some circumstances is n_1F when $n_2 = \infty$. The number of degrees of freedom associated with the within-groups sum of squares is in this case infinite, because we calculate a theoretical variance based on some hypothesis, usually the binomial. If χ^2 exceeds a certain value we conclude, as in the F test, that the groups are heterogeneous.

F. Small Samples

When dealing with large samples from a normally distributed population samples of several hundreds, the standard deviation may be used with sufficient exactitude to predict the proportion of the sample that will fall within specified limits with the mean as a center. Thus, about 68% of all observations will fall within the limits $\overline{Y} \pm s$, where s is our estimate of σ, the true standard deviation. About 95% of all observations will fall within $\overline{Y} \pm 2s$, and 99.7% within $\overline{Y} \pm 3s$. When small samples are dealt with, s is a very approximate estimate of σ and the limits must be widened at each level of probability. The effect of this is shown in Table IV, which gives values of t and the limits of error of a mean,

TABLE IV

VALUES OF t AND LIMITS OF ERROR OF A MEAN $(\overline{Y} = 100)^a$

Sample size	Sy	t	Limits of error and t for:		
			$P = 0.95$	t	$P = 0.99$
2	7.06	12.71	10.3–189.7	63.66	−349.4–549.4
4	5.00	3.18	84.1–115.9	5.84	70.8–129.2
8	3.54	2.57	90.9–109.1	4.03	85.7–114.4
16	2.50	2.37	94.1–105.9	3.50	91.2–108.8
32	1.77	2.04	96.4–103.6	2.75	95.1–104.9
64	1.25	2.00	97.5–102.5	2.66	96.7–103.3
∞	0.00	1.96	—	2.58	—

^{a} Population variance of 100, derived from small samples.

assumed to be 100, with a population standard deviation of 10, when derived from small samples. The limits of error are given for the 5% $(P = 0.95)$ and 1% $(P = 0.99)$ levels of probability, and it is seen how wide these become when sample sizes are small.

It will be noted that in all these calculations it has been assumed that the within-groups variance is homogeneous, even though the means for groups may differ significantly. Fisher (1954) has discussed the likelihood of obtaining misleading values of t because of heterogeneity in this variance, and finds that it is very unlikely to be a source of practical trouble. However, when any doubt arises, it is possible, and advisable to test the assumption. Thus, the analysis is not applicable if variance is correlated with response to any marked degree, and it may be necessary to transform the response so that this is no longer the case. A transform frequently used is log response, which may then be related to log dose in the usual manner. Any transform which equalizes variances may be employed, although it may then be necessary to confine experimental observations to a particular linear segment of the dose-response line.

G. Quantal Responses

It has become conventional to analyze assays involving all-or-none responses in quite a different way from those in which continuous variation is measured. The usual transform employed is the *probit*, based on the *normal equivalent deviation* of Gaddum (1933). At an earlier time of writing (Emmens, 1950) it was possible only to remark that, apart from such observations as those of Finney in Table I, nothing seemed to have been done about the possibilities of using simpler techniques. It was remarked also that the angular transformation (cf. Fisher and Yates, 1957) might prove useful, having the advantage of a constant variance at all levels of response, which the probit has not.

Since 1950, a greater effort has been made to explore the possibilities of other transforms, a project which has in particular been stimulated by the difficulties of probit analysis when attempts are made to use factional or other complex designs, and its virtual inapplicability to crossover or repeat tests of a quantal nature when the same animal can be used more than once. As it stands, probit analysis cannot usefully be applied to the calculation of *within-animal* variation (Claringbold, 1956; Emmens, 1957; Claringbold and Emmens, 1961). The substitution of logits (Berkson, 1949) is no help in this regard.

On the assumption that the distribution of individual effective doses is log-normal, the appropriate theoretical transform is indeed the probit. Finney (1952a, b) has described the operations of probit analysis, taking it as far as simple factorial tests, when calculation commences to be especially tedious. The probit corresponding to a given percentage of reactors is

$$5 + Y = 5 + (X - X_0)/\sigma_x,$$

where X is the log dose causing the percentage of reactors in question and X_0 the log dose causing 50% of reactions (it being assumed that nil dose causes no reactions). The quantity, 5, is added to keep the probit positive under all ordinary circumstances.

In practice, however, we do not know X_0, and the equation,

$$P = \frac{1}{\sqrt{2\pi}} \int_{-\infty}^{V} e^{-\frac{1}{2}Y^2} dY$$

is employed. It derives Y, the normal equivalent deviate, or probit minus 5, from P, the percentage of reactors. After fitting a dose-response line, or lines, to the responses expected on the hypothesis, the adequacy of the transform is checked by a χ^2 test, a "goodness of fit" test, to see if the points fit the calculated line well enough. Unfortunately the inconstant variance of the probit, which is least at 5 and greater the farther from 5 one goes, makes calculations very tedious if many are to be done, or if a test is complex in design. Analysis of variance is inapplicable, at least in theory, but in fact it may be used as a short cut if extreme percentages are not frequent in the data, perhaps finally to be rounded off with a single cycle of probit operations. Otherwise, cycles of calculation have to be repeated until successive estimates agree within reasonable limits. With few points, this may involve several repetitions, but fortunately, estimates for larger assays usually settle down rapidly.

The angular transformation was investigated recently by Claringbold *et al.* (1953), who showed that transformation of *observed* responses (Eisenhart, 1947) leads to a rapid, noniterative, but approximate solution, and transformation of *expected* responses (as is usual in the probit method) to an exact, iterative maximum likelihood solution. In practice the two methods gave almost identical results, and with the addition of one cycle of the maximum likelihood solution following the method of Eisenhart, this method is fully adequate. To overcome difficulties with regions of 0 or 100% response, parallelogram designs were introduced for assays or experiments, in which the *region of useful observation* was covered by dosage groups, avoiding expected responses of less than, say 10% or more than 90%.

Despite the advantage of the angular transformation, it is still inadequate for some types of work. Claringbold (1955) showed that the within-animal variation, over a period of 5 weeks, was only 29% of the between-animal variation in the response of ovariectomized mice to estrone, which is quantal. He then proceeded to investigate the possibilities of within-animal bioassays with quantal responses (Claringbold, 1956) and confirmed that a 4-point cross-over design had about 25% of the variance seen in standard designs of the same type. But in such an assay, solution in terms of probits would imply a group size of unity, since a constant must be fitted for each individual (Finney, 1952b), and in the standard maximum likelihood solution estimates of more parameters would be needed than there were animals in the test. Estimation with the angular transformation would be very awkward also, because a working angle would have to be computed for each observation with a "group" response always of either 0 or 100%. Instead the simple approach was made of scoring each response as either zero or one, and performing an analysis of variance. Although open to some theoretical objections, this method gives reliable results.

A comparison of the angular transformation; (0, 1) or (0, 1, 2) scoring was made by Emmens (1957), again in cross-over tests with ovariectomized mice and is used as an example below. In these tests, a repeat smear from each mouse on each occasion made the (0, 1, 2) score possible, so that a semiquantal assay was also performed. This test was over an extended period of 16 weeks, but still showed a twofold gain in information as a result of within-animal estimates. It also demonstrated how (0, 1) or (0, 1, 2) scores make possible the estimation of slopes and relative potency in the presence of heterogeneity, when either probits or angles would demand the use of a heterogeneity factor and an estimate of error based on very few degrees of freedom. The analysis of complex tests is only feasible with such methods, while that of simpler tests is very much facilitated, with a possible gain in information as well.

We are therefore faced with a choice of methods in presenting the results of quantal assays. There is no doubt that very complex designs can only in practice be analyzed by other than probit methods, and that the same methods are useful in simpler cases, either on their own or, if desired, as a basis for a cycle of probit calculations for those who feel the need of reassurance about the agreement between methods.

III. Measuring Responses

A. GRADED AND QUANTAL RESPONSES

Since graded (continuous) responses such as organ weights or blood-sugar levels give more information per observation than do quantal responses, they are in general to be preferred. As is apparent from above, it is also easier to apply the full possibilities of modern design to graded assays. It may be shown that a graded response gives about twice the information per test object that a quantal response gives, over the range of about 20–80% of reactions on the quantal scale, but in addition to this, graded responses can usually be measured over a more extended scale and thus their usefulness is likely to be even greater than is implied.

When there is a variety of ways in which a response may be measured, it is often difficult to decide between them and experiment may repay the trouble involved. The ideal response is easy to measure, has a small error, changes rapidly with dose of over a linear segment of a dose-response line, which is wide enough to make assays practicable without much difficulty in finding the useful response range on each occasion. These desiderata are rarely found all together. A simple measurement is as likely to give good results as a complicated one, and it is usually best to avoid subjective decisions wherever possible.

There is sometimes justification for expressing responses in relation to such measures as body weight of the animals, such as crop-gland weight in gm./100-gm. body weight in the pigeon assay of prolactin (this volume,

Chapter 18). It should never be assumed that this is so, however, and the technique of *covariance analysis* should be used to decide if it is applicable, or whether some other adjustment should be made. It will also be apparent that the arbitrary decision to give doses in terms of so much per 100-gm body weight is open to the same objection. It is usually best to keep dosage as simple as possible until adequate information is available from which any necessary adjustment can be made.

Covariance analysis extends the methods of the analysis of variance to include estimates of the influence of one or more variables which were not rigidly controlled in the assay. A frequent covariate is body weight, as previously mentioned. It is often impossible or inconvenient to select all animals of the same body weight, or if such selection is made they may differ by the end of an assay. Any regular influence such a factor may have on response can be eliminated in the analysis by entering it as a concomitant variable, usually on the assumption of a linear effect, but this is not essential. By this technique, assumption about the nature of the dependence of response on the concomitant variable is avoided, and correction is made from the internal evidence of the test.

When it is possible to measure changes in the test object, such as a gain in body weight, blood sugar before and after insulin injection, or comb size in a capon before and after hormone treatment, it is often assumed that such measurements of differences must be better than final body or organ weights, or final measurements of any kind, unrelated to some initial measurement. This point has been discussed by Emmens (1948) who showed that there must be a sufficiently high correlation between initial and subsequent readings to compensate for the additional variance introduced by the initial measurement. The variance of a difference (or sum) of two uncorrelated observations is their added variances, and thus an assay may have a substantially increased error if little correlation exists. The variance of a ratio is also greater than that of its components, and similar arguments apply. Data of Marks (Emmens, 1948) showed that, in the assay of insulin by the rabbit blood-sugar method, final blood-sugar readings at the second hour after injection gave as precise an assay as the far more complex procedure usually employed. This involved measurement of blood sugar before and several times after injection, the postinjection mean fall was then expressed as a percentage of the initial reading and then corrected by covariance for the initial reading. The introduction of initial blood-sugar measurements in the manner described served only to increase error, but the increase was removable by covariance analysis, bringing the error down again to that of a final reading, or group of readings.

The commonest qualitative data are quantal, occasionally more than two grades can be used in an assay, as with estrogen determination. If there are several grades it is possible to give them scores, other than purely arbitrary scores, by discriminant analysis (Fisher, 1954), but this has rarely been done. The estimation of anaphylactic effects by Claringbold and Sobey (1957) provides an example. There is however no guarantee that a dose-response line based on scores assigned by such a technique will be linear, unless this condition is imposed in their estimation; but this may be done. However, a sufficiently linear segment of the line is likely to be found even if it is not.

Sometimes quantal data may be avoided with a little ingenuity, such as employing reaction time instead. If it is feasible to measure time to death for instance, a more accurate assay may be performed. This is done in the assay of adrenal hormones with adrenalectomized rats or drakes (Bülbring, 1937). The assay of melanophore-expanding hormone, based on the time required for the melanophores of hypophysectomized frogs to return to the contracted state (Calloway *et al.*, 1942) also uses a reaction time. In such assays, either time or log time has been successfully used as the dependent variate.

B. Transformations

Whatever response is measured attention must be paid to attaining linearity of a sufficient segment of the dose-response line for useful assays, either with the response as measured or a transform of it, to attaining a constant or near-constant variance at all levels of response employed, and as steep a line as possible in relation to the magnitude of the variance, i.e., the quantity s/b should be minimal, where b is the slope of the dose-response line. Transforms to bear in mind are:

1. *Log response,* useful when the standard deviation is a constant fraction of the response, whereupon the standard deviation of log responses will be constant.

2. *The square root* of the response, useful when the response is dependent on a factor like a cell count, when the square root should have constant variance.

3. *Angular transformation,* useful not only in straightforward quantal assays, but also in responses dependent on enumeration or estimates thereof, such as a percentage live sperm count.

If no transform can be found which at least approximately equalizes variance throughout the dose-response line, the fitting of the line should in theory follow a series of successive approximations resembling probit analysis. Fortunately, in balanced assays, when the potency of the unknown has been well judged and responses to it and to the standard are much the same, quite large inequalities in variance may safely be ignored with little or no bias in the assessment of relative potency. This may not be true with more complex designs, such as a Latin square, where equality of variance is particularly important to avoid bias.

The amount of information per test object is b^2/s^2, and the quantity s/b mentioned above, often called λ, is a direct guide to the precision of assays. The value of λ differs greatly from one method to another, and it is generally felt that if it exceeds 0.4 the assay is not likely to be very useful.

In quantal assays, equality of variance is not expected, unless the angular transformation is used. That is the great advantage of this transform over the probit, but as has been discussed above, simpler scoring still, although involving inequality in variance, offers great advantages. In such assays, s has either a theoretical value (probit, angles) or an experimental one (0, 1 transform) according to the method of analysis. If probits or angles are used, the steepness of the dose-response line alone determines the value of λ when comparing various techniques.

If the response is found to be linearly related to dose (*not* log dose) other techniques may be used. Such a response seems hardly ever to occur in hormone assays, but if it does, the papers of Finney (1945), Wood (1946), and Wood and Finney (1946) should be consulted (also Claringbold), for more recent methods of analysis.

C. Between- and Within-Animal Variation

Whenever the same animal can be used in repeated or simultaneous tests, or the same test object or its parts, such as a strip of gut, can receive simultaneous or successive treatments, the advantage of planning within-animal assays should be considered. Examples of this method are given by Bliss and Marks (1939a, b), Bliss and Rose (1940), and Bliss (1940), who did much of the pioneer work in this field. Another possibility is the use of within-litter variation, which is also usually less than otherwise encountered. Curiously, the use of inbred lines has not been found to give regular gains of this nature (Emmens, 1939; Biggers and Claringbold, 1954) apparently because genetic homogeneity is often accompanied by instability in response to small environmental changes. Instead, first crosses of inbred lines frequently give more stable and useful stocks for experimental work, including bioassay. The use of within-animal assays frequently gives a four- to sixfold gain over those between animals, and within litters a corresponding gain of two- to fourfold. Examples are given by Emmens (1960). An assay based on quantal responses between animals tends to be at one extreme of precision (or imprecision) and one based on graded responses within animals at the other.

IV. Assays Based on Graded Responses

A. Balanced Designs

The simplest valid assay, depending on its own internal evidence for a check of parallelism of dose-response lines and for an estimate of error, is the 4-point assay, with two groups on the unknown and two on the standard. It should have equal numbers in each group, and equal log spacing of doses for the two compounds (i.e., if the standard is given at doses of 1 and 2 mg.; the unknown must be given in doses of x and $2x$ units). In such an assay, the calculations are minimal (Irwin, 1937; Bliss and Marks, 1939a, b). If there are n_p test objects in each group, the estimate, s, of the error of the assay, is based on $4(n_p - 1)$ degrees of freedom, and on the within-group variance. If the totals of responses in the four groups are S_1 and S_2 for the low and high doses of the standard preparation and U_1 and U_2 for those of the unknown, the remaining three degrees of freedom can be isolated as follows, and are the components of the *between-group* variance:

1. The difference between the over-all potencies of the substances is represented by the total difference in response:

$$(U_1 + U_2) - (S_1 + S_2) = 2D \tag{1}$$

2. The slope of the combined dose-response line is represented by the total difference in response between high and low doses:

$$(S_2 + U_2) - (S_1 + U_1) = 2B \tag{2}$$

3. The difference between the individual slopes for the standard and unknown is represented by the difference between the corresponding estimates:

$$(U_2 - U_1) - (S_2 - S_1) \tag{3}$$

This is a simple example of *factorial analysis,* in which each individual degree of freedom for the sum of squares between groups has been separately examined in a meaningful way. To each of the quantities (1), (2), and (3) can be attributed a standard error derived from s, by which their significance is evaluated. If (3) is significantly large, the two preparations cannot be supposed to have the same dose-response relationship and thus no valid assay is possible on the evidence available.

The slope of the combined dose-response line, b, is such that:

$$b = (S_2 + U_2 - S_1 - U_1)/2In_p \tag{4}$$

where I is the log dose ratio, or difference between log doses, necessarily the same for each substance. The precision of the assay λ, depends on b and s as usual.

The log ratio of the potency of the unknown to that of the standard is represented by M, such that:

$$M = (\overline{X}_s - \overline{X}_u) + (\overline{Y}_u - \overline{Y}_s)/b \qquad (5)$$

where $\overline{X}_s$ and $\overline{X}_u$ are the mean log doses of the standard and unknown, respectively, and $\overline{Y}_s$ and $\overline{Y}_u$ are the mean responses to the standard and unknown, all groups combined. This relationship is true whatever the number per group or the number of groups. With a 4-point assay, the value of M reduces to ID/B. It is then assumed that one unit of the unknown equals one unit of the standard, and the expression for M is very simple. The antilog of M is the number of units of the standard required to give the same response as one unit of the unknown, or the relative potency, R.

The standard error of M, s_M, is approximately given by the equation:

$$s_M^2 = VM = s^2 I^2 (B^2 + D^2)/B^2 \qquad (6)$$

This quantity is used in conjunction with t, based on $4(n_p - 1)$ degrees of freedom, giving as the limits of error of M:

$$(M + ts_M) \quad \text{and} \quad (M - ts_M),$$

where t is taken at any required level of probability, usually $P = 0.95$ or 0.99 (or 0.05 and 0.01—the two ways of expressing the probability level; both mean that there is about a 5 or 1% likelihood that the true value lies beyond the stated limits). These are log limits, just as M is a log relative potency, and the ordinary arithmetic value R and its limits of error are obtained by taking antilogs. The lower limit is therefore always nearer to R than is the upper limit.

This method of fixing limits of error is not sufficiently accurate unless the assay has given a value of b/s_b exceeding about 8, where s_b is the standard error of the slope. Methods for examining b/s_b and the procedure for calculating limits of error (fiducial limits) when it takes a lower value than 8 are discussed below.

When more than 2 doses are used per substance, the arithmetic remains simple, but requires modification. If 3 doses are used per substance, there are 5 degrees of freedom associated with differences between groups, so that in addition to the components isolated above, two additional components may be isolated so that (4) the possible departure of the combined dose-response line from linearity, and (5) the possible opposed curvature of the two separate dose-response lines may be examined. Details of such isolations are given by Bliss and Marks (1939b), Emmens (1948), and Finney (1952b) together with full computations.

It is unusual to employ more than 3 dosage groups per substance in an assay, as apart from the exploration that may precede the establishment of an assay method, but where it is desirable an extension of the same methods may be used. Equation (5) is not affected, but Eqs. (1), (2), (4), and (6) are modified to take account of the larger number of groups. As long as components (3) or higher are insignificant, the modified forms of (1) and (2) are always used to form estimates of D and B, when Eqs. (4) and (6) become

$$b = B/In_pSk^2 \tag{4a}$$

for an odd number of dosage groups, and

$$b = 2B/In_pSk^2 \tag{4b}$$

for an even number of dosage groups, where Sk^2 is the sum of the factorial coefficients (Bliss and Marks, 1939b) used in analysis. Then,

$$VM = s_M^2 = s^2K^2I^2(B^2 + D^2)/B^2 \tag{6a}$$

where K is a constant depending on the number of dosage groups. The limits of error are calculated exactly as before.

An example previously given by Emmens (1950) and modified from Bliss and Marks (1939b) is repeated here, as it remains as good an exposition of these methods as is available. Eight rabbits were used

TABLE V

ASSAY OF INSULIN POTENCY BY RABBIT BLOOD-SUGAR METHOD[a]

Dose	Standard (units)			Unknown (mg.)		
	0.25	0.5	1.0	0.8	1.6	3.2
	11.2	16.5	32.7	19.8	37.7	45.4
	21.2	23.2	14.0	21.7	40.7	28.6
Per cent fall in	18.7	25.6	28.9	26.1	29.3	50.4
blood sugar	2.8	12.7	40.2	32.2	48.1	47.7
	27.2	39.8	35.1	28.5	45.6	50.0
	25.1	28.4	36.2	20.2	35.3	12.4
	25.8	40.0	37.8	35.7	14.2	39.0
	2.2	2.4	39.4	26.1	7.9	38.1
Mean fall	16.8	23.6	33.0	26.3	32.4	39.0

[a] Adapted from Bliss and Marks (1939b).

per group in the estimation of the potency of a sample of insulin in terms of the standard; 3 dosage levels were used per substance and each dose was twice the preceding one. The response is the mean per cent fall in blood sugar over a 5-hour period following injection and has been remarked on above. The basic data are given in Table V, and an analysis of variance in Table VI. From the latter, it is seen

TABLE VI

ANALYSIS OF VARIANCE OF THE DATA IN TABLE V

Source of variation	Degrees of freedom	Sum of squares	Mean square	F
Between samples	1	780.9	780.9	6.2*
Slope of D/R line	1	1673.3	1673.3	13.3**
Departure from parallelism	1	25.9	25.9	0.2
Combined curvature	1	6.8	6.8	0.05
Opposed curvature	1	3.0	3.0	0.02
Error	42	5286.8	125.9	—
	47	7776.7	—	—

* $P < 0.05$
** $P < 0.01$

that a highly significant dose-response slope was obtained, and that the doses of the preparations as given may have differed in mean potency. Departures from linearity and parallelism are negligible, in fact they are somewhat smaller than might be expected from the magnitude of the error term, but not significantly so, as the value of F with 42 and 1 degrees of freedom for the larger and smaller variances, respectively, has to be very large for significance—greater than 250, even at the 5% level.

The modification of (5) to be used in determining M when there are 3 dosage groups per substance is

$$M = \sqrt{8/3}\ ID/B$$
$$= \sqrt{8/3} \times 0.3010 \times \sqrt{790.9}/\sqrt{1673.3}$$
$$= 0.336$$

Hence the log of the potency of 3.2 mg. of the unknown, which was assumed equal to 1 unit of the standard in setting up the test, is 0.336, antilog 2.17. Therefore 3.2 mg. is equivalent to 2.17 units of the standard and 1 mg. = 0.68 units.

The standard error of M is approximately as in Eq. (6a), where $K = \sqrt{8/3}$, whence $s_m = 0.167$. The value of t for 42 degrees of freedom at $P = 0.95$ is 2.02; the limits of error of the determination of potency are thus the antilogs of $0.336 \pm (2.02 \times 0.167)$, or 1.00 and 4.71 units approximately per 3.2 mg.; 0.31 to 1.47 units per 1 mg. The percentage accuracy at $P = 0.95$ is therefore 46–218% approximately.

If an assay like this had unbalanced dosage groups, and/or unequal spacing of doses, the calculations would be tedious and the total yield of information less. It has been stressed above that this can normally be avoided, and even the loss of one or two observations does not prohibit the application of the methods just employed. Missing values can be supplied from the internal evidence of the test, allowance being made for the loss in precision in the estimation of error (Snedecor, 1956; Emmens, 1948).

B. Increasing Precision

Various ways of increasing the precision of assays have already been mentioned—care in randomizing, selection of the response and perhaps of a transform of it, the use of concomitant variables, use of balanced designs, and the use of within-animal or within-litter estimates of error. We are usually concerned with trying to guarantee the homogeneity of the biological material entering assays, or to take such measures as covariance analysis to reduce the effects of measurable heterogeneity. The same is achieved by segregation of possible sources of heterogeneity in the design of assays, some types of which may allow quite heterogeneous material to be used if there are no interactions with dosage levels.

Whenever the test objects can be subdivided into several groups believed to be more homogeneous than the whole, or whenever a test object can be used more than once, various *restrictions* in the design of assays become possible, which will usually contribute materially to the reduction of error. It may also be possible to give different doses to different animals in the same subclass, after preliminary knowledge of individual response levels (Bliss and Marks, 1939b; Claringbold, 1955).

A simple instance is provided by litter mates. If it is possible to place one litter mate into each dosage group in an assay, then a series of litters may be used to build up a test in which differences within litters are used in the estimation of potency and error. Each litter may be regarded as a complete assay in itself, since every dose is represented, but there will be no estimate of error from each individual litter, since only one animal is in each group. However, the degrees of freedom which represent over-all response differences between dosage groups may be examined separately, leaving other degrees of freedom associated with *litter-dose interactions,* which it will usually be profitable to use as an estimate of error. The interaction measured is that concerned with the extent to which different litters reacted differently to the various doses, irrespective of the general level of response of each litter. An example may make things clear, as in Table VII, which gives the responses of eight litters of ovariectomized

TABLE VII

RESPONSES OF LITTER-MATE RATS TO INJECTED ESTRONE

Litter No.	Dose of estrone (μg.)			Totals, T_l
	0.2	0.4	0.8	
1	106	116	145	367
2	72	88	135	295
3	42	68	115	225
4	64	111	136	311
5	70	111	133	314
6	56	68	85	209
7	42	63	87	192
8	65	70	150	285
T_p	517	695	986	2198 (T)

a Adapted from Bülbring and Burn (1935); uterine weights are given in milligrams.

rats to estrone, which when injected causes uterine enlargement. There were three levels of estrone in geometrical progression. These data are not an assay, but half of an assay, showing only responses to a standard (adapted from Bülbring and Burn, 1935).

From Table VII it will be seen that litter 1 gave a much greater mean uterine weight than litter 7, but the changes caused by differences in dosage level are much the same—an increase of 39 mg. in litter 1 from 0.2 to 0.8 μg. of estrone, and one of 45 mg. in litter 7. The other litters give a similar picture and when this occurs, the elimination of the mean levels of response of whole litters is required to reduce the estimate of error, which would otherwise be artificially inflated by the very procedure designed to reduce it. The form of the appropriate analysis is shown in Table VIII, where the 23 degrees of freedom available in the assay are segregated into 7 associated with differences between litters, 2 with differences between doses, and the remaining

TABLE VIII

ANALYSIS OF VARIANCE OF THE DATA IN TABLE VII

Source of variation	Degrees of freedom	Sum of squares	Mean square	F
Between litters	7	8509	1216	7.1**
Between doses				
(a) Linear regression	1	13748	13748	80.3***
(b) Curvature	1	266	266	1.6
Within litters (error)	14	2396	172	—
	23	24918	—	—

* $P < 0.01$.
** $P < 0.001$.

14 with variation within litters. The variation between litters is significantly greater than that within them ($F = 7.1$, $P < 0.01$) and a gain in information has thus been achieved. Had litter mates been ignored, the sum of squares for error would have been 10905 with 21 degrees of freedom, and a mean square of 519.4, three times as large as the proper term for error. This failure in segregation could occur at either of two stages: (1) by omitting to allocate litter mates properly in the design of the assay, or (2) by failing to segregate the appropriate sum of squares in analysis.

In the assay of insulin, as described above, the same rabbits may be used repeatedly, and differences between individuals are commonly segregated in analysis. In one example, Bliss and Marks (1939b) found the mean square between rabbits to be 845 and that within rabbits 41.4. The between-rabbit sum of squares was 9296.9, associated with 11 degrees of freedom; that within rabbits was 3149.5, associated with 76 degrees of freedom, so that an estimate ignoring the structure of the assay would have associated 9296.9 plus 3149.5 with 87 degrees of freedom, giving a mean square of 143.1, three and a half times the real error of the assay.

The *Latin square* is a popular example of the type of restriction under discussion, first used extensively in agricultural research, where it had a physical application. If a square or rectangular field of crops is subdivided into a number of smaller rectangles (plots) like a chessboard, the yield per acre will be more uniform in any one plot than over the field as a whole. Then if experimental treatments are so allotted to these plots that each falls into one row and one column, as in Fig. 3, any regular gradients across or down the field may be eliminated in part or whole by segregating sums of squares in analysis which represent differences between rows and columns. The 36 plots in Fig. 3 yield 35 degrees of freedom which may then be subdivided into 5 between rows, 5 between columns, 5 between treatments, and 20 for

```
C   F   A   B   E   D
B   E   C   F   D   A
D   B   F   C   A   E
E   D   B   A   C   F
F   A   E   D   B   C
A   C   D   E   F   B
```

FIG. 3. A 6 × 6 Latin square.

the estimation of error. These 20 degrees of freedom represent complex interactions between rows, columns, and treatments and the design will succeed in its purpose of reducing the magnitude of the error term only in so far as these are smaller than the fertility differences over the whole field. If replicates (repeat measurements) are possible from within plots, a true estimate of error is available from which to assess the magnitude of the interactions.

In assays, the physical layout of rows and columns may be represented by positions in an animal house, but will more often be replaced by litters, times of injection, etc.

Such an arrangement must retain randomization, but within the restrictions imposed by design. It will still be true that each test object is as likely to receive any given dose as another, and the appropriate square would be selected at random from all possible squares by such methods as described by Fisher and Yates (1957). In an assay, a 4-point design could be accommodated by a 4 × 4 Latin square, with 4 test objects per dose, a 6-point design by a square such as that in Fig. 3, when the three doses each of the standard and unknown would be allotted at random to the letter A-F, if rows represented, say, litters and columns order of infection. When the same test object can be used repeatedly, it may form a row or column of such a square. Greater numbers of test objects per dosage groups may be desirable, if so, several ways of doubling-up or more are available. As just mentioned, each plot may receive more than one test object, or further squares may be added to the first as in the example by Bliss and Rose (1940) of the assay of parathyroid hormone in dogs. These authors used a series of 4 × 4 Latin squares in 4-point assays, so that 12 dogs in all were used, each at every dosage level on different occasions. In the general run of biological tests interaction is minimal, often completely absent, and a design like the Latin square succeeds frequently in achieving the desired control of error, even without intraplot replication.

C. Utilizing Restricted Material

When the maximum number of test objects which fall naturally into a homogeneous group, such as a litter or a set of twins is small, it may be necessary to balance an assay in a different way from those already discussed. *Incomplete blocks,* none of which contain the full range of doses, may be used, so that in sum they provide the necessary information because of the balance in design. *Symmetrical pairs* form a special case of a balanced incomplete block design, and were described by Bliss and Rose (1940). Table IX gives an example of the

TABLE IX

Assay Schemes: One Complete Replicate of Each Symmetrical Pair or Trio Is Shown

Pair No.	Doses		Trio No.	Doses		
1	U_1	U_2	1	U_1	U_2	S_1
2	U_1	S_1	2	U_1	U_2	S_2
3	U_1	S_2	3	U_1	S_1	S_2
4	U_2	S_1	4	U_2	S_1	S_2
5	U_2	S_2	—		—	
6	S_1	S_2	—		—	

layout of an assay using symmetrical pairs, where twin pairs of animals were used in a 4-point assay. Any pair, used once only in this assay, could receive no more than two doses of the standard and/or unknown, but the arrangement in Table IX of the six pairs of animals is such that every possible combination of doses is given to a pair. Table IX also gives a similar scheme for using trios of animals. Symmetrical pairs must be used in multiples of six, and trios in multiples of four. The analysis of these designs is not simple, and if they are employed it is recommended that professional assistance be sought.

Cross-over tests were first used in the assay of insulin, which still provides the neatest example in the twin cross-over test of Smith *et al.* (1944). The neat feature of the test is the confounding of differences between rabbits with departure from parallelism of dose-response lines, in a test in which the slope of the dose-response line is known with virtual certainty to be the same for both substances, both being pure or nearly pure insulin. A more accurate estimate of the value for the combined slope and potency differences is available from the within-rabbits sum of squares, while a difference in combined slope on the 2 days of the assay does not affect the results. Table X illustrates

TABLE X

SCHEME FOR A TWIN CROSS-OVER TEST

Group	First day	Second day
1	S_2	U_1
2	S_1	U_2
3	U_2	S_1
4	U_1	S_2

the layout of such a test. Four groups, each of 3 rabbits, receive doses as in the table, the high dose of the unknown and the low dose of the standard are crossed over in two of them, and the reverse cross is made in the other two groups, the test occupying 2 days. Differences between days are then eliminated in analysis, while a difference in the number of animals per group does not affect the working in a particular test.

Comparisons which can be built up from differences between successive responses from the same group are *within-animal* comparisons, those built up from the sums of successive responses from the same group are *between-animal* comparisons, with a lower precision. For rapid calculation the sums (Y) and differences (y) are determined and given suffixes corresponding with their group numbers in Table X. Then:

$$M = ISy/y_2 + y_3 - y_1 - y_4),$$

where I is the log dose interval as usual, V_y is estimated from the differences for individual animals within groups, with $(Sn_p - 4)$ degrees of freedom.

Departure from parallelism is measured by the quantity,

$$(Y_1 + Y_4) - (Y_2 + Y_3)$$

and has a variance $(VY)S(1/n_p)$ based on between-animal sums of squares, also associated with $(Sn_p - 4)$ degrees of freedom. Limits of error are calculated as follows:

1. F for 1 and $(Sn_p - 4)$ degrees of freedom is taken from the table of F at the required level of P.

2. $U^2 = (y_2 + y_3 - y_1 - y_4)^2 - (FVy)S(1/n_p)$ at the chosen level of P.

3. $UT = (y_2 + y_3 - y_1 - y_4) Sy - (FVy)(1/n_2 + 1/n_3 - 1/n_1 - 1n_4)$ is also calculated.

4. The *fiducial* limits of error are the roots of the equation:

$$U^2m^2 - 2UTIm + T^2I^2 = 0, \text{ solving for } m.$$

D. Groups of Assays

Groups of assays may combine several estimations of potency of different substances at the same time, serial estimates of potency of the same substance at different times or in different places, or combinations of these. The object of simultaneously testing several compounds is to save time and material, in that one set of test objects on the standard may suffice for all unknowns. Various designs will suggest themselves for this purpose, and if restrictions are to be included in design, as in a Latin square, a suitable type must be chosen so that

TABLE XI

Penicillin Assay by the Cylinder Plate Method[a]

Sample	Dose of solution (ml.)		
	0.8	1.0	1.25
Standard	607	673	740
	577	615	645
	605	643	700
	1789	1931	2085
U_1	614	661	742
	582	615	652
	590	630	689
	1786	1906	2083
U_2	608	652	758
	580	611	633
	605	630	684
	1793	1893	2075
U_3	606	661	723
	568	596	637
	562	584	659
	1736	1841	2019

[a] An assay of three samples. From Emmens (1948).

all dosage levels of all substances contribute equally to the summed totals for various integral restrictions. There is a limit to this, and groups of tests made simultaneously are most often of fairly simple structure.

The results of a group of simultaneous tests can be pooled, if they turn out to be reasonably homogeneous in respect of error terms, to give improved estimates of slope and error, or of any departures from parallelism, or curvature, that may occur.

Table XI gives an example from Emmens (1948) in which three simultaneous assays of penicillin samples were made on an agar plate, the drug inhibiting the growth of *Staphylococcus aureus* to an extent depending on potency. Circular areas of inhibited growth of the seeded culture are scored according to their respective diameters. The diameter increases with increasing dose and is linearly related to the log dose over a wide range. The analysis of variance is shown in Table XII,

TABLE XII

ANALYSIS OF VARIANCE OF THE DATA IN TABLE XI

Source of variation	Degrees of freedom	Sum of squares	Mean square	F
Between doses				
Linear regression	1	55873	55873	44.2***
Combined curvature	1	697	697	0.6
Between substances	3	2944	981	0.8
Dose/substance interaction	6	194	32	0.03***
Error	24	30332	1264	—
	35	90040	—	—

*** $P < 0.001$.

in which the combined linear regression for the standard and three unknowns is shown to be highly significant, but terms representing curvature and differences between substances are not significant. The dose/substance interaction, with 6 degrees of freedom, is also highly significantly less than expectation, which is the same as the error term. This arises because in actual fact the different doses and substances were not randomized on the surface of the agar plate, but were placed systematically, so that they sampled the irregularities of the medium more effectively than should occur by chance. However, they were not arranged in a design which allows segregation of the systematic effects, and so an error term resulted which is in excess of the value it should have, so that a precise assay has been accompanied by a decrease in apparent precision.

If we assume an unbiased estimate of error, this combined term for all substances would be used together with the combined estimate of slope for determining the potencies and limits of error for the three substances under test by the usual means, with the advantage that a larger number of degrees of freedom is available for estimation than would otherwise be the case.

In a series of tests made over a period or in different places, a very similar structure may be used if the assays are logically planned, U_1, U_2, U_3, etc., being replaced by T_1, T_2, T_3, etc., representing different times or places; and consistency of estimates and a combined estimate for all assays are easy to compute. With different places of testing, care should in particular be taken to check homogeneity of variance. Even when such tests are made on different plans, combined estimates of slope and of error may still be justified, with improved over-all accuracy. Methods for testing various aspects of homogeneity in combined assays are given by Emmens (1948).

It should also be noted that, for maximal efficiency in simultaneous tests, although not usually for maximum ease of computation with most designs, there should be more test objects on the standard preparation than on each unknown. If N is the number of unknowns, $\sqrt{N}$ times the number of observations on any one unknown should be made with the standard. With any but simple or special designs, it is easier to forego this advantage for the others consequent upon more balanced assays.

E. FIDUCIAL LIMITS OF ERROR

Until the paper by Irwin (1943), it was not commonly realized that the formula using s_M and t as above is misleading when calculating limits of error of M, unless b/s_b exceeds about 8, when some 5% error is involved at the most. The approximate formula gives finite limits of error at levels of P at which the slope itself may not differ from zero. Accurately calculated limits, which take the error of b into account, are called *fiducial limits of error* to indicate their greater precision. Corresponding *confidence limits* were calculated by Bliss (1946) when referring to factorially designed assays and have essentially the same meaning. These limits must be calculated anew for each value of P, as in the example above dealing with twin cross-over tests.

The calculation of fiducial limits for the assay of insulin on page

28, for which the approximate limits were 46–218% gives, for example, new limits of 53–374%, which are not only wider than before but are different in range. The estimate of relative potency is not affected, only its limits of error. In this assay b/s_b is only 3.6, hence the big difference. Irwin (1943) gives a table of examples showing how the value of b/s_b affected the comparison of approximate and fiducial limits of error at $P = 0.95$ and $P = 0.99$; these results are shown in Table XIII.

TABLE XIII

COMPARISON OF FIDUCIAL AND APPROXIMATE LIMITS OF ERROR[a]

b/s_b	$P = 0.95$		$P = 0.99$	
	Fiducial %	Approx. %	Fiducial %	Approx. %
2.74	19–143	58–172	0–155	49–204
2.76	72–117	85–117	24–127	81–123
3.64	53–128	72–139	29–136	65–155
3.76	80–128	82–123	71–148	77–131
3.90	76–122	82–123	63–131	77–131
3.98	83–119	85–117	75–129	81–123
4.08	83–123	84–119	77–137	80–125
4.05	83–121	85–118	75–131	80–125
4.75	83–116	86–117	76–122	82–122
5.17	88–116	88–114	83–122	85–118
5.36	85–116	87–116	80–123	83–121

[a] The median fertility dose of vitamin E in rats. Modified from Irwin (1943).

V. Assays Based on Quantal Responses

A. BALANCED DESIGNS

Just as with graded response assays, the simplest valid assay with quantal responses is the 4-point design, again with equal numbers per group and equal log spacing of doses. If probits or logits are then used, the calculations are not as simple as with graded responses, as the variance differs at different levels of response, and the error variance is supplied theoretically; the goodness of fit of the data to that theory is tested by χ^2. If this test indicates heterogeneity, and the fact that the theoretical variance is exceeded in the data, any single assay when so treated is unlikely to give much information, as a heterogeneity factor has to be introduced which not only incorporates the increased estimate of variance, but also the very few degrees of freedom on which it is based (only 2 in 4-point assay).

When probits are used, the following steps must be taken:

1. Two parallel straight lines are drawn by eye, or with the help of formulas (Emmens, 1948), one to fit the data for the standard and the other that for the unknown, as well as can be managed. Allowance is made for 0 or 100% responses, but only by slightly altering the slope if these occur at the end of the dose range.

2. The provisional lines are then used to read off the *expected probit* at each dosage level used. (The observed probits are called the *empirical probits*.) From these two, *corrected probits* are calculated from tables such as those of Bliss (1938) or Fisher and Yates (1957). These are then used in conjunction with corresponding weighting factors, which allow for the variance of the probits concerned, to compute a first approximation to the common slope and separate positions of the dose-response lines.

3. If the provisional slope and the first calculated approximation differ by more than a small amount, which is not usually specified however, a second cycle has to be computed, and so on until successive approximations agree satisfactorily (a process of *iteration*). It may be necessary to go through four or five cycles, but fortunately not often. If the data are homogeneous and based on reasonable numbers—say, several groups per substance of 20 observations each—one or two computed cycles are often sufficient.

4. The final approximations to the dose-response lines are then tested for goodness of fit by χ^2 and for the tenability of the assumption that they are in fact parallel. Suitable methods are given in the references above, or by Finney (1952a, b).

5. The log ratio of potency is given by Eq. (5) (page 25); $\bar{Y}_u$ and $\bar{Y}_s$ are now the mean probits for the unknown and standard, respectively. With equal numbers per group and the same assumed dosage units, the equation does not simplify, as $\bar{X}_s$ and $\bar{X}_u$ are not the same unless the responses are identical at all corresponding levels, because of the introduction of the weighting factors in step 2. The variance of M is calculated integrally in performing the operations listed above, but it is based on the theoretical variances of the probits and used with infinite degrees of freedom in determining approximate limits of error. Fiducial limits of error should be calculated by the same methods as outlined above.

If the angular transformation is used, calculations are simplified, even with the above procedure, because the variance remains constant at all levels of response. As also indicated above, this transformation (and also the probit) may be used in two ways. Transformation of the *expected response* gives an exact iterative solution, but transformation of the *observed response* (or *empirical angle*) gives a rapid, noniterative procedure due to Eisenhart (1947). Claringbold *et al.* (1953) have pointed out that the two methods are very similar in practice, and it may be noted that Gaddum (1933) used the empirical probits when first evolving the method. However, if complete assurance is required, a single cycle of iteration by the exact method seems all that is required. This at least reduces even the full maximum likelihood solution to two cycles of computation, one of them very rapid. When this is done, exact fiducial limits may be calculated. If the noniterative procedure alone is used, despite its giving almost identical results, exact fiducial inference is not theoretically possible.

Claringbold *et al.* (1953) applied the approximate method with angles

TABLE XIV

COMPARATIVE VALUES OF REGRESSION COEFFICIENTS AND χ^2 FOR GOODNESS OF FIT[a]

Expt.	Eisenhart method b	Eisenhart method s_b	Fisher-Bliss method First cycle b	Fisher-Bliss method Second cycle b	Fisher-Bliss method Second cycle s_b
1	1.6	2.4	1.8	1.8	2.3
	12.7	2.1 $\chi_{[16]}^2 = 16.2$	12.6	12.6	2.0 $\chi_{[16]}^2 = 14.0$
	−6.9	2.1 $0.5 > P > 0.3$	−6.4	−6.4	2.0 $0.5 > P > 0.3$
	−11.4	2.1	−11.5	−11.5	2.0
2	2.8	2.1	2.7	2.7	2.0
	13.7	2.1 $\chi_{[17]}^2 = 7.3$	13.3	13.3	2.0 $\chi_{[17]}^2 = 8.8$
	10.4	2.4 $0.98 > P > 0.95$	10.1	10.1	2.3 $0.95 > P > 0.9$
	−9.1	2.1	−8.5	−8.6	2.0
3	−0.3	2.4	−0.6	−0.6	2.3
	10.9	2.1 $\chi_{[18]}^2 = 14.7$	10.9	11.0	2.0 $\chi_{[18]}^2 = 12.1$
	−14.6	2.1 $0.7 > P > 0.5$	−14.9	−15.0	2.0 $0.9 > P > 0.8$
4	7.0	1.5 $\chi_{[7]}^2 = 4.6$	7.1	7.0	1.4 $\chi_{[7]}^2 = 3.6$
	−7.2	1.5 $0.8 > P > 0.7$	−7.4	−7.4	1.4 $0.9 > P > 0.8$
5	17.7	3.3 $\chi_{[10]}^2 = 9.2$	17.6	17.6	3.2 $\chi_{[10]}^2 = 7.8$
	9.8	1.5 $0.7 > P > 0.5$	9.7	9.7	1.4 $0.7 > P > 0.5$
6	12.7	1.4	12.6	12.6	1.3
	3.1	1.1 $\chi_{[10]}^2 = 7.5$	2.6	2.7	1.1 $\chi_{[10]}^2 = 7.7$
	−2.7	0.9 $0.7 > P > 0.5$	−2.7	−2.8	0.9 $0.7 > P > 0.5$

[a] Six factorial experiments were analyzed by the method of Eisenhart (1947) and followed by two cycles of the Fisher-Bliss method (Claringbold, *et al.*, 1953).

in various designs leading to an analysis of variance (not possible with the weighted probit technique) and compared it with other transforms. Table XIV from this paper demonstrates that the approximate method, when applied in six factorial experiments and compared with two *further* cycles of the Fisher-Bliss method, gives very useful results. The table compares goodness of fit at the three stages of computation, which is perfectly satisfactory in all. There was no sensible difference between the two Fisher-Bliss cycles. However, had an attempt been made to start off with the usual probit technique, fitting complex provisional grids in several dimensions to the data, no such agreement could have been expected between the two cycles and difficulties would have been encountered in the calculations, which could not have been based on an analysis of variance.

The advantage of the angular transformation is thus rapidity and ease of calculation, applicability of the analysis of variance, and results which are in practice indistinguishable from those obtained with probits.

B. WITHIN-ANIMAL QUANTAL ASSAYS

These advantages are not enough, however, particularly when crossover quantal tests are possible, or tests in which any series of individual responses may be examined. It is then necessary, if analysis is to be at all feasible, to pass to the (0, 1) or (0, 1, 2) etc., methods of scoring described above. A within-animal bioassay with quantal responses was first performed by Claringbold (1956), who determined the approximate individual sensitivity of his animals (ovariectomized mice) in estrogen tests. He had already shown that about a fourfold gain in precision was to be expected if this were done (Claringbold, 1955). The results obtained in the 4-point cross-over assay are shown in Table XV. The design was in 6 Latin squares, each 4 × 4, so that each mouse received all dose levels of the standard and unknown by the end of the assay, but although the actual doses were in the same ratio throughout, each mouse was given an individual set of doses scaled to its own level of sensitivity, as are rabbits in the assay of insulin. Each mouse therefore yielded a total score which varied between zero and four, since it was scored only zero or one on each occasion. Very few examples of zero or four occurred, however, because of the scaling of doses, thus making the test more useful than if it had had many of them.

The data were then subjected to analysis of variance as shown in Table XVI, using 0 or 1 as the basic variate. Since the dose-response lines were not significantly different in slope, relative potency was computed and found to be 1.52 (1.16–1.99, $P = 0.95$), whereas the

TABLE XV

FOUR-POINT CROSS-OVER ASSAY WITH QUANTAL RESPONSES[a]

Latin square	Mouse No.	Mean sensitivity $(10^{-4} \mu g.)$	Order of tests				Responses to doses			
			1	2	3	4	S_1	S_2	U_1	U_2
I	1	4	S_1	S_2	U_1	U_2	0	1	0	0
	2	2	U_1	S_1	U_2	S_2	0	1	1	1
	3	8	U_2	U_1	S_2	S_1	0	1	0	1
	4	23	S_2	U_2	S_1	U_1	0	1	1	0
II	5	8	S_2	U_2	S_1	U_1	0	1	0	1
	6	6	U_1	S_2	U_2	S_1	0	1	0	1
	7	4	U_2	S_1	U_1	S_2	0	0	1	1
	8	4	S_1	U_1	S_2	U_2	0	1	0	1
III	9	3	U_2	S_2	S_1	U_1	0	0	0	1
	10	11	S_2	U_2	U_1	S_1	0	1	0	1
	11	3	S_1	U_1	S_2	U_2	0	1	1	1
	12	11	U_1	S_1	U_2	S_2	0	1	1	1
IV	13	8	U_2	S_2	S_1	U_1	0	1	0	1
	14	16	U_1	S_1	S_2	U_2	1	1	1	1
	15	4	S_1	U_2	U_1	S_2	0	1	0	1
	16	8	S_2	U_1	U_2	S_1	0	0	1	1
V	17	3	U_1	S_1	U_2	S_2	0	1	0	1
	18	23	U_2	U_1	S_2	S_1	0	1	1	1
	19	1	S_2	U_2	S_1	U_1	0	1	0	1
	20	23	S_1	S_2	U_1	U_2	0	1	1	1
VI	21	6	S_1	U_2	S_2	U_1	1	1	1	1
	22	1	U_2	S_2	U_1	S_1	0	0	1	1
	23	3	U_1	S_1	U_2	S_2	0	1	0	1
	24	11	S_2	U_1	S_1	U_2	0	1	0	1

[a] Modified from Claringbold (1955).

true figure was known to be 1.414. This assay entailed 96 observations, 4 with each of 24 mice, and was compared with an assay of normal design using 400 observations, 1 with each of 400 mice, analyzed by probits. This assay gave an estimate of 1.38 (1.02–1.85, $P = 0.95$), fiducial limits of error being calculated in each case. The ranges are almost the same, with over 4 times as many observations in the second assay.

The use of this type of score, with cross-over tests, was extended by Emmens (1957), who tested the effect on precision of analyzing the same extensive data from estrogen tests by analyses of variance

TABLE XVI

ANALYSIS OF VARIANCE OF THE DATA IN TABLE XV[a]

Source of variation	Degrees of freedom	Mean square	F
Between animals	23	0.12	0.9
Between times	3	0.05	0.4
Linear regression	1	9.38	68.0***
Parallelism	1	1.50	10.9**
Between substances	1	0.38	2.8
Error	66	0.138	—

[a] Claringbold (1955).
** $P < 0.01$.
*** $P < 0.001$.

employing the angular transformation, (0, 1) and (0, 1, 2) scoring, *without* adjustment of dosage for individual mice. As the tests took 16 weeks to perform, and all mice received the same doses, it was a matter for conjecture whether any great advantage would accrue. First, mice might not remain steady in relative sensitivity for so long a

TABLE XVII

RESPONSES OF MICE TO INTRAVAGINAL ESTROGENS[a]

Test	Estrogen				Proestrogen			
	1	2	3	4	5	6	7	8
Group I	9(2)	17(4)	12(3)	2(1)	4(1)	13(3)	17(4)	11(2)
II	19(4)	14(3)	7(1)	11(2)	18(4)	12(2)	12(1)	17(3)
III	8(1)	14(2)	17(4)	11(3)	10(2)	7(1)	20(3)	17(4)
IV	8(3)	10(1)	9(2)	17(4)	15(3)	18(4)	16(2)	10(1)
	Proestrogen				Estrogen			
V	9(1)	20(3)	15(2)	22(4)	19(4)	8(2)	14(3)	7(1)
VI	14(2)	12(1)	21(4)	19(3)	18(3)	14(4)	6(1)	11(2)
VII	15(3)	23(4)	7(1)	16(2)	11(1)	8(3)	14(2)	13(4)
VIII	15(4)	19(2)	16(3)	11(1)	5(2)	5(1)	16(4)	13(3)
Doses			1	2	3	4		
Response to estrogen			57	81	98	132		
Response to proestrogen			72	113	135	151		

[a] Twenty-four animals per group, in cross-over tests, showing group totals only for quantal (0, 1) scores, with dosage groups 1–4 in parentheses. Modified from Emmens (1957).

TABLE XVIII

ANALYSIS OF VARIANCE OF ANGULAR TRANSFORMATION[a]

Source of variation	Degrees of freedom	Sum of squares	Mean square	F
Tests	7	44.17	6.31	4.2***
Doses	7	268.45	38.35	25.7***
Groups	7	23.25	3.32	2.2*
Interaction	42	61.29	1.46	1.0
Theoretical variance	—		1.49	—

[a] Data in Table XVII, determined from group responses. From Emmens (1957).
*$P < 0.05$.
***$P < 0.001$.

period, although the data of Emmens (1939) indicated that they would, and second, too many 0 or 100% responses might occur. The chance of this was, however, minimized in the design of the test since each mouse was used eight times.

These tests were not assays, because they investigated the slope differences between estrogens and proestrogens (Emmens, 1941), but they were in all other respects of the same design as an assay would be, were slopes the same. The design is shown in Table XVII, with 0, 1 response scoring as an example. Tables XVIII to XX give analyses of variance for the angular transformation, (0, 1) scoring and (0, 1, 2) scoring, respectively.

Analysis with the angular transformation showed that there was indeed heterogeneity in response, differences between groups giving an

TABLE XIX

ANALYSIS OF VARIANCE OF (0, 1) SCORING[a]

Source of variation	Degrees of freedom	Sum of squares	Mean square	F
Tests	7	6.39	0.91	4.7***
Doses	7	40.77	5.82	29.8***
Interaction	42	8.89	0.21	1.1
Residual (= error 1)	1288	251.85	0.20	—
Groups	7	3.13	0.45	1.2
Animals within groups (= error 2)	184	69.74	0.38	—

[a] Data in Table XVII, based on individual scores. From Emmens (1957).
*** $P < 0.001$.

TABLE XX

ANALYSIS OF VARIANCE OF (0, 1, 2) SCORING[a]

Source of variation	Degrees of freedom	Sum of squares	Mean square	F
Tests	7	17.29	2.47	4.8***
Doses	7	156.04	22.29	43.7***
Interaction	42	22.64	0.54	1.1
Residual (= error 1)	1288	652.66	0.51	—
Groups	7	6.70	0.96	0.9
Animals within groups (= error 2)	184	193.30	1.05	—

[a] Data in Table XVII, based on individual scores, from Emmens (1957).
*** $P < 0.001$.

$F = 2.2$, $P < 0.05$. This would preclude assay, except with a heterogeneity factor of 2.2 and, in this rather extensive experiment, only 7 degrees of freedom for error. Analysis with the (0, 1) or (0, 1, 2) scores gets over this difficulty, in addition to making computation much easier. Because it is now practicable to use all of the 1535 degrees of freedom in the tests, variation both between and within individual animals, not groups of animals, is examined. In both Tables XIX and XX, we see that differences between groups are associated with approximately the same variance as differences between animals within groups, which in turn is about double the residual error (error 1 in the tables). The residual error, representing differences *within* animals and applicable to the within-animal comparisons of primary interest, is usable even in the presence of the heterogeneity between animals which confused the issue with angular analysis, with more than a twofold gain in precision, since the heterogeneity factor of 2.2 is accompanied by so few degrees of freedom.

VI. The Design of Assays

A. EXPLORING METHODS

When a general method of assay occurs to the investigator as being likely to prove fruitful, he usually needs to explore the variables which may be associated with it. The number and spacing of doses, the vehicle and method of administration, the time of final examination, the age or weight of animals, the effects of body weight, and the methods of measuring response are among the common factors which may need investigation. They often form a large array, complete examination of which may seem forbidding. Many workers have, in the past, spent up to several years investigating such variables, often in an incomplete fashion because of the methods employed.

If classic techniques are practiced, varying one thing at a time and keeping others constant, it will indeed be a long task to investigate a series of variables, and even then there will be no guarantee that the particular set of conditions chosen as optimal are in fact so. On the contrary, there is usually a greater likelihood that the optimum set of conditions within the system investigated has been missed. Factorial analysis of such situations was advocated by Fisher some time ago, and has been utilized widely in agricultural and some other fields, relatively little in bioassay other than in the restricted sense used above, in the factorial analysis of dose-response lines. What is needed in exploration is factorial planning of reasonable large-scale experiments designed to look into the possibilities of a general technique, varying as many factors as is feasible in each experiment. The advantages of such methods were pointed out by Fisher and many subsequent workers. Standard texts, such as Cochran and Cox (1950), may be consulted for details of the methods, but it seems worth while to point out briefly the advantages they convey.

A factorial experiment, whether involving an assay technique or otherwise, explores the possible effects of a number of variables simultaneously, in all possible combinations. Thus, the number of doses into which the material is subdivided for administration, the time over which they are spaced, and the total dose administered may form the subject of one factorial test. Suppose we decided to try 2, 3, and 4 doses per total amount administered, spaced equally over 1, 2, or 3 days, and totaling 1, 2, or 4 mg. It is usually best to do a few very simple pilot tests, with one or two test objects per group, before embarking on such a factorial experiment, so that we know roughly where the useful regions of response lie. Then such a test would have as a unit component $3 \times 3 \times 3$, or 27 test objects, each receiving a different combination of treatments, and would be referred to as a 3^3 factorial. It is most satisfactory to allot at least two test objects per treatment combination, and so advisable to have not less than 54 in such a test. In certain circumstances, particularly when it seems advisable to crowd as many factors in as possible above time, *replication* in this manner may be omitted, and each treatment combination may then be given to one test object only, and interaction used as a measure of error. In special circumstances, *partial replication,* which implies the use at any one time of an incomplete simple replicate, may be practiced, with the sacrifice of certain predetermined comparisons.

In the normal case, however, we shall have every treatment combination represented by several test objects and the within-cell variation can be used as error. Since every test object receives one level or another of every factor under test, each factor is investigated as fully as if the test were devoted to it alone, and, at the same time, its interaction with other factors is investigated. If there is no interaction between particular pairs of factors, we conclude that the test is indifferent to the particular combination of them we choose to use, whenever there is interaction, we can see its effect and decide at which levels to design the assay, and similarly with other higher combinations of factors.

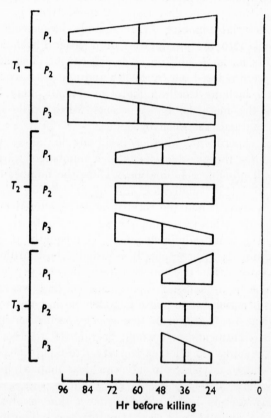

Fig. 4. Diagrammatic representation of the treatments in the experiment by Claringbold and Lamond (1957). Ordinates represent the proportion (M) of the total dose given at any one time.

Thus, the dose-response line may be steepest when 4 doses are given over 2 days, but had we made 1-factor tests all the time we might have explored the effect of doses over 3 days, and the effect of number of days at 2 doses, and so never have hit on the best combination. Had we built up a complete factorial by such methods, taking a long time and many tests to do it, we should still have confused time-to-time variation with the factors under examination and still be uncertain about the real magnitude of the effects we measured. Factorial experiments are thus more informative and economical of both time and material compared with other tests.

A practical example of a very similar experiment to that just discussed is provided by Claringbold and Lamond (1957), in designing an assay for gonadotropins—substances which stimulate testis or ovary growth and function in vertebrates. This particular test used a secondary response, growth of the uterus subsequent upon stimulation of the ovaries of mice. Figure 4 shows the plan of the test, which involved three ways of giving a total dose in three injections, namely in increasing, equal, or decreasing amounts, three spacings of dosage, over 72, 48, or 24 hours (T) and three dosage levels (P). The test was made with four mice per treatment combination. The mice were killed 24 hours after the last injection in all instances. Since variance depended on the level of response, the uterine weights were transformed to logarithms before analysis, a procedure giving approximately equal variances. The analysis of variance of the transformed data is given in Table XXI from which it will be seen that each factor gave highly significant effects. The conclusions were that:

(1) Administration of doses over a short period (24 hours) gave the highest responses.

(2) Three equal doses gave a greater response than either of the unequal dosage schedules (i.e., the quadratic term in the partitioning of doses was significant).

(3) The log dose response was linear over all combinations of treatments, but increased in slope as more of the dose was given in the first injection.

(4) Only one interaction in 20 was significant, and that only at the 5% level, which could readily have happened by chance.

The error mean square in this list was computed from the 3 degrees of freedom at each treatment combination, minus 3 degrees of freedom for missing values.

This experiment therefore demonstrated that a sensitive assay resulted from equal spacing of doses over a short period, although greater accuracy could be obtained if more of the dose were given

TABLE XXI

ANALYSIS OF VARIANCE[a]

Source of variation	Degrees of freedom	Mean square	F
Time base			
Linear	1	2532.3	10.9***
Quadratic	1	176.0	0.7
Partition			
Linear	1	93.4	0.4
Quadratic	1	1768.2	7.5**
Levels			
Linear	1	40375.3	170.8***
Quadratic	1	210.0	0.9
Interactions			
$P_L \times L_L$	1	1575.5	6.7*
Remainder	19	134.9	0.6
Error	77	236.5	—

[a] Data from the experiment illustrated in Fig. 4. Adapted from Claringbold and Lamond (1957).

* $P < 0.05$.
** $P < 0.01$.
*** $P < 0.001$.

early. Further tests showed the advantage of giving only one dose and killing the animals 44 hours later, omitting any later doses, which was the final form of the assay.

Another example of factorial analysis, this time at an even earlier stage of investigating a proposed assay technique, is provided by Lamond and Emmens (1959), when assays using hypophysectomized mice were in planning, but poor results were being obtained at operation, many of the animals dying within the first 24 hours after their pituitary glands had been removed. The factors thought most likely to be affecting survival were the duration of anesthesia, the age of the mouse, the air temperature, and adrenal insufficiency. Since the mice were to be used for pituitary-gonad investigations it was felt that cortical hormone therapy should be avoided, but glucose could be injected. Consequently, the basal anesthetic Avertin was used alone, or in a half-dose plus ether anesthesia, giving a briefer total period of anesthesia; mice were used at 18 or 25 days of age; air temperatures of 78° or 87° Fahrenheit were tried; and 0.3 ml. of 5% glucose was given intraperitoneally after the operation in half of the cases. This was therefore a 2^4 factorial test, the results of which are shown in Table

TABLE XXII

GROUPS OF TEN SURVIVAL[a]

Anesthetics	Age (days)	Air temp., °F.	Glucose?	24 hr	48 hr	75 hr[b]
Avertin	18	78	+	4	1	1(1)
(0.01 ml./gm.)			−	5	4	3(2)
		87	+	2	2	2(2)
			−	5	4	3(2)
	25	78	+	9	7	7(4)
			−	7	7	7(6)
		87	+	7	7	7(2)
			−	8	8	7(4)
Avertin	18	78	+	9	6	6(5)
(0.005 ml./gm.)			−	9	7	6(5)
plus ether		87	+	9	9	8(7)
			−	10	10	10(8)
	25	78	+	10	9	9(8)
			−	9	9	9(5)
		87	+	10	10	10(7)
			−	9	9	9(6)

The header for the surviving mice columns: "Treatments" spans Air temp./Glucose; "Surviving mice at" spans 24 hr / 48 hr / 75 hr.

[a] Hypophysectomized mice after various operational procedures. From Lamond and Emmens (1959).

[b] Figures in parentheses show completely hypophysectomized survivors, upon which analysis is based.

XXII, using 10 mice per group. The figures themselves demonstrate unequivocally that the anesthetic technique was at fault in earlier trials; reducing the period of anesthesia resulted in far fewer deaths over all the other treatment combinations, which did not themselves differ significantly. Summing totals over each pair of factors, we get, among the completely hypophysectomized survivors:

	Living mice
Effect of anesthesia	23:51
Effect of age	32:42
Effect of temperature	36:38
Effect of glucose	36:38

The data were converted to angles to equalize variances, the analysis of variance is shown in Table XXIII and confirms the conclusions above. The suspicion of an age effect is seen not to be confirmed.

TABLE XXIII

Analysis of Variance[a]

Source of variation	Degrees of freedom	Mean square	F
Anesthetics	1	1853	22.6***
Age	1	251	3.1
Temperature	1	11	0.1
Glucose therapy	1	13	0.2
Interactions	11	84	1.0
Error	∞	82	—

[a] Data in Table XXI (complete hypophysectomy). From Lamond and Emmens (1959).

*** $P < 0.001$.

B. Regions of Useful Response

In factorial tests, or in assays based upon them, one is likely to encounter the difficulty that certain regions of the design are liable to give no response or maximal responses, and to convey little information at the same time as making analysis difficult because of problems concerning equalization of variance. This is particularly acute when quantal responses are in question. To overcome this trouble, *parallelogram* designs were introduced by Claringbold *et al.* (1953). Consider an $n \times m$ factorial design as in Fig. 5, where whole areas are

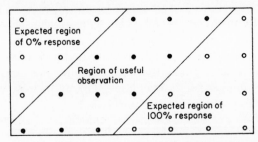

Fig. 5. Region of useful response in a parallelogram design. From Claringbold *et al.* (1953).

expected to give 0 or 100% responses. Then doses of X_1 and X_2 can be given which avoid these regions, as do the solid dots in the figure. The analysis of variance is treated in detail by Claringbold *et al.* (1953) and presents no difficulties; the following example is taken from the same paper (Table XXIV). This table shows the effect of the time interval (X_1) and dosage of estrone (X_2) or the response

TABLE XXIV

THE EFFECT OF THE INTERVAL OF TIME (X_1) BETWEEN DIVIDED DOSES OF ESTRONE ON THE PERCENTAGE VAGINAL RESPONSE IN OVARIECTOMIZED MICE[a]

Dose estrone (10^{-4} μg.)	Time interval (hr.)			
	0.89	2.67	8.0	24.0
1				20
2				45
4			15	50
8			30	70
16		30	35	
32		55	65	
64	25	60		
128	30	70		
256	6)			
512	85			

[a] From Claringbold et al. (1953).

of ovariectomized mice in the vaginal smear test, scored quantally. At short time intervals, a much higher dose is needed than at longer intervals, so that the dosage scale must be ascended as the interval lengthens, in order to obtain useful responses. This experiment, when analyzed by taking empirical responses (Eisenhart, 1947), gave the results shown in Table XXV, demonstrating a highly significant linear dose-response relationship unaffected in slope by the time interval chosen. The position effect has been absorbed by the design of the test and does not appear in the analysis.

TABLE XXV

ANALYSIS OF VARIANCE BY EMPIRICAL ANGLES[a]

Source of variation	Degrees of freedom	Sum of squares	Mean square	F
Doses				
Linear	1	1883.7	1883.7	44.7***
Quadratic	1	3.1	3.1	0.1
Cubic	1	23.5	23.5	0.6
Time interval	3	254.5	84.8	2.1
Interactions	9	191.0	21.2	0.5
Theoretical variance	—		41.0	—

[a] From Claringbold et al. (1953).
*** $P < 0.001$.

It is easy to extend this design to many dimensions, as in 2^n or 3^n, etc., factorials; or to extend it, should it be necessary, to curvilinear relationships.

C. MIXTURES OF SUBSTANCES

A considerable literature has accumulated on tests of joint action of hormones, insecticides, and other substances, reviewed by Finney (1952a). Its importance to assay is that methods are offered by which, in certain circumstances, the similarity of action of substances under assay may be examined. If two substances are acting in the same manner, such that one may be assayed in terms of the other, a test involving mixtures of the two should reveal comparable activity to that shown by either one alone. If antagonism or potentiation of any kind is seen, the similarity of their action should be doubted, whereas if like action is indicated the evidence is of a stronger nature than mere parallel dose-response lines. Even so, care must be taken in the interpretation of such tests.

Joint action tests may be quite complex; the principle however is simple. If dose A of substance 1 is equivalent in effect to dose B of substance 2, and if the dose-response lines are parallel (as they will be in a valid assay), we may investigate mixtures of 1 and 2 to see if the dose-response lines remain linear and parallel to the originals. One such mixture could be $A/2 + B/2$, others $A/4 + 3B/4$, and so on, where A and B may then take a series of values up the dose-response lines. If substances 1 and 2 act either antagonistically or co-operatively, mixtures giving lesser or greater responses than might be expected, the dose-response lines will curve, or, alternatively, mixtures expected to give a constant level of response will fail to do so. Thus, in the examination of gonadotropin action on the mouse uterus as in assays cited above, Lamond and Claringbold (1958) found that various mixtures of gonadotropins acted in a purely additive manner, indicating, in this assay at least, similar action. Figure 6 gives examples of two such mixtures, with the responses shown diagrammatically in the form of fitted regression surfaces. In the HMG:HCG mixtures (mixtures of human menopausal and human chorionic gonadotropins), equivalent doses were misjudged, but this merely resulted in a skew surface, with linearity unaffected.

It is of great interest that other evidence (Lamond and Emmens, 1959) clearly demonstrates the *dissimilarity* of action of some of these substances in a different type of test, also on the mouse uterus, but

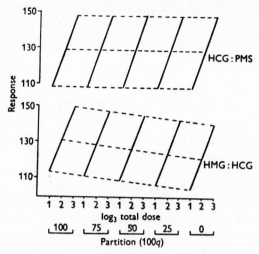

F<small>IG</small>. 6. Regression surfaces fitted to the data of Lamond and Claringbold (1958) by the authors, showing equivalence of action of all mixtures of various gonadotropins in pairs (HCG, PMS, and HMG).

in hypophysectomized animals. In the tests of Lamond and Claringbold (1958), intact animals were used, whose own hormone secretions entered the picture and entirely changed the action of injected substances in some cases. This finding is a warning to be very cautious about accepting even seemingly convincing evidence of a purely statistical nature in the hormone field. Parallel dose-response lines and apparently complete similarity of action did not, in this case, guarantee that the pairs of substances act alike on the ovary in all circumstances, let alone that one could be regarded as a dilution of the other.

D. PREDICTING REQUIREMENTS

When an assay method has been established, the characteristics of the dose-response line may be used to predict requirements in future assays, on the assumption that these characteristics remain constant. It is also necessary to assume that the responses to the doses of the standard and unknown(s) to be given will not differ greatly and will fall within predetermined limits.

The minimal possible error occurs if the mean responses to the standard and unknown are equal, and if the same number of responses are obtained to each. The standard error of M is then

$$s_M{}^2 = 2s^2/nb^2,$$

where s^2 is the error variance and n is the total number of responses to one preparation.

The least number of observations required with each substance to obtain a given level of accuracy is such that

$$n = 2s^2/b^2 s_M{}^2,$$

where s_M is to be assigned the desired value. The calculated limits of error in an assay which turns out to have the s and b postulated may unfortunately not be as narrow as predicted, unless previous experience is taken into account and lower errors for b, in particular, can be assigned. In an assay with a relatively small number of observations, even s may be associated with too few degrees of freedom to give narrow limits of error when the internal evidence of that test alone is utilized. However, a prediction assuming a constant s and b can validly be accompanied, when the assay fulfills the prediction, by the use of average values based on past experience.

Suppose we require limits of about 83–120% in an assay. This corresponds with a log standard error of 0.04, hence the limits of error of M will be $M \pm 2ts_M$ at $P = 0.95$, or $M \pm 0.08$, approximately, if n is fairly large (say, greater than 20). Then if s^2 is 50, and b is 20, we have

$$n = (2 \times 50)/(20^2 \times 0.04^2)$$
$$= 100/0.8^2$$
$$= 157 \text{ observations per substance, a rather imprecise assay method.}$$

In quantal assays, $s^2 = 1$, if probits or angles are employed, and an average value must be assumed for the weighting factor. This is usually taken as 0.5, the approximate factor for 20 or 80% of responses, intermediate responses carrying somewhat higher weights, up to 0.637 for 50%. The approximate equation for n is then:

$$n = 2/wb^2 s_M{}^2$$

where w is the weighting factor.

Thus, in a quantal assay with a slope of 5 probits and an assumed w of 0.5, limits of error of 83–120% ($P = 0.95$) can be expected if not less than $2/(0.5 \times 5^2 \times 0.04^2)$ observations are made per substance, or $n = 100$.

In assays where litter mates are used, the appropriate design and analyses must be applied in any future work, if previous experience is to be used for prediction, when the error mean square as derived in typical tests may, if homogeneous, be used in such predictions. If crossing-over has been done then similar cross-over tests may also be expected to show the same mean square for error, on the average, but differently designed assays, taking account of other or additional factors to those appearing in earlier work, may have quite different limits of error.

The number of animals needed in practice in various biological assays is very variable. Although an assay with a λ value of more than 0.4 is frowned upon, some techniques such as the intravaginal estimation of estrogen have proved essential as research tools and thus have continued in use despite very poor precision. Such an assay, with a slope of 2 and a λ of 0.5 may need several hundred animals per substance, unless within-animal estimates are used, when at least 100 observations will still be needed for reasonable precision, say 80–125% limits (Claringbold, 1956). At the other end of the scale, some remarkably precise assays have been recorded even without within-animal estimates. Such are the assay of serum gonadotropin, using litter-mate rats (British Pharmacopoeia, 1948), where about 6 animals per substance give limits of error of 80–125%, and even without litter mates only about 13 per substance are needed (in practice, 12 or 14). Adrenal cortical activity as measured by the total hepatic fermentable sugar in the rat requires only about 16 rats per substance for comparable precision, again using random animals. Other assay range between these extremes, more typical values lying between 25 and 50 animals per substance for the limits quoted. It is rare for adequate numbers to be used in the laboratory to give such precise results, limits more like 50–200% are frequently accepted in both clinical and fundamental work, particularly in the former, where limited material often prohibits any attempt at high accuracy. It is unfortunate that high sensitivity (response to small quantities of hormone) seems usually to be accompanied by poor accuracy, so that many test objects must be used in an attempt to gain precision and thus the total quantity of the unknown required may still be substantial.

REFERENCES

Berkson, J. (1949). *J. Am. Statist. Assoc.* 44, 273.

Biggers, J. D. (1951). *J. Endocrinol.* 8, 169.

Biggers, J. D., and Claringbold, P. J. (1954). *Nature* 174, 596.

Bliss, C. I. (1938). *Quart. J. Pharm. Pharmacol.* 11, 192.

Bliss, C. I. (1940). *J. Am. Statist. Assoc.* 35, 498.

Bliss, C. I. (1944). *J. Am. Statist. Assoc.* 33, 225.

Bliss, C. I. (1946). *Biometrics* 1, 57.

Bliss, C. I., and Marks, H. P. (1939a). *Quart. J. Pharm. Pharmacol.* 12, 82.

Bliss, C. I., and Marks, H. P. (1939b). *Quart. J. Pharm. Pharmacol.* 12, 182.

Bliss, C. I., and Rose, C. L. (1940). *Am. J. Hyg.* 31, 79.

Bülbring, E. (1937). *J. Physiol.* (*London*) 89, 64.

Bülbring, E. and Burn, J. H. (1935). *J. Physiol. (London)* **85**, 320.

Burn, J. H. (1937). "Biological Standardization," 288 pp. Oxford Univ. Press, London and New York.

Calloway, N. O., McCormack, R. M., and Singh, N. P. (1942). *Endocrinology* **30**, 423.

Claringbold, P. J. (1955). *J. Endocrinol.* **13**, 11.

Claringbold, P. J. (1956). *J. Roy. Statist. Soc. B*, **18**, 133.

Claringbold, P. J., and Emmens, C. W. (1961). In press.

Claringbold, P. J., and Lamond, D. R. (1957). *J. Endocrinol.* **16**, 86.

Claringbold, P. J., and Sobey, W. R. (1957). *Australian J. Biol. Sci.* **10**, 360.

Claringbold, P. J., Biggers, J. D., and Emmens, C. W. (1953). *Biometrics* **9**, 467.

Cochran, W. G., and Cox, G. M. (1950). "Experimental Designs," 454 pp. Wiley, New York.

Dorfman, R. I. (1950). *In* "Hormone Assay" (C. W. Emmens, ed.), Chapter 14, pp. 326-362. Academic Press, New York.

Eisenhart, C. (1947). *In* "Techniques of Statistical Analysis," Chapter 16. McGraw-Hill, New York.

Emmens, C. W. (1939). *Med. Research Council (Brit.) Spec. Rept. Ser.* **234**.

Emmens, C. W. (1941). *J. Endocrinol.* **2**, 444.

Emmens, C. W. (1948). "Principles of Biological Assay," 206 pp. Chapman and Hall, London.

Emmens, C. W. (1950). *In* "Hormone Assay" (C. W. Emmens, ed.), pp. 1-32. Academic Press, New York.

Emmens, C. W. (1957). *J. Endocrinol.* **16**, 148.

Emmens, C. W. (1960). *Biometrics* **16**, 161.

Finney, D. J. (1945). *Quart. J. Pharm. Pharmacol.* **18**, 77.

Finney, D. J. (1952a). "Probit Analysis," 2nd ed., 318 pp. Cambridge Univ. Press, London and New York.

Finney, D. J. (1952b). "Statistical Methods in Biological Assay," 661 pp. Griffin, London.

Fisher, R. A. (1954). "Statistical Methods for Research Workers," 12th ed., 356 pp. Oliver and Boyd, Edinburgh.

Fisher, R. A., and Yates, F. (1957). "Statistical Tables," 5th ed., 138 pp. Oliver and Boyd, Edinburgh.

Gaddum, J. H. (1933). *Med. Research Council (Brit). Spec. Rept. Ser.* **183**.

Irwin, J. O. (1937). *J. Roy. Statist. Soc. Suppl.* **4**, 1.

Irwin, J. O. (1943). *J. Hyg.* **43**, 121.

Lamond, D. R., and Claringbold, P. J. (1958). *J. Endocrinol.* **16**, 298.

Lamond, D. R., and Emmens, C. W. (1959). *J. Endocrinol.* **18**, 251.

Pedersen-Bjergaard, K. (1939). "Comparative Studies Concerning the Strengths of Estrogenic Substances." Oxford Univ. Press, London and New York.

Smith, K. W., Marks, H. P., Fieller, E. C., and Broom, W. A. (1944). *Quart. J. Pharm. Pharmacol.* **17**, 112.

Snedecor, G. W. (1956). "Statistical Methods," 5th ed., 485 pp. Iowa State College Press, Ames, Iowa.

Wood, E. C. (1946). *Analyst.* **71**, 1.

Wood, E. C., and Finney, D. J. (1946). *Quart. J. Pharm. Pharmacol.* **19**, 112.

PART II

Steroid Hormones and Related Substances

Chapter 2

Estrogens

C. W. Emmens

I. Introduction

Estrogens may be assayed biologically or chemically, and the choice of methods depends on the particular requirements of an investigation.

Biological assays as such, and experiments of the same character as assays, continue in use when very high sensitivity is needed, even if preceded by chemical extraction and purification. They also continue in use in investigations demanding the demonstration of estrogenic activity or its potentiation or inhibition; much new investigation thus demands a biological approach at least in the first instance.

Some biological methods of assay are still very much more sensitive than chemical or physical methods. The most sensitive biological methods described below cover the range 5×10^{-6} to 10^{-4} μg. approximately, or 5 to 100 picagrams (pg.) of estradiol or estrone per mouse. However, a colony of mice must be used in such assays, with an accuracy of 80–125% ($P = 0.95$) attainable with about 12 mice per group. If a mean dose of 30 pg. is given, a total of 30×24 pg., or allowing for wastage, of about 1000 pg. or 0.001 μg. will be needed per complete assay. This is still below the best available chemical or physical methods. These sensitive biological techniques are fortunately more precise than those previously available. The great drawback of the intravaginal method of assay using cornification as a response (Emmens, 1950a) was its variability and the need for many animals per assay. Despite this, it was and still is necessary as a research tool, although rarely seeing use in routine assays.

For laboratory research and clinical investigation, therefore, it seems likely that the newer biological techniques will see considerable use, sometimes in conjunction with some of the older methods, and with chemical, particularly radiochemical methods. They have the advantage of high precision, speed, high sensitivity, and freedom from interference from various steroidal and other substances which may occur in clinical material. If these methods can be adapted for the direct or semidirect assay of urinary and blood estrogens with a minimum of extraction, they will contribute a great deal. It is fortunate that we are now departing from the situation which has obtained since Emmens (1939a,b) and Pedersen-Bjergaard (1939) investigated the assay of estrogenic substances and concluded that the effects of variation in technique were so great that an estrogenic preparation could only be validly assayed biologically if the chemical nature of the estrogens present were known and each was isolated. This arose because different estrogens were affected quite differently by changes in the medium and the number and spacing of injections, so that while reproducible estimates could be obtained with any one method, unless the nature of the estrogen was known, it was not possible to estimate the amount present. It was easily shown that intravaginal assay is relatively free from this drawback, in that all potent estrogens have about the same activity and the newer methods employing intravaginal application also have that advantage. This means that a mixture of estrogens may be assayed and that, with little margin of error, an over-all figure can be given for the total amount present, whatever the ratio of any one to the others may be. There is, however, some interaction as discussed on p. 78. On the other hand, if chemical separation is made, each estrogen may be assayed with precision, and probably without purification, in terms of any chosen standard.

II. Types of Estrogen

A. NATURAL SUBSTANCES

The natural estrogens of animal origin so far isolated are all steroids, possessing the cyclopentanoperhydrophenanthrene nucleus, as in Fig. 1.

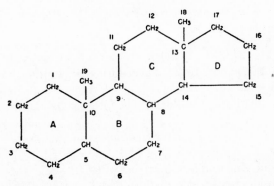

FIG. 1. The steroid nucleus, showing the nomenclature of the rings and carbon atoms. From Emmens (1959).

Some plant estrogens are not steroids, although others are. In contrast to the androgens and progesterone, estrogenic steroids have a phenolic A-ring, and a carbon atom in position 18 but not in position 19. (Some of the new synthetic steroids, e.g., 19-nortestosterone, possessing a variety of androgenic, progestational, and estrogenic actions, also lack a carbon atom in position 19.)

Estradiol-17β [Fig. 2(1)] is formed by the ovaries and is the most potent natural estrogen by nearly all test methods. It would seem to be the only estrogen produced by the ovaries, and it is also produced by the adrenals, the placenta, and the testes of the stallion. Its stereoisomer, estradiol-17α, is found in the urine of pregnant mares and is much less potent. Some estradiol-17β occurs in human urine.

Estrone [Fig. 2(2)] is found in urine, the adrenals, and the placenta. In most tests involving parenteral injection it is less active than estradiol-17β, but in intravaginal tests of all types it is only a little less active, the ratio of estradiol-17β: estrone potency being about 1.5. The slopes also differ slightly but significantly.

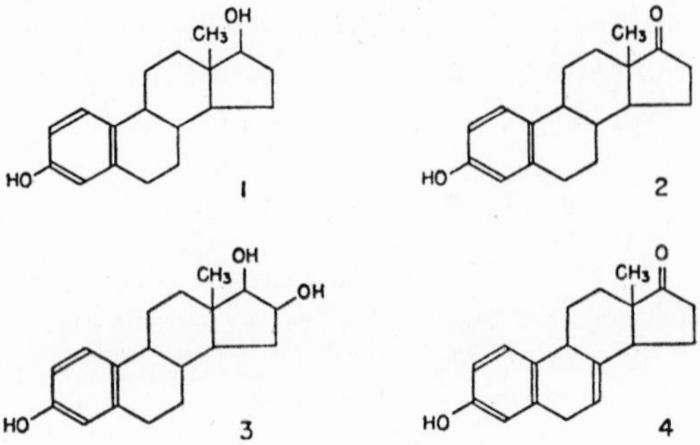

FIG. 2. Four important natural estrogens: (1) estradiol; (2) estrone; (3) estriol; (4) equilin. From Emmens (1959).

Estriol [Fig. 2(3)] is found in urine and is less active than estrone in all but intravaginal tests under optimal conditions, when the two are of equal potency (Biggers and Claringbold, 1954c; Martin and Claringbold, 1960; Martin 1960). The potency estimates by older test methods are completely dependent on test conditions and vary between 1.0 and 250 for the estrone:estriol ratio. Both estrone and estriol are formed *in vivo* from estradiol and are excreted in the urine mainly as sulfates and glucuronides (Marrian, 1948).

Various other newly identified steroids, such as 16β-hydroxyestrone (Layne and Marrian, 1958) have now been found in human urine, while *equilin* [Fig. 2(4)] and *equilenin* have been known for some time and are found in the urine of pregnant mares.

Some of the androgens, notably *trans*-androstenediol, 17-methyl-androstane-17-ol-3-one, ethinyltestosterone, and both 19-nortestosterone and 17-ethinyl-19-nortestosterone are estrogenic, but are active only in relatively large doses and almost certainly by virtue of a metabolite (Emmens, 1941b, 1942a,b, 1943).

B. Synthetic Substances

Dodds and his co-workers (1939) first produced a series of synthetic compounds with potent estrogenic activity and with no apparent qualitative differences in action from the natural estrogens. A very large number of such compounds is now known, although many are far less potent than the natural estrogens and the majority are almost certainly estrogenic by virtue of their metabolites. This has not been fully recognized by reviewers such as Solmssen (1945) and Grundy (1957) in their otherwise comprehensive accounts of the synthetic estrogens.

Important members of the synthetic series are:

Diethylstilbestrol [Fig. 3(1)], which is active by oral administration as well as by injection, in contrast to the natural estrogens which lose

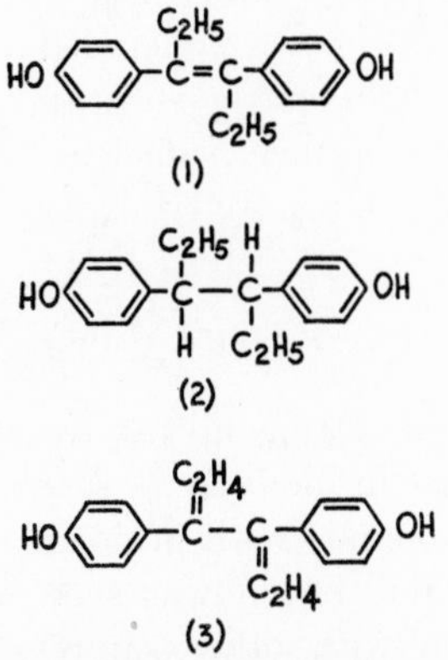

(1)

(2)

(3)

Fig. 3. Three commonly used synthetic estrogens: (1) diethylstilbestrol; (2) hexestrol; (3) dienestrol.

much of their potency when given by mouth unless they are protected by some means. It has a potency, when injected, between that of estrone and estradiol, and a potency equal to that of estrone in intravaginal tests.

Hexestrol [Fig. 3(2)] and *dienestrol* [Fig. 3(3)] are very similar in structure to diethylstilbestrol and share its properties. They are of about the same potency in most tests, but hexestrol seems to be less potent orally in the human than is diethylstilbestrol.

The high potency of this type of compound has led to speculation about the structure which must be possessed by a substance if it is to show estrogenic activity. When the proestrogens (Emmens, 1941b) are eliminated, it seems that we are left with substances much resembling diethylstilbestrol, which may be thought to copy the structure of estradiol-17β much more closely than at first appears (Fig. 4).

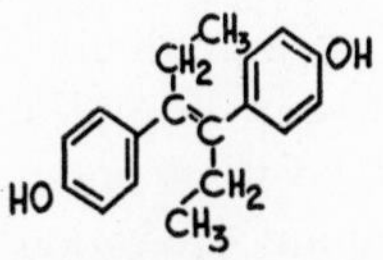

Fig. 4. Supposed configuration of diethylstilbestrol, resembling estradiol.

Studies of the stilbestrol series by Emmens and his colleagues (Emmens, 1957; Emmens and Cox, 1958; Emmens *et al.*, 1959, 1960) have recently shown that it contains not only proestrogens and estrogens, but also anti-estrogens. Some compounds exhibit both proestrogenic and anti-estrogenic activity, and the peak of each type of activity is found in one of three adjacent compounds of the series. Thus, diethylstilbestrol exhibits maximal estrogenic potency, methylethylstilbestrol exhibits maximal proestrogenic potency, and dimethylstilbestrol exhibits maximal anti-estrogenic potency. It is concluded that the unchanged anti-estrogens in this series are the active substances and that those that are proestrogens in addition produce sufficient estrogenic metabolites to overcome their anti-estrogenic activity except in special circumstances.

C. Esterified Compounds

It was recognized when setting up international standards for estrogenic activity that, at least in bioassay, a separate standard or standards would be needed for compounds with prolonged action. Estradiol benzoate was at that time chosen, but it was soon apparent that it could be used only for comparison with other samples of the same compound. This is true as long as parenteral methods of assay are under consideration, but the question of the effects of esterification is not a pressing one now that pure characterized substances are usually being handled, except in the parallel case of the natural conjugates. A discussion of the general biological effects of esterification is given in Emmens (1950a).

Estrone sulfate or estriol glucuronide may require assay by biological techniques, and it is unfortunate that no very exhaustive tests have been made to determine whether these naturally occurring substances are potent estrogens when assayed by the intravaginal route. Robson and Adler (1940) concluded that estriol glucuronide is about as effective as the free compound in causing vaginal cornification when given locally, and Emmens (1941b) showed that esterification is almost or completely without effect when aliphatic esters of the natural or synthetic estrogens are tested under the same conditions, but neither estrone sulfate nor estriol glucuronide were tested. Later (unpublished) tests have thrown doubt on the intravaginal activity of these two compounds, but have themselves been the subject of some doubt because of uncertainty about the purity of preparations, some samples giving completely negative results and others partially positive ones. It seems very likely, however, that the two predominant excretion products in the urine are not active locally and that they therefore differ in this respect from the general run of esters; neither is, of course, an ester in the usual sense of the word.

III. Vaginal Cornification

A. CORNIFICATION IN RODENTS

The Allen-Doisy test for vaginal cornification in rodents (Allen and Doisy, 1923) was based on the observations of Stockard and Papanicolaou (1917), who first reported the cyclic vaginal cornification of guinea pigs. In the rat or mouse, used by Allen and Doisy, very clear vaginal changes occur, and these may be initiated in the castrate female by dosage with estrogen. Very many modifications of the Allen-Doisy test have been made, sometimes employing immature animals instead of castrates, but all depending on the induction of the characteristic vaginal changes, occurring some 60–80 hours after injection and somewhat earlier after intravaginal dosage. Our knowledge of the factors affecting estrogen assays is almost confined to variants of this test, and our decision that many compounds are estrogens (or antiestrogens) has been dependent on it. Detailed discussion may be found in Marrian and Parkes (1929), Emmens (1939a, 1950a), and Pedersen-Bjergaard (1939). Useful studies in addition are those of Allan *et al.* (1930), de Jongh *et al.* (1932), and Hain and Robson (1936). These studies are primarily concerned with administration routes other than intravaginal, in rats or mice.

Much of the earlier work was done with rats, which are still used for the test, but less so than previously. There seems little to recommend the rat unless large amounts of crude material are to be injected. Otherwise, the mouse is easier to handle, requires much less room and less hormone, and can thus be used in sufficient numbers for reasonably precise work. The response of the mouse is also easier to classify than is that of the rat.

B. SPAYING THE RAT OR MOUSE

Ovariectomy, or spaying, is easiest in the immature female, shortly after weaning. A single transverse incision across the mid-line is made in the skin of the back, with the animal under any convenient but short-acting anesthetic. The incision may be shifted readily from one side to the other so as to lie over each ovary in turn. A small puncture is then made over the site of the ovary, which can usually be seen through the abdominal wall, embedded in a pad of fat. The tip of a pair of fine forceps is introduced grasping the fat around the ovary, care being taken not to rupture the capsule of the ovary itself. In the rat, the tip of the uterine horn is then crushed in a pair of artery forceps, and the ovary together with the Fallopian tube is removed with a single cut with a scalpel or safety razor blade. In the mouse, a similar procedure may be followed if desired, but alternatively the ovary plus tube may be snipped off with a pair of fine scissors and the uterus allowed to slip back into place. There is usually insufficient bleeding to matter, even with the latter technique, which is quicker. In the rat, the abdominal wall may need a single suture; in the mouse it does not. On completion of the operation, the skin incision may be closed by 1 or 2 interrupted sutures, but with skill, in the mouse, a sufficiently small incision may be made so as to need no suturing. Aseptic precautions are not necessary; speed and gentle handling are more important. With practice, up to 70 mice per hour may be spayed if sutures are omitted and the anesthetic is administered by an assistant. Age and weight at ovariectomy do not affect responses as much as might be expected (Biggers and Claringbold, 1954a).

C. PREPARATION OF SOLUTIONS

Most estrogens are soluble in organic solvents, and stock solutions are usually made in alcohol and stored cold. These may be added to oil, saline, distilled water, or mixtures of water and glycerol or propylene glycol for tests. The final concentration of ethyl alcohol should not exceed 2% by volume for oral administration, 10% for parenteral administration, or 5% for intravaginal administration. It should also be kept uniform in any one test. Although in local Allen-Doisy tests it has not been shown that propylene glycol solutions up to 50% have any effect on response, tests of mitotic responses have been impaired with more than 25% of propylene glycol in the medium (Martin, 1960).

These solutions must be thoroughly mixed, if in glycerol-water media or oil, by gentle warming for a prolonged period over a sand bath or hot plate, with care taken to adjust the final volume if necessary. Most commonly used oils will not mix with more than 5% of alcohol (olive, arachis, or sesame oil). Alcohol stock solutions of estrone were found by Rowlands and Callow (1935) to remain stable for several months, even at 37°C., but Wilder-Smith and Williams (1947) found that solutions of dienestrol and diethylstilbestrol at both 1 and 100 μg. per milliliter lost potency when kept at room temperature either in water or alcohol. Estrone, hexestrol, and estradiol were found to be more stable under the same conditions for up to 32 weeks, but still showed a slight potency loss. All five estrogens were little affected if kept in sesame oil at room temperature or in men's urine in a refrigerator. Aeration, the presence of benzoyl peroxide or hydrogen peroxide increased the rate of inactivation of dienestrol and diethylstilbestrol, while hydroquinone decreased it. Emmens (1950b) found that the very dilute solutions used in intravaginal work may lose potency in a few weeks, but found no instability in more concentrated alcoholic or oily solutions kept cold for up to 12 months. It is thus reasonable to keep relatively concentrated stock solutions in the refrigerator for several months; at room temperature for only short periods; and not to keep very dilute solutions for more than a single test unless they are deep frozen, when they presumably last for a longer period.

D. Preparation of Test Animals

After spaying, the animals should not be used for about 2 weeks, but they may be given a "priming" injection of 1 μg. of any potent estrogen in 0.05 to 0.1 ml. of oil, subcutaneously, before this time. This injection helps to ensure maintenance of sensitivity, and greater uniformity of response. It is necessary to prime at about 6-week intervals, unless a particular group has responded positively within that period (Emmens, 1939a) and this makes it advisable to prime at regular intervals in order to avoid heterogeneity in the colony. After positive intravaginal responses (Emmens, 1950b) no priming action occurs, and it is necessary to prime periodically whatever the responses in a colony used for intravaginal work. Palmer (1941) found greater uniformity of response if mice were selected, by priming, then giving a threshold dose a week later, and rejecting any mice not responding positively on both occasions. This is a step toward the use of individual dose levels (Claringbold, 1955a). Assays should not follow each other closer than at about 2-week intervals with the same mice, unless one is prepared to make statistical allowance for carry-over effects from one assay to another.

Uniformity of response is worth striving for, particularly if the response must be scored quantally. It is therefore advisable to keep the test animals under as uniform a set of conditions as possible, to minimize time-to-time variation and to maximize the slope of the dose-response line. Randomizing animals, or at least boxes of 5 animals or some such small number to dosage groups is essential if heterogeneity is to be avoided. However, the use of inbred lines is questionable. Emmens (1939c) found the one inbred line of mice he used to be more variable than randomly bred albinos, and Biggers and Claringbold

(1954b) and others have made similar observations. It now seems to be felt that selected F_1 hybrids are much better for assay work than inbred lines.

After observing the above precautions, it is best to test a colony for satisfactory response to a known estrogen by establishing a dose-response line with, say, estradiol. This will check technique and homogeneity, and give a base line from which to plan assays. The probit-$\log_{10}$ dose line should have a slope of between 5 and 6, in subcutaneous tests, but only of about 2 in intravaginal tests. The X^2 test for homogeneity should reveal no significant departure from linearity, and in order to test this effectively, the initial dose-response line should comprise at least 5 or 6 groups. If the angular transformation is used in computations, the corresponding slopes should be about 100 and 35, and if 0,1 scoring (see below) is used, they should be about 1.0 and 0.4 for subcutaneous and intravaginal testing, respectively.

E. A Typical Test

The method now in use for subcutaneous Allen-Doisy tests in the author's department will be described. Solutions for injection are made up in arachis oil (sesame, olive, or other oils can be used) and adjusted so that a volume of 0.05 ml. is given per injection. Exceptionally, up to 0.2 ml. may be given, but it tends to leak from the site of injection, or, even if it does not, to retain some of the estrogen. Also exceptionally, water-soluble material may be given, in distilled water or saline, or in mixtures of water and glycerol or propylene glycol. The same volumes per injection are used, but with such material it is usual to give four injections instead of two.

Injections are made at about 10 A.M. on Monday and Tuesday, if four are to be given, these are added at about 5 P.M. on the same days. Smears are taken with a specially ground fine metal spatula at 5 P.M. on Wednesday and 10 A.M. on Thursday. Other smears have been found to contribute very little to the final result, although maximal sensitivity may usually be gained by postponing the Wednesday smear to later in the evening if convenient. Precision is not affected. All smears are taken with a saline-moistened spatula as gently as possible, transferred to a glass slide, and stained for 10 minutes with 5% aqueous methylene blue solution. They are then washed and scored when dry under a low power of the microscope.

In its original form, the test score records only whether the rat or mouse has or has not responded positively to the dose administered, thus taking several smears merely increases sensitivity so that few positive reactions are missed. In the author's experience, the two smears recommended catch nearly all positives but may be considered separately in order to obtain more information per animal (see Chapter 1, this volume). This however is only possible if quantal scoring and the usual probit or similar type of analysis is abandoned. A positive smear contains nucleated or cornified epithelial cells, and no leucocytes; a full proestrous smear is thus scored as positive. Biggers and Claringbold (1954c) have shown that subdivisions of scoring for individual smears, such as a four-way score of presence or absence of leucocytes plus presence or absence of nucleated or cornified epithelial cells, adds nothing to the information obtained—in fact it is the presence or absence of leucocytes that governs the score, as nucleated or cornified cells are nearly always present if leucocytes are absent—if they are not, it usually means that an effective smear has not been taken.

Assays follow standard methods as outlined in Chapter 1 (this volume). Groups containing less than 20 animals are unlikely to give satisfactory assays with quantal responses, and the probability of obtaining 0 or 100% of positive responses rises as group size decreases. If 20 animals are used per group with a dose ratio of 2 with each substance a valid assay will usually result, with fiducial limits of error between about 70 and 140%, or narrower in range if an estimate of the slope of the typical dose-response line is available from previous assays and is found to apply. The position of the line is subject to time-to-time variation, but the slope is usually not.

Even under fairly constant conditions, such as rooms regulated by thermostats, a constant daily period of illumination, constant diet and routine, and the maintenance of priming, time-to-time variation occurs in sensitivity. It is not usually as marked, however, as reported by earlier investigators, nor is it seasonal. Changes in sensitivity are only a nuisance if they cause groups to react with 0 or 100% positive responses and so tend to invalidate assays. They do not seriously affect the precision of assays when responses within the useful range have been obtained.

IV. Modifications of the Allen-Doisy Test

A. METHODS OF ADMINISTRATION

Estrogens may be given by mouth, subcutaneously, percutaneously, intramuscularly, intraperitoneally, intravenously, or intravaginally in the cornification test. The last-named method is of considerable importance and will be dealt with below. Peroral administration may be in any of the media mentioned for subcutaneous injection, or even in pure propylene glycol or glycerol. With mice, a metal tube, about 1.5 mm. in diameter, with a blunt end and a side outlet of "organ-pipe" design is best. It is easiest to keep the tube fixed and to thread the mouse onto it than the reverse. Up to 0.5 ml. may be given at each administration. An elastic catheter may be used as a stomach tube for rats.

Subcutaneous dosage needs no further comment. Percutaneous administration was shown by Emmens (1941a) to be remarkably effective if in organic solvents. Applied once daily to the shaved skin of mice, estrogens in alcohol or benzene give as sensitive a test as by injection in oil, but there is no merit in the method for ordinary purposes. Oily solutions are not absorbed as efficiently and the response is poor. Pincus and Werthessen (1938) showed that the potency of some synthetic compounds is increased 50- to 300-fold if they are injected intraperitoneally instead of subcutaneously. Pedersen-Bjergaard (1939) has reported results using intravenous dosage.

With different investigators, the number and spacing of injections varies from a single injection (usually only employed with esterified compounds in oily solution) to six or even eight spaced out over 2–3 days. From the studies mentioned above, it is clear that multiple injections increase sensitivity, by making more hormone available over the critical period, but that a peak is soon reached with oily solutions, except in the case of estriol. Little is otherwise to be gained by giving more than two injections. With aqueous media, however, multiple injections continue to give improved sensitivity and at least four injections are advisable.

Administration may be modified also in a different way, so as to budget for individual sensitivity and to utilize within-animal information. This will usually be followed by a considerable reduction in error. Claringbold (1955a) studied the individual median effective dose (IMED) in spayed mice, using the intravaginal method of administration which is more fully discussed below, but the same principle may be applied whatever the route. The individual effective dose (IED) is the minimal dose required to cause vaginal cornification at any one time. It cannot be determined, but the IMED can be determined. This is the quantity which causes an individual to respond in 50% of all trials, if it can be tested on several occasions. The IMED is likely to be of use if the variation in response of the same animal at different times is less than the variation in response of different animals at the same time. It usually is; Claringbold's estimate was 29% of the usual variation between animals. Two methods for locating the IMED within reasonable limits are given.

The utilization of within-animal information in a quantal assay was first demonstrated by Claringbold (1956), who used mice for which IMED estimates were available in the assay of estrone. The design was a cross-over, reproduced in Table XV, Chapter 1 (this volume), where it is used as statistical example. It is sufficient to emphasize here that the assay, which was highly successful, gave an answer with 4 times the precision of ordinary estrogen assays of the same type, using the same number of observations. The method is slow, however, since each animal must be used repeatedly in the same determination of relative potency.

B. Taking and Scoring Smears

The method described above for taking vaginal smears is rapid and convenient. Various authors have felt, however, that a gentler technique is desirable and have used cotton wool pledglets or swabs, or have pipetted a little saline into the vagina and back onto a slide, perhaps after a few sucks back and forth. These methods are both much more time consuming, as new material has to be used for each smear. Even with the swab method, Wade and Doisy (1935) reported that frequent smearing—3 times daily for 3 or 4 days—produces 25% false positives. However, the few smears taken by the spatula in the method described above do not produce false positives. It would nevertheless be wise to check this possibility with any particular method adopted in new hands. Some workers do not stain smears, but staining is so easy that it seems hardly worth while to omit it, as scoring is harder with unstained material, even under the phase microscope. Rat smears may perhaps be handled without staining more successfully than with the mouse.

Some workers have attempted to gain greater precision or sensitivity by scoring smears in one or more of a series of grades between the conventional negative and positive. Mühlbock (1940) used 7 grades, a to g, only the last representing a full reaction. Sulman (1952) has attempted to gain sensitivity by defining a positive smear as one containing more than 50% nucleated or cornified cells in the presence of leucocytes and mucin. The work of Biggers and Claringbold (1954c) mentioned above, clearly showed that vaginal cornification is a strictly quantal response, that proestrous smears should be classed as positive, and that the absence of leucocytes is a critical factor governing classification. Four sets of data were subjected to discriminant analysis, examining the efficiency of a 4-fold classification obtained by a double dichotomy of the usual quantal score. The four classes are:

Score

0—diestrous smear, mainly leucocytes, few epithelial cells

x—mixture of leucocytes and epithelial cells

y—proestrous smear, nucleated or nucleated plus cornified cells, no
    leucocytes

1—estrous smear, cornified cells only

The values of x and y were then estimated for maximal discrimination
in analysis, and turned out to be -0.03 and 0.99. Clearly $x = 0$ and
$y = 1$ is a valid decision to make, giving only the two classes normally
employed and a fully quantal response.

Other criteria of action on the epithelium of the vagina have been
suggested, but until the studies of Martin and Claringbold (1958, 1960)
and Martin (1960) no effective use seems to have been made of alternative responses.

If the quantal response is used, as seems most appropriate from all
the evidence, it is still possible to use the information from individual
smears. There are, for instance, at least two components of the reaction—
did it take place, and if so, how long did it last? There is evidence
that these factors are to an extent independent. Thus Emmens (1957)
compared the information obtained from 0,1 or 0,1,2 scoring in typical
but very large bioassays designed to extract within-animal estimates
of error, and found that 0,1,2 scores differentiated more successfully
between substances, the F values for the sum of squares for the dose-
response relationships of two preparations were, for instance, 84.7 and
149.0 as against 76.2 and 87.4, respectively, with 0,1 scoring and 64.2
and 80.4 with the angular transformation. The 0,1,2 score thus has an
advantage over simple quantal analysis, whether by 0,1 score or by
angles.

V. Interpreting Allen-Doisy Tests

It has been pointed out above that quite different answers may be
obtained in vaginal cornification tests when technique is varied, except
perhaps in intravaginal tests on mice. There is still little to report in
the way of detailed investigation of other than intravaginal tests since
the work of Emmens (1939a) and Pedersen-Bjergaard (1939). Tables
I and II are reprinted from Emmens' monograph to illustrate the
position. They show such wide discrepancies, depending on the author
quoted and the particular technique employed, that it is obvious that
it is not possible to assay accurately the potency of estrogenic material of either known or unknown constitution in terms of, say,

TABLE I

THE RATIO OF POTENCIES OF ESTRIOL AND ESTRONE FOUND BY DIFFERENT
INVESTIGATORS WORKING WITH OVARIECTOMIZED RATS
IN THE ALLEN-DOISY TEST[a]

Number and nature of injections	Estrone: estriol ratio	Reference
3 Aqueous	250	Meyer et al. (1936)
3 Aqueous	2	Curtis and Doisy (1931)
4 Aqueous	2	Cohen and Marrian (1934)
4 Aqueous	1	Burn and Elphick (1932)
1 Oily	4.5	Burn and Elphick (1932)
1 Oily	100	Butenandt and Störmer (1932)
3 Oily	90	Meyer et al. (1936)
? Oily	2	Marrian (1930)

[a] From Emmens (1939a).

estrone. Studies by both authors of impure urinary extracts from women
and mares agreed in showing that with such biological methods, it
was impossible to arrive at a trustworthy estimate of the nature or
amounts of the estrogens present, and that the two international standards then in use could only be employed for comparison with preparations known to be of identical constitution. Pedersen-Bjergaard (1939)

TABLE II

THE RATIO OF POTENCIES OF ESTRADIOL AND ESTRONE FOUND BY DIFFERENT
INVESTIGATORS USING OVARIECTOMIZED RATS OR MICE
IN THE ALLEN-DOISY TEST[a]

Animals	Number and nature of injections	Estradiol: estrone ratio	Reference
Rats	3 Oily	6	Schoeller et al. (1935)
Rats	6 Aqueous	7	Schoeller et al. (1935)
Mice	3 Oily	0.8	Schoeller et al. (1935)
Mice	6 Aqueous	3	Schoeller et al. (1935)
Rats	1 Oily	3	David et al. (1935)
Mice	1 Oily	2	David et al. (1935)
Mice	3 Oily	2	David et al. (1935)
Mice	6 Aqueous	2	David et al. (1935)
Mice	5 Oily	5–10	Dirscherl (1936)
Rats	3 Oily (β-form)[b]	12	Whitman et al. (1937)
Rats	3 Oily (α-form)	0.3	Whitman et al. (1937)

[a] From Emmens (1939a).
[b] Modern nomenclature.

found, for example, that an extract of human pregnancy urine assayed at from 158 to 75,900 international units (I.U.) per gram according to the assay method used. It was also shown by Emmens that, in addition to the discrepancies occurring among the different pure estrogens, the responses to impure urinary extracts were modified by the presence of augmenting substances which were present in varying amounts according to extraction technique.

These findings led to a concentration by others on chemical methods for identification and assay of urinary and other estrogens, with good success. Since these also necessitate, as things stand, the separation and the part purification of the estrogens concerned, bioassay can be used instead of colorimetry or other methods, if so desired. There is usually no advantage in this unless minute quantities must be assayed, or there is a question of checking the estrogenic activity of the substances concerned. There still remains, however, the possibility of biological assay of crude materials, which may give a quick, if approximate answer. If conditions are used under which the various natural estrogens give much the same response, and if this response is not affected, or much affected, by contaminants likely to be present, it may be worth while to have the rapid, approximate estimate available without chemical fractionation and semi-purification. Standard Allen-Doisy tests do not hold much attraction, although useful work has been possible on crude material with their aid, and the modification next to be discussed offers much better possibilities. This in turn, however, is much improved by changing the end point as in the other assays below.

VI. Intravaginal Allen-Doisy Tests

A. Local Application

A summary of the history of local techniques with estrogens is given by Emmens (1950a) to that date. Since then, a considerable volume of work has been done to enlarge the older viewpoint, which will be briefly summarized here. Freud (1939) and Mühlbock (1940) investigated some of the variables of the method and the latter showed that, in the mouse, administration in 50% aqueous glycerol gives consistent responses of very high sensitivity. Robson and Adler (1940) made the important observation that natural and (some) synthetic estrogens act locally without absorption in significant amounts, since a separate vaginal pocket formed from the lower vagina was practically unaffected in spayed mice receiving effective doses into the upper vagina. Emmens (1941b) confirmed these results, obtaining almost identical activities for the three natural estrogens to those reported by Mühlbock (1940), who found the MED for estrone, estradiol, and estriol to be approximately 250, 500, and 750 pg., respectively, in two applications of either saline or aqueous glycerol. Assay by intravaginal administration is thus much more sensitive than by subcutaneous injection; it gives more consistent results and does not show much difference in potency between the natural estrogens.

Further investigations by Emmens (1941b, 1942a, b, 1943, 1947) showed that with the exception of the weakly estrogenic androgens, all the natural estrogens examined, and the most potent synthetic estrogens, are alike in potency by intravaginal assay and are true estrogens, as opposed to proestrogens, which must be metabolized in the body before exhibiting estrogenic activity and which do not show very high intravaginal potencies. It was also established that esterification does not affect intravaginal assays, if the addition to the molecule of an ester chain is allowed for in computations of potency. It was thus concluded that intravaginal assay offered a method that was extremely sensitive, differentiated little between the natural and commonly used synthetic estrogens, and was insensitive to esterification or to the presence of substances which interfere with subcutaneous assays. The drawbacks were a low slope, requiring many animals per test, and uncertainty about the parallelism of slope for different natural substances. In some tests (Emmens, 1941b), the slopes appeared to be different, but in later tests (Emmens, 1950b) these differences were not found to be significant.

Systematic investigation of the intravaginal method was then undertaken by Biggers and Claringbold, in various papers cited below. Using aqueous egg albumin as the vehicle for administration Biggers (1951, 1953a) found that, with a two-injection technique, the potency of estrogens is enhanced. It was thought that the protein bound the estrogen and prevented rapid loss from the site of action, thus maintaining more effective local concentrations. Using bovine plasma albumin, Biggers (1953a) found erratic responses to estrogens in 0.1% solutions, but an enhanced potency with 0.01%. Biggers and Claringbold (1954c) repeated and extended some of this work to show that the relative potencies of various estrogens other than estradiol under presumably optimal or near-optimal conditions were not significantly different. Their work also showed that multiple intravaginal doses reach a maximal efficiency at four injections spread over 36 hours, while more than four proved less effective with all estrogens studied. However, estriol remained less potent than the rest, except with 1% egg albumin, when with four injections as above, it equaled them in potency. The relative activities of a variety of estrogens under these conditions are given in Table III. It will be seen that estradiol still shows greater activity under optimal conditions of administration. This agrees with other evidence, presented in the same paper, which shows that estradiol differs

TABLE III

RELATIVE ACTIVITY OF VARIOUS ESTROGENS USING ESTRONE AS A STANDARD, WHEN GIVEN INTRAVAGINALLY IN 4 INJECTIONS IN THE ALLEN-DOISY TEST[a]

Estrogen	Solvent	MED ratio	Fiducial limits ($P = 0.95$)
Estradiol-3,17β	Water	1.37	1.04–1.81
Estriol	Water	0.09	0.04–0.21
Diethylstilbestrol	Water	0.76	0.51–1.39
Estradiol-3,17β	1% Egg albumin	1.57	1.03–2.37
Estriol	1% Egg albumin	1.13	0.72–1.76
Diethylstilbestrol	1% Egg albumin	0.82	0.57–1.19
Equilin	1% Egg albumin	0.84	0.60–1.20
Equilenin	1% Egg albumin	0.65	0.37–1.15

[a] After Claringbold (1954).

in slope and in response to time interval changes between injections, from the other estrogens examined.

Biggers (1952, 1953b) also demonstrated by histological studies that the morphological response of the vaginal epithelium is the same to estrogens administered by either the subcutaneous or intravaginal route, although the response occurs earlier with intravaginal application.

There then followed a number of studies on factors other than technique which may affect the intravaginal response. They are of importance in assays only in so far as they demonstrate the need for environmental and treatment stability, as it was shown that thyroid status (Biggers and Claringbold, 1953), insulin, phlorizin (Claringbold, 1954), potassium cyanide, and the metabolic inhibitors, sodium monocodoacetate, sodium azide, and 2,4-dinitrophenol influence responses (Claringbold, 1953). Moreover, the responses to estradiol were not affected in the same way as those to estrone, leading the authors to conclude that estrone is probably converted in part or whole to estradiol before exerting its action. The general conclusions from these studies were that estrogens are absorbed at a critical rate from the lumen of the vagina and in order to initiate the typical cornification response a threshold level (for each individual) must be present for 36 to 48 hours. Meaningful studies of relative potency must be carried out utilizing responses to locally administered hormones under optimal conditions of action. The studies with such substances as insulin and metabolic inhibitors indicated the importance of mitosis and active metabolic processes, and led indirectly to the development of other tests.

B. An Assay Technique

Apart from the difference in slope (and activity) of estradiol from the others, assays may validly be performed by the intravaginal method. They have, for instance, been used throughout the work quoted above, even when it has been necessary to compare ED_{50}'s (doses needed to elicit 50% of positive responses) rather than to compute relative potency, because of slope differences. It must however be stressed that, in the author's present opinion, intravaginal assays are much better carried out by the techniques described in Sections VII and VIII, unless performed for special purposes such as those specifically requiring the particular response of cornfication and leucocyte withdrawal.

Applications in 50% glycerol or up to 25% propylene glycol are to be preferred to water or saline, but only because they are better retained in the vagina. Careful technique avoids the preference. The spayed mouse vagina cannot retain more than 0.02 ml., and 0.01 ml. is much safer and is recommended for routine administration. This is delivered by a micrometer syringe, such as the "Agla," using a blunt-end wide-bore needle with a side aperture near the end, like a smaller version of the equipment for oral dosage. It is best to withdraw the needle slightly as the dose is delivered, to make room for it. Applications are made at 10 A.M. on Monday and Tuesday as with injections; if four are to be given, these are added at 5 P.M. Smears must be taken earlier, on Wednesday at 10 A.M. and 5 P.M., two being sufficient. Staining and scoring is exactly as with other tests, and with careful technique the log-dose-response line is straight throughout the whole effective range, whichever transform is used of those mentioned.

Emmens (1950b) showed that mice used in intravaginal tests need regular *subcutaneous* priming; positive responses do not suffice when they are to intravaginal dosage. The slope of the dose-response line is only about 2 instead of 5 to 6 as with subcutaneous assays, and many animals per group are needed for high precision. Thus, in an assay of estrone against itself using 400 animals (100 per group in a 2×2 design), Claringbold (1956) found percentage limits of error ($P = 0.95$) of 74–134%, and in the within-animal cross-over test described above, 24 animals and 96 observations in total gave percentage limits of error ($P = 0.95$) of 76–131%.

Mixtures of the natural estrogens may be assayed by the subcutaneous route as if they were one substance—the pure compounds have the same slope and so do mixtures between them (Claringbold, 1955b). However, this is not true of mixtures when they are given intravaginally; these give lower responses than would be expected from the activities of the constituents. This further complicates the attempted assay of any but pure substances by this technique. In other tests, Claringbold and Biggers (1955) also showed that when a single estrogen is given, partly subcutaneously and partly intravaginally, the response is greatest when most of the effective dose is given intravaginally, but a small portion is given subcutaneously. The amount of subcutaneous estrogen is far below that required to produce responses on its own, and the effect was presumed to be on blood flow to the vagina and perhaps on vaginal connective tissue, producing potentiation of the intravaginal dose by a subthreshold subcutaneous dose. The effect is illustrated in Fig. 5.

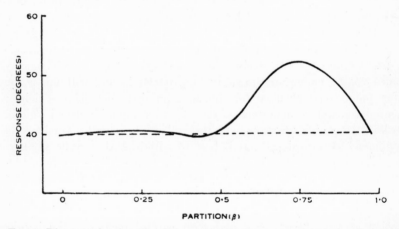

Fig. 5. Diagram showing the increased response to estrone in vaginal smear tests when part of the effective dose is given subcutaneously, but most of it intravaginally (Claringbold and Biggers, 1955).

The slope of the intravaginal dose-response line may be increased by selection of the mice into more homogeneous groups (Biggers *et al.*, 1954). When this was done by selecting mice into those responding twice, once, and not at all in two successive intravaginal tests, the slope within such groups was 77 ± 7 (by the angular transformation) as against an original slope of 35 ± 11, a highly significant improvement. The higher slope was maintained for 3 months in intravaginal tests, but the corresponding slope for subcutaneous assays with the same mice was unaffected. Converse tests, in which the subcutaneously determined slope improved as a result of selection from 98 ± 8 to 153 ± 14 gave similar results, with no effect on intravaginal slopes, as shown in Fig. 6. This independence of responses to the two methods of administration illustrates that the response to a dose of estrogen may be affected by factors

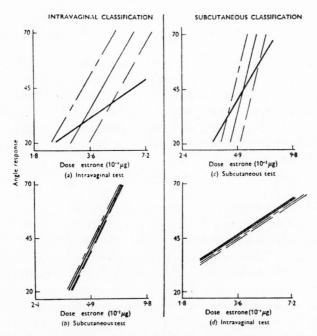

FIG. 6. Schematic diagram of the effects of classification by intravaginal and subcutaneous routes of administration: control (——); ++ (— — —); + — (——); — (— — — —) (Biggers *et al.* 1954).

such as rates of absorption, metabolism, and effects on systems other than the vagina, which are not the same for the two routes. Other studies in this laboratory have shown that these factors are even independently inherited (Biggers and Claringbold, 1955a).

C. INTRAVAGINAL PELLETS

Attempts were made quite early to assay blood estrogens by introducing pellets of dried material into the vaginae of spayed rats. Albrieux (1941a, b) obtained positive responses with the blood and serum of non-pregnant women and concluded that the corpuscles contain most of the estrogen. Krichesky and Glass (1947) confirmed the practicability of this method, and reported results with rabbit and human blood. A brief account of the technique was presented by Emmens (1950a), which will not be repeated here as little further work seems to have been done, and it was never placed on a fully quantitative basis.

VII. Vaginal Mitosis and Epithelial Thickness

A. Early Vaginal Changes

Few studies have been made of the early changes which take place in the vagina after the administration of estrogens. Changes in alkaline phosphatase and cytoplasmic ribonucleic acid were described by Jeener (1947) at 24 hours after injection, and changes in carbohydrate and glycogen content by Biggers (1953b) and Balmain et al. (1956a, b). Allen et al. (1937) studied the mitotic activity of the vaginal epithelium with the colchicine technique and concluded that cell division commences less than $9\frac{1}{2}$ hours after a subcutaneous injection of 5 μg. of estrone, reaches a maximum at 37 hours, and declines by 48 hours. Biggers and Claringbold (1955b) investigated this response when estrone was given intravaginally, finding that mitosis did not commence until at least 18 hours after dosage with 6.4×10^{-3} μg.

Martin and Claringbold (1958, 1960) then made a quantitative investigation of the mitotic rate of the vaginal epithelium 16 to 36 hours after hormone administration. Randomly bred ovariectomized albino mice were used, of the SW (Sydney White) stain, primed 2 weeks before intravaginal dosage with 1 μg. of estrone in peanut oil. Estrone or other

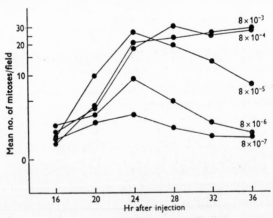

Fig. 7. Increase in mitosis in the mouse vaginal epithelium after the intravaginal administration of estrone in the doses indicated (μg.) (Martin and Claringbold, 1960).

hormones were placed in the vagina in 0.01 ml. of distilled water as in the usual assay, and 0.1 μg. of colchicine was injected 7 hours before killing the animals. After dissection, the vaginae were placed in an automatic tissue processor which carried them through fixative and alcohols to wax, overnight. Sections were cut at 6 μ from blocks containing 6 or 8 vaginae in one experimental group, and were stained in Heidenhain's hematoxylin and differentiated and counterstained in Van Geison's picrofuchsin. They were ready for examination 24 hours after killing the mice.

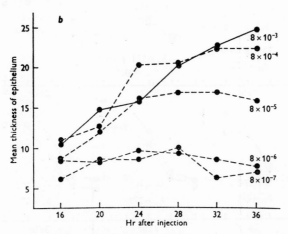

FIG. 8. Increase in epithelial thickness in the mouse vagina after the intravaginal administration of estrone in the doses indicated (μg). The solid line is used only for clarity (Martin and Claringbold, 1960).

Two types of observation were made:

(a) *Arrested mitoses.* Each animal provided at least 5 sections for examination, from which 5 fields were selected in as random as possible a manner and the total number of mitoses scored in each field at $\times 720$.

(b) *Epithelial thickness.* The thickness of the epithelium was measured with a micrometer eyepiece in similarly selected fields and expressed in arbitrary units. An increase seen in epithelial thickness during the experimental period is due to an increase in cell size, little or no actual division having occurred because of treatment with colchicine.

Preliminary work showed that at 16 hours the dose-response lines for mitoses and epithelial thickness had slopes differing insignificantly from zero. After 16 hours mitotic rate increases rapidly, lower dosage groups reaching a maximum at 24 hours, higher ones at 28–36 hours after instillation. Similar results were seen with epithelial thickness (Figs. 7 and 8). The effective doses ranged from about 1 to 100 pg. above which no further increases were seen, but instead a decrease. If mitotic rate is expressed in logs, such that the index $Y = \log_{10} (Z + 2)$, where Z is the mean number of arrested mitoses per field, Y is linearly related to log dose in about the range 10–100 pg. for periods up to 28 hours, and in about the range 10–1000 pg. after that time. Sensitivity, however, declines after 24 hours.

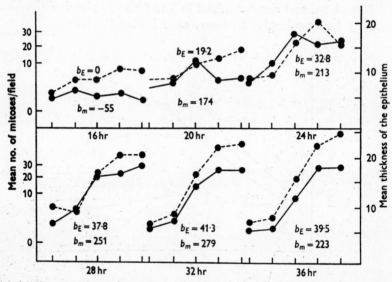

Fig. 9. Dose-response lines for intravaginal estrone in mitotic count (—) and epithelial thickness (– – –) assays at various times after administration. Doses were 8×10^{-7} to 8×10^{-3} μg. of estrone. b_m = slope for the interval 8×10^{-6} to 8×10^{-5} μg. for mitosis, b_E = corresponding slope for epithelial thickness (Martin and Claringbold, 1960).

If epithelial thickness is expressed directly in the arbitrary units used, they are linearly related to log dose over somewhat wide ranges at most times (Fig. 9). The appearance of the epithelium at 24 hours after doses of 4, 20, and 100 pg. is shown in Figs. 10 to 12.

B. An Assay Technique

Since sensitivity and slope were both satisfactory at the convenient time of 24 hours after injection, it was decided to base an assay method on this period. It was shown that injection of the estrone in albumin, to delay absorption, did not improve responses, and so a single injection of hormone in 0.01 ml. distilled water was chosen. A dose-response line is illustrated in Table IV, based on 16 animals per group, in steps of five-

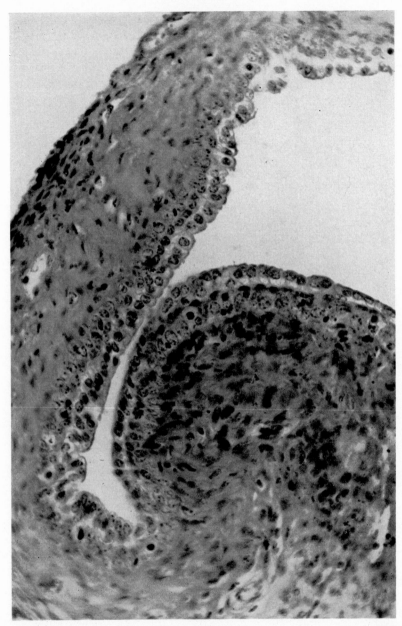

Fig. 10. Appearance of the vaginal epithelium 24 hours after the local administration of 4×10^{-6} μg. of estrone in distilled water (Martin and Claringbold, 1960).

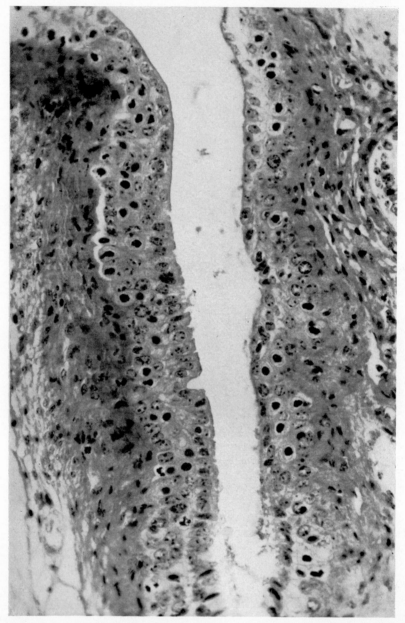

FIG. 11. Appearance of the vaginal epithelium 24 hours after the local administration of 2×10^{-5} μg. of estrone in distilled water (Martin and Claringbold, 1960).

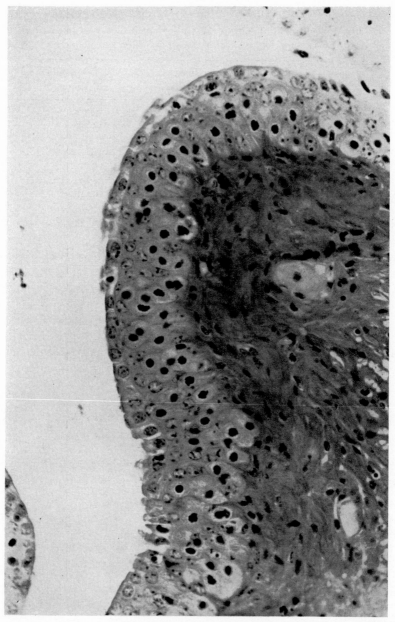

FIG. 12. Appearance of the vaginal epithelium 24 hours after the local administration of 1×10^{-4} μg. of estrone in distilled water (Martin and Claringbold, 1960).

TABLE IV

Dose-Response Line for Counts of Arrested Mitoses and for
Epithelial Thickness[a] with 16 Animals per Group

Dose of estrone (pg.)	Mean number of mitoses per field	Mean epithelial thickness
4	6.2	16.3
20	17.1	23.1
100	22.5	27.9
500	16.4	28.0
2500	12.6	26.3

[a] After Martin and Claringbold (1960).

fold dosage over the range 4–2500 pg. This confirms the falling-off in mitotic count and warns against assaying with only one dosage group, which should never be done anyway. The epithelial thickness measurements do not fall so markedly. The cause of the mitotic count decrease is not clear, and it eventually reaches a peak at all dosage levels, but not within 24 hours.

An example of the use of the technique is seen in Table V in which a group of tests of various estrogens is shown. The slopes sometimes differed significantly, particularly of the rest from that for estrone, which would appear to be an unfortunate substance to use as a standard. The

TABLE V

The Relative Activity of Various Estrogens Using Estrone as a Standard,
When Given Intravaginally in One Injection in the Mitotic Count
and Epithelial Thickness Tests[a]

Estrogen	Test	MED ratio	Limits of error (P = 0.95)
Estradiol-3,17β	Mitosis	1.86	1.17–2.96
Estriol	Mitosis	0.99	0.72–1.36
Dienestrol	Mitosis	0.89	0.64–1.24
Hexestrol	Mitosis	1.02	0.74–1.41
Diethylstilbestrol	Mitosis	1.08	0.78–1.49
Estradiol-3,17β	Epithelial thickness	0.99	0.68–1.45
Estriol	Epithelial thickness	0.69	0.45–1.05
Dienestrol	Epithelial thickness	0.57	0.38–0.86
Hexestrol	Epithelial thickness	0.68	0.47–0.98
Diethylstilbestrol	Epithelial thickness	1.12	0.75–1.38

[a] After Martin and Claringbold (1960).

authors, however, chose to express results in terms of the ratio of the MED to that for estrone, giving this ratio fiducial limits of error as in Table V. Even this necessarily rather imprecise measure has reasonable limits of error with only 8 animals per group, and it is clear that in the mitotic count assays, as in intravaginal assays using cornification as the end point, estradiol stands out as being more potent than the other estrogens, which do not differ among themselves. In the epithelial thickness assay, however, estradiol was not found to be more potent than estrone, whereas dienestrol and hexestrol were significantly less potent. Repeat assays confirmed the greater potency of estradiol by the mitotic count technique.

The heterogeneity seen in these tests indicates the need for further studies and for improvements in technique. The authors themselves suggest that it may arise from the practice of cutting all the sections for one dosage group from the same block, whereby chance variation in the thickness might affect group responses as a whole and give a greater variability than should otherwise occur.

C. VARIATIONS IN TECHNIQUE; SPECIFICITY

The effects of variation in the dose and route of administration of colchicine was found to be negligible within the range 0.5–50 μg., intravaginally, but subcutaneous administration of 0.1 mg. was preferred because of its convenience. Total counts are somewhat greater by the intravaginal method, but not enough to matter.

The alternative vehicles of administration tried were 1% aqueous egg albumin, mentioned above, 25, 50, and 100% propylene glycol in water, and peanut oil. Peanut oil was found to be useless, in conformity with other intravaginal results (Emmens, 1939a), but egg albumin and 25% propylene glycol did not affect the assay. Higher percentages of propylene glycol reduced the slope of the dose-response line and 100% propylene glycol partially destroyed the epithelium, but caused about 100% mitoses in the remaining cells.

In Allen-Doisy tests, inhibition of responses to estrogens is seen with high doses of androgens or progesterone (Courrier and Cohen-Solal, 1937a, b; Courrier, 1950), with cortisone and hydrocortisone (Szego and Roberts, 1953), with various newer steroids related to 19-nortestosterone (Edgren, 1957; Edgren and Calhoun, 1957; Emmens et al., 1960), and with various synthetic compounds related to diethylstilbestrol (Emmens and Cox, 1958; Emmens et al., 1959). These are effective in causing inhibition of vaginal cornification to varying degrees in both subcutaneous and intravaginal tests. Various tests were therefore made of their possible inhibitory effects in the present assay, but none except the synthetics had any effect. Up to 1 mg. of progesterone, testosterone, or hydrocortisone either subcutaneously or intravaginally was tested, and up to 1 μg. of 19-nortestosterone, 17-ethyl-19-nortestosterone, and 17-ethinyl-19-nortestosterone. No inhibition was seen in any test, but the higher doses of most compounds caused mitotic increases instead. This is in line with the finding that some of the 19-norsteroids are estrogenic in moderate doses, although they will inhibit at lower doses in the vaginal smear test (Emmens *et al.*, 1960). Vitamin A was also found to be without effect. In Allen-Doisy tests, it suppresses vaginal cornification when administered locally (Kahn and Bern, 1950; Kahn, 1954a,b). It may be concluded, therefore, that the mitotic rate assay and the epithelial thickness assay are less subject to interference from likely contaminants, and less affected than Allen-Doisy tests by variation in technique.

These assay methods thus seem to possess considerable advantages over the conventional Allen-Doisy technique used intravaginally or subcutaneously. They are approached in sensitivity only by the intravaginal method, but are still 10 times as sensitive and about 4 times as accurate, a saving of fortyfold in terms of material to be assayed, and fourfold in terms of animals. The high potency of estriol and the lack of influence of albumin solutions as the vehicle of administration in these tests indicate that differences in potency due to differential rates of loss of substance from the vagina are minimized. The lack of interference from any but the synthetic inhibitors has made these assays very useful tools for the analysis of anti-estrogenic activity, in that they appear to be affected only by analog-type inhibitors of the natural and synthetic estrogens.

VIII. Vaginal Metabolic Activity

A. VAGINAL METABOLISM

Manometric studies in this laboratory indicated that vaginal respiration is elevated within 24 hours after estrogen treatment, although it was not possible to distinguish between an epithelial response and that of the whole vagina. Attempts at elaborating an assay method based on micromanometry were unsuccessful and it was felt that a dyestuff undergoing color changes with reduction or oxidation might prove useful instead. In consequence, Martin (1960) studied the reduction of 2,3,5-triphenyltetrazolium chloride (tetrazolium) as a possible method of following changes in the metabolism of the vagina after estrogenic stimulation. Tetrazolium is a pale yellow, nontoxic, water-soluble compound which interacts with a number of intracellular reductases as a hydrogen acceptor. It is reduced to a stable, insoluble, deep red pigment, a formazan, which is precipitated at the site of reaction. The formazan is soluble in a number of organic solvents and may be extracted from tissues and estimated colorimetrically. The method has been used in the localization of enzymes within the cell and the identification of actively growing tissues (see Martin, 1960, for summary).

Initial tests were made by introducing 0.5 mg. of tetrazolium in 0.02 ml. of distilled water into the vagina 30 minutes before killing the mouse and extracting the tetrazolium with an organic solvent. The best method was found to be to dissect out the vaginae, cut them open and wash away any excess of tetrazolium, dry on filter paper and place in 1 ml. of 3:1 ethanol:tetrachloroethylene (Jardetsky and Glick, 1956). The formazan was then estimated colorimetrically in a "Uvispeck" spectrophotometer at 500 mµ. The relationship between optical density and the weight of formazan in control solutions was found to be linear over the range 0–40 µg. per milliliter (Fig. 13); hence direct readings have been used as an

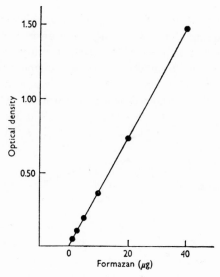

Fig. 13. Relationship between weight of formazan and optical density (Martin, 1960).

index of formazan formation, and converted to logs for graphing and analysis.

These tests showed that formazan formation increased linearly after a single dose of intravaginal estrone for the next 30 hours at least (Fig. 14). The highly significant effect at 6 hours shows that biochemical

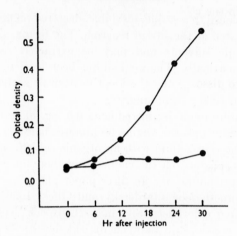

Fig. 14. Increase in tetrazolium reduction by vaginal epithelium of mouse at various times after a single injection of estrone. Top line: 1×10^{-4} μg.; bottom line: 4×10^{-6} μg. (Martin, 1960).

changes occur very early and greatly precede mitosis and other gross morphological changes. The slope of the dose-response line increases steadily and is about maximal at 24 hours. A study of the effect of correcting for vaginal weight showed that this influences response, but only slightly, so that correcting for it is not worth while in ordinary circumstances. Frozen sections showed heavy deposition of formazan in the epithelium; but not in the tissues beneath; the basement membrane was

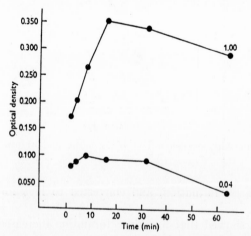

Fig. 15. Effect of time of injection of tetrazolium on tetrazolium reduction by vagina stimulated with 1.0 and 0.04×10^{-4} μg. estrone (Martin, 1960).

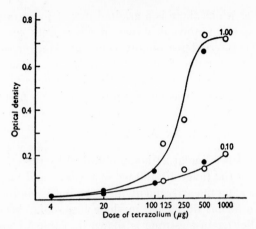

Fig. 16. Effect of dose of tetrazolium on reduction of tetrazolium after stimulation with 1.0 and 0.1 × 10⁻⁴ µg. estrone, ●, first experiment; ○, second experiment (Martin, 1960).

quite clearly marked by formazan crystals. In sections of unstimulated vaginae, only scattered small crystals of formazan were seen.

Further tests showed that the rather arbitrary 0.5 mg. of tetrazolium and a 30-minute period for reduction were in fact nearly optimal, and so they were retained. Tetrazolium reduction actually ceases after about

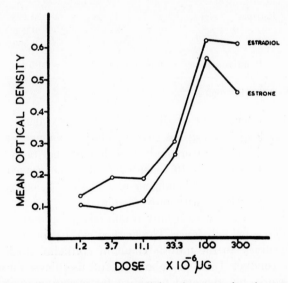

Fig. 17. Dose-response lines for estradiol and estrone by the tetrazolium technique. These differ significantly.

16 minutes, after which there is a gradual loss of formazan (Fig. 15), but 30 minutes is a more convenient period when work must be staggered to keep such an interval reasonably constant. Since a small proportion of the tetrazolium is reduced, it was somewhat surprising to find that if less than 0.5 mg. is used, a great reduction in formazan formation occurs (Fig. 16) and the author was clearly fortunate in his first guesses.

B. AN ASSAY TECHNIQUE

The dose-response line at 24 hours obtained by the methods described above is linear in the range 10–100 pg. of estrone, and may extend above the upper limit. The linear segment for estradiol is similar if not identical, and no significant difference in slope has so far been detected. An assay of estradiol against estrone is shown in Table VI and Fig. 17, and

TABLE VI

THE RELATIVE POTENCY OF ESTRADIOL WITH ESTRONE AS A STANDARD
BY THE TETRAZOLIUM REDUCTION ASSAY[a] WITH 5 ANIMALS PER GROUP

Estrogen	Dose (pg.)	Mean optical density
Estradiol-3,17β	11	0.189
	33	0.304
	100	0.622
Estrone	11	0.118
	33	0.263
	100	0.566
Relative potency = 1.40 (0.79 − 2.48; $P = 0.95$)		

[a] Martin (1960).

gave a relative potency of 1.40 (limits 0.79–2.48; $P = 0.95$), while one of diethylstilbestrol against estrone gave a relative potency of 2.80 (2.57–3.05, $P = 0.95$), which is surprisingly high but has not been repeated.

The slope for estrone in 10 repeated assays has proved both linear over the range quoted, and homogeneous. The 3×2 assay of estradiol against estrone was done with only 5 animals per group; that of stilbestrol was a 2×2 assay with only 6 animals per group, with totals of 15 and 12 animals per substance. The method is thus comparable in sensitivity and accuracy to the mitotic count of epithelial thickness assays, and easier to conduct. Decisions about its full usefulness must obviously await more work, but the evidence is so far encouraging. No extensive studies have yet been made of the vehicle of administration, but propylene glycol has been shown to decrease formazan production if present in high concentration.

Specificity might be expected to accompany that for the other assays depending on early responses, and it has so far been established that progesterone, testosterone, and hydrocortisone do not affect tetrazolium reduction in intravaginal doses up to 0.1 μg., and that the 19-norsteroids mentioned above do not inhibit the responses to estrone in similar doses. However, 17-ethinyl-19-nortestosterone and 19-nortestosterone increased reduction at the highest doses tested, as they do the mitotic count and epithelial thickness. Dimethylstilbestrol, the only synthetic of the potent series of inhibitors tested by Emmens *et al.* (1960), inhibits in the tetrazolium test. There is thus so far complete agreement between the methods of assay depending on early vaginal responses, as far as specificity and the actions of other steroids and inhibitors are concerned.

IX. Uterine Weight

Very little use of uterine weight assays has been seen in the last two decades, although studies such as those of Huggins *et al.* (1954) of the so-called "impeded" estrogens have used the uterus; these have not been aimed at bioassay. They have confirmed, however, that the shape of the dose-response lines for the natural estrogens are not identical, and that it may be no more feasible to assay one estrogen in terms of another with uterine weight tests than it is with many of the others. Another peculiarity of uterine weight tests, at least in the rat, is the greater potency of both estradiol and estriol compared with estrone, as seen below.

The account which follows therefore differs only in part from that of Emmens (1950a), where such tests were surveyed. The data there presented still seem worth repeating, as the assay methods, for particular purposes including studies of the actions of sex hormones on the uterus per se, are still worth consideration. The Dorfman and Dorfman (1954) work is of course new.

A. FOUR-DAY TESTS

Bülbring and Burn (1935) described a test in which young female rats were spayed at about 40 gm. weight and injected 2 days later for 4 consecutive days with estrogen in olive oil. On the eighth day from operation, the uteri were excised, fixed, and weighed, after drying with filter

paper. This and similar tests are cumbersome and take rather a long
time to complete. Later investigators have successfully used immature
intact rats, mice, or guinea pigs in shorter tests.

Using the immature, 22- to 23-day-old albino rat, weighing 34–39 gm.,
Lauson *et al.* (1939) developed a 4-day test. The animals were injected
twice daily for 3 days with 0.5 ml. of an aqueous solution of estrogen
and killed on the fourth day (72–75 hours after the first injection). The
uteri were separated from the vaginae by cutting through the cervix, the
surrounding tissue was stripped off, and the uterotubal junction severed.
They were then weighed fresh, after pressing out the intra-uterine fluid
on moistened blotting paper, using a Roller-Smith torsion balance.
Weights of uteri before expressing the intra-uterine fluid were found to
be valueless. Results with estradiol and estrone are shown in Table VII.

TABLE VII

UTERINE AND VAGINAL RESPONSE TO ESTRADIOL AND ESTRONE[a]

Substance	No. of rats	Total dose (μg.)	Mean uterine weight (mg.)	S.D.	No. of vaginae open
Estradiol	55	0	19.6	2.63	0
	13	0.025	27.5	3.20	0
	14	0.05	36.3	5.90	0
	14	0.10	50.0	5.80	0
	14	0.15	62.3	6.97	1
	14	0.20	67.4	5.43	9
	14	0.30	88.1	6.99	13
	14	0.40	92.8	8.57	14
	14	0.75	90.0	9.30	14
Estrone	15	1.0	41.1	9.06	0
	15	2.0	52.7	10.93	0
	15	3.0	60.3	8.43	2
	15	4.0	77.6	14.41	8
	15	6.0	91.6	9.58	12
	15	8.0	101.7	9.98	15
	15	10.0	105.4	10.40	15

[a] From Lauson *et al.* (1939).

Vaginal opening was also noted and is shown in the table. Estriol was
also investigated, and was found to produce uteri with a maximal mean
weight of about 50 mg., in contrast to the 90- to 100-mg. levels found
with the higher doses of estradiol and estrone. This confirms the finding
of Dorfman *et al.* (1936), who used the difference as a means of distin-

guishing estriol from estrone. On the ascending portion of the curve, the approximate equivalents of 1 μg. of estradiol are 6 μg. of estriol and 20 μg. of estrone. The greater potency of estriol as compared with estrone is a peculiarity of this type as assay.

The dose-response curves are of a type which lend themselves to an assay using uterine weight and log dose, with groups on the standard and unknown, but this method was not employed by the authors. Later, check assays with pure estrogens were made against the previously determined curves, with from 4 to 26 rats per dose. These gave a wide splay of errors, as would be expected from the conditions of testing, only 21 out of 25 assays of estrone and 25 out of 34 assays of estradiol coming within ±50% of the correct figure. From the data supplied by Lauson *et al.* (1939), it is however possible to calculate approximately the precision an assay of any given type would have. The standard deviations shown in Table VII, although rather higher on the average for estrone, are fairly constant for any one substance. An assay of estrone against estradiol would have an average unit variance of about 75, and a slope of about 60 (uterine weight increase per tenfold dose increase). If a total of 40 animals were used in a 4-point assay, the expected minimal limits of error are therefore approximately ($P = 0.95$) 81–124%, a reasonably low error. The fiducial limits of error, if not founded on a well-established slope from other similar assays, would be wider. It should be noted, however, that the marked dissimilarity in dose-response curves for estradiol and estriol would preclude the assay of one in terms of the other, and presumably of urine or other extracts in terms of a crystalline standard.

The use of oil solutions was also investigated, and it was found that rats receiving a daily injection in 0.2 ml. of oil (type not stated) gave uterine weights similar, dose for dose, to those shown above. The authors also noted changes in sensitivity of the animals from time to time, a strong pointer, if any be necessary, to the need for the simultaneous assay of unknown against standard on each occasion.

The uterine reaction to gonadotropin in the mouse was studied by Hamburger and Pedersen-Bjergaard (1937) and many others later, as it is a standard method for both clinical and research studies. The mouse is more sensitive than the rat, as in Allen-Doisy tests, and in gonadotropin assays it gives a more uniform response. Evans *et al.* (1941), therefore, tried the mouse uterine assay for estrogens (the gonadotropin assay utilizes the production of estrogens by the stimulated gonads). Their figures suggest that the mouse assay is more accurate than the assay using rats as described by Lauson *et al.* (1939) but this is an inference from the scatter of points about dose-response lines they present, made from tests with a similar injection and time schedule to that just described. Unfortunately, Evans *et al.* (1941) do not give sufficient details for a critical appraisal of their results, and no useful estimate can be made of the probable accuracy of tests.

The mouse uterine weight curves also seem to show differences in shape between the natural estrogens, but it is not certain, from the data presented, that this is not merely a reflection of differences in potency, as no flat maxima are shown for estriol and estrone. The order of activity, in contrast to the rat uterine tests, is estradiol, estrone, and estriol (the weakest).

Uterine weight can be increased by androgens and progestogens, in considerably higher doses than are needed of the commonly encountered estrogens. These tests are therefore not completely specific, although the presence of sufficient androgenic or progestational material to augment the effects of estrogen seems unlikely, even in unfractionated urine extracts. Thus, Evans *et al.* (1941) found that the metrotropic activity of androsterone is less than one ten-thousandth that of estrone, and in tests in which androsterone and dehydroisoandrosterone were added to injections of estrone in ratios likely to be found in human urine, Evans and his colleagues found no significant effect.

Dorfman and Dorfman (1954) have used the immature rat uterus in the assay of estrogens, both by subcutaneous and oral administration. The rats were 22 or 23 days old at the start of tests and were injected once daily for 3 days with estrogen sulfates in 0.1 ml. oil, or fed once daily for 4 days by stomach tube with the same substance in 1 ml. of water. The uteri were removed 24 hours after the last injection, blotted, and weighed to 0.5 mg. Body weights were also determined and the results expressed as 100 times the uterine weight in milligrams per gram body weight.

Table VIII shows the results obtained with various preparations by the oral route, and Table IX a series of assays of sodium estrone sulfate against itself in 4-point or 6-point assays. These appear satisfactory— the potency should of course be 100%, but the authors stated that if less than 8 animals were used per group, unsatisfactory assays resulted which sometimes showed significant slope differences. The method gave a linear log dose-response relationship with subcutaneous estrone from 0.6 to 2.4 μg. and with oral estrone from 2.5 to 20 μg. In a series of 10 runs in which estrone was assayed against itself by subcutaneous injection, using 8 rats per group (32 in all), the maximum standard error of the potency was 22%.

Interest in oral dosage of estrogens for cattle and other livestock has recently led to various methods being evolved for feeding natural or synthetic estrogens to rats or mice, usually measuring uterine weight. Assays

TABLE VIII

RAT UTERINE RESPONSE TO ORALLY ADMINISTERED SODIUM ESTROGEN SULFATES[a]

Preparation	Total dose (μg.)	No. of rats	Mean uterine ratio $\pm$ S.E.
—	0	11	54 $\pm$ 3.7
—	0	13	56 $\pm$ 1.6
Sodium estrone sulfate	2.5	17	77 $\pm$ 5.7
	5.0	22	108 $\pm$ 9.4
	10.0	32	141 $\pm$ 7.8
	20.0	11	184 $\pm$ 12.3
Sodium equilin sulfate	4.0	10	75 $\pm$ 2.6
	8.0	17	108 $\pm$ 5.2
	16.0	10	144 $\pm$ 3.8
	32.0	9	188 $\pm$ 9.3
Reduced sodium equilin sulfate	2.0	9	151 $\pm$ 6.0
	4.0	17	191 $\pm$ 4.6
	8.0	9	196 $\pm$ 5.8
	16.0	7	216 $\pm$ 10.2

[a] After Dorfman and Dorfman (1954).

of essentially standard design have been used with such techniques by Stot et al. (1954), Turner (1956), Preston et al. (1956), and Umberger et al. (1958). Diethylstilbestrol and other synthetics are more effective by mouth than the natural estrogens, and so it is a reasonable way of approaching problems of bioassay of residual material in muscle, fat, etc.

TABLE IX

THE ORAL ASSAY OF SODIUM ESTRONE SULFATE AGAINST ITSELF IN FOUR-POINT ASSAYS WITH THE RAT UTERINE WEIGHT ASSAY[a]

No. per group	Doses (μg.)	Slope	λ	t	% potency $\pm$ S.E.
5	10; 20	106	0.352	2.84	67 $\pm$ 28
5	10; 20	179	0.191	0.68	127 $\pm$ 26
8	2.5; 5	105	0.117	0.96	104 $\pm$ 28
8	2.5; 10	120	0.103	0.33	99 $\pm$ 25
10	5; 10	86	0.397	1.14	127 $\pm$ 39
10	5; 10	102	0.428	0.25	75 $\pm$ 25
20	5; 10	100	0.369	0.54	96 $\pm$ 18

[a] After Dorfman and Dorfman (1954).

B. ASTWOOD'S SIX-HOUR TEST

Astwood (1938a) studied the early effects of estrogen on the uterus of the immature rat, and showed that a rapid increase in weight occurs during the first few hours after an injection. This increase is due almost entirely to the accumulation of water, as is shown in Fig. 18. The increase has been made the basis of a 6-hour test for estrogenic activity (Astwood, 1938b), at which time the early weight increase is at a maximum.

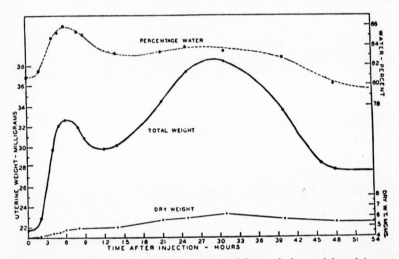

FIG. 18. Changes in per cent water, total weight, and dry weight of immature rat uteri during 48 hours following a single subcutaneous injection of 0.1 μg. of estradiol in oil. The curve represents mean figures from 370 rats (Astwood, 1938b).

In Astwood's original work, all doses were given in a single injection of 0.1 ml. sesame oil under the skin of the back. Female albino rats 21–23 days old were used, weighing 25–49 gm. (mean 36 gm.). After 6 hours, the animals were killed with chloroform, and the uteri were dissected out by cutting at the uterotubal junctions, stripping the mesometria, and trimming the vagina from its attachment to the cervix. After blotting on absorbent paper, the uteri were quickly weighed on a damped analytical balance. Water determinations were made by desiccating the weighted uteri in an oven at 110°C. Astwood then "partially corrected" for variation in the sizes of the rats by expressing all uterine weights in terms of an animal of a standard body weight of 36 gm. He noted that the correction tended to overcorrect for animals at the extremes of the normal range. The crude data were then further treated in producing assay curves by using the percentage increase in uterine weight as a criterion of response, but as this was apparently done on the basis of a single group of controls, common to all assays, it would not be a source of time-to-time variation and would presumably leave the nature and accuracy of the dose-response line unaffected.

Estradiol and estrone were shown to have similar dose-response curves; that for estradiol is shown in Fig. 19. This is a standard curve

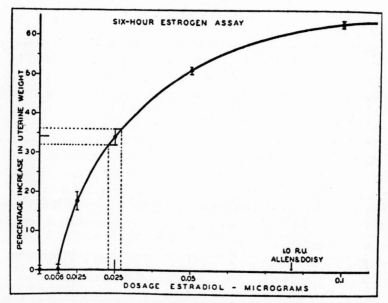

FIG. 19. Standardization curve from 300 rats in the Astwood 6-hour test (Astwood, 1938b).

based on data accumulated over a period, with standard errors of the means shown graphically. Astwood does not give his data in such a form as to allow of calculations relating to the probable errors of assays, and one can only judge roughly from the figures and data given that the method is probably fairly accurate. No subsequent critical applications of the method seem to have been made.

In the hands of its author, the Astwood test covered a range of doses of from 0.006 to 0.1 μg. of estradiol, and from about 0.07 to 1.2 μg. of estrone, which has one-twelfth the potency of estradiol. Four assays of the potency of estrone in terms of estradiol, each on only 5–7 animals, made by reading from the standard curve, gave estimates of 12.7, 12.2, 11.4, and 13.6, mean 12.4 μg. estrone = 1 μg. estradiol. The wide dose range over which estimates may be made is a recommendation, although a more orthodox method of conducting the assay is to be desired. It seems probable that a 4-point assay using crude uterine weight as the criterion of response, with covariance for body weight correction, instead of the arbitrary method described above, would give reasonably precise estimates of potency. It may be noted that, from Astwood's data, the log dose-response relationship is linear and adaptable to such an assay.

X. Vaginal Opening

Data such as those in Table VII are sometimes given, including observations of the incidence of vaginal opening, although not used by the authors for the estimation of relative potency. From the results of Lauson *et al.* (1939) it can nevertheless be seen that vaginal opening may be a sensitive and accurate index of estrogenic activity. The slope of the probit-log dose line in this instance is approximately 7.8, steeper than an Allen-Doisy test, which is usually 5 to 6, and indicating that an assay based on vaginal opening might have greater accuracy than an Allen-Doisy assay. A further advantage of such a method of assay would be a saving of animals, which need not be killed at the end of the test.

Interest in such assays was aroused by the reports of Hartman and his colleagues that vaginal opening could be stimulated in immature

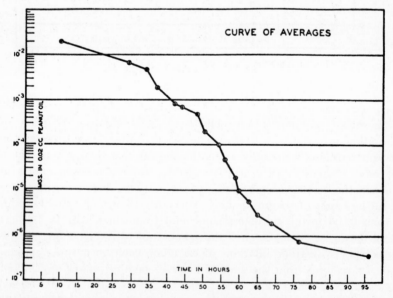

FIG. 20. Dose-response curve for the weanling guinea pig test using estradiol dipropionate in peanut oil (Hartman *et al.*, 1946).

rodents by the local injection of very small quantities of estrogen (Hartman and Littrell, 1945), or of 0.02 ml. of finger blood from a woman. The estrogen or test material was injected around the region of the future vaginal opening in the 21-day-old female rat and then was followed in 4 to 5 days by premature vaginal opening. Recognizable changes were described within 1 day, the first being a crescent-shaped transverse dimpling at the future site of opening, followed by pin-point punctures with oozing of fluid. Large doses caused complete opening within 24 hours.

The same method was then explored in the guinea pig by Littrell *et al.* (1946a, b). One-half of the total dose is injected with a short beveled needle on each side of the vulva. Five stages of response are described, four being short of complete opening. The assay may also be based on the time taken to a given level of response, that for full opening is shown in Fig. 20. It is based on only 1 to 3 observations per point and has a very gentle slope.

Lloyd *et al.* (1946) report poor results with the Hartman test in the rat, and it does not seem to have been used by others.

XI. *In Vitro* Assays

Estradiol-17β has been shown by Villee (1955) and Villee and Gordon (1955) to stimulate a reaction in human term placental extracts mediated by a diphosphopyridine nucleotide (DPN) dependent isocitric dehydrogenase. DPN is reduced to DPNH and the product can be measured by absorption at 340 mμ in a spectrophotometer (Gordon and Villee, 1955), the rate of DPN reduction being a function of the concentration of estradiol in the medium. Estrone is as potent as estradiol in this system, but no other steroid tested (including estriol) stimulates DPNH production. The authors therefore propose (Gordon and Villee, 1956) that the system can provide a sensitive *in vitro* method for assaying estradiol and estrone. The dose-effect curve covers 0.1 to 0.5 μg. over its steepest portion.

The placental extract is prepared by cutting human term placentae, obtained as soon as possible after delivery, into 3- to 5-cm. pieces and washing in ice-cold physiological saline. The pieces are then sliced and dried, the gross connective tissue discarded, and the rest homogenized in cold 0.25 M sucrose. Cellular debris and residual connective tissue are separated by centrifuging at 2000 g for 10 minutes at 5°C. The supernatant is then centrifuged at 57,000 g for 60 minutes to remove mitochondria and microsomes. The clear, reddish fluid ($S_{57,000}$) is stored at 0°C. until use, and retains maximum activity for at least 6 to 8 hours.

Steroid suspensions or solutions must be in aqueous media and suspensions are made by homogenizing for 2 to 3 minutes with a Teflon pestle and stored at 5°C.

In Gordon and Villee's (1956) estimations, the reduction of DPN was measured in a Beckman model DU at 340 mμ. The reaction mixtures were incubated at room temperature in quartz cuvettes with a 1-cm. light path, with a blank, control, and estrogen sample (3 cuvettes) used to make each measurement. Each received 1.0 ml. of 0.3 M tris(hydroxymethyl)aminomethane (Tris) buffer acidified to pH 7.4, 0.1 ml. of 0.1 M $CoCl_2$, and 0.3 ml. of 0.02 M isocitrate, but these were mixed before partitioning between buffers as small changes in $CoCl_2$ concentration affect results. The solution or suspension to be tested for estrogenic activity was added (0.1 to 0.5 ml.) to the estrogen cuvette, followed by 1 ml. of $S_{57,000}$ and then water to give a final volume of 3 ml. was added to each cuvette, while 0.1 ml. of the DPN solution (7.5 mM DPN) was added to the control and estrogen cuvettes to start the reaction. The cuvettes were inverted several times for mixing, and the optical densities recorded 1 and 20 minutes after mixing.

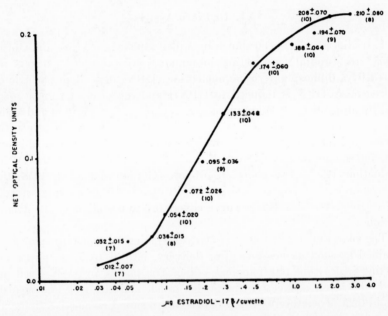

FIG. 21. DPN reduction by the placental $S_{57,000}$ fraction as a function of estradiol concentration. Net optical density units (ordinate) is defined in the text. The numbers are the means ± standard error of determinations with the number of different placental preparations shown in parentheses (Gordon and Villee, 1956).

A standard curve was made for each placental preparation with 5 concentrations of estradiol in the range 0.075–0.5 μg. per cuvette. The response is the optical density at 20 minutes minus that at 1 minute for the estrogen cuvette, minus the same figure (20 minutes − 1 minute) for the control, or: $E20 − C20 + C1 − E1$, where E and C have obvious meanings. It is not clear why a blank was included, and it also seems likely that $E20 − C20$ would give a better index.

Results from a number of placental preparations are given in Fig. 21; the number of preparations used at each point is shown in brackets under the mean response and its standard error. This is clearly not the standard error to be attached to the mean in a properly balanced assay, whether using one or more placental extracts, because an assay would (or should) be founded on *within-extract* comparisons. The authors state that an analysis of their data according to the method of Bliss (1944) showed an index of precision (λ) of 0.106 when the responses to 0.1, 0.15, 0.3, and 0.5 μg. of estradiol were compared in alternate series of experiments using different placental extracts in each series. The meaning of this is not clear, but it would seem that a precise assay could be based on this method, although it is not very sensitive, and direct chemical methods can already rival it.

Results with other steroids are shown in Table X. Estrone has a

TABLE X

THE EFFECT OF STEROIDS, SINGLY AND IN COMBINATION, ON DPN REDUCTION
BY THE PLACENTAL $S_{57,000}$ FRACTION[a]

Steroid	μg. per cuvette	Δ O.D. at 340 mμ	Steroid pair	μg. per cuvette	Δ O.D. at 340 mμ
Control	—	0.012	Control	—	0.014
Estradiol	0.3	0.224	Estradiol	0.3	0.190
Estrone	0.3	0.190			
Estriol	15.0	0.006	Estradiol and	0.3	0.160
17α-Ethinylestradiol	15.0	0.084	estriol	12.0	
Stilbestrol	15.0	0.016	Estradiol and	0.3	0.201
Estradiol-17β	15.0	−0.004	progesterone	12.0	
Progesterone	15.0	0.016			
Testosterone	15.0	0.167	Estradiol	0.3	0.212
Cortisone	15.0	0.006	and cortisol	12.0	
Cortisol	15.0	0.046			
Cholesterol	15.0	0.015	Estradiol and	0.3	0.273
			testosterone	15.0	

[a] From Gordon and Villee (1956).

relative potency of about 0.9 compared with estradiol, while, of the other compounds tested, testosterone, cortisol, and 17-ethinyl estradiol had measurable stimulatory effects, but only in large amounts. Estriol, inactive alone, seemed to inhibit estradiol slightly. Assays of human urine extracts prepared by the method of Smith and Smith (1952) and compared with assay by the vaginal smear technique gave fair to good agreement for the estradiol and estrone fractions, but not of course for the estriol fraction (Table XI).

TABLE XI

COMPARISON OF ESTROGEN CONTENT OF URINE FRACTIONS BY A RAT VAGINAL SMEAR ASSAY[a] AND THE *in Vitro* PLACENTAL EXTRACT TECHNIQUE[b]

| | | μg./ml. of hormone | |
Urine fraction	Hormone present	Placental extract technique	Rat vaginal smear assay
1	Estradiol	0.60	0.50–0.59
2	Estrone	3.87	4.0–5.2
3	Estriol	0.00	200–250
4	Estriol	0.00	200–250
5	Estradiol	4.70	3.35–4.50
6	Estradiol	1.12	0.67–0.78

[a] Smith and Smith (1952).
[b] From Gordon and Villee (1956).

XII. Oral Dosage to Chicks

Dorfman and Dorfman (1953) described an assay method using various estrogens and estrogen sulfates added to the diet, which gave surprisingly precise results. This method does not control individual dosage, hence there is some surprise at its accuracy.

Four-point assays with dose ratios of 2:1 or 4:1 were usually employed, with sex-linked pullets from a commercial hatchery. The end point was oviduct weight, expressed as a ratio to body weight. The chicks were placed on the diets containing estrogen for 13 days, commencing 2 to 3 days after hatching, and then were killed.

Some results with natural estrogens are shown in Table XII, and some relative potencies are shown in Table XIII (p. 106). It will be seen from these tables that the method is not suitable for small quantities of active material, but that it gives valid assays of various estrogens against each other, with reasonably narrow limits of error in view of the numbers

TABLE XII

CHICK OVIDUCT RESPONSES TO NATURALLY OCCURRING ESTROGENS
AND DERIVATIVES IN THE DIET[a]

Preparation	Dose (mg./kg.)	No. of chicks	Mean oviduct ratio ± S.E.
—	0	32	16 ± 0.5
—	0	24	16 ± 0.5
—	0	32	14 ± 0.5
Sodium estrone sulfate (pure)	40	30	31 ± 4.0
	80	30	115 ± 11.0
	80	16	117 ± 17.0
	160	16	466 ± 90.0
Estrone	20	25	24 ± 2.0
	40	26	40 ± 3.0
	80	27	149 ± 24.0
	160	24	278 ± 21.0
Estradiol dipropionate	80	23	77 ± 6.0
	160	24	202 ± 38.0

[a] From Dorfman and Dorfman (1953).

of chicks used. It is not clear whether the method of expressing uterine weight in terms of body weight improved the results, or whether a technique such as covariance analysis would have improved them further.

XIII. Duration of Action

Diczfalusy et al. (1957) have described an assay based on the duration of vaginal cornification in mice when using long-acting compounds. Adult females were spayed and used 2 to 4 weeks later without priming. Following a single subcutaneous injection, smears were taken daily and the duration of cornification recorded for each mouse. A symmetrical 4-point assay was used, with up to 20 animals per dosage level.

A straight dose-response line was obtained for polyestradiol phosphate or ethinyl estradiol when log time was plotted against log dose, or when the reciprocal of time was plotted against log dose, but in the latter instance the precision of assays was less. The two dose-response lines for ethinyl estradiol are shown in Fig. 22. Valid assays seemed possible when different long-acting estrogens were compared with one another and if different vehicles were used. With 60 to 80 mice per assay, the fiducial limits of error ($P = 0.95$) were around 85–118%.

TABLE XIII

RELATIVE POTENCIES OF ORALLY ADMINISTERED ESTROGENS IN CHICKS[a]

Standard	Unknown	Doses (mg./kg.)	No. of chicks	Potency	% Limits of error ($P = 0.95$)
Stilbestrol		80:160	72		
	Sodium estrone sulfate	80:160	62	87	$-12; +14$
Stilbestrol		20:40	152		
	Ethinyl estradiol	10:20	62	226	$-9; +10$
Stilbestrol		40:80	111		
	Estrone	80:160	51	74	$-14; +17$
Estrone		40:80:160	77		
	Estradiol dipropionate	80:160	47	64	$-18; +22$
Sodium estrone sulfate		80:160	62		
	MDDA[b]	80:160	39	100	$-12; +13$
Sodium estrone sulfate		40:80:160	60		
	Sodium estradiol sulfate	40:80:160	59	100	$-16; +19$

[a] From Dorfman and Dorfman (1953).
[b] Methoxybisdehydrodoisynolic acid.

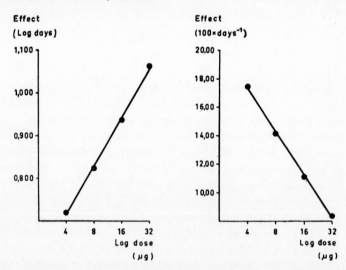

FIG. 22. Different transformations of the relationship between dose and response for ethinyl estradiol in tests of duration of action (Diczfalusy *et al.*, 1957).

XIV. Estrogen Inhibition

Many of the assay methods outlined above may be used to measure the inhibition of estrogens. Examples are given in Chapter 1 (this volume), from Claringbold *et al.* (1953) and by Emmens and Cox (1958) for the Allen-Doisy technique, worked out either by angles, or 0,1,2, scores. Examples using vaginal mitosis, epithelial thickness or tetrazolium reduction are given by Emmens *et al.* (1959, 1960). The main point about inhibition assays is that it is not very satisfactory to inhibit the effects of a single dose of estrogen, as the nature of the hormone-inhibitor relationship is not thereby elucidated. Instead, a factorial scheme should be employed, so that simultaneously a series of dose-response lines for the estrogen and for the inhibitor is established. Table XIV from Emmens and Cox

TABLE XIV

INHIBITION OF INTRAVAGINAL ESTRONE BY DIMETHYLSTILBESTROL (DMS) IN ALLEN-DOISY TESTS[a]

(Scores are for groups of 10 mice by the 0, 1, 2 system)

Total doee DMS (μg.)	Total dose estrone in μg. $\times 10^{-4}$			
	6	12	24	48
0.0	12	12	17	19
0.02	4	10	13	19
0.20	0	2	7	14

	Analysis of variance			
Source of variation	DF	Sum of squares	Mean square	F
Estrone				
Linear	1	24.40	24.40	55.5***
Quadratic	1	0.41	0.41	0.9
Cubic	1	0.01	0.01	0.0
DMS	2	17.45	8.73	19.8***
Interaction	6	2.35	0.39	0.9
Residual (error)	108	47.65	0.44	—

[a] From Emmens and Cox (1958).
*** $P < 0.001$.

(1958) shows the inhibition of estrone by dimethylstilbestrol, and the analysis of variance indicates that a series of parallel dose-response lines for the estrogen has been achieved, with no significant curvature or inter-action. The action of the inhibitor may thus be assumed to be the same at all dose levels and at the two levels of inhibition. Figure 23, from Emmens *et al.* (1959), shows a similar set of responses in the mitotic

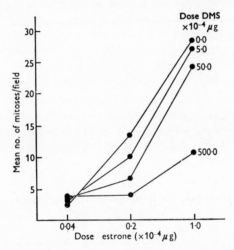

Fig. 23. Inhibition of estrone-stimulated mitosis in the mouse vagina by dimethyl-stilbestrol (DMS) (Emmens *et al.,* 1959).

index test, but this time there is a significant curvature of the dose-response line for estrone, when inhibition is partial, and the situation is not simple. Over the greater part of the dose range, however, parallel lines are in fact seen, and the curvature is due to the almost zero responses to the lowest dose of estrone and the highest dose of inhibitor.

References

Albrieux, A. S. (1941a). *J. Clin. Endocrinol.* **1**, 889.

Albrieux, A. S. (1941b). *J. Clin. Endocrinol.* **1**, 893.

Allan, H., Dickens, F., and Dodds, E. C. (1930). *J. Physiol. (London)* **68**, 22.

Allen, E., and Doisy, E. A. (1923). *J. Am. Med. Assoc.* **81**, 819.

Allen, E., Smith, G. M., and Gardner, W. U. (1937). *Am. J. Anat.* **61**, 372.

Astwood, E. B. (1938a). *Anat. Record* **70**, Suppl. 3, 5.

Astwood, E. B. (1938b). *Endocrinology* **23**, 25.

Balmain, J. H., Biggers, J. D., and Claringbold, P. J. (1956a). *Australian J. Biol. Sci.* **9**, 139.

Balmain, J. H., Biggers, J. D., and Claringbold, P. J. (1956b). *Australian J. Biol. Sci.* **9**, 147.

Biggers, J. D. (1951). *J. Endocrinol.* **7**, 163.

Biggers, J. D. (1952). *Nature* **170**, 895.

Biggers, J. D. (1953a). *J. Endocrinol.* **9**, 136.

Biggers, J. D. (1953b). *J. Anat.* **87,** 327.

Biggers, J. D., and Claringbold, P. J. (1953). *Australian J. Biol. Sci.* **6,** 305.

Biggers, J. D., and Claringbold, P. J. (1954a). *Australian J. Exptl. Biol. Med. Sci.* **32,** 33.

Biggers, J. D., and Claringbold, P. J. (1954b). *Nature* **174,** 596.

Biggers, J. D., and Claringbold, P. J. (1954c). *J. Endocrinol.* **11,** 277.

Biggers, J. D., and Claringbold, P. J. (1955a). *J. Endocrinol.* **12,** 1.

Biggers, J. D., and Claringbold, P. J. (1955b). *J. Anat.* **89,** 124.

Biggers, J. D., Claringbold, P. J., and Emmens, C. W. (1954). *J. Endocrinol.* **11,** 26.

Bliss, C. I. (1944). *Science* **100,** 577.

Bülbring, E., and Burn, J. H. (1935). *J. Physiol. (London)* **85,** 320.

Burn, J. H., and Elphick, G. K. (1932). *Quart. J. Pharm. and Pharmacol.* **5,** 192.

Butenandt, A., and Störmer, I. (1932). *Z. physiol. Chem., Hoppe-Seyler's* **208,** 129.

Claringbold, P. J. (1953). *Australian J. Biol. Sci.* **6,** 657.

Claringbold, P. J. (1954). *J. Endocrinol.* **11,** 36.

Claringbold, P. J. (1955a). *J. Endocrinol.* **13,** 11.

Claringbold, P. J. (1955b). *Australian J. Biol. Sci.* **8,** 396.

Claringbold, P. J. (1956). *J. Roy. Statist. Soc.* **B18,** 133.

Claringbold, P. J., and Biggers, J. D. (1955). *Australian J. Biol. Sci.* **8,** 407.

Claringbold, P. J., Biggers, J. D., and Emmens, C. W. (1953). *Biometrics* **9,** 467.

Cohen, S. L., and Marrian, G. F. (1934). *Biochem. J.* **28,** 1603.

Courrier, R. (1950). *Vitamins and Hormones* **8,** 179.

Courrier, R., and Cohen-Solal, G. (1937a). *Compt. rend. soc. biol. (Paris)* **118,** 683.

Courrier, R., and Cohen-Solal, G. (1937b). *Compt. rend. soc. biol.* **118,** 686.

Curtis, J. M., and Doisy, E. A. (1931). *J. Biol. Chem.* **91,** 647.

David, K., de Jongh, S. E., and Laqueur, E. (1935). *Arch. intern. pharmacodynamie* **51,** 137.

de Jongh, S. E., Laqueur, E., and de Fremery, P. (1932). *Biochem. Z.* **250,** 448.

Diczfalusy, E., Magnusson, A. M., Nilsson, L., and Westman, A. (1957). *Endocrinology* **60,** 581.

Dodds, E. C., Golberg, L., Lawson, W., and Robinson, R. (1939). *Proc. Roy. Soc.* **B127,** 140.

Dirscherl, W. (1936). *Z. physiol. Chem., Hoppe-Seyler's* **239,** 53.

Dorfman, R. I., and Dorfman, A. S. (1953). *Endocrinology* **53,** 301.

Dorfman, R. I., and Dorfman, A. S. (1954). *Endocrinology* **55,** 65.

Dorfman, R. I., Gallagher, T. F., and Koch, F. C. (1936). *Endocrinology* **19,** 33.

Edgren, R. A. (1957). *Acta Endocrinol.* **25,** 365.

Edgren, R. A., and Calhoun, D. W. (1957). *Proc. Soc. Exptl. Biol. Med.* **94,** 537.

Emmens, C. W. (1939a). *Med. Research Council (Brit.) Spec. Rept. Ser.* **234.**

Emmens, C. W. (1939b). *J. Endocrinol.* **1,** 142.

Emmens, C. W. (1939c). *J. Endocrinol.* **1,** 373.

Emmens, C. W. (1941a). *J. Endocrinol.* **2,** 368.

Emmens, C. W. (1941b). *J. Endocrinol.* **2,** 444.

Emmens, C. W. (1942a) *J. Endocrinol.* **3,** 168.

Emmens, C. W. (1942b). *J. Endocrinol.* **3,** 174.

Emmens, C. W. (1943). *J. Endocrinol.* **3,** 316.

Emmens, C. W. (1947). *J. Endocrinol.* **5,** 170.

Emmens, C. W., ed. (1950a). "Hormone Assay," Chapter XVI. Academic Press, New York.

Emmens, C. W. (1950b). *J. Endocrinol.* **6,** 302.

Emmens, C. W. (1957). *J. Endocrinol.* **16**, 148.

Emmens, C. W. (1959). *In* "Reproduction in Domestic Animals" (H. H. Cole and P. T. Cupps, eds.), Chapter 4. Academic Press, New York.

Emmens, C. W., and Bradshaw, T. E. T. (1939). *J. Endocrinol.* **1**, 378.

Emmens, C. W., and Cox, R. I. (1958). *J. Endocrinol.* **17**, 265.

Emmens, C. W., Cox, R. I., and Martin, L. (1959). *J. Endocrinol.* **18**, 372.

Emmens, C. W., Cox, R. I., and Martin, L. (1960). *J. Endocrinol.* **20**, 198.

Evans, J. S., Varney, R. F., and Koch, F. C. (1941). *Endocrinology* **28**, 74(.

Freud, J. (1939). *Acta brevia Neerl. Physiol. Pharmacol. Microbiol.* **9**, 11.

Grundy, J. (1957). *Chem. Revs.* **57**, 281.

Gordon, E. E., and Villee, C. A. (1955). *J. Biol. Chem.* **216**, 215.

Gordon, E. E., and Villee, C. A. (1956). *Endocrinology* **58**, 150.

Hain, A. M., and Robson, J. M. (1936). *J. Pharmacol. Exptl. Therap.* **57**, 337.

Hamburger, C., and Pedersen-Bjergaard, K. (1937). *Quart. J. Pharm. and Pharmacol.* **10**, 662.

Hartman, C. G., and Littrell, J. L. (1945). *Science* **102**, 175.

Hartman, C. G., Littrell, J. L., and Tom, J. (1946). *Endocrinology* **39**, 120.

Huggins, C., Jensen, E. V., and Cleveland, A. S. (1954). *J. Exptl. Med.* **100**, 225.

Jardetsky, C. D., and Glick, D. (1956). *J. Biol. Chem.* **218**, 283.

Jeener, R. (1947). *Nature* **159**, 579.

Kahn, R. H. (1954a). *Am. J. Anat.* **95**, 309.

Kahn, R. H. (1954b). *Nature* **174**, 317.

Kahn, R. H., and Bern, H. A. (1950). *Science* **111**, 516.

Krichesky, B., and Glass, S. J. (1947). *Endocrinology* **40**, 192.

Lauson, H. D., Heller, C. G., Golden, J. B., and Severinghaus, E. L. (1939). *Endocrinology* **24**, 35.

Layne, D. S., and Marrian, G. F. (1958). *Nature* **182**, 50.

Levin, L., and Tyndale, H. H. (1937). *Endocrinology* **21**, 619.

Littrell, J. L., Tom, J., and Hartman, C. G. (1946a). *Federation Proc.* **5**, 65.

Littrell, J. L., Tom, J., and Hartman, C. G. (1946b). *Anat. Record* **94**, 25.

Lloyd, C. W., Rogers, W. F., and Williams, R. H. (1946). *Endocrinology* **39**, 256.

Marrian, G. F. (1930). *Biochem. J.* **24**, 1021.

Marrian, G. F. (1948). *J. Endocrinol.* **5**, lxxi.

Marrian, G. F., and Parkes, A. S. (1929). *J. Physiol.* (*London*) **67**, 27.

Martin, L. (1960). *J. Endocrinol.* **20**, 187.

Martin, L., and Claringbold, P. J. (1958). *Nature* **181**, 620.

Martin, L., and Claringbold, P. J. (1960). *J. Endocrinol.* **20**, 173.

Meyer, R. K., Miller, L. C., and Cartland, G. F. (1936). *J. Biol. Chem.* **112**, 597.

Mühlbock, O. (1940). *Acta brevia Neerl. Physiol. Pharmacol. Microbiol.* **10**, 42.

Palmer, A. (1941). *Univ. California* (*Berkeley*) *Publs. Pharmacol.* **1**, 375.

Pedersen-Bjergaard, K. (1939). "Comparative Studies Concerning the Strengths of Oestrogenic Substances." Oxford Univ. Press, London and New York.

Pincus, G., and Werthessen, N. T. (1938). *Proc. Roy. Soc.* **B126**, 330.

Preston, R. E., Cheng, C. D., Story, P. H., Pauls, J., and Burroughs, W. (1956). *J. Animal Sci.* **15**, 3.

Robson, J. M. (1936). *Proc. Soc. Exptl. Biol. Med.* **35**, 49.

Robson, J. M. (1937). *J. Physiol.* (*London*) **90**, 15 P.

Robson, J. M. (1938). *J. Physiol.* **92**, 371.

Robson, J. M., and Adler, J. (1940). *Nature* **146**, 60.

Rowlands, I. W., and Callow, R. K. (1935). *Biochem. J.* **29**, 837.

Schoeller, W., Dohrn, M., and Hohlweg, W. (1935). *Med. J. and Record* **132**, 487.
Smith, O. W., and Smith, G. V. (1952). *Recent Progr. in Hormone Research* **7**, 209.
Solmssen, U. V. (1945). *Chem. Revs.* **37**, 481.
Stockard, C. R., and Papanicolaou, G. N. (1917). *Am. J. Anat.* **22**, 225.
Stot, M., Andrews, F. N., and Zarrow, M. X. (1954). *Am. J. Vet. Research* **15**, 319.
Sulman, F. G. (1952). *Endocrinology* **50**, 61.
Szego, C. M., and Roberts, S. (1953). *Recent Prog. in Hormone Research* **8**, 419.
Turner, C. W. (1956). *J. Animal Sci.* **15**, 13.
Umberger, E. J., Gass, G. H., and Curtis, J. M. (1958). *Endocrinology* **63**, 806.
Villee, C. A. (1955). *J. Biol. Chem.* **216**, 171.
Villee, C. A., and Gordon, E. E. (1955). *J. Biol. Chem.* **216**, 203.
Wade, N. J., and Doisy, E. A. (1935). *Proc. Soc. Exptl. Biol. Med.* **32**, 707.
Whitman, B., Wintersteiner, O., and Schwenk, E. (1937). *J. Biol. Chem.* **118**, 789.
Wilder-Smith, A. E., and Williams, P. C. (1947). *J. Endocrinol.* **5**, 152.

Chapter 3

Anti-Estrogenic Compounds

RALPH I. DORFMAN

I. Introduction

For the purpose of this chapter, anti-estrogenic substances are defined as compounds which interfere with any action of an estrogen at a peripheral level. Inhibition of estrogen action has been shown for androgenic substances (Robson, 1938; Emmens and Bradshaw, 1939; Velardo *et al.*, 1955; Edgren and Calhoun, 1957; Dorfman *et al.*, 1960a,b), progestational substances (Robson, 1938; Astwood, 1940; Szego and Roberts, 1948; Courrier, 1950; Mardones *et al.*, 1954; Huggins and Jensen, 1955b; Edgren and Calhoun, 1957; Dorfman *et al.*, 1960a,b), estrogens (de Fremery *et al.*, 1934; Allen and Meyer, 1935; Hisaw *et al.*, 1954), and corticoids (Robson, 1939; Szego and Roberts, 1948; Szego, 1952; Talalay *et al.*, 1952; Roberts and Szego, 1953; Beyler and Szego, 1954; Huggins and Jensen, 1955b; Velardo, 1955; Velardo and Sturgis, 1955; Velardo *et al.*, 1955; Velardo, 1956; Velardo and Sturgis, 1956). The relative effectiveness of corticoids has been summarized by Velardo (1959) as 9α-fluoroprednisolone > 9α-fluorocortisol > cortisol > cortisone

> prednisone > prednisolone >deoxycorticosterone. Neither the pituitary nor the adrenal were necessary for the reaction.

The substance MER-25 [1-(p-2-diethylaminoethoxyphenyl)-1-phenyl-2-p-methoxyphenyl ethanol], is unique since inhibition of estrogen action to the extent of 90–100% has been described (Lerner et al., 1958). The substance has a low uterotrophic activity and anti-pituitary gonado-tropin action. MER-25 is the best studied anti-estrogenic substance, and it is effective in intact and castrated rats, mice, monkeys, chicks, and rabbits. Lerner et al. (1958) have further demonstrated that the compound is effective against steroidal and nonsteroidal estrogens.

Recently a group of papers have appeared dealing with the anti-estrogenic activity of certain synthetic steroids which show intense activity (Payne et al., 1956; Edgren and Calhoun, 1957; Sturtevant, 1957; Edgren, 1958; Edgren et al., 1959). Edgren et al. (1959) reported that certain 17α-alkyl derivatives are extremely active, that the nature of the alkyl group has an important effect on the potency, and that the dihydro-19-nortestosterone as well as the $\Delta^{5(10)}$ isomers are much less active than the Δ^4 steroids. These studies, as with older studies, suffer from the fact that the stimulating and suppressing compounds were injected as a single solution at a single site. This technique may be faulty due to the fact that the action of the inhibitor may be by way of interference with estrogen absorption. Certain synthetic compounds such as (di-p-hydroxyphenyl)-butane: -pentane: -hexane: and -1,4-pentanedien-3-one inhibit the proliferation and cornification in the vaginal epithelium of rats treated subcutaneously with estradiol benzoate (Banay et al., 1955). Villee (1957a, b) has shown that certain anti-estrogenic activity may be detected with an in vitro test employing the estrogen isocitric acid dehydrogenase reaction from human placental tissue.

The assay of anti-estrogenic compounds has been described and implied in various publications by in vivo and in vitro methods. The in vivo methods are not quantitative techniques but rather qualitative tests suitable to establish an approximate rank order of relative potency. Some of these methods will be discussed and described in this chapter.

A rather wide range of compounds possessing this property have already been listed. In addition, it is known that folic acid is required for estrogen activity (Hertz and Sebrell, 1944; Hertz, 1945; Kline and Dorfman, 1951; Davis et al., 1956; Davis, 1957). No obvious interrelationship between the folic acid antagonists and the known anti-estrogens of the steroid type is apparent.

Emmens and his co-workers (Emmens and Cox, 1958; Emmens et al., 1959) have indicated that substances such as testosterone and progesterone inhibit the action of estrogens with respect to their cornification action on the vaginal epithelium but fail to interfere with the mitosis caused by estrogens. On the other hand, three stilbestrol derivative products including dimethylstilbestrol, ethylstilbestrol, and n-propylstilbestrol, do interfere with the mitotic stimulation caused by estrogens when the agents are administered intravaginally.

II. *In Vivo* Assays

A. VAGINAL RESPONSE IN SPAYED RATS (INJECTION)

(Lerner *et al.*, 1958)

Spayed adult rats (Rolfsmeyer Rat Company and Hamilton Laboratory Animals) are injected subcutaneously with estradiol-17β in olive oil solution at time zero. The inhibitor is injected subcutaneously twice: at zero and 8 hours. Vaginal smears are obtained at 56, 64, and 72 hours. Positive smears are those containing nucleated or cornified epithelial cells and not more than a few leucocytes.

Typical results are illustrated in Table I. MER-25 at doses from 0.04

TABLE I

THE INHIBITION OF ESTRADIOL-17β VAGINAL STIMULATION
BY MER-25 IN THE SPAYED RAT (INJECTION)[a]

Total dose of MER-25 injected (mg.)	Total dose of estradiol-17β injected (μg.)	Number of rats	Positive vaginal response (%)
0	0	10	0
0	0.6	10	100
0.04	0	10	0
0.2	0	10	0
1.0	0	10	0
0.04	0.6	10	90
0.2	0.6	10	10
1.0	0.6	10	0

[a] Adapted from Lerner *et al.* (1958).

to 1.0 mg. showed no vaginal response, but a dose of 0.2 mg. produced a highly significant inhibition.

B. Vaginal Response in Spayed Rats (Gavage)

(Lerner et al., 1958)

The method is the same as described above (Vaginal Response in Spayed Rats—Injection) except that the test compound is administered in olive oil solution by gavage at zero and 8 hours. A dose of 0.4 mg. of MER-25 was effective in inhibiting the estrogenic action of 0.6 μg. of estradiol-17β. One milligram of this compound almost completely inhibited the same dose of estradiol-17β (Table II).

TABLE II

The Inhibition of Estradiol-17β Vaginal Stimulation
by MER-25 in the Spayed Rat (Gavage)

Total dose of MER-25 by Gavage (mg.)	Total dose of estradiol-17β injected (μg.)	Number of rats	Positive vaginal response (%)
0	0	10	0
0	0.6	10	100
0.4	0	10	0
1	0	10	0
2	0	10	0
0.4	0.6	10	70
1	0.6	10	10
2	0.6	10	0

C. Uterine Response in Spayed Rats (Injection)

(Velardo et al., 1956)

Virgin ovariectomized rats, 100 days of age, are injected subcutaneously once daily with 0.1 μg. of estradiol-17β contained in 0.1 ml. of sesame oil for 3 days starting one week after surgery. The test compounds are dissolved in 0.2 ml. of sesame oil or aqueous media administered once daily for 3 days but at separate sites. Twenty-four hours after the last injection, the uteri are removed and weighed both wet and dry.

D. Uterine Response in Hypophysectomized Rats (Injection)

(Huggins and Jensen, 1955a)

Female rats, 22 days of age, were placed on a synthetic diet consisting of casein 254 gm., dextrin 468 gm., corn oil 38 gm., Alphacel 50 gm., mixed vitamins 10 gm., salt mixture 40 gm., oleum percomorphum 3 drops, water 140 ml., and vitamin K 50 μg. The steroids were contained in a mixture of 10% ethanol in sesame oil. The stimulating estrogen and inhibitor were injected in a single solution.

The rats were hypophysectomized at 24 days of age and the test compounds in 0.2 ml. of vehicle were injected once daily for 7 days when the rats were 38 days of age. The uteri were removed at 45 days of age, one day after the last injection. Those animals which had a body weight of 75 gm. or a spleen weight of 200 mg. were discarded to avoid the possibility of using rats which were not completely hypophysectomized. In addition to the determination of wet uterine weight the nitrogen content of uterus was determined.

Typical results are presented in Table III which indicates that a

TABLE III

INHIBITION OF ESTRONE-INDUCED UTERINE GROWTH BY VARIOUS STEROIDS[a]

Steroid injected	Daily dose (μg.)	Inhibition of uterus (%)	
		Weight	Nitrogen content
Estriol	2.5	33	35
16-Epiestriol	2.5	40	37
17-Epiestriol	2.5	31	29
Estradiol-16α	5.0	37	38
Estradiol-16β]	5.0	26	26
6-Ketoestrone	5.0	43	42
6-Ketoestradiol-17β	1.0	32	28

[a] Stimulating dose of estrone = 0.5 μg. per day for 7 days. Six or more rats per group. Data from Huggins and Jensen, 1955a).

variety of relatively "weak" estrogenic substance could inhibit the action of estrone, a "strong" estrogen. Huggins and Jensen (1955a) choose to name these phenolic steroid inhibitors "impeded estrogens" since, in the words of the authors, "after a moderate increase of uterine weight (about one-third of maximal growth) has been induced by steroids in this class, a tenfold increase in dosage causes little or no increment in growth."

E. UTERINE RESPONSE IN IMMATURE MICE (INJECTION)

(Edgren and Calhoun, 1957)

Mice 23 to 25 days of age are injected once daily for three days with 0.1 ml. of corn oil containing estrone alone or in combination with the test material. The total dose of estrone is 0.3 μg. In each experiment, groups of 8–10 mice were treated with estrone alone and estrone in combination with a series of doses of the test compound. One group of mice, receiving only corn oil, served as controls. At autopsy, 24 hours after the last injection, uterine weight was determined.

Figure 1 indicates some typical results obtained with the method of Edgren and Calhoun (1957) for testosterone propionate, progesterone,

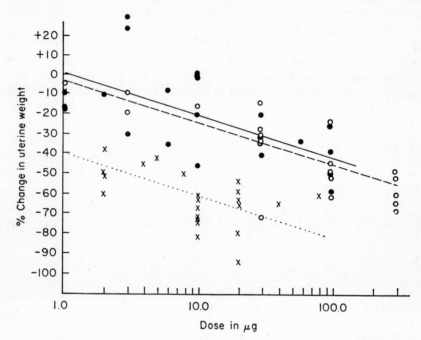

Fig. 1. Anti-uterotrophic action of steroids. Effects of testosterone propionate (dots and solid line), progesterone (circles and dashed line) and 17-ethyl-19-nortestosterone (crosses and dotted line) on estrone-induced uterine growth of intact, immature mice. 0% change = response of uterus to 0.3 μg of estrone; −100% change = control uterine level (Edgren and Calhoun, 1957).

and 17-ethyl-19-nortestosterone. Progesterone was judged to be 1.4 times as active as testosterone propionate, whereas the 19-nor compound was found to be about 70 times as potent.

F. UTERINE RESPONSE IN IMMATURE MICE (INJECTION)
(Dorfman et al., 1960a)

Twenty- to twenty-two-day-old Swiss albino mice are injected subcutaneously once daily with estrone for 3 days. The total dose of 0.4 μg.

is contained in 0.3 ml. of sesame oil and 0.1 ml. is injected daily. Control groups of mice receive only sesame oil. The test substance is injected subcutaneously daily in 0.1 ml. of an aqueous suspending medium at a different site from that used for the estrone injection. The aqueous suspending fluid consists of sodium chloride (0.9%), polysorbate 80 (0.4%), carboxymethylcellulose (0.5%), and benzyl alcohol (0.9%). One day after the last injections the animals are sacrificed and the uterine weights and body weights determined.

The assays may be conveniently run in groups of 132 mice which are divided into 14 groups. One group of 12 mice serve as sesame oil-injected control animals. Another group of 12 mice receive a total dose of 0.4-μg. estrone. The remaining ten groups of 9 mice each receive the test compounds. Usually a single compound is studied at three or more concentrations in any specific assay. To arrive at the relative activity of a given compound, all the data for a specific compound at a specific dose are combined. Compounds are compared on the basis of the minimum weight necessary to produce a statistically significant inhibition ($P = 0.02$) and by the maximum intensity of the inhibition at any dose. Sample relative potency data attainable with this method are presented in Table IV.

TABLE IV

RELATIVE ANTI-ESTROGENIC ACTIVITIES OF VARIOUS STEROIDS (INJECTION)[a]

Steroid	Total number of mice	Dosage range studied (μg.)	Minimum dose to produce inhibition (μg.)	Maximum inhibition (%)
2α, 17α-Dimethyl-17β-hydroxyandrostan-3-one	81	2–4000	2	30
Norethisterone	180	1–4000	16	56
Testosterone	99	64–4000	500	36
Progesterone	129	10–4000	500	56
Deoxycorticosterone	245	2–4000	1000	21

[a] Dorfman et al. (1960a).

G. UTERINE RESPONSE IN IMMATURE MICE (GAVAGE)

(Dorfman et al., 1960b)

This method is practiced precisely the same as that described for the injection method in immature mice by the same authors (Dorfman et al., 1960a), except that the total dose of test compound is dispersed in 0.6 ml.

of aqueous medium and 0.2 ml. are administered daily by gavage for 3 days. Representative data are presented in Table V.

TABLE V

RELATIVE ANTI-ESTROGENIC ACTIVITIES OF VARIOUS STEROIDS (GAVAGE)[a]

Various steroids	Total number of mice	Dose range studied (μg.)	Minimum dose to produce inhibition (μg.)	Maximum inhibition (%)
Norethisterone	238	2–1000	32	40
17-Methyltestosterone	270	4–2000	250	36
Deoxycorticosterone	118	10–4000	2000	30
Ethisterone	103	50–4000	4000	20

[a] Dorfman et al. (1960b).

H. MITOSIS METHOD IN SPAYED MICE (INTRAVAGINALLY)
(Emmens et al., 1959)

The authors recommend a colony of ovariectomized randomly bred albino mice which are used one every 14 days. The intravaginal applications are made in 0.01-ml. 25% aqueous propylene glycol solutions. Two smears are taken at approximately 10 A.M. and 4 P.M. on the third day and are scored as 0, 1, or 2, according to whether a positive reaction occurred in no smear, in one, or both. When mitotic counts were studied, the ovariectomized mice are primed with 1 μg. estrone dissolved in peanut oil, and the test solutions are administered intravaginally in 0.005-ml. doses. The stimulating dose of estrone and the inhibitor are administered intravaginally in a single solution. Colchicine (0.1 mg. in 0.05-ml. water) is injected subcutaneously 7 hours before autopsy to arrest mitosis. The estrogen and inhibitor are administered 24 hours before autopsy, at which time the vagina is removed, fixed in Barr's fixative, and embedded in wax. Transverse sections, 6 μ thick, are stained in Heidenhain's hematoxylin and counterstained in van Gieson's picro-acid fuchsin.

Observations are made on the number of mitoses and the thickness of the epithelium. The final mitotic score of each animal is the sum of five fields. For the purpose of analysis the authors employed the transformation $Y = \log_{10} (Z + 2)$ (where Z is the number of mitoses per field). The thickness of the epithelium is measured with an eyepiece micrometer

TABLE VI

INHIBITORY EFFECT OF DIMETHYLSTILBESTROL ON INTRAVAGINAL
RESPONSE TO ESTRADIOL-17β IN OVARIECTOMIZED MICE[a]

Dose of estradiol-17β (μg. $\times 10^{-4}$)	Dose of dimethyl- stilbestrol	Total scores for 10 mice
6	0	8
	0.2	2
	0.4	0
12	0	16
	0.2	8
	0.4	1

[a] Data of Emmens *et al.* (1959).

and expressed in arbitrary units. The score for each mouse was the average of five observations.

Typical data for the inhibitory effect of dimethylstilbestrol on intravaginal response to estradiol-17β in ovariectomized mice is presented in Table VI. Figure 2 (see also Fig. 23 of Chapter 2) indicates the inhibitor effect of estrone-stimulated mitosis and epithelial growth.

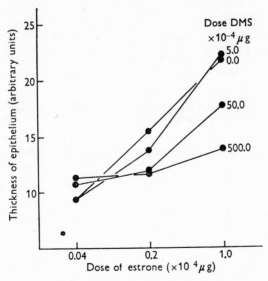

FIG. 2. Inhibition of estrone-stimulated growth by dimethylstilbestrol (Emmens *et al.*, 1959).

I. Chick Oviduct (Injection)

(Adapted from Lerner et al., 1958)

Seven-day-old pullet chicks are injected subcutaneously twice daily with oil solutions of both estradiol-17β and the test compound for 6 days. The daily dose of each compound is contained in 0.1 to 0.2 ml. of oil.

TABLE VII

The Inhibitory Activity of MER-25 on the Oviduct
of Estradiol-17β Stimulated Chicks[a]

Estradiol-17β injected (mg.)	MER-25 injected (mg.)	Number of chicks	Mean body weight (gm.)	Mean oviduct weight (mg.)
0	0	8	93	11
0	3	8	88	11
0.6	0	8	84	169
0.6	3	8	80	61

[a] Lerner et al. (1958).

One day after the last injections the animals are sacrificed and weights of the body and oviduct determined. The synthetic compound, MER-25, produced inhibition of the estradiol-17β action on the oviduct when this method was used (Table VII).

TABLE VIII

Inhibitory Effect of Various Steroids on the Action of Stilbestrol
on the Chick's Oviduct[a]

Total dose of stilbestrol (mg.)	Total dose of inhibitor		Number of chicks	Body weight (gm. $\pm$ S.D.)	Oviduct weight (mg. $\pm$ S.D.)
	Compound	mg.			
0	0	0	Not given		22
2	0	0	10	208 $\pm$ 17	1122 $\pm$ 199
2	Progesterone	1	11	209 $\pm$ 21	578 $\pm$ 86
2	Progesterone	5	5	189 $\pm$ 21	468 $\pm$ 35
2	11-Deoxycortisol	1	13	200 $\pm$ 23	825 $\pm$ 111
2	11-Deoxycortisol	5	9	216 $\pm$ 20	590 $\pm$ 115

[a] Tullner and Hertz (1956).

J. CHICK OVIDUCT (INJECTION)
(Hertz *et al.*, 1947; Tullner and Hertz, 1956)

Female New Hampshire Red chicks are maintained on commercial starting mash and controlled lighting of 12 hours light and 12 hours of darkness. Starting at 2 weeks of age the chicks are injected subcutaneously once daily for 8 days with 0.25-mg. stilbestrol in 0.1 ml. of corn oil. The test compounds as oil suspensions are injected subcutaneously at a separate site once daily for 8 days. Twenty-four hours after the last injections the chicks are sacrificed and the weights of the body and oviduct determined. Typical results with inhibitory steroids are indicated in Table VIII.

III. *In Vitro* Assays

A. PLACENTAL ISOCITRIC DEHYDROGENASE
(Villee and Hagerman, 1957)

Term human placentas are homogenized within 5 minutes of delivery and a particle-free fraction prepared by ultracentrifugation. Homogenates are prepared containing 20% (weight per volume) of placenta in ice-cold 0.25 M sucrose. This is done in a smooth glass homogenizer fitted with a Teflon pestle for 20 seconds and centrifuged at 2000 g in an angle hand centrifuge in the cold room. The sediment and connective tissue is discarded and the particle free supernatant ($S_{57,000}$) prepared in a Spinco model L preparative ultracentrifuge is used for the incubations (Villee, 1955). The incubations are carried out in air at 37°C. in 30-ml. beakers shaken at 45 cycles per minute in a Dubnoff incubator. The beakers contain 1.0 ml. of $S_{57,000}$ (particle-free supernatant), 1.0 ml. of a buffer containing 30 micromoles K$^+$, 10 micromoles Mg^{++}, 20 micromoles Cl$^-$, and 20 micromoles of phosphate buffered at pH 7.4, 3.0 micromoles of citrate, *cis*-aconitate or *d*-isocitrate, or 6.0 micromoles of *dl*-isocitrate, 0.75 micromoles of DPN, estrogen and anti-estrogens added as aqueous suspensions prepared by homogenization, and water to a total of 3 ml. After incubating for one hour, the following analyses are done: citric acid (Natelson *et al.*, 1948), α-keto acids (Friedemann and Haugen, 1943), and nitrogen by digestion and Nesslerization.

The results obtained with the *in vitro* method are not necessarily correlated with the *in vivo* studies. Estriol is an example of an estrogen in the classic sense; that is, it causes stimulation of female sex structures, which in the intact animal can also suppress the action of a more active estrogen such as estradiol-17β. The *in vitro* enzyme studies show the same properties (Table IX). However, other substances such as proges-

TABLE IX

Influence of Estriol and Estradiol-17β Alone and in Combination on the Placental Isocitric Dehydrogenase System[a,b]

Concentration of estriol added (μg./ml.)	Estradiol-17β added (μg./ml.)		
	0	0.1	1.0
0	0.22	0.42	0.47
0.33	0.29	0.41	0.47
3.3	0.34	0.38	0.44
33.0	0.38	0.35	0.40

[a] Villee and Hagerman (1957).

[b] Figures are micromoles α-ketoglutaric acid produced per 1 mg. N per hour (mean of 8 determinations).

terone and cortisone, which are grossly classified as anti-estrogens on the basis of the *in vivo* studies, neither stimulate the placental isocitric acid dehydrogenase system nor inhibit the action of the estradiol-17β.

IV. Conclusion

The assay methods developed for the determination of anti-estrogenic action of steroidal and nonsteroidal compounds have not been developed to the point of desired precision, nor is there adequate information as to the meaning of the inhibition observed, except that in all the tests described it is believed that the effect is at the peripheral level. The number of substances that show anti-estrogenic effects is great indeed, and their mechanisms of action not necessarily similar. This is illustrated by a compound such as dimethylstilbestrol which has the ability to inhibit the action of estrogens on the cornification reaction of the vagina, on mitosis stimulation, and on the growth of epithelial layer of the vagina. Testosterone and progesterone can produce certain inhibitory actions but are unable to inhibit the mitosis produced by estrogens. Only future studies, most likely those involving the elucidation of the mechanism(s) of estrogen action, will lead to more definitive anti-estrogen assays.

REFERENCES

Allen, W. M., and Meyer, R. K. (1935). *Anat. Record* **61**, 427.

Astwood, E. B. (1940). *Am. J. Physiol.* **129**, 302.

Banay, E., Morsing, P., Müller, W., Stallberg, G., and Stenhager, E. (1955). *Acta Soc. Med. Upsaliensis* **60**, 69.

Beyler, A. L., and Szego, C. M. (1954). *Endocrinology* **54**, 334.

Courrier, R. (1950). *Vitamins and Hormones* **8**, 179.

Davis, J. S. (1957). *Proc. Soc. Exptl. Biol. Med.* **95**, 247.

Davis, J. S., Meyer, R. K., and McShan, W. H. (1956). *Endocrinology* **59**, 505.

de Fremery, P., Kober, S., and Tausk, M. (1934). *Acta Brevia Neerl. Physiol. Pharmacol., Microbiol.* **4**, 119.

Dorfman, R. I., Kincl, F. A., and Ringold, H. J. (1960a). *Endocrinology* **68**, 17.

Dorfman, R. I., Kincl, F. A., and Ringold, H. J. (1960b). *Endocrinology* **68**, 43.

Edgren, R. A. (1958). *Endocrinology* **62**, 689.

Edgren, R. A., and Calhoun, D. W. (1957). *Proc. Soc. Exptl. Biol. Med.* **94**, 537.

Edgren, R. A., Calhoun, D. W., Elton, R. L., and Colton, F. B. (1959). *Endocrinology* **65**, 265.

Emmens, C. W., and Bradshaw, T. E. T. (1939). *J. Endocrinol.* **1**, 378.

Emmens, C. W., and Cox, R. I. (1958). *J. Endocrinol.* **17**, 265.

Emmens, C. W., Cox, R. I., and Martin, L. (1959). *J. Endocrinol.* **18**, 372.

Friedemann, T. E., and Haugen, G. E. (1943). *J. Biol. Chem.* **147**, 415.

Hertz, R. (1945). *Endocrinology* **37**, 1.

Hertz, R., and Sebrell, W. H. (1944). *Science* **100**, 293.

Hertz, R., Larsen, C. D., and Tullner, W. W. (1947). *J. Natl. Cancer Inst.* **8**, 123.

Hisaw, F. L., Velardo, J. T., and Goolsby, C. M. (1954). *J. Clin. Endocrinol. and Metabolism* **14**, 1134.

Huggins, C., and Jensen, E. V. (1955a). *J. Exptl. Med.* **102**, 335.

Huggins, C., and Jensen, E. V. (1955b). *J. Exptl. Med.* **102**, 347.

Kline, I. T., and Dorfman, R. I. (1951). *Endocrinology* **48**, 345.

Lerner, L. J., Holthaus, F. J. Jr., and Thompson, C. R. (1958). *Endocrinology* **63**, 295.

Mardones, E., Iglesias, R., and Lipschütz, A. (1954). *Nature* **174**, 839.

Natelson, S., Pincus, J. B., and Lugovoy, J. K. (1948). *J. Biol. Chem.* **175**, 745.

Payne, R. W., Hellbaum, A. A., and Owens, J. N. Jr. (1956). *Endocrinology* **59**, 306.

Roberts, S., and Szego, C. M. (1953). *J. Biol. Chem.* **201**, 21.

Robson, J. M. (1938). *J. Physiol.* (*London*) **92**, 371.

Robson, J. M. (1939). *J. Physiol.* (*London*) **96**, 21P.

Sturtevant, F. M. (1957). *J. Pharmacol. Exptl. Therap.* **121**, 369.

Szego, C. M. (1952). *Endocrinology* **50**, 429.

Szego, C. M., and Roberts, S. (1948). *Am. J. Physiol.* **152**, 131.

Talalay, P., Dobson, M. M., Ebersole, C. M., and Huggins, C. (1952). *Endocrinology* **50**, 574.

Tullner, W. W., and Hertz, R. (1956). *Endocrinology* **58**, 282.

Velardo, J. T. (1955). *Anat. Record* **122**, 478.

Velardo, J. T. (1956). *Am. J. Physiol.* **186**, 468.

Velardo, J. T. (1959). *Ann. N. Y. Acad. Sci.* **75**, 385.

Velardo, J. T., and Sturgis, S. R. (1955). *Am. J. Physiol.* **183**, 259.

Velardo, J. T., and Sturgis, S. R. (1956). *J. Clin. Endocrinol. and Metabolism* **16,** 496.

Velardo, J. T., Hisaw, F. L., and Bever, A. T. (1955). *Anat. Record* **117,** 552.

Velardo, J. T., Hisaw, F. L., and Bever, A. T. (1956). *Endocrinology* **59,** 165.

Villee, C. A. (1955). *J. Biol. Chem.* **215,** 171.

Villee, C. A. (1957a). *Cancer Research* **17,** 507.

Villee, C. A. (1957b). *Endocrinology* **60,** 552.

Villee, C. A., and Hagerman, D. D. (1957). *Endocrinology* **60,** 552.

Chapter 4

Progestational Substances

Tamotsu Miyake

I. Introduction

Gestagens, progestins, progestogens, or luteoids, by definition are substances which possess characteristic biological activity affecting the fertility of female animals. Corner (1928) first demonstrated that corpus luteum hormone has not only the properties of establishing ova implantation and maintaining the pregnancy of ovariectomized animals but also produces the characteristic endometrial histology which has been recognized as progestational or pseudopregnant proliferation.

Thus the Corner-Allen (1929) test was established as the first progestin assay based on the endometrial proliferation. Progestational activity has traditionally been estimated by the Clauberg (1930d) test or McPhail (1934) test, either of which is essentially a modification of Corner-Allen test. These assay methods were of great importance for the

127

isolation of progesterone and the discovery of numerous synthetic progestins.

Until recently [since the isolation of progesterone in 1934 (Allen and Wintersteiner, 1934; Butenandt, 1934; Slotta *et al.*, 1934)] progesterone was the only naturally occurring gestagen; no potent synthetic gestagens were available. Accordingly, there had been little need of clinical evaluation or biological standardization for progestational substances, and more attention was paid to other types of investigation.

Most of the earlier methods belong to the classic type of assay based on the all-or-none judgment or the semiquantitative evaluation. These methods have been thoroughly described by C. W. Emmens (1950), who stated that no studies were known on the bioassay of progesterone employing a modern statistical assay design. During the last decade, however, a variety of steroids with progesterone-like activity have been synthesized by steroid chemists. The excited interest in synthetic progestins has necessarily stimulated the search for an accurate bioassay method for progestational substances.

II. Progestational Substances

A. Natural Progestins

Progesterone (Δ^4-pregnene-3,20-dione) is a naturally occurring gestagen normally secreted from the corpus luteum and is essential for the establishment and maintenance of pregnancy. During pregnancy, the placenta also produces progesterone, the amount of which depends upon the placental growth (Zander and von Münstermann, 1956); and, further, there is indirect evidence that the adrenal cortex produces progesterone

TABLE I[a]

NATURALLY OCCURRING GESTAGENS: BIOLOGICAL ACTIVITY
COMPARED WITH PROGESTERONE

Compound	Mouse (Hooker-Forbes test)	Rabbit (Clauberg test)	Man
Progesterone	1	1	1
20α-Hydroxy-Δ^4-pregnen-3-one	$\frac{1}{5}$	$\frac{1}{2}$–$\frac{1}{3}$	As cyclopentyl propionate less active than progesterone
20β-Hydroxy-Δ^4-pregnen-3-one	2	$\frac{1}{5}$–$\frac{1}{10}$	As cyclopentyl propionate less active than progesterone

[a] From J. Zander (1959).

(Balfour *et al.*, 1957; Davis *et al.*, 1952; Klopper *et al.*, 1957; Zander, 1952).

It has recently been demonstrated that there are two other natural gestagens in the organism, 20α-hydroxy-Δ⁴-pregnen-3-one and 20β-hydroxy-Δ⁴-pregnen-3-one, which are metabolites of progesterone (Zander, 1959; Zander *et al.*, 1957, 1958; Zander and von Münstermann, 1954). Both compounds are active in the Hooker-Forbes (1947) test and in the Clauberg (1930d) test as indicated in Table I. The structures of these natural progestins are illustrated in Fig. 1.

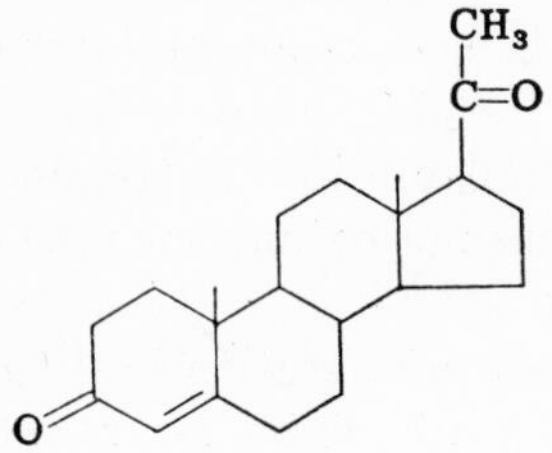

CH₃ C=O

Progesterone

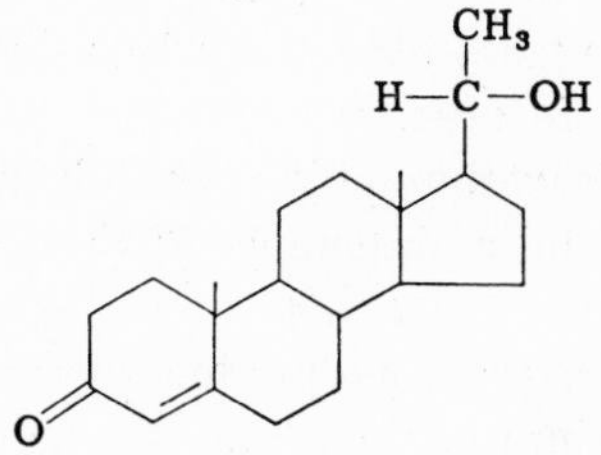

CH₃ H—C—OH

20α-Hydroxy-Δ⁴-pregnen-3-one

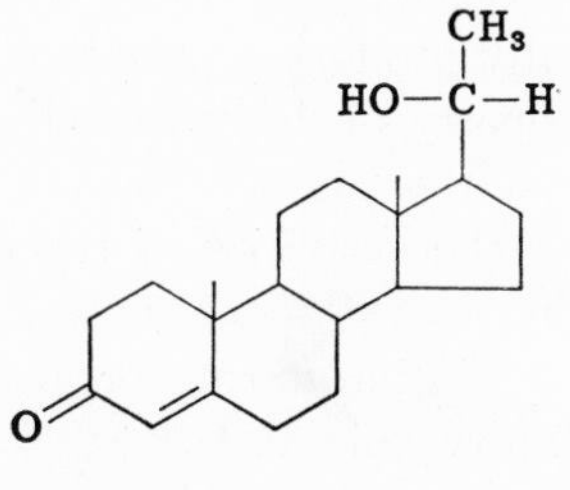

CH₃ HO—C—H

20β-Hydroxy-Δ⁴-pregnen-3-one

Fig. 1. Structures of naturally occurring progestins.

Progesterone not only plays an important role in the female reproductive physiology as a circulating hormone, but also serves as a versatile intermediate in the production of steroid hormones such as corticoids, androgens, and estrogens in all steroid-forming tissues including the gonads, adrenals, and placenta.

Circulating progesterone is rapidly inactivated, chiefly in the liver and kidney. This is the reason for the oral ineffectiveness of this natural hormone. The principal urinary metabolites of progesterone are pregnane-3,20-dione, 3α-hydroxypregnan-20-one, pregnane-3α,20α-diol, and their isomers, the structures of which are illustrated in Fig. 2 (Davis and Plotz, 1957). All these compounds have been detected in the urine of healthy pregnant women. The two principal metabolites, pregnane-3α,20α-diol and 3α-hydroxypregnan-20-one, are excreted as glucuronides.

The biological actions of progesterone can be briefly summarized as follows.

1. Progesterone is a significant conditioning substance for normal mating reflexes in a number of animals.

2. Progesterone has its special effect upon both tubal and uterine contraction while the eggs and sperm are traveling through the oviduct.

3. Progesterone, in certain dosage levels, acts as an inhibitor of fertilization *in vivo*.

4. Progesterone is essential for ovum implantation, blastocyst development, and maintenance of the fetus and the normal uterine tone during pregnancy.

5. Progesterone produces pseudopregnant proliferation in the uterine endometrium of the adult estrous or estrogen-primed immature rabbit.

6. Progesterone causes the deciduomata in the traumatized uterine horn of estrogen-primed rodents.

7. Progesterone causes the mucification of vaginal epithelium if administered following sensitization with estrogen.

8. Progesterone alters the reactivity of the myometrium and inhibits the uterine contraction normally produced by oxytocin.

9. Progesterone has a property of delaying delivery at the termination of pregnancy.

10. Progesterone influences the activities of relaxin and plays a role in parturition.

11. Progesterone inhibits ovulation during pregnancy, and can do so on administration to preovulatory animals.

12. Progesterone, as well as the other sexagens, inhibits the secretion of pituitary gonadotropin that is primarily responsible for the menstrual cycle in the female and for the inhibition of this cycle during gestation.

13. Progesterone either antagonizes or potentiates the activity of estrogen according to the balance between their dosages.

14. Progesterone, in a large amount, acts as an anesthetic agent and an inhibitor of the salt-retaining corticoids.

In clinical observations, the secretory changes in the endometrium, the inhibition of vaginal cornification induced by estrogen, the prevention of ferning of cervical mucus, the elevation of basal body temperature, and the prolongation of the menstrual cycle are usually obtained by treatment with progestational substances. Recently, evidence for the ovulation-inhibiting effect of progesterone or synthetic progestins has

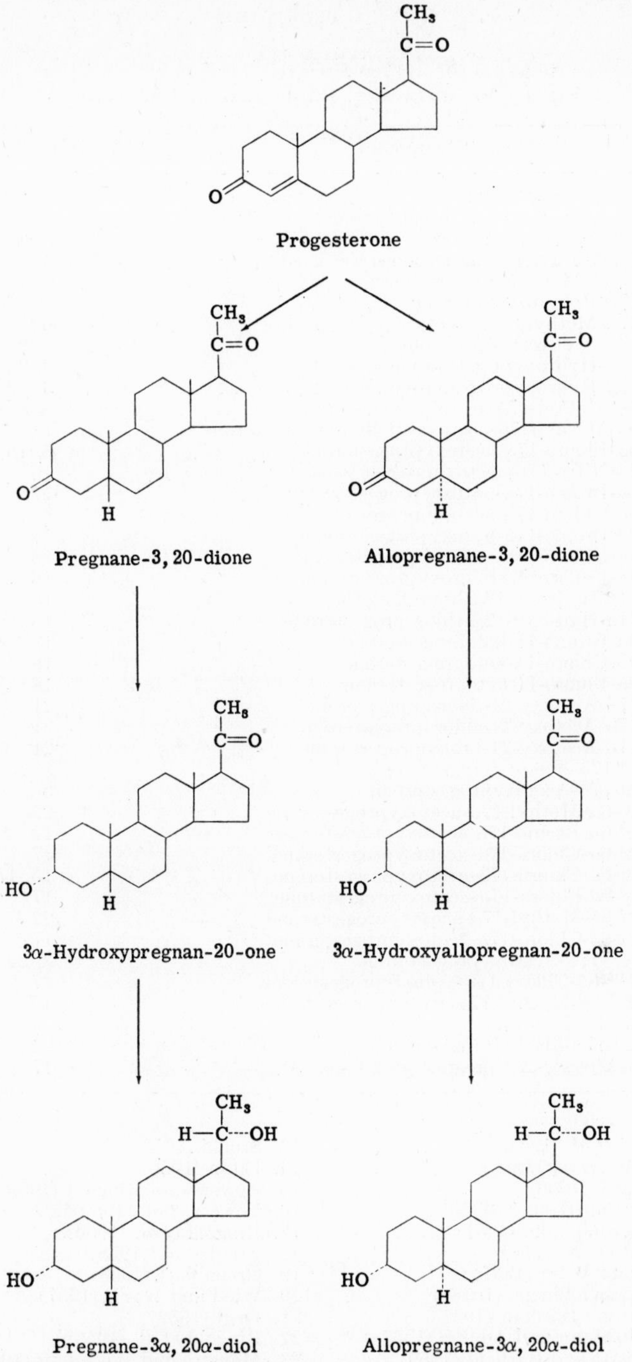

Fig. 2. Urinary metabolites of progesterone.

131

TABLE IIA

Synthetic Gestagens: Progesterone Derivatives

No.	Compound	References[a]
1	19-Norprogesterone	1–4
2	17α-Acetoxy-19-norprogesterone	3
3	16α-Methylprogesterone	3
4	1,2-Methylen-progesterone	3
5	16,17-Methylen-progesterone	3
6	17α-Bromoprogesterone	5
7	17α-Methylprogesterone	6
8	17α-Acetoxyprogesterone	7, 8
9	17α-Hydroxyprogesterone caproate	3, 9, 10
10	17α-Hydroxyprogesterone formiate	3
11	6α-Methyl-17α-acetoxyprogesterone	3, 8, 11–13
12	6α-Methyl-17α-acetoxy-21-fluoroprogesterone	14
13	6α-Fluoro-17α-acetoxyprogesterone	3, 15
14	6α-Nitro-17α-acetoxyprogesterone	16
15	6α-Bromo-17α-acetoxyprogesterone	17
16	6α-Chloro-17α-acetoxyprogesterone	3, 17
17	9α-Bromo-11β-hyroxyprogesterone	18
18	9α-Chloro-11β-hydroxyprogesterone	18
19	9α-Fluoro-11β-hydroxyprogesterone	18
20	11β-Hydroxy-12α-bromoprogesterone	18
21	11β-Hydroxy-12α-chloroprogesterone	18
22	9α-Bromo-11-ketoprogesterone	13, 18–20
23	9α-Chloro-11-ketoprogesterone	18
24	9α-Fluoro-11-ketoprogesterone	18
25	17α-Acetoxy-21-fluoroprogesterone	21
26	17α-Acetoxy-21-chloroprogesterone	21
27	17α-Acetoxy-21-bromoprogesterone	21
28	Δ^1-17α-Acetoxyprogesterone	3
29	Δ^6-17α-Acetoxyprogesterone	3
30	Δ^1-6α-Methyl-17α-acetoxyprogesterone	22
31	Δ^1-6α-Bromo-17α-acetoxyprogesterone	17
32	Δ^1-6α-Chloro-17α-acetoxyprogesterone	17
33	Δ^1-6α-Fluoro-17α-acetoxyprogesterone	15, 17
34	Δ^6-6β-Fluoro-17α-acetoxyprogesterone	17
35	Δ^6-6β-Methyl-17α-acetoxyprogesterone	22
36	Δ^6-6β-Chloro-17α-acetoxyprogesterone	17
37	$\Delta^{1,6}$-17α-Acetoxyprogesterone	3, 22
38	$\Delta^{1,6}$-6β-Chloro-17α-acetoxyprogesterone	17
39	$\Delta^{1,6}$-6β-Methyl-17α-acetoxyprogesterone	17
40	Δ^{11}-Progesterone	23
41	Δ^{11}-17α-Methylprogesterone	24
42	3-Acetoxy-$\Delta^{3,5}$-pregnadien-20-one	17

[a] Key to references: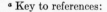

1. Djerassi et al. (1954)
2. Jadrijevic et al. (1956)
3. Junkmann (1959)
4. Tullner and Hertz (1957)
5. Engel and Jahnke (1957)
6. Heusser et al. (1950)
7. Davis and Wied (1957)
8. Miyake and Pincus (1958a)
9. Kessler and Borman (1957)
10. Lutwak-Mann and Adams (1957a)
11. Greenblatt and Barfield (1959)
12. Sala et al. (1958)

13. Stucki (1958)
14. Elton (1959)
15. Bowers and Ringold (1958)
16. Bowers et al. (1959)
17. Ringold et al. (1959a)
18. Fried et al. (1958)
19. Greenblatt (1958)
20. Wied and Davis (1957)
21. Drill (1959)
22. Ringold et al. (1959b)
23. Meystre and Wettstein (1948)
24. Engel et al. (1956)

been accumulated not only by animal experiments but also by clinical investigations on normally ovulating women (Drill, 1959; Hoagland, 1959; Pincus, 1959; Pincus *et al.*, 1959a,b; Rakoff, 1958, 1959; Saunders and Elton, 1959; Tyler, 1959).

B. SYNTHETIC PROGESTINS

Up to 1950, ethisterone (17α-ethynyltestosterone) was the only synthetic gestagen. It is much less active than progesterone systemically, but presented an important advance in therapeutic convenience because of its oral activity. Since 1950, the number of progestational steroids parenterally more potent than progesterone or orally more active than ethisterone has increased geometrically. The list of these is still growing. They are classed by their chemical structures into the three groups, progesterone derivatives, ethisterone derivatives, and 19-nortestosterone analogs as presented in Tables IIA, B, and C, respectively.

TABLE IIB

SYNTHETIC GESTAGENS: ETHISTERONE DERIVATIVES

No.	Compound	References[a]
43	6α-Methylethisterone	1–3
44	6β-Methylethisterone	1
45	6α-21-Dimethylethisterone	4
46	6α-Methyl-21-ethylethisterone	4
47	21-Methylethisterone	3, 4
48	21-Ethylethisterone	3, 4
49	21-Propylethisterone	4
50	17α-Ethynyl-Δ^4-androstene-$3\beta,17\beta$-diol	5

[a] Key to references:
1. Campbell *et al.* (1958)
2. Byrnes and Meyer (1951)
3. Drill (1959)
4. David *et al.* (1957)
5. Sondheimer and Klibansky (1959)

Both laboratory and clinical workers have recently shown marked renewal of interest in these synthetic compounds with progestational activity. This is not only due to the therapeutic advantages, such as prolonged action and high oral potency of the compounds, but also to their properties that differ from the natural hormone, progesterone, and from each other in their biological actions in animals and in humans, and also in their metabolism and excretion products. For example, the use of

TABLE IIC

SYNTHETIC GESTAGENS: 19-NORTESTOSTERONE ANALOGS

No.	Compound	References[a]
51	17α-Ethynyl-19-nortestosterone	1–15
52	17α-Vinyl-19-nortestosterone	8, 13, 16, 17
53	17α-Methyl-19-nortestosterone	3, 8, 9, 18–20
54	17α-Ethyl-19-nortestosterone	3, 5, 8, 10, 11, 13, 14, 21
55	17α-Propyl-19-nortestosterone	8, 9, 13, 17
56	17α-Propinyl-19-nortestosterone	8
57	17α-Allyl-19-nortestosterone	17
58	17α-(1-Methally)-19-nortestosterone	9, 14, 22
59	17α-(2-Methally)-19-nortestosterone	22, 23
60	19-Nor-3-(3-oxo-17β-OH-4-androstene-17α-yl)-propionic γ-lactone	24
61	17α-Ethynyl-Δ⁴-19-norandrostene-3β,17β-diol	25
62	17α-Ethynyl-3-deoxy-19-nortestosterone	26
63	17α-Methyl-3-deoxy-19-nortestosterone	26
64	17α-Ethyl-3-deoxy-19-nortestosterone	26
65	17α-Propyl-3-deoxy-19-nortestosterone	26
66	17α-Butyl-3-deoxy-19-nortestosterone	26
67	17α-Allyl-3-deoxy-19-nortestosterone	26, 30
68	17α-Ethynyl-Δ⁵⁽¹⁰⁾-estren-17β-ol-3-one	5, 9–11, 14, 17, 21, 27, 28
69	17α-Methyl-Δ⁵⁽¹⁰⁾-estren-17β-ol-3-one	16, 29
70	17α-Ethyl-Δ⁵⁽¹⁰⁾-estren-17β-ol-3-one	16, 29
71	17α-Propyl-Δ⁵⁽¹⁰⁾-estren-17β-ol-3-one	16, 29

[a] Key to references:

1. Baquero (1957)
2. Edgren (1958)
3. Ferin (1957)
4. Greenblatt (1956)
5. Greenblatt (1958)
6. Hertz et al. (1954)
7. Hertz et al. (1956)
8. Junkmann (1959)
9. Miyake and Pincus (1958a)
10. Pincus et al. (1956a)
11. Pincus et al. (1956b)
12. McGinty and Djerassi (1958)
13. Saunders et al. (1957a)
14. Saunders and Drill (1958)
15. Tullner and Hertz (1957)
16. Drill (1959)
17. Drill and Riegel (1958)
18. Ferin (1956)
19. Kotsalo (1957)
20. Moggian (1959)
21. Stucki (1958)
22. Saunders (1958)
23. Elton and Edgren (1958)
24. Hertz and Tullner (1958)
25. Sondheimer and Klibansky (1959)
26. de Winter et al. (1959)
27. Kistner (1958)
28. Kupperman and Epstein (1957)
29. Saunders et al. (1957b)
30. Madjerek et al. (1960)

19-norsteroids, norethisterone, and norethynodrel as oral contraceptive agents has been discussed in the last few years (Hoagland, 1959; Pincus et al., 1959b; Tyler, 1959). This accounts for the renewed pharmacological interest in the biological analysis and standardization of progestins.

III. Progestational Proliferation

A. Corner-Allen (1929) Test

This test is only of historic interest. Adult female rabbits are spayed 18 hours after having been mated during estrus. The substance to be tested is then injected, subcutaneously, daily for 5 days. The minimum amount necessary to cause complete progestational proliferation of the endometrium is taken as one unit. This is now known to require 1 to 2 mg. of progesterone in the average rabbit.

B. Clauberg (1930d) Test

Of the several bioassay methods for progesterone, the Clauberg (1930a, b, c, d) method has been the most popular. This is based on the changes in endometrial histology of the estrogen-primed immature rabbit following 5 consecutive days of subcutaneous treatment with the substance to be tested. The total dose necessary to produce a definite progestational transformation of the endometrium is taken as the unit. This corresponds to 0.75 mg. of progesterone.

C. McPhail (1934) Test

McPhail (1934) systemically examined the factors concerned in the results obtained by the Clauberg (1930d) test, and set up the optimal condition for this test in order to achieve further consistency and accuracy. The test is performed on immature female rabbits, weighing 750 to 950 gm., treated with 150 I.U. of estrone subcutaneously over a period of 6 days. After this period of estrogen-priming, the compound to be tested is administered intramuscularly once daily for 5 days. In the graded scale ranging from 0 to 4+ of progestational proliferation observed in the uterine section, the average reaction of 2+ is taken as the unit. This corresponds to 0.75 mg. of progesterone. McPhail's five stages, together with a control, are shown in Fig. 3. The dose-response curve with 5 rabbits per group is shown in Fig. 4. No indication of variability is presented.

In this type of assay, evaluation of the progestational activity of unknown samples is based on their minimal effective dose which produces a certain grade of response, but theoretically it must depend on the calculation of ED_{50}. Comparison of the minimal effective dose would be practicable for the screening tests, but it cannot achieve accurate evaluation of comparative potency of the unknown against the standard preparation. On the other hand, the calculation of ED_{50} needs many test animals for each set of experiments. Furthermore, there is a problem in

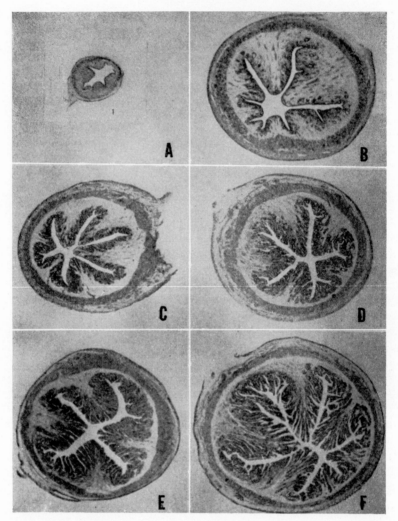

Fig. 3. The standard scale of progestational proliferation in the McPhail test. Section A, no treatment; Section B, estrogen above; Sections C–F, reactions 1, 2, 3, and 4, respectively, following the administration of progesterone (McPhail, 1934).

the objectiveness for scoring the proliferation in the uterine section. Accordingly, this method cannot be a standard assay procedure.

D. McGinty Test (McGinty et al., 1939)

McGinty et al. (1939) established a local progestational test which involves the direct injection of progesterone into an uterine segment.

The test is performed on the estrogen-primed immature rabbits recommended by McPhail (1934). On the day following the last priming of estrogen, the uterus is exposed by laparotomy. An upper middle segment of each horn, 3 to 4 cm. long, is ligated without disturbance of blood cir-

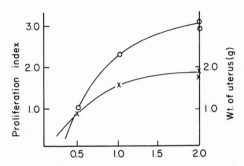

FIG. 4. Proliferation index and uterine weight of rabbits receiving different doses of progestogen over 5 days (McPhail, 1934).

culation. Progesterone, dissolved in 0.1 ml. of peanut oil or lanolin, is injected into the lumen of one segment through the lower ligature which was left loose before injection. As the injection is completed, the lower ligature is drawn tight. The procedure is repeated with the opposite horn, injecting only the vehicle as a control. Three days after this operation, the rabbits are killed and the uterine segments are sectioned for microscopic examination. The degree of progestational response is scored by the McPhail scale (Fig. 3).

TABLE III

RESPONSE TO INTRA-UTERINE PROGESTERONE[a]

Dose of progesterone (μg.)	Number of observations	Responses obtained with				
		Peanut oil		Number of observations	Lanolin	
		Mean	Range		Mean	Range
20	2	3.5	$3\frac{1}{2}$	2	3.5	3–4
10	10	2.7	$\frac{1}{2}$–4	2	3.8	$3\frac{1}{2}$–4
5	6	2.3	2–3	6	3.3	2–4
1	6	2.2	2–$2\frac{1}{2}$	8	2.0	1–$3\frac{1}{2}$
0.5	4	1.8	1–$2\frac{1}{2}$	6	2.0	1–$2\frac{1}{2}$
0.25	10	0.9	0–1	6	0.8	$\frac{1}{2}$–2
0.125	4	1.3	1–$1\frac{1}{2}$	—	—	—

[a] Adapted from McGinty et al. (1939). Half Values Were Scored by the authors as, e.g., 2–3.

The results of McGinty *et al.* (1939) are summarized in Table III. The data suggest that the minimum effective dose in this test is in the range of 0.125 to 0.5 µg. of progesterone.

TABLE IV

RESPONSE TO INTRA-UTERINE PROGESTERONE[a]

Dose of progesterone[b] (µg.)	Number of observations	Proliferation index		Endometrial carbonic anhydrase activity (EU/gm. wet tissue)[c]
		Mean	Range	
500	10	3.6	2–4	126.1 ± 19.6[d]
50	10	2.6	1–4	71.0 ± 6.8
5	10	1.9	1–3	62.9 ± 8.4
1	8	1.4	$\frac{1}{2}$–2	38.2 ± 5.3
0.5	8	0.5	0–1	21.9 ± 3.7
0	6	0.1	0–$\frac{1}{2}$	12.6 ± 2.2

[a] Miyake and Nagata (1960). Half-values were scored by the authors as, e.g., 2–3.
[b] Vehicle: sesame oil; volume: 0.25 ml.
[c] EU/gm.: see Section IV.
[d] Mean ± S.E.

Table IV is the data of Miyake and Nagata (1960), who injected progesterone in a volume of 0.25 ml. of sesame oil into uterine segments throughout the total length of the horn, for the convenience of simultaneous measurement of endometrial carbonic anhydrase. The responses are lower than those reported in Table III. This may be due to the use of the whole length of the uterine horn.

TABLE V

RESPONSE TO INTRA-UTERINE PROGESTERONE[a]

Dose of progesterone[b] (µg.)	Volume of injection (ml.)	Number of observations	Proliferation index (average)	Endometrial carbonic anhydrase (EU/gm.)[c]
0	0.05	5	0	15.4 ± 3.6[d]
0	0.25	3	0	14.8 ± 6.8
5	0.05	8	0.06	19.4 ± 3.6
5	0.1	9	0.05	18.4 ± 4.6
5	0.25	9	1.6	101.9 ± 13.9

[a] From Miyake and Nagata (1960).
[b] Vehicle: sesame oil.
[c] EU/gm.: see IV. Carbonic Anhydrase Test.
[d] Mean ± S.E.

In the local test, it is important to adjust the injection volume to the size of the uterine segment. The data of Miyake and Nagata (1960) presented in Table V suggest that an adequate volume of vehicle is necessary to produce an adequate progestational response.

The interest recently excited in the McGinty test is not due to its remarkable sensitivity for progesterone, but to the fact that the local progestational response of the synthetic gestagens does not always parallel their systemic response. Saunders and Elton (1959) have reported that only substances which exhibit a progestational reaction by the local test are able to maintain pregnancy in ovariectomized pregnant rabbits or rats. The mechanism of this phenomenon is not clear. At any rate, the importance of the local activity test will be raised not only for the quantification but also for the qualification of the various progestins.

E. PINCUS-WERTHESSEN (1937) TEST

Pincus and Werthessen have enhanced the objective aspects of the Corner-Allen (1929) test by measuring the diameter of flushed ovum and the ratio of G/M, which means the area of glandular (G) proliferation against total mucosa (M). Rabbits spayed 18 to 20 hours after mating are injected subcutaneously with progesterone twice daily on the second, third, and fourth days after copulation. Animals are sacrificed on the fifth day when the uterus is flushed for ova. A section of the uterus is saved for study of the endometrium. The diameter of the ovum, exclusive of the albumen coating, is measured and the mean ovum diameter per individual is calculated. A representative cross section of the uterus is projected and traced, the mucosa being divided into glandular and stromal portions as indicated in Fig. 5. The areas of the various portions

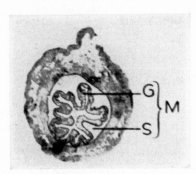

FIG. 5. Cross section of the uterus of an ovariectomized rabbit which had received 0.42 mg. progesterone, illustrating the method of dividing the uterine mucosa (M) into glandular (G) and stromal (S) portions (Pincus and Werthessen, 1937).

are measured with a planimeter. The dose-response data are presented in Fig. 6. About 0.4 mg. of progesterone can be detected by this technique. However, the comparative assay of one compound against another has not been attempted. The blastocyst measurement has been used by

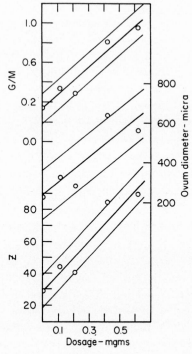

FIG. 6. The regression of G/M (glandular area divided by total mucosa area), upper curve, ovum diameter, middle curve, and their combined index, z, lower curve, on progesterone dosage. The two lines parallel to the calculated regression line are drawn at a distance equal to the standard deviations of the respective sets of measurement (Pincus and Werthessen, 1937).

Werthessen *et al.* (1945) who studied the effect of estrogens on the early development of the rabbit blastocyst. Complexity and variability has limited the further use of this method for quantitative purposes.

F. PINCUS-MIYAKE TEST (PINCUS *et al.*, 1957)

Pincus and associates (1957) have improved the quantitative aspects of the McPhail (1934) test by the use of planimetric measurement of endometrial proliferation and a modern statistical assay design. The test is carried out on immature albino rabbits weighing about 1 kg. The rabbits are injected subcutaneously once daily with 5 μg. of estradiol for 6 days. After this period of estrogen-priming, the rabbits are injected subcutaneously, or force fed by gavage, once daily with various doses of progesterone or the unknown compound to be tested. All compounds are dissolved in sesame oil or suspended in an aqueous solution which consists of sodium chloride (0.9%), polysorbate 80 (0.4%), carboxymethylcellulose (0.5%), and benzyl alcohol (0.9%). Animals are sacrificed 24 hours after the last administration.

After the rabbits are bled thoroughly, the uteri are isolated and rinsed with cold saline. Small pieces of the mid-sections of both horns are cut off, fixed in Bouin's solution, embedded in paraffin, sectioned at 10 μ, and stained by hematoxylin and eosin. A series of sections are projected on a sheet of white paper. The best section for each horn is selected and traced, the mucosa being divided into the glandular and stromal portions as indicated in Fig. 5. Planimetry is then carried out for each area of the various portions. The average G/M ratio (glandular portion/total mucosa) for both horns serves as an indicator of progestational proliferation for the individual rabbit.

This assay has been established along with a new method, the endometrial carbonic anhydrase test, by simultaneous measurements of the enzyme concentration and G/M ratio in samples of the same uteri. The data concerned with the dose-response relationship for progesterone and an example of comparative assay on Δ^4-pregnenolone (3β-hydroxy-Δ^4-pregnen-20-one) against progesterone are presented, in the Section IV, together with the assay data obtained by the determination of endometrial carbonic anhydrase.

The G/M assay technique as described appears to be the quantitative method of choice as a test to evaluate endometrial histology in spite of the extensive labor involved.

IV. Endometrial Carbonic Anhydrase

Lutwak-Mann (1955) has recently found that measurement of carbonic anhydrase activity of rabbit endometrium can be used as a basis for progestin assay. Pincus et al. (1957) and Miyake and Pincus (1958a) have confirmed the findings of Lutwak-Mann using the conventional Clauberg rabbit and developed the carbonic anhydrase method as a standard assay procedure.

The usefulness of the endometrial carbonic anhydrase measurement for progestin assay purposes resides in: (a) the intensity and range of response to varying progesterone dosages, (b) the relative ease and speed of the enzyme determination, (c) the satisfying accuracy and reproducibility of the test, (d) the response correlating with progestational proliferation in the endometrial histology, (e) the considerable specificity of the test for progestational compounds, (f) the organo-specificity of the enzyme synthesis by progesterone, and (g) the possible role of the enzyme on the blastocyst implantation and the placental function.

The test is performed on albino immature female rabbits weighing about 1 kg. pretreated with estrogen over a period of 6 days. The mode of hormone treatment is the same as that described in the Pincus-Miyake test (Section III, F) (Pincus *et al.*, 1957). Extraction and determination of carbonic anhydrase are as follows.

Extraction of carbonic anhydrase:

1. Sacrifice rabbits by breaking the neck and cutting carotid artery.

2. Isolate uteri immediately after bleeding the rabbits thoroughly.

3. Rinse uteri once with cold saline.

4. Save small pieces of uterine sections in Bouin's solution for histological examination.

5. Open the uteri longitudinally with scissors.

6. Rinse them once with a small amount of cold saline.

7. Dissect endometrium from uterus with scissors on the filter paper moistened with cold saline.

8. Weigh each wet endometrial tissue on a torsion balance.

9. Wash the tissue mass with cold distilled water from the weighing pan into a suitable glass homogenizer (working volume 7–10 ml.) kept in an ice bath.

10. Grind and homogenize tissue with 10- to 20-fold volume of cold distilled water in ice bath.

11. Transfer the homogenate into a 15-ml. graduated centrifuge tube.

12. Centrifuge at 1500 r.p.m. for 15 minutes.

13. Record the volume of fluid.

14. Transfer the supernatant into a 10-ml. Erlenmeyer flask.

The supernatants are used for the determination of enzyme activity. The enzyme extracts are stable and retain their activity for several days if they are kept in the refrigerator.

Estimation of carbonic anhydrase activity: The colorimetric method of Philpot and Philpot (1936) is used.

(A) Reagents:

1. Solution A_1—solution saturated with Na_2CO_3 and $NaHCO_3$ at 5°C.

2. Solution A_2—27.3 vol. % of solution A_1.

3. Solution B—$NaHCO_3$ 0.221 gm. in 1000 ml. distilled water.

4. BTB—Bromothymol blue, 0.1%, aqueous.

(B) Procedure:

1. Half fill a 500-ml. aspirator bottle with solution B.

2. Open the CO_2 tank and start the gas bubbling in order to saturate solution B with CO_2 (about 1 bubble/second for 10–15 minutes).

3. Put 0.1 ml. of BTB in each test tube (1.5 × 15 cm.).

4. Fill burette (50 ml.) with solution B saturated with CO_2.

5. Put 4 or 5 ml. of CO_2-saturated solution B into each test tube.

6. Stopper each test tube immediately.

7. All test tubes must be kept in an ice bath.

8. Fill completely a 100-ml. graduated cylinder with water. Adjust regulating tube at approximately the 35-ml. level.

9. Connect all tubing as shown in Fig. 7.

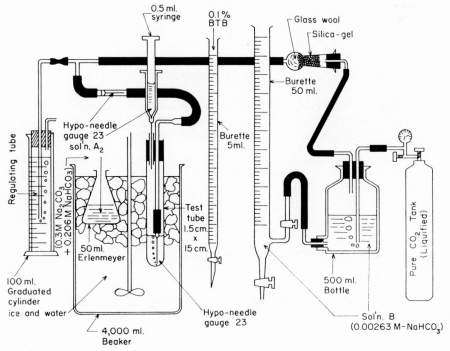

Fig. 7. Determination of carbonic anhydrase activity by Miyake's modification of Philpot and Philpot (1936) (Miyake and Pincus, 1958).

10. Make an ice bath in a 4000-ml. beaker and start stirrer.

11. Put solution A_2 in 50-ml. Erlenmeyer flasks and keep in ice bath.

12. Start the control measurement.

    a. Add distilled water to test tube 5.6 ml.

    b. Add 1 drop octyl alcohol to prevent foaming.

    c. Put test tube in ice bath and bubble CO_2 through it for 2 minutes to bring about equilibrium.

    d. Add 0.5 ml. of solution A_2 to test tube and at the same time start the stop watch.

    e. When color turns green-yellow from initial blue, record the elapsed time.

    f. Repeat, adjusting the regulator until the reaction time is 65–75 seconds. This is the control reaction time.

  13. Start measurement of enzyme activity.

    a. Substitute the enzyme extract for distilled water and proceed as in step 12 (a through e).

    b. Adjust the dilution of enzyme extract until the reaction time is 25–30 seconds (one enzyme unit = 1 EU).

  14. The enzyme unit per gram wet tissue (EU/gm.) is calculated as follows:

$$\text{EU/gm.} = \frac{1000}{C \cdot V} \cdot \frac{1}{2}, \tag{A}$$

where C = concentration of extract (mg./ml.), and

    V = volume of extract which is required to shorten the reaction time from 65–75 to 25–30 seconds (ml./EU).

Because the volume of the reaction medium is reduced to one half the original of Philpot and Philpot (1936), the factor $\frac{1}{2}$ is used in the calculation in order to make it equivalent to the definition of the enzyme unit of Keilin and Mann (1940).

    The following definition of the enzyme unit is also available in the routine estimation of enzyme activity.

$$\text{EU/gm.} = \frac{t_0 - t}{t} \cdot \frac{1000}{C \cdot V}, \tag{B}$$

where t_0 = reaction time without enzyme (constant),

    t = reaction time with enzyme,

    C = concentration of extract (mg./ml.),

    V = volume of extract.

In the determination of enzyme activity, the value "t" is kept constant for 60 to 90 seconds and V and C are adjusted to get "t" in the range of 10 to 40 seconds, whereby a linear relationship is obtained between $(t_0 - t)/t$ and the concentration of enzyme as shown in Fig. 8. The data obtained according to formula (B) are approximately 3 times higher than those obtained by formula (A). The enzyme determination is speeded up by the use of formula (B), but formula (A) is recommended for better test accuracy.

The main sources of error in this technique are supposed to originate in steps 1 and 2 and 7, in the extraction of the enzyme. It has been confirmed that the activities which could be derived from the blood never exceed one tenth of the activities of the endometrial extracts.

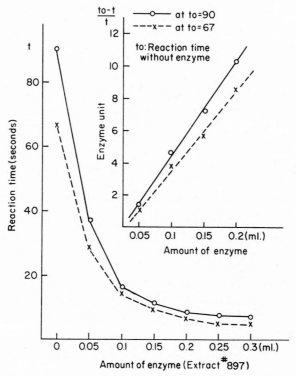

FIG. 8. The relationship between $(t_0 - t)/t$ in formula (B) and amount of enzyme (Miyake and Pincus, 1958).

It is, however, always important to bleed rabbits as thoroughly as possible in order to keep blood contamination in the extract at a minimum.

At step 7, dissection of endometrium from the uterus should be carried out very carefully so that hardly any muscle layer is mixed into the tissue to be ground at the next step. For dissecting off the endometrium, it is recommended that a pair of small curved scissors be used which should be repeatedly moved with a half-cutting of the

TABLE VI

The Dose-Response Relationships of Progesterone for Carbonic Anhydrase
Activity and the G/M Ratio of Clauberg Rabbits' Endometrium
(Subcutaneous Test)[a]

Dosage (mg./rabbit)	Number of rabbits	Carbonic anhydrase activity (EU/gm. wet tissue)[b]	G/M ratio of uterus[c]
0	14	17.45 ± 1.25[d]	0.426 ± 0.018[d]
0.25	6	36.30 ± 2.05	0.506 ± 0.042
0.5	9	36.14 ± 6.27	0.501 ± 0.029
1.0	6	59.67 ± 6.08	0.636 ± 0.037
2.0	10	88.05 ± 7.05	0.746 ± 0.025
4.0	12	140.03 ± 9.48	0.717 ± 0.009
8.0	6	179.57 ± 42.38	0.689 ± 0.044

[a] From Pincus *et al.* (1957).
[b] EU/gm. wet tissue is defined by formula (A) in the text.
[c] G/M ratio is estimated by the Pincus-Werthessen technique (see Section III, E).
[d] Mean ± S.E.

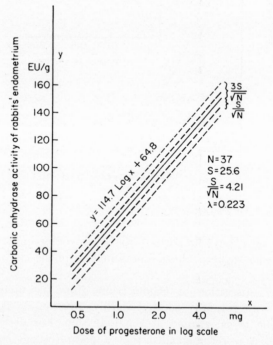

Fig. 9. Dose-response regression line of progesterone. Dose range: 0.5–4.0
mg./rabbit, subcutaneous. EU/gm. is defined by formula (A) in the text (Pincus
et al., 1957).

tissue and a half-sliding over the endometrial surface of the opened uterus.

In the process of enzyme determination, caution has to be paid to the step 12 (c and d). The tip of the hypodermic needle, through which CO_2 comes out, must be kept touching the center of the bottom of the test tube to keep the mixing efficiency and the speed of CO_2 bubbling constant. When solution A_2 is added to the test tube, the plunger of the syringe must be pushed down as quickly as possible and the solution should not slide down the wall of the test tube.

Table VI presents the data on carbonic anhydrase activity and G/M ratio in samples of the same uteri of control and progesterone-injected animals. The dose-response regressions are illustrated in Figs. 9 and 10.

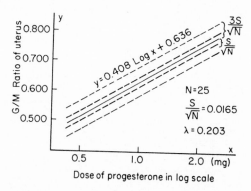

FIG. 10. Dose-response regression line of progesterone. Dose range: 0.5–2.0 mg./rabbit, subcutaneous (Pincus *et al.*, 1957).

The lambda values of 0.223 and 0.203 for the two types of measurement indicate a comparable degree of accuracy. The greater intensity and the wider range of response in terms of enzyme activity confer useful advantages to the enzyme measurements for quantitative bioassay. Tables VII and VIII present the data on a four-point comparative assay of Δ^4-pregnenolone against progesterone. Both types of measurement give entirely similar comparative potency ratios of 1.18 and 1.16, similar limits of error at $P = 0.95$.

These data indicate the complete agreement of the endometrial carbonic anhydrase titers with the glandular development. This has been clearly established by the data (Table IX) of Lutwak-Mann and Adams (1957a). The parallel increase of both measurements, the enzyme activity and progestational proliferation, is observed not only with subcutaneous injection but also with the intra-uterine application of progesterone, as previously presented in Table IV. This parallelism is also observed in the data of Miyake (1959) (Table X) on the time-action relationships of progesterone and 6α-methyl-17α-acetoxyprogesterone injected into the Clauberg rabbits.

TABLE VII

COMPARATIVE ASSAY OF Δ^4-PREGNENOLONE (3β-HYDROXY-Δ^4-PREGNEN-20-ONE) AGAINST PROGESTERONE BY ENDOMETRIAL CARBONIC ANHYDRASE METHOD (SUBCUTANEOUS)[a]

Sample:	Progesterone		Δ^4-Pregnenolone	
Dose:	2 mg.	0.5 mg.	2 mg.	0.5 mg.
	112.7	22.6	108.3	28.0
	118.8	71.2	76.7	50.1
Response	67.4	33.7	79.2	34.7
(EU/gm. tissue)[b]	68.8	26.7	138.1	21.7
	75.2	38.6	134.4	32.3
	81.6		116.3	
Mean	87.4	38.6	108.8	33.4

Difference between dosage:	62.1
Difference between samples:	8.1
Logarithmic ratio of dosage:	0.6
Slope of combined line:	103.44
Logarithm of potency ratio:	0.0724

Potency ratio: $\dfrac{\Delta^4\text{-Pregnenolone}}{\text{Progesterone}} = \dfrac{1.182}{1.0}$.

Limit of error at $P = 0.95$: $64.9 \sim 154.2\%$
Parallelism of both lines is significant at $P = 0.95$

[a] From Pincus et al. (1957).
[b] EU/gm. tissue is defined by formula (A) in the text.

Miyake and Pincus (1958a) have tested various compounds including two progesterone derivatives and eight 19-norsteroids to demonstrate progestational activity by their standardized method. Table XI deals with the comparative potency ratios of 19-norsteroids and progesterone derivatives calculated according to a four-point assay procedure in the range of dosage in which their dose-response curves are parallel with that of the compound used as the standard. Progesterone and 17-hydroxyprogesterone acetate are used as standards in the subcutaneous and the oral assays, respectively. The data demonstrate that the relative potencies by the enzyme test correspond roughly to those

TABLE VIII

COMPARATIVE ASSAY OF Δ^4-PREGNENOLONE (3β-HYDROXY-Δ^4-PREGNEN-20-ONE) AGAINST PROGESTERONE BY ENDOMETRIAL G/M RATIO METHOD (SUBCUTANEOUS)[a]

Sample:	Progesterone		Δ^4-Pregnenolone	
Dose:	2 mg.	0.5 mg.	2 mg.	0.5 mg.
Response (G/M ratio)[b]	0.734	0.489	0.733	0.562
	0.657	0.633	0.693	0.585
	0.711	0.574	0.789	0.557
	0.696	0.515	0.792	0.468
	0.661	0.531	0.688	0.494
	0.689		0.772	
Mean	0.691	0.548	0.745	0.533

Difference between dosage: 0.1775
Difference between samples: 0.02
Logarithmic ratio of dosage: 0.6
Slope of combined line: 0.296
Logarithm of potency ratio: 0.0659

Potency ratio: $\dfrac{\Delta^4\text{-Pregnenolone}}{\text{Progesterone}} = \dfrac{1.164}{1.0}$

Limit of error at $P = 0.95$: $67.8 \sim 147.5\%$
Parallelism of both lines is significant at $P = 0.95$

[a] From Pincus et al. (1957).
[b] The G/M ratio is measured by the Pincus-Werthessen technique (see Section III, E).

TABLE IX

STANDARD REFERENCE DATA ON THE CORRELATION BETWEEN CARBONIC ANHYDRASE AND PROLIFERATION[a]

Number of observations	Proliferation scale reading[b]	Carbonic anhydrase activity (EU/gm. mucosa)	
		Average	Range
5	I	9	8– 10
21	II	13	12– 22
19	III	22	16– 36
10	IV	62	50– 75
7	V	114	96–125
6	VI	127	100–142

[a] From Lutwak-Mann and Adams (1957a).
[b] Histological appearance of the endometrium: I, as in untreated rabbits; II, as in estrogen-primed rabbits; III, at the onset; IV, V and VI, at successive stages of increasing glandular development.

TABLE X

TIME-ACTION RELATIONSHIPS OF PROGESTERONE
AND 6α-METHYL-17α-ACETOXYPROGESTERONE[a]

Treatment	Days after injection[b]	Number of rabbits	Uterine weight (gm.)	Endometrial carbonic anhydrase (EU/gm.)[c]	G/M ratio
Control	0	5	2.3 ± 0.3[d]	18 ± 3[d]	0.267 ± 0.017[d]
(sesame oil)	3	5	1.5 ± 0.2	40 ± 7	0.319 ± 0.040
	6	5	1.3 ± 0.1	27 ± 5	0.289 ± 0.021
Progesterone	3	10	2.7 ± 0.11	204 ± 17	0.594 ± 0.028
(5 mg.)	6	9	1.2 ± 0.1	313 ± 56	0.537 ± 0.029
	9	5	1.0 ± 0.01	25 ± 10	0.311 ± 0.024
	12	4	0.6 ± 0.01	17 ± 2	0.351 ± 0.015
6α-Methyl-	3	5	4.3 ± 0.35	226 ± 13	0.633 ± 0.021
17α-acetoxy-	6	6	3.8 ± 0.45	601 ± 54	0.707 ± 0.011
progesterone	9	7	1.3 ± 0.13	54 ± 13	0.422 ± 0.013
(5 mg.)	12	6	1.1 ± 0.14	26 ± 11	0.405 ± 0.027

[a] From Miyake (1959).

[b] Hormone injection: Single, subcutaneous, at the end of the period of estrogen priming.

[c] EU/gm. is defined by formula (B) in the text.

[d] Mean ± S.E.

obtained with the G/M ratio either in the subcutaneous or in the oral assay.

The anti-progestational activity of four estrogens, estrone, estradiol, estriol, and stilbestrol, administered subcutaneously along with progesterone, has also been demonstrated by estimation of endometrial carbonic anhydrase and simultaneous measurement of uterine G/M ratio (Fig. 5). Intensity of inhibition depends upon the dosage of estrogen as shown in Table XII. The data in Table XIII indicate that these estrogens, when administered alone, produce no significant change in either carbonic anhydrase titers or G/M ratios of the endometrium. Therefore, if the compound essentially has estrogenicity or contaminates estrogen, its progestational activity would be masked or underestimated in this test. The linear dose-response relationship with a negative slope for each estrogen, as illustrated in Fig. 11, indicates that carbonic anhydrase method is also useful as an assay procedure for the anti-progestational compound.

The specificity of the carbonic anhydrase test is shown in Table XIV

TABLE XI

RELATIVE PROGESTATIONAL POTENCY OF 19-NORSTEROIDS
AND PROGESTERONE DERIVATIVES[a]

	Progestational potency			
	Subcutaneous injection		Oral administration	
Compound	Enzyme test	G/M test	Enzyme test	G/M test
Progesterone	1.0[b]	1.0[b]	—[c]	—[c]
17-Ethynyl-19-nortestosterone	0.1	0.2	1.0	0.5
17-Ethynyl-5(10)-estrenolone	—[c]	—[c]	0.3	0.5
17-Methyl-19-nortestosterone	0.1	0.1	1.5	2.0
17-Ethyl-19-nortestosterone	2.6	2.6	3.2	4.4
17-Propyl-19-nortestosterone	2.9	2.6	1.7	1.2
17-Allyl-19-nortestosterone	5.8	2.7	1.3	1.1
17-(1-Methallyl)-19-nortestosterone	3.5	2.4	1.3	2.2
17-(2-Methallyl)-19-nortestosterone	16.8[d]	9.9[d]	14.5[d]	5.7[d]
17-Acetoxyprogesterone	7.3	3.3	1.0[e]	1.0[e]
17-Acetoxy-6α-methylprogesterone	44.1	33.8	13.6	13.0

[a] From Miyake and Pincus (1958a).
[b] Standard in subcutaneous injection.
[c] Potency too low to calculate.
[d] Unpublished data.
[e] Standard in oral administration.

obtained by summarizing the data of Lutwak-Mann and Adams (1957a)
and of Miyake and Pincus (1958a).

As indicated in Table XV it has been made clear that progesterone
produces marked increase in the content of endometrial carbonic anhydrase, the magnitude of which suggests new synthesis of enzyme in
the uterus, without any significant increase in the enzyme content of
the blood, liver, kidney, and adrenals (Miyake, 1959; Pincus et al.,
1957).

The significance of carbonic anhydrase on the reproductive physiology has been discussed in the comprehensive work of Lutwak-Mann
(1955). The uterine endometrium, placental tissue, and oviducts have
been established as the main localities of carbonic anhydrase activity
in the female reproductive tract of a variety of mammals. Lutwak-
Mann (1955) has assumed that the level of endometrial carbonic anhydrase reflects the pattern of circulating progestin level. It is, however,
more correct to say that the enzyme level in the uterine mucosa is

TABLE XII

INHIBITORY EFFECT OF ESTROGEN ON PROGESTERONE IN CARBONIC ANHYDRASE
ACTIVITY AND G/M RATIO OF CLAUBERG RABBITS' ENDOMETRIUM[a]

Dose of progesterone (mg./rabbit)	Treatment of estrogen (mg./rabbit)	Number of rabbits	EU/gm. wet tissue[b]	G/M ratio
2.0	Control (sesame oil)	18	492 ± 18^c	0.732 ± 0.013^c
2.0	Estrone			
	0.0025	6	345 ± 22	0.626 ± 0.031
	0.025	5	194 ± 16	0.628 ± 0.022
	0.25	5	108 ± 13	0.467 ± 0.049
2.0	Estradiol			
	0.0025	5	388 ± 34	0.629 ± 0.024
	0.025	5	281 ± 23	0.658 ± 0.023
	0.25	5	141 ± 13	0.447 ± 0.039
2.0	Estriol			
	0.0025	6	387 ± 26	0.665 ± 0.018
	0.025	6	304 ± 26	0.675 ± 0.016
	0.25	5	75 ± 9	0.459 ± 0.038
2.0	Stilbestrol			
	0.0025	6	400 ± 27	0.657 ± 0.015
	0.025	5	158 ± 14	0.559 ± 0.059
	0.25	6	67 ± 7	0.384 ± 0.032

[a] From Miyake and Pincus (1958b).
[b] EU/gm. wet tissue is defined by formula (B) in the text.
[c] Mean ± S.E.

TABLE XIII

EFFECT OF ESTROGEN ON CARBONIC ANHYDRASE ACTIVITY AND G/M RATIO
OF CLAUBERG RABBITS' ENDOMETRIUM[a]

Compound	Dose (mg./rabbit)	Number of rabbits	EU/gm. wet tissue[b]	G/M ratio
Control	Sesame oil	17	23 ± 3^c	0.234 ± 0.019^c
Estrone	0.25	5	23 ± 3	0.231 ± 0.016
Estradiol	0.25	5	22 ± 2	0.226 ± 0.014
Estriol	0.25	5	27 ± 2	0.233 ± 0.010
Stilbestrol	0.25	5	26 ± 3	0.238 ± 0.013

[a] From Miyake and Pincus (1958b).
[b] EU/gm. wet tissue is defined by formula (B) in the text.
[c] Mean ± S.E.

TABLE XIV

SPECIFICITY OF RABBIT ENDOMETRIAL CARBONIC ANHYDRASE TEST

Compound	Response	References[a]
Progesterone	+	1, 2, 3
Δ^4-Pregnenolone	+	2
17α-Hydroxyprogesterone	−	1
17α-Hydroxyprogesterone caproate	+ (long acting)	1
17α-Acetoxyprogesterone	+	1, 3
17α-Acetoxy-6α-methylprogesterone	+ (potent)	3, 6
17β-Acetoxyisoprogesterone	−	1
2α-Acetoxyprogesterone	−	1
2β-Acetoxyprogesterone	−	1
3-Acetoxypregna-3,5-diene-20-one	−	1
3α-Hydroxypregnane-12,20-dione	−	1
12α-Hydroxypregnane-3,12,20-trione	−	1
Deoxycorticosterone	−	1
Deoxycorticosterone acetate	+ (slight)	1
Testosterone propionate	−	1
19-Nortestosterone phenylpropionate	+ (slight)	7
17α-Ethynyltestosterone	+	1
17α-Methyltestosterone	+	1
17α-Ethynyl-19-nortestosterone	+	1, 3
17α-Ethynyl-5(10)-estrenolone	+ (slight)	3
17α-Methyl-19-nortestosterone	+	1, 3
17α-Ethyl-19-nortestosterone	+	3
17α-Propyl-19-nortestosterone	+	3
17α-Allyl-19-nortestosterone	+	3
17α-(1-Methallyl)-19-nortestosterone	+	3
17α-(2-Methallyl)-19-nortestosterone	+ (potent)	5, 7
17α-Hydroxy-16β-thiocyanatoprogesterone	−	7
5α-Thiocyanato-17α-ethynylestrenolone	+	7
19-Nortestosterone	+	7
5α-Thiocyanatopregnan-3,20-dione	+	7
16β-Mercapto-17α-hydroxyprogesterone	−	7
11β-Mercapto-12α-hydroxypregnan-3,20-dione	−	7
6β-Acetylthioprogesterone	+	7
5α-Hydroxy-6β-Acetylthiopregnan-3,20-dione	−	7
Estrone	−	4
Estradiol	−	4
Estriol	−	4
Stilbestrol	−	4
17β-Hydroxyandrostan-3-one	+ (slight)	7

[a] Key to References:

1. Lutwak-Mann and Adams (1957)
2. Pincus *et al.* (1957)
3. Miyake and Pincus (1958a)
4. Miyake and Pincus (1958b)
5. Elton and Edgren (1958)
6. Sala *et al.* (1958)
7. Miyake (unpublished)

under the control of both sexagens, progestin and estrogen, as the estrogen-progesterone interaction has been demonstrated both in the rabbit and in the rat (Miyake and Pincus, 1958b, 1959). Recently, Böving (1959) has set up an hypothesis by histochemical approach, suggesting the role of carbonic anhydrase on the mechanism of blastocyst implantation. Nagata and Miyake (1960) have recently demonstrated histochemical evidence that the remarkable biosynthesis of

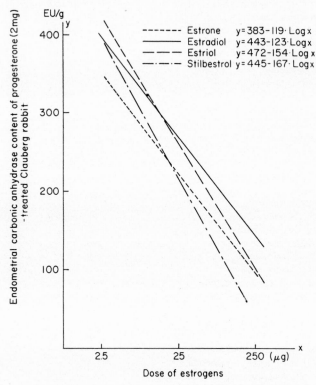

FIG. 11. Dose-response regression lines of estrogens on anti-progestational activity. EU/gm. is defined by formula (B) in the text (Miyake and Pincus, 1958).

carbonic anhydrase produced by progesterone takes place in the glandular portion of uterine mucosa (Fig. 12) and the precipitation of manganese granules resulting from the enzyme reaction are concentrated in the epithelial cells (Fig. 13).

The direct or indirect evidence, which has been found for hormone-specific and organ-specific changes of the carbonic anhydrase level, the localization of enzyme synthesis, and the possible role of the enzyme in the female reproductive cycle, intensifies the physiological significance

TABLE XV

EFFECT OF PROGESTERONE ON THE CARBONIC ANHYDRASE CONTENT ON THE
UTERINE ENDOMETRIUM, THE LIVER, KIDNEY, ADRENAL, AND BLOOD[a]

Organs tested	Carbonic anhydrase activity (EU/gm. wet tissue)	
	Control (sesame oil)	Progesterone (2 mg./rabbit)
Endometrium	14 ± 4[b]	450 ± 7[b]
Adrenals	28 ± 11	35 ± 3
Kidney	267 ± 22	302 ± 27
Liver	105 ± 12	121 ± 12
Number of rabbits	7	11
Endometrium	17.5 ± 1.1[b]	127.2 ± 12.5[b]
Blood[c]	5.3 ± 0.16	5.5 ± 0.23
Number of rabbits	6	6

[a] From Pincus *et al.* (1957) and Miyake (1959).

[b] Mean + S.E.

[c] EU/mg. Hb (Enzyme unit/mg. hemoglobin). Enzyme activity is expressed by using formula (B) in the upper set of experiments and by using formula (A) in the lower set of experiments.

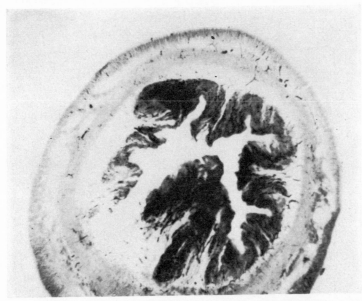

FIG. 12. Uterine section of progesterone-treated Clauberg rabbit. Glandular portion is densely stained by Häusler's (1958) cobalt sulfate histochemical test for carbonic anhydrase (Nagata and Miyake, 1960).

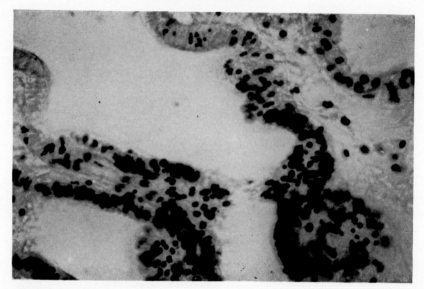

Fɪɢ. 13. Magnified endometrium of progesterone-treated Clauberg rabbit, stained by Kurata's (1953) manganese chloride method for carbonic anhydrase. Manganese granules chiefly concentrate in the epithelial cells (Nagata and Miyake, 1960).

of the endometrial carbonic anhydrase method for evaluation of progestational activity of gestagen.

V. Stromal Nuclear Hypertrophy

Hooker and Forbes (1947) demonstrated that a minute amount of progesterone injected into the lumen of a ligated uterine segment

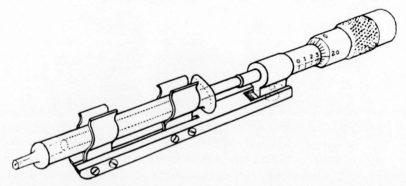

Fɪɢ. 14. Apparatus for intra-uterine injections (Hooker and Forbes, 1947).

of the ovariectomized mouse produced an apparent specific response consisting in hypertrophy of the stromal nuclei in the endometrium. They reported that it requires only a very small amount of progesterone (as little as 0.0002 μg.) to produce the positive reaction.

The instrument illustrated in Fig. 14 is used for the intra-uterine injection of test material. It is a tuberculin syringe, with a micrometer, the bolt of which controls the plunger of syringe. Hormone is dissolved in sesame oil. The standard volume of injection should not exceed 0.0006 ml.; a volume over this produces undesirable distention of the uterine segment.

The test is performed on an adult female mouse, ovariectomized 16 days earlier. Sixteen days is said to be the minimal interval after ovariectomy. Under ether anesthesia, one uterine horn is exposed through a midventral incision. The test material is then injected into the uterine segment, 5 mm. in length, according to the technique illustrated in Fig. 15. In such a microtechnique, it is most important to keep the

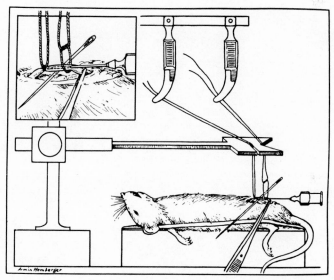

FIG. 15. Method for intra-uterine injection (Hooker and Forbes, 1947).

segment of uniform length, to adjust the micrometer-bolt gently, and to prevent leakage of injected material.

The animal is sacrificed 48 hours after injection, and the injected segment is fixed in Lavdowsky's fluid, which consists of formaldehyde 10 vol., 95% alcohol 50 vol., glacial acetic acid 3.5 vol., and distilled water 40 vol. Paraffin sections 6 μ in thickness are stained with Harris'

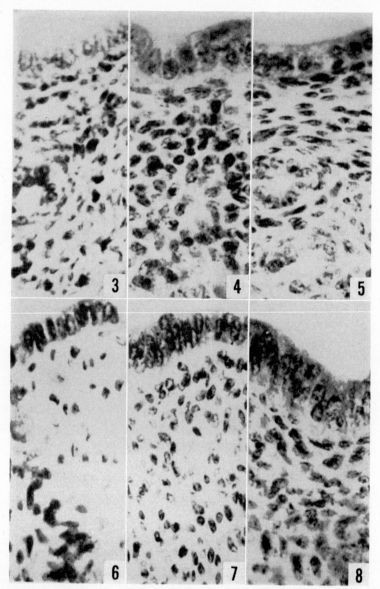

Fig. 16. Sections of endometria of mice ovariectomized 16 days previously (Hooker and Forbes, 1947). 3. No treatment. The stromal nuclei are shrunken and have clumped chromatin. 4. After intra-uterine injection of 0.00075 μg. of progesterone. A characteristic stromal nucleus is oval and has a conspicuous nucleolus and fine, evenly dispersed chromatin particles. 5. After sesame oil alone. The stromal nuclei are spindle-shaped. 6. After 6.0 μg. of deoxycorticosterone acetate. Edema is conspicuous; the stromal nuclei show little change. Part of a gland appears at the left. 7. After 0.48 μg. of testosterone. In being smaller and wrinkled, the stromal nuclei fail to meet the criteria for a positive response. 8. After 0.0075 μg. of estradiol. The chief response is heightening of the epithelium. The stromal nuclei are somewhat enlarged.

hematoxylin and eosin. For microscopic examination, the thinner sections appear to be the better.

The original figures illustrating the response are reproduced in Fig. 16. It is necessary to distinguish between the stromal nuclei and the nuclei of glandular epithelium. The latter do not appear to be affected by progesterone and can be recognized as belonging to uterine glands, if necessary, by examining adjacent serial sections. In the uterus affected by progesterone, the stromal nuclei enlarge and appear smooth, elongated, and oval in outline, whereas control sections show shrunken nuclei with clumped chromatin. In the stimulated nuclei, the chromatin particles are fine and evenly distributed, and there is a conspicuous nucleolus.

For the estimation of progesterone-like activity, the material must be serially diluted and injected in a consistent volume of 0.0006 ml. per uterine segment until negative results are obtained. The minimal effective dose is defined as the least amount which would induce a positive response of any stromal nuclei. The minimal effective dose of progesterone is reported to be equal to 0.0002 μg. in the test with the CHI strain mice.

Hooker and Forbes (1947) have mentioned that 100% positive responses can be expected with doses of 0.0002 μg. or higher, and no amount less than the minimal effective dose shows a response in 16 mice. However, they have not attempted the estimation of the 50% effective dose and the slope of the dose-response line, so that the accuracy of this method has not been clarified.

The specificity of the test has been examined in detail by Hooker and Forbes (1949b). They have demonstrated that up to 6 μg. of deoxycorticosterone acetate or of up to 0.48 μg. of testosterone injected into the uterine segment produces a negative response, and neither estradiol nor estrone will duplicate the action of progesterone on the stromal nuclei. Furthermore, the action of progesterone is never affected by the presence of estrogens. Table XVI shows the results of further tests made by them on various steroids in this respect (1949b). The Hooker-Forbes test, with its remarkable sensitivity and specificity, has been used for the detection and/or determination of the substance with a progesterone-like activity in the blood and tissues of animals and man (Forbes, 1951; Hooker and Forbes, 1949a).

In spite of the sensitivity and specificity of the Hooker-Forbes test, it has some disadvantages that have restricted its usefulness. These are (a) the time and labor required, (b) a reaction based on all-or-none basis, and (c) the difficulty of reading slides of uterine sections.

The reliability of the Hooker-Forbes test has been questioned in

TABLE XVI

SUCCESS (+) OR FAILURE (−) OF COMPOUNDS IN EVOKING A NUCLEAR RESPONSE IDENTICAL WITH THAT PRODUCED BY PROGESTERONE[a]

	mg./I.U. (Selye and Masson)	Intra-uterine injection (mg.)		Subcutaneous administration (mg.)	
		−	+	−	+
Progesterone	1	0.0001	0.0002	0.375, 0.875, 0.875	1.5, 0.75 0.375, 0.375
Anhydrohydroxy-progesterone (Ethynyltestosterone)	10	Less than 0.006		Small amount from pellets (2 mice)	
Deoxycorticosterone acetate	10	6, 3, 0.6		5, 2.5, 1.25	5, 2.5
Deoxycorticosterone		6, 3, 1.5			
Methyltestosterone	30	15, 3, 0.6		25, 12.5, 6.25, 1,	25, 12.5,
Testosterone propio-nate	50	15, 15, 3, 3, 0.6, 0.6		9.5, 3.125, 1.563, 1, 0.75	6.25, 6.25, 6.25
Testosterone dipro-pionate		3, 0.6, 0.12			
Δ⁵-Pregnenolone	40–100	5.7, 2.9, 1.4		5, 5, 2.5	
Testosterone	140–200	0.48, 0.24, 0.16, 0.12		2.5, 2.5, 2.5	
cis-Testosterone		Approx. 8, 8, 4, 4			
Pregnanediol	0	Unknown concn.			
Pregnanedione	0	3, 1, 0.005	12?, 6?		
Allopregnanedione		6, 3, 1, 0.005	12?		
Allopregnanolone		12, 6, 3, 1, 0.005			
Androsterone	0	6, 6, 3, 1.5			
Dehydroisoandros-terone	0	6.3			
Cholesterol	0	5.2, 2.6, 1.3			
Oily adrenal cortical extract		Undild., ½ dild.			
Aqueous adrenal corti-cal extract		½ dild.	Undild.?		
Estrone		0.6, 0.3, 0.15			
Estradiol	0	0.000000023–0.00075 (36 mice)			
Estradiol benzoate				0.0488, 0.0488, 0.0488	
Estradiol dipropionate				0.0001 (6 mice)	
Ascorbic acid in water		171, 85.5			

[a] From Hooker and Forbes (1949).

recent years. Olsen *et al.* (1952) have shown that progesterone can be inhibited by estrogen in the Hooker-Forbes assay with the ratio of 1:200 (estradiol-17β:progesterone). On the other hand, Ober *et al.* (1954) have found that the sensitivity of the progesterone assay can be increased as much as fivefold when the optimal ratios of 1:500 (estradiol:progesterone) or less are tested. These results do not agree with the findings of Hooker and Forbes (1947).

Most recently, Zarrow *et al.* (1957) have indicated that 17α-hydroxy-progesterone is 60 times as active as progesterone in the Hooker-Forbes test with Rockland Swiss mice, whereas Forbes (1959) has mentioned that the compound is entirely inactive in the same test with CHI strain mice. Whether such a severe discrepancy presented here is merely due to the difference in mouse strain or not, awaits further investigation.

VI. Deciduoma Formation

The various deciduoma tests are based on the fact that the endometrium of the estrogen-primed, progesterone-treated rodent is so sensitive to any local stimuli, such as scratching, chemical irritation, and electrical stimulation, that it produces a deciduoma, that is a maternal placental tumor.

The quantitative aspect of this phenomenon was first investigated by Astwood (1939). It was found that consistent deciduoma formation occurred when pseudopregnant animals were ovariectomized and then injected with progesterone. Adult female rats, 3 to 5 months old, weighing 150–200 gm. are used. Animals in estrus receive cervical stimulation of the uterus by a faradic current, as described by Greep and Hisaw (1938). Four days later, the rats are ovariectomized and the endometrium of one horn is simultaneously traumatized. By inserting a needle through the cut tubal end down as far as the cervix and then withdrawing it at an angle, the antimesometrial side of the uterine horn is scratched throughout its length. Injection of progesterone is now started once daily and continued for 3 days. The animals are killed on the day following the last injection. The degree of swelling is scored in the range of 1 to 4 by comparison with deciduoma produced in intact and uninjected pseudopregnant female by similar traumatization. The score 1 is given to uteri showing a questionable reaction. The scores 2, 3, and 4 are given to those equivalent to 1, 2, and 3 days normal deciduoma, respectively. With Astwood's technique, the reaction 3 to 4 is produced by 0.5 to 1 mg. of progesterone, 2 to 3 with 0.25 mg., and 0 to 1 with 0.1 mg. per day.

TABLE XVII

DECIDUOMA FORMATION IN INTACT PSEUDOPREGNANT RATS
24, 48, AND 72 HOURS AFTER UTERINE TRAUMATIZATION[a]

			Mean diameters	
Number of rats	Hours after uterine traumatization	Decidual rating	Traumatized horn (mm.)	Contralateral horn (mm.)
11	24	+2	2.9 ± 0.20	1.9 ± 0.17
12	48	+3	3.6 ± 0.34	2.1 ± 0.19
15	72	+4	4.8 ± 0.35	2.2 ± 0.22

[a] From Velardo and Hisaw (1951).

Velardo and Hisaw (1951) demonstrated that the diameter of the traumatized uterine horn correlated well with the grade of deciduoma development scored by Astwood's scale. Their data are shown in Tables XVII and XVIII.

Velardo and Hisaw (1951; Hisaw and Velardo, 1951) demonstrated that rat deciduoma reaction with progesterone in the Astwood test was inhibited by estrogen, testosterone, pregnanediol, deoxycorticosterone acetate, cortisone acetate, and ACTH, but not by pregnanedione and pregnenolone.

TABLE XVIII

EFFECT OF GRADED AMOUNTS OF PROGESTERONE ON THE DECIDUAL RESPONSE
IN OVARIECTOMIZED PSEUDOPREGNANT RATS[a]

	Amount of progesterone each day for three days (mg.)		Mean diameters[b]	
Number of rats		Decidual rating	Traumatized horn (mm.)	Contralateral horn (mm.)
11	0.25	+1	2.4 ± 0.22	1.9 ± 0.20
12	0.50	+2	2.8 ± 0.17	1.8 ± 0.19
11	0.75	+3	3.4 ± 0.23	1.8 ± 0.21
12	1.00	+3	3.5 ± 0.18	1.9 ± 0.20
15	1.25	+3	3.8 ± 0.17	2.0 ± 0.21
16	1.50	+4	4.5 ± 0.25	2.2 ± 0.21
10	1.75	+4	5.1 ± 0.22	2.1 ± 0.23
11	2.00	+4	5.3 ± 0.44	2.2 ± 0.18

[a] From Velardo and Hisaw (1951).
[b] Necropsies performed 72 hours after uterine traumatization.

Recently, Zarrow *et al.* (1958) have reported another method for the deciduoma formation test, in which intra-uterine injection of histamine, instead of uterine traumatization, serves as a stimulus to produce decidual reaction. The significance of histamine on the induction of decidual reaction has been studied by Shelesnyak (1957) in relation to the mechanism of ova implantation.

Either adult rats or mice can be used in this test. The animals are ovariectomized and one week later treated with estrone (1 μg. per rat or 0.2 μg. per mouse) once daily subcutaneously for 4 days, followed by 9 days of progesterone or the test compound. The uterus is exposed on the fifth day of progesterone treatment and histamine dihydrochloride (1 mg. per rat or 0.2 mg. per mouse) is injected into the lumen of one horn. The animals are sacrificed after the last treatment. Two uterine horns are removed and weighed, and the degree of deciduomatogenesis is evaluated by the percentage of increase in the weight of the histamine-injected uterine horn as compared with the control horn. The dose-response curves of progesterone obtained by this method are illustrated in Figs. 17 and 18. In the rat test, progesterone dissolved in oil gives a good dose-response curve over the dosage range of 0.2 to 2 mg. per day (Fig. 17). Suspension of the hormone in saline containing

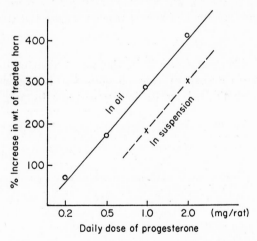

FIG. 17. Dose-response curve of progesterone on the decidual growth of castrated rats (adapted from Zarrow *et al.,* 1958).

"Tween 80" decreases the activity of the hormone by approximately 50%. In the mouse test, however, an excellent dose-response curve for progesterone in suspension is obtained over the dosage range of 0.4 to 1.6 mg. per day with an intensity of 891% at the high dosage (Fig. 18).

It has been demonstrated by Selye (1940) and Hooker (1941) that the pretreatment or simultaneous administration of estrogen is not essential for the induction of deciduoma with progesterone, as long as an adequate amount of progesterone is used.

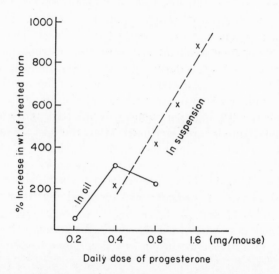

Fig. 18. Dose-response curve of progesterone on the decidual growth of castrated mice (adapted from Zarrow *et al.,* 1958).

In spite of the great interest in the mechanism of deciduoma formation, the practical use of this phenomenon for quantitative assay purposes is rather limited by its low sensitivity to progesterone.

VII. Pregnancy Maintenance and Parturition Delay

It is a well-known fact that an ovariectomy performed during the first half of pregnancy terminates gestation, but the operation performed during the second half of pregnancy does not always result in abortion, because of the capacity of placenta to produce some progestin and estrogen. It has been firmly established by many investigators (Allen and Corner, 1930; Chang, 1951; Lyons, 1943; Pincus *et al.,* 1956b) that either implantation of blastocyst or maintenance of pregnancy in the ovariectomized animal can be achieved by sufficient quantities of exogenous progestin with and without estrogen.

Although there are no technical difficulties in the assay procedure of a pregnancy maintenance test, the requirement of large numbers of

animals, large amounts of test materials, and long-term experiments
have restricted the use of this test for quantitative aspects. However,
the importance of the pregnancy maintenance test has been re-empha-
sized by the recent appearence of many synthetic progestins. The assay
procedures used by Saunders and Elton (1959) and by Stucki (1958)
are introduced here.

For the rat experiment, normal adult female rats are mated, and
breeding is checked by taking vaginal smears to detect sperm. The
day on which sperm are detected is defined as day 1. On the eighth
day of gestation, the rats are spayed bilaterally by the dorsal approach,
care being exercised to avoid traumatizing the uterine horn or disrupting
the uterine blood supply. The animals are then injected subcutaneously,
once daily, with the test compound in oil or in suspension. All animals
are sacrificed on the eighteenth day (Saunders and Elton, 1959) or
on the twenty-first day (Stucki, 1958) of pregnancy. The uteri are
isolated, placed in 70% alcohol for 24 to 48 hours, and then weighed.
The placentas and/or implantation sites are counted and measured.
The fetuses are dissected out and weighed individually.

Stucki (1958) has presented the "net success index" calculated by
the following formula, as the criteria of pregnancy-maintaining activity
of various progestins.

$$\frac{\text{Living young/group}}{\text{Number of mothers/group} \times 11 \text{ implantation sites}} \times 100$$

The above formula is based on Stucki's experiment in which 70 normal
pregnant rats contained an average of 11 implantation sites and 68
out of 70 delivered an average of 10.3 live young each. The net success
indices of the compound are expressed as percentages of theoretical
maximum success (one live fetus for each of 11 expected implantations).

For the rabbit experiment, does are mated and the ovaries are
removed on the 10th to 14th day of pregnancy. In all cases, pregnancy
is established by the observation of placental sites at the time of
ovariectomy. Daily subcutaneous injections are started on the day of
operation. Laparotomy is performed 7 to 10 days after ovariectomy and
the condition of the conceptuses determined. If normal-appearing fetuses
are present, gestation is permitted to continue until the thirtieth day.

McGinty (1959) has recommended the pregnancy-maintaining test
in mice ovariectomized at mid-gestation, in which progesterone at a
dose of 1 mg. daily in oil subcutaneously maintains pregnancy in 90%
of treated mice.

Tables XIX and XX are the data of Saunders and Elton (1959)
on the effect of ovariectomy on the rat pregnancy and on the effective-

TABLE XIX

EFFECT OF OVARIECTOMY ON THE COURSE OF
PREGNANCY IN RATS[a]

	Controls	
	Intact	Spayed[b]
Number of rats	10	10
Number with placentas	10	1
Average number of placentas	10.7	11
Uterine weight range (gm.)	14.3–34.6	0.11–0.22
Number with fetuses	10	0
Average number of fetuses	9.2	—
Average fetal weight (mg.)	909.5	—
Fetal weight range (mg.)	507–1290	—

[a] From Saunders and Elton (1959).
[b] Spaying was performed on the 8th day and the rats
were sacrificed on the 18th day of pregnancy.

ness of progesterone in maintaining pregnancy of spayed rats, respectively. Stucki's data, shown in Table XXI, on the effectiveness of
progesterone in various dosages, are similar to those (Table XX) of
Saunders and Elton (1959).

Relatively fair correlation between reported potency in the rabbit
endometrial assay and pregnancy-maintaining activity seems to exist

TABLE XX

EFFECTIVENESS OF PROGESTERONE IN MAINTAINING PREGNANCY IN RATS SPAYED
ON THE EIGHTH DAY OF PREGNANCY[a]

	Daily dose (mg./kg.)				
	1	5	10	20	50
Number of rats[b]	7	7	10	10	10
Number with placentas	0	2	10	10	10
Average number of placentas		7.5	8.1	9.3	10.3
Uterine weight range (gm.)	0.095–0.262	0.191–0.291	0.277–9.6	0.632–30.4	16.3–41.5
Number with fetuses			2	4	10
Average number of fetuses			2.5	9.0	8.5
Average fetal weights (mg.)			737	1034	850
Fetal weight range (mg.)			550–983	233–1361	84–1253

[a] From Saunders and Elton (1959).
[b] Rats were sacrificed on the 18th day after mating.

TABLE XXI

MAINTENANCE OF PREGNANCY IN RATS CASTRATED ON EIGHTH DAY OF PREGNANCY.
RESULTS OBTAINED WITH COMPOUNDS WHICH MAINTAINED LIVE YOUNG[a,b]

Daily doses		Successful pregnancies per number of "tries"	Live young per successful pregnancy	Net success index
Progesterone[c] (mg.)	Estrone (μg.)			
8	—	5/5	4	36
4	—	4/5	2.5	18
2	—	1/5	2	4
8	1	4/5	5.5	40
4	1	5/5	6.8	62
2	1	5/5	3.6	33
1	1	2/5	4.5	16

[a] Adapted from Stucki (1958).

[b] Autopsy on 21st day of pregnancy.

[c] Progesterone was administered subcutaneously once daily as suspension in CMC (CMC: 10 mg. carboxymethylcellulose, 4 mg. polysorbate 80, and 0.42 mg. propylparaben/ml.).

for 6α-methyl-17α-acetoxyprogesterone (Saunders and Elton, 1959), 17α-(2-methallyl)-19-nortestosterone (Saunders and Elton, 1959), 9α-bromo-11-ketoprogesterone (Stucki, 1958), and deoxycorticosterone acetate (Stucki, 1958). There is, however, some evidence that the ability of gestagen to maintain pregnancy cannot be surmised from the property to produce pseudopregnant proliferation in the Clauberg rabbit. It has been clearly demonstrated by Saunders and Elton (1959), Stucki (1958), and by Stucki and Forbes (1960) that the well-marked oral progestins evaluated by endometrial proliferation, such as 17α-ethynyl-19-nortestosterone, 17α-ethynyl-5(10)-estrenolone, 17α-acetoxyprogesterone and its caproate, are incapable of maintaining pregnancy of spayed rats and rabbits even in large dosages.

Lyons (1943) has reported that a small amount of estrogen administered along with progesterone greatly enhances the ability of progesterone to maintain pregnancy of hypophysectomized, ovariectomized rats, while estrogen by itself has no effect in this respect. Stucki (1958) has confirmed the finding of Lyons (1943) and has further extended the estrogen progestin synergism on pregnancy maintenance to several synthetic progestins. This phenomenon, however, can not explain the fact that 17α-ethynyl-5(10)-estrenolone, the compound having either estrogenic or progestational activity, shows no pregnancy-maintaining activity in spayed rats.

Saunders and Elton (1959) have suggested that the only compounds which exhibit a progestational reaction by the local test of McGinty *et al.* (1939) are effective in maintaining pregnancy in the rat or rabbit, as indicated in Table XXII.

TABLE XXII

QUALITATIVE EFFECTS OF VARIOUS GESTAGENS
IN SEVERAL EXPERIMENTAL PROCEDURES[a]

Compound	Endometrial development		Maintenance of pregnancy	
	Subcutaneous or oral	Intra-uterine	Rat	Rabbit
Progesterone	+	+	+	+
17-Hydroxyestrenolone:				
17-Ethynyl, $\Delta^{4(5)}$	+	0	0[b]	0[b]
17-Ethynyl, $\Delta^{5(10)}$	+	0	0	0
17-Methyl, $\Delta^{5(10)}$	+	0	0	
19-Nortestosterone:				
17-Ethyl	+	+	+	+
17-Butyl	+	+	?[c]	
17-Allyl	+	+	+	+
17-(1-Methallyl)	+	+	+	+
17-(2-Methallyl)	+	+	+	+
17-Hydroxyprogesterone:				
17-Acetate	+	+	?[c]	
17-Caproate	+		?[c]	
6-Methyl, 17-acetate	+	+	+	+

[a] From Saunders and Elton (1959).
[b] Some placental development but no fetuses maintained.
[c] Inactive at doses used. May be active at higher levels.

McGinty (1959) has mentioned that certain progestational steroids exhibit activity when administered in such a way as to provide a more or less continuous supply of hormone for the organism whether by constant feeding or by depot form of injection, whereas the same substance may appear to be inactive when administered intermittently in single daily doses. These facts lead to an attractive speculation that the different substances, progesterone and its metabolites, may be involved in controlling the different stages of normal pregnancy.

Parturition delay, as well as endometrial proliferation and pregnancy maintenance, is also considered as one of the progestational properties involved in the therapeutic value of a steroid in habitual or threatened abortion.

For the evaluation of parturition-delaying activity, inseminated females receive the test compound daily beginning at various stages of pregnancy, and the treatment is continued through the expected day of parturition or until parturition occurs. The rate of parturition-delayed animals in the compound-treated group is obtained by comparison with the normal range of delivery days in the control group. This is used as an indicator of parturition inhibition. It is not a completely specific response to progesterone, because Stucki and Forbes (1960) have found that not only progestins but also testosterone propionate administered at the late stage of pregnancy are capable of delaying parturition of intact rats. These findings indicate that endometrial proliferation, pregnancy maintenance, and parturition inhibition appear to be separable effects.

The mechanism of the action of progesterone in maintaining pregnancy or inhibiting parturition is still unknown. However, Caspo (1959) has recently proposed an unique explanation for the mechanism of pregnancy maintenance and parturition onset. This is based on his experimental evidence that progesterone has a property of blocking the conductive capacity and thus reducing the reactivity of uterine myometrium. Progestin withdrawal is thought to remove the "block" against contractile stimulants, such as oxytocics, and the block against propagation of coordinated contractile waves. The possibility of the "progesterone block" as a criterion of the quantitative assay of progestational substances awaits further investigation.

VIII. Anti-Fertility

The assays on the activities presented in this category are useful for the characterization of progestational substances rather than for the quantification of the compounds.

A. OVULATION INHIBITION

It has been clearly demonstrated that progestational steroids have a property of inhibiting ovulation and thus act as anti-fertility agents in animals and man (Drill, 1959; Hoagland, 1959; Pincus, 1959; Pincus et al., 1956a, b, 1959a, b; Rakoff, 1958; Rakoff, 1959; Saunders and Elton, 1959; Tyler, 1959). The methods for estimating the inhibitory effect on ovulation and fertility uesd by Pincus and associates (1956b) are as follows. Following the Friedman (1932, 1939) test, post-partum female rabbits are injected with the test substance 24 hours before mating to a fertile male. Laparotomy is performed 24 hours after mating to determine the presence or absence of ovulation points on the ovary.

In the rat test, mature breeding females are treated with the test compound and placed with fertile males at the time of treatment. The latent period between cohabitation with the male and the successful mating that culminates in pregnancy serves as an indicator of anti-fertility effect, resulting most likely from ovulation inhibition. This test is not specific for progestins, because the other sexagens, estrone and testosterone, are much more potent than progesterone in this anti-fertility test as demonstrated by Saunders and Drill (1958).

Norethisterone (17α-ethynyl-19-nortesterone) and norethynodrel (17α-ethynyl-5(10)-estrenolone) are reported to be clinically active progestins from the standpoint of fertility control.

B. Pituitary Gonadotropin Inhibition

Ovulation inhibition produced by endogenous or exogenous sexagens is due to the suppression of secretion of pituitary gonadotropin, the regulation of which is responsible for the cycle of the female. Pituitary-gonad relationship has been firmly established as one of the typical feed-back principles in the organism.

The effect of steroids on gonadotropin storage is estimated as follows. Intact adult male rats are treated with the test substance daily for a certain period. The pituitaries of these animals are removed and homogenized with saline. Immature female rats are treated with donor pituitary and administered in multiple injections over a certain period. The recipients are sacrificed; the ovarian and uterine weights are used as the indicators of gonadotropic activity of pituitary homogenates.

The inhibition of pituitary gonadotropin secretion is also inferred from the reduction in gonadal weight observed in intact rats treated with the test substances.

The most sensitive and quantitative method is that which uses parabiotic animals, rats or mice. The significance and consequence of the use of parabiosis in the study of pituitary-gonad relations are thoroughly investigated by Greep and Jones (1950) and reviewed by Finerty (1952). A detailed analysis of the use of the parabiosis method is discussed by Dr. Shipley in Chapter 5.

The parabiotic operation of Bunster and Meyer (1933), the most popular technique at present, which was designed for use on rats or mice, briefly consists of: (a) removal of hair from the right half of one and the left half of the other animal; (b) longitudinal incision of the skin from ear to base of tail; (c) union of the ventral edges of the skin incisions with small wound clips; (d) incision of the abdominal wall from last rib to ilium; (e) union of the four edges of the abdominal wall with either continuous or interrupted sutures; (f) tying the lateral aspects of the adjacent scapulas of the two animals firmly together with gut; and, (g) union of the dorsal edges of the skin incision with wound clips. The operation is performed under anesthesia with ether or short-acting narcotics such as methylhexabital sodium or thiopenthal sodium.

The method of Byrnes and Meyer (1951) is ordinarily used for the determination of gonadotropin inhibition on the parabiotic rats. Thirty-day-old immature male and female rats are used. A castrated male or female is united in parabiosis to a female litter-mate partner. The test compounds are administered once daily subcutaneously or orally for 10 days to the castrated partner, beginning on the day of operation. The animals are sacrificed on the eleventh day; the ovaries and uteri are removed and weighed. The pairs treated with vehicle only serve as the control. A number of natural sexagens and synthetic steroids including 19-norsteroids have been tested in this manner by many investigators (Biddulph et al., 1940; Byrnes and Meyer, 1951; Epstein et al., 1958; Goldman et al., 1957; Hertz and Meyer, 1937; Lerner et al., 1959).

More recently, Miyake (1961) has set up the method of gonadotropin inhibition test on the parabiotic mice. The assay procedures are quite similar to those on the rats. The advantages of using parabiotic mice for the determination of pituitary gonadotropin inhibiting activity of various steroids, reside in; (a) no need of litter mates as far as inbred mice are used; (b) low mortality; (c) relative ease and speed of the parabiotic operation; and, (d) economic aspect.

Table XXIII indicates the preliminary data on various progestins, injected subcutaneously, showing gonadotropin inhibition on parabiotic mice. The activity of test compound is presented by the percentage inhibition of ovarian growth of the intact female partner, which is calculated by the formula: $100 \times (V - C)/(V - Vi)$, where V, C, and Vi indicate the average ovarian weights of the intact partner united with the vehicle-injected castrated male, the compound-injected castrated male, and the vehicle-injected noncastrated male, respectively.

Anti-gonadotropin activities of progesterone derivatives correlate well with their progestational potencies on the endometrial response described

TABLE XXIII

ANTI-GONADOTROPIN ACTIVITY OF VARIOUS STEROIDS ON PARABIOTIC MICE[a]

Compound	Logarithm of dose (mg.)[b]								
	1	0	−1	−2	−3	−4	−5	−6	−7
Estradiol					+++	+	−		
Estrone						+++	+++	±	±
Estriol			+++		−	−			
Ethynylestradiol					+++	+++	±	±	
17-Ethynylestradiol-3-methyl ether					+++	+++	−	−	
Diethylstilbestrol					+++	+++	±	±	−
Progesterone	+++	+	−						
17-Acetoxyprogesterone		+++	±						
17-Acetoxy-6-methyl-progesterone				+++	+++	+	−		
Δ⁴-Pregnenolone	+	−	−						
17-Ethyl-19-nortestosterone			+++	+++	+	−			
17-Ethynyl-19-nortestosterone			+++	+++	+				
17-Ethynyl-5(10)-estrenolone					+++	+++	+	+	−
17-(1-Methallyl)-19-nortestosterone			+++	±					
17-(2-Methallyl)-19-nortestosterone			++	±					
Testosterone propionate		+++	++	−					
Methyltestosterone			+++	+++	−				
Methylandrostenediol			+++	+++	−				
Ethynyltestosterone			+++	+++	±				
2-Hydroxymethylen-17-methyldihydrotestosterone			+++	±					
2,17-Dimethyldihydro-testosterone			+++	±					
2-Methyldihydrotestosterone			+++	±					
Cortisone acetate		−	−	−					
Hydrocortisone acetate		−	−	−					
Deoxycorticosterone acetate		+	±	±					

NOTE: The per cent inhibition of ovarian growth is calculated according to the formula: $100 \times (V - C)/(V - Vi)$, where V, C, and Vi indicate the average ovarian weights of the intact partner united with the vehicle-injected castrated male, the compound-injected castrated male and with the vehicle-injected noncastrated male, respectively.

KEY: − : No inhibition
± : Up to 25% inhibition of ovarian growth
+ : 26 to 50% inhibition of ovarian growth
++ : 51 to 75% inhibition of ovarian growth
+++ : 76 to 100% inhibition of ovarian growth

[a] From Miyake (1961).
[b] Subcutaneous injection, daily for 10 days, in suspension.

previously (Table XI). In the 19-norsteroids, however, 17α-(2-meth-allyl)-19-nortestosterone, an extremely active progestin, does not show a superiority in the gonadotropin inhibition test, whereas 17α-ethynyl-5(10)-estrenolone, the weakest progestin in the compounds tested, shows a remarkable anti-gonadotropin activity which is nearly equivalent to the activity of ethynyl-estradiol, although a part of the activity may be derived from the small amount of aromatic steroids contaminated this compound.

As far as the animal experiment is concerned, it seems likely that the pituitary gonadotropin inhibiting potencies of the compounds correlate well with their anti-fertility or ovulation inhibiting activities.

The mechanism of gonadotropin release and the sites of action of "feed-back" steroids have been actively studied in recent years with either histochemical methods or electrophysiological techniques. At the present time, however, none of the modern techniques, neither histochemical nor electrographical, are available for the quantitative determination of steroid activity.

IX. Clinical Evaluation of Progestational Agents

From the clinical point of view, the most satisfactory bioassay is that based on the induction of the following responses: (a) transformation of a proliferative endometrium to a secretory one; (b) desquamation of the superficial cells of the vaginal mucosa; (c) inhibition of ferning of the cervical mucus; (d) induction of a thermogenic response; and, (e) occurrence of uterine bleeding following withdrawal of medication in amenorrheic females. These clinical indicators give direct evidence of progestational activity in human female, but for obvious reasons, it is not suitable for accurate quantitative assays on a statistically significant basis.

Recently, Greenblatt *et al.* (1958) have proposed a simple test for efficacy of progestational compounds. This test is based on the fact that removal of the corpus luteum any time after ovulation induces uterine bleeding within 48 hours. Menstruation itself is thought to be the result of withdrawal of hormonal support of the endometrium by the rapid regression of the corpus luteum. Progestational substances adequately substituted for the loss of endogenous progestin, will prevent the onset of the ensuing menstrual period.

In the test, the administration of test compound is started at day 20 or 21 of a regular 28-day cycle or 6 to 7 days after ovulation, and continued for 3 or more weeks. If the compound is active, the menses will be postponed until 2 or 3 days after cessation of the treatment. According to Greenblatt *et al.* (1958), the continuous daily oral administration of 30-mg. norethisterone (17α-ethynyl-19-nortestosterone) from about day 20 or 21 (or about 6 or 7 days after ovulation) adequately substitutes for corpus luteum function by sustaining the endometrium and prevents the onset of menses at the expected time during the period of medication. It has been reported, however, that ethisterone, 17α-acetoxyprogesterone, progesterone suppositories, and oral 17α-hydroxyprogesterone caproate do not meet this test even when very large dosages are employed.

X. Concluding Remarks

At the present time, there is no single assay method for a progestational substance that is satisfying in all respects, such as accuracy, sensitivity, specificity, reproducibility, and simplicity.

The only statistically evaluable method is the test developed by Pincus and Miyake (Miyake and Pincus, 1958a; Pincus *et al.*, 1957) who used simultaneous measurements of the G/M ratio and carbonic anhydrase in samples of the same endometrium. Both measurements are not completely parallel but are roughly correlated with each other according to the individual synthetic progestins. The objective estimation and graduated response in the test are of great advantage for the quantitative bioassay of progestational agents.

According to Saunders and Elton (1959), the intra-uterine progestational activity of the compound estimated by the McGinty test (McGinty *et al.*, 1939) is thought to reflect the potency of pregnancy maintenance, which would be an essential property of progestational agents. It is, therefore, indicated that combination of the histological investigation with the biochemical approach, such as carbonic anhydrase determination, to the endometrial responses in accordance with the different routes of administration (systemic, oral, and intra-uterine) is very promising not only for quantification but also for qualification of progestational substances.

The Hooker-Forbes (1947) test, which is based on the stromal nuclear hypertrophy of spayed mouse endometrium, appears to be an extremely sensitive method, but the accuracy and specificity of the test has not been thoroughly clarified. However, this is the only method suitable for biological detection of a minute amount of the substance with progesterone-like activity and should be used as such rather than for comparative assay of various compounds.

The decidual formation in the rat or mouse uterus seems to be a good index of progestational activity, but the sensitivity of the response to progesterone is much lower than that of endometrial proliferation in the rabbit.

From the qualitative point of view, there is a serious problem in that the ability of progestational steroids to maintain pregnancy cannot be assessed by their relative potency in the rabbit endometrial proliferation test. Obvious qualitative as well as quantitative differences in various biological properties of synthetic progestins have raised the most fundamental questions in the field of hormone-tissue interactions and also in the definition of progestational activity. The diversity of biological actions induced by progesterone-like substances leads to the forecast of the multiplicity of the active forms, of the sites, and modes of action.

It is naturally urged that the wide spectrum of biological activities including those of the other steroid hormones such as corticoids, androgens, and estrogens is necessary for the qualification of the "tailor-made" progestins. Accordingly, in spite of incomplete standardization, each of the assay methods described in this chapter will be more and more valuable for the characterization of the steroids affecting pregnancy or fertility.

REFERENCES

Allen, W. M., and Corner, G. W. (1930). *Proc. Soc. Exptl. Biol. Med.* **27**, 403.
Allen, W. M., and Wintersteiner, O. (1934). *Science* **80**, 190.
Astwood, E. B. (1939). *J. Endocrinol.* **1**, 49.
Balfour, W. E., Comline, R. S., and Short, R. V. (1957). *Nature* **180**, 1480.
Baquero, R. (1957). *Rev. colombiana endocrinol.* **1**, 209.
Biddulph, C., Meyer, R. K., and Gumbreck, L. G. (1940). *Endocrinology* **26**, 280.
Böving, B. G. (1959). In "Recent Progress in the Endocrinology of Reproduction" (C. W. Lloyd, ed.), p. 205. Academic Press, New York.
Bowers, A., and Ringold, H. J. (1958). *J. Am. Chem. Soc.* **80**, 4423.
Bowers, A., Ibanez, I. C., and Ringold, H. J. (1959). *J. Am. Chem. Soc.* **81**, 3707.
Bunster, E., and Meyer, R. K. (1933). *Anat. Record* **57**, 339.
Butenandt, A. (1934). *Wien. klin. Wochschr.* **47**, 936.
Byrnes, W. W., and Meyer, R. K. (1951). *Endocrinology* **48**, 133.
Campbell, J. A., Babcock, J. C., and Hogg, J. A. (1958). *J. Am. Chem. Soc.* **80**, 4717.
Caspo, A. (1959). *Ann. N.Y. Acad. Sci.* **75**, 790.
Chang, M. C. (1951). *Endocrinology* **48**, 17.
Clauberg, C. (1930a). *Klin. Wochschr.* **9**, 2004.

Clauberg, C. (1930b). *Zentr. Gynäkol.* **54,** 7.

Clauberg, C. (1930c). *Zentr. Gynäkol.* **54,** 1154.

Clauberg, C. (1930d). *Zentr. Gynäkol.* **54,** 2757.

Corner, G. W. (1928). *Am. J. Physiol.* **86,** 74.

Corner, G. W., and Allen, W. M. (1929). *Am. J. Physiol.* **88,** 326.

David, A., Hartley, F., Millson, D. R., and Petrow, V. (1957). *J. Pharm. and Pharmacol.* **9,** 929.

Davis, M. E., and Plotz, E. J. (1957). *Recent Progr. in Hormone Research* **13,** 347.

Davis, M. E., Test, C. M., Navori, C. A., Hryse, B., Pottinger, R. E., and Dunkele, F. (1952). *J. Clin. Endocrinol. and Metabolism* **12,** 697.

Davis, M. E., and Wied, G. L. (1957). *J. Clin. Endocrinol. and Metabolism* **17,** 1237.

de Winter, M. S., Siegmann, C. M., and Szpilfogel, S. A. (1959). *Chem. & Ind. (London)* July 11, p. 905.

Djerassi, C., Miramontes, L., Rosenkranz, G., and Sondheimer, F. (1954). *J. Am. Chem. Soc.* **76,** 4092.

Drill, V. A. (1959). *Federation Proc.* **18,** 1040.

Drill, V. A., and Riegel, B. (1958). *Recent Progr. in Hormone Research* **14,** 29.

Edgren, R. A. (1958). *Endocrinology* **62,** 689.

Elton, R. L. (1959). *Proc. Soc. Exptl. Biol. Med.* **101,** 677.

Elton, R. L., and Edgren, R. A. (1958). *Endocrinology* **63,** 464.

Emmens, C. W. (1950). "Hormone Assay," pp. 419-441. Academic Press, New York.

Engel, C. R., and Jahnke, H. (1957). *Can. J. Biochem. Physiol.* **35,** 1047.

Engel, C. R., Jennings, K. F., and Just, G. (1956). *J. Am. Chem. Soc.* **78,** 6153.

Epstein, J. A., Kupperman, H. S., and Cutler, A. (1958). *Ann. N.Y. Acad. Sci.* **71,** 560.

Ferin, J. (1956). *Acta Endocrinol.* **22,** 303.

Ferin, J. (1957). *J. Clin. Endocrinol. and Metabolism* **17,** 1252.

Finerty, J. C. (1952). *Physiol. Revs.* **32,** 277.

Forbes, T. R. (1951). *Endocrinology* **49,** 218.

Forbes, T. R. (1959). *In* "Recent Progress in the Endocrinology of Reproduction" (C. W. Lloyd, ed.), p. 279. Academic Press, New York.

Fried, J., Kessler, W. B., and Borman, A. (1958). *Ann. N.Y. Acad. Sci.* **71,** 494-499.

Friedman, H. M. (1932). *J. Pharmacol. Exptl. Therap.* **45,** 7.

Friedman, H. M. (1939). *Endocrinology* **24,** 617.

Goldman, J. N., Epstein, J. A., and Kupperman, H. S. (1957). *Endocrinology* **61,** 166.

Greenblatt, R. B. (1956). *J. Clin. Endocrinol. and Metabolism* **16,** 869.

Greenblatt, R. B. (1958). *Am. J. Obstet. Gynecol.* **76,** 626.

Greenblatt, R. B., and Barfield, W. E. (1959). *Southern Med. J.* **52,** 345.

Greenblatt, R. B., Jungck, E. C., and Barfield, W. E. (1958). *Ann. N.Y. Acad. Sci.* **71,** 717.

Greep, R. O., and Hisaw, F. L. (1938). *Proc. Soc. Exptl. Biol. Med.* **39,** 359.

Greep, R. O., and Jones, I. C. (1950). *Recent Progr. in Hormone Research* **5,** 197.

Häusler, G. (1958). *Histochemie* **1,** 29.

Hertz, R., and Meyer, R. K. (1937). *Endocrinology* **21,** 756.

Hertz, R., and Tullner, W. W. (1958). *Proc. Soc. Exptl. Biol. Med.* **99,** 451.

Hertz, R., Tullner, W. W., and Raffelt, E. (1954). *Endocrinology* **54,** 228.

Hertz, R., Waite, J. H., and Thomas, L. B. (1956). *Proc. Soc. Exptl. Biol. Med.* **91,** 418.

Heusser, A., Engel, C. R., Herzig, P. T., and Plattner, P. A. (1950). *Helv. Chim. Acta* **33**, 2229.

Hisaw, F. L., and Velardo, J. T. (1951). *Endocrinology* **49**, 530.

Hoagland, H. (1959). *Federation Proc.* **18**, 1039.

Hooker, C. W. (1941). *Proc. Soc. Exptl. Biol. Med.* **46**, 698.

Hooker, C. W., and Forbes, T. R. (1947). *Endocrinology* **41**, 158.

Hooker, C. W., and Forbes, T. R. (1949a). *Endocrinology* **44**, 61.

Hooker, C. W., and Forbes, T. R. (1949b). *Endocrinology* **45**, 71.

Jadrijevic, D., Mardones, E., and Lipschütz, A. (1956). *Proc. Soc. Exptl. Biol. Med.* **91**, 38.

Junkmann, K. (1959). *Japan. Med. Congr., Proc. 15th Congr., Tokyo* p. 61.

Keilin, D., and Mann, T. (1940). *Biochem. J.* **34**, 1163.

Kessler, W. B., and Borman, A. (1957). *Proc. Soc. Exptl. Biol. Med.* **94**, 820.

Kistner, R. W. (1958). *Am. J. Obstet. Gynecol.* **75**, 264.

Klopper, A., Strong, J. A., and Cook, L. R. (1957). *J. Endocrinol.* **15**, 180.

Kotsalo, K. (1957). *Nord. Med.* **58**, 1813.

Kupperman, H. S., and Epstein, J. A. (1957). *Proc. Symposium on 19-Nor Progestational Steroids, Chicago* pp. 32-45.

Kurata, Y. (1953). *Stain Technol.* **28**, 231.

Lerner, L. J., Holthaus, F. J., Jr., and Thompson, C. R. (1959). *Endocrinology* **64**, 1010.

Lutwak-Mann, C. (1955). *J. Endocrinol.* **13**, 26.

Lutwak-Mann, C., and Adams, C. E. (1957a). *J. Endocrinol.* **15**, 43.

Lutwak-Mann, C., and Adams, C. E. (1957b). *Acta Endocrinol.* **25**, 405.

Lyons, W. R. (1943). *Proc. Soc. Exptl. Biol. Med.* **54**, 65.

McGinty, D. A. (1959). *Federation Proc.* **18**, 1048.

McGinty, D. A., and Djerassi, C. (1958). *Ann. N.Y. Acad. Sci.* **71**, 500.

McGinty, D. A., Anderson, C. P., and McCollough, N. B. (1939). *Endocrinology* **24**, 839.

McPhail, M. K. (1934). *J. Physiol. (London)* **83**, 145.

Madjerek, Z., de Visser, J., van der Vies, J., and Overbeek, G. A. (1960). *Acta Endocrinol.* **35**, 8.

Meystre, C., and Wettstein, A. (1948). *Helv. Chim. Acta.* **31**, 1465.

Meystre, C., Tschopp, E., and Wettstein, A. (1948). *Helv. Chim. Acta.* **31**, 1465.

Miyake, T. (1959). *Intern. Conf. on Planned Parenthood, Proc. 6th Conf., New Delhi.* Report of the Proceedings, IPPF (London), p. 328.

Miyake, T. (1961). *Endocrinology* **69**, 534, 547.

Miyake, T., and Nagata, G. (1960). *Shionogi's Ann. Rept.* **10**, 185.

Miyake, T., and Pincus, G. (1958a). *Endocrinology* **63**, 816.

Miyake, T., and Pincus, G. (1958b). *Proc. Soc. Exptl. Biol. Med.* **99**, 478.

Miyake, T., and Pincus, G. (1959). *Endocrinology* **65**, 64.

Moggian, G. (1959). *Endocrinology* **64**, 363.

Nagata, G., and Miyake, T. (1960). *Endocrinol. Japon.* **7**, 202.

Ober, K. G., Klein, I., and Weber, M. (1954). *Arch. Gynäkol.* **184**, 543.

Olsen, A. G., Salhanick, H. A., and Hisaw, F. L. (1952). *Endocrinology* **51**, 519.

Overbeek, G. A., and de Visser, J. (1956). *Acta Endocrinol.* **22**, 318.

Philpot, F. J., and Philpot, J. St. L. (1936). *Biochem. J.* **30**, 2191.

Pincus, G. (1959). *Vitamins and Hormones* **17**, 307-324.

Pincus, G., and Werthessen, N. T. (1937). *Am. J. Physiol.* **120**, 100.

Pincus, G., Chang, M. C., Hafez, E. S. E., Zarrow, M. X., and Merrill, A. (1956a). *Science* **124**, 890.

Pincus, G., Chang, M. C., Zarrow, M. X., Hafez, E. S. E., and Merrill, A. (1956b). *Endocrinology* **59**, 695.

Pincus, G., Miyake, T., Merrill, A. P., and Longo, P. (1957). *Endocrinology* **61**, 528.

Pincus, G., Rock, J., Chang, M. C., and Garcia, C. R. (1959a). *Federation Proc.* **18**, 1051.

Pincus, G., Rock, J., and Garcia, C. R. (1959b). *Intern. Conf. on Planned Parenthood, Proc. 6th Conf., New Delhi.* Report of the Proceedings, IPPF (London), p. 216.

Rakoff, A. E. (1958). *Ann. N.Y. Acad. Sci.* **71**, 479–806.

Rakoff, A. E. (1959). *Federation Proc.* **18**, 1066.

Ringold, H. J., Perez, J., Batres, E., and Djerassi, C. (1959a). *J. Am. Chem. Soc.* **81**, 3485.

Ringold, H. J., Perez, J., Batres, E., and Djerassi, C. (1959b). *J. Am. Chem. Soc.* **81**, 3712.

Sala, G., Camerino, B., and Cavallero, C. (1958). *Acta Endocrinol.* **29**, 508.

Saunders, F. J. (1958). *Endocrinology* **63**, 561.

Saunders, F. J., and Drill, V. A. (1958). *Ann. N.Y. Acad. Sci.* **71**, 516.

Saunders, F. J., and Elton, R. L. (1959). *In* "Recent Progress in the Endocrinology of Reproduction" (C. W. Lloyd, ed.), pp. 227–253. Academic Press, New York.

Saunders, F. J., Colton, F. B., and Drill, V. A. (1957a). *Proc. Soc. Exptl. Biol. Med.* **94**, 717.

Saunders, F. J., Edgren, R. A., and Drill, V. A. (1957b). *Endocrinology* **60**, 804.

Selye, H. (1940). *Proc. Soc. Exptl. Biol. Med.* **43**, 343.

Shelesnyak, M. C. (1957). *Recent Progr. in Hormone Research* **13**, 269.

Slotta, K. H., Ruschig, H., and Fels, E. (1934). *Ber.* **67**, 1270.

Sondheimer, F., and Klibansky, Y. (1959). *Tetrahedron* **5**, 15.

Stucki, J. C. (1958). *Proc. Soc. Exptl. Biol. Med.* **99**, 500.

Stucki, J. C., and Forbes, A. D. (1960). *Acta Endocrinol.* **33**, 73.

Tullner, W. W., and Hertz, R. (1957). *Proc. Soc. Exptl. Biol. Med.* **94**, 298.

Tyler, E. (1959). *Intern. Conf. on Planned Parenthood, Proc. 6th Conf., New Delhi.* Report of the Proceedings, IPPF (London), p. 237.

Velardo, J. T., and Hisaw, F. L. (1951). *Endocrinology* **49**, 732.

Werthessen, N. T., Gargill, S. L., Berman, S., and Greenberg, B. (1945). *Endocrinology* **36**, 110.

Wied, G. L., and Davis, M. E. (1957). *Obstet. and Gynecol.* **10**, 411.

Zander, J. (1952). *Klin. Wochschr.* **30**, 873.

Zander, J. (1959). *In* "Recent Progress in the Endocrinology of Reproduction" (C. W. Lloyd, ed.), p. 256. Academic Press, New York.

Zander, J., and von Münstermann, A. M. (1954). *Klin. Wochschr.* **32**, 894.

Zander, J., and von Münstermann, A. M. (1956). *Klin. Wochschr.* **34**, 494.

Zander, J., Forbes, T. R., Neher, R., and Dessaulles, P. (1957). *Klin. Wochschr.* **35**, 143.

Zander, J., Forbes, T. R., von Münstermann, A. M., and Neher, R. (1958). *J. Clin. Endocrinol. and Metabolism* **18**, 337.

Zarrow, M. X., Neher, G. M., Lazowasem, E. A., and Salhanick, H. A. (1957). *J. Clin. Endocrinol. and Metabolism* **17**, 658.

Zarrow, M. X., Peters, L. E., and Caldwell, A. L. (1958). *Ann. N.Y. Acad. Sci.* **71**, 532.

Chapter 5

Anti-Gonadotropic Steroids, Inhibition
of Ovulation and Mating

Elva G. Shipley

I. Introduction

The scope of this discussion will be limited to inhibition of gonadotropin activity of the pituitary gland by steroids, and some of the methods which have been used to detect and assay gonadotropin inhibition. Only a few of the methods to be discussed have been developed into quantitative assays; many of them, however, show potential for quantitative measurement and each of the methods will be useful for specific situations. It is hoped that no important innovations in testing procedures have been overlooked.

The dual role of steroids, in stimulation and inhibition of the production and/or release of gonadotropins from the pituitary gland, have been well recognized, although all aspects of pituitary gonadotropin activity are not clearly elucidated.

Differences in the potency and/or activity of pituitary glands of male and female animals is also well recognized; notice has been taken of qualitative and quantitative differences in responses of pituitary glands of male and female animals given androgen, estrogen, or progesterone. Many of the variations in conclusions probably have been reached as a result of (1) differing conditions of assay, particularly as related to dose levels and length of treatment, or (2) animal variations. The latter point is often raised, but it cannot be too strongly stressed. Over a period of 10 to 15 years changes have been noted in degrees of responsiveness of rats from commercial strains; strain selection has been practiced on the basis of "good breeders"; although the offspring are descendants of the original stock, the increased productivity has carried with it such changes as increased gonadotropic activity and earlier maturity. Occasionally a "new colony" has been developed from closely inbred rats of a given strain and is used to replace old breeding stock (Fischer, 1960). Such colony changes produce altered sensitivity of test animals. One noteworthy example is seen in changed sensitivity to steroid so that the dosage required to prevent castration hypersecretion in parabiotic rats, as well as the normal ovarian weights, have altered markedly. (This will be referred to again in the discussion of parabiosis.)

It is now generally agreed that administration of appropriate doses of gonadal hormones will depress the rate of growth and development of ovaries and testes, and that no sex specificity occurs as far as inhibition of gonads by heterologous hormones are concerned, although a large degree of sex specificity exists in responses of accessory reproductive structures to estrogens, androgens, and progestogens. Marked differences exist also in potency of various steroids as inhibitors of gonadotropins.

Through early investigations it has been established that (1) the pituitary glands of very young animals are highly sensitive to inhibitory effects of steroids and that the sensitivity decreases in a given species with increasing age and/or size; (2) pituitary gonadotropin inhibition in young animals has longer lasting effects than in older animals; (3) castration changes, such as castration hypersecretion and pituitary morphology, can be more readily prevented if treatment is started immediately postcastration than if the postcastration changes are already established prior to treatment. These basic physiological findings can be used advantageously in selecting methods most suited to the phase of gonadotropin inhibition that is to be tested.

II. Parabiotic Technique

A widely used technique for testing the anti-gonadotropic properties of steroids is by use of parabiotic rats. The technique involves surgical union of two rats of the same age (usually 30 days of age) ; one member of each pair is castrated at the time of surgical union. The technique described by Bunster and Meyer (1933) specified that litter-mate animals be used; in recent years the highly inbred strains of rats commercially available have made it possible to eliminate that specification. Currently in use are nonlitter mates, 30 days of age, weighing 75 to 80 gm. at the time of parabiosis. It is of importance to have the two members of a pair closely matched in weight. Parabiotic pairs may be composed

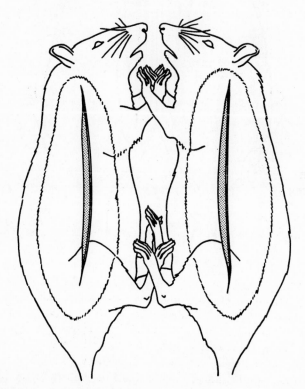

FIG. 1. Parabiosis: Area of clipped fur and skin incisions.

of 2 females, 2 males, or 1 female and 1 male; the choice of pairings can be made to suit the test materials to be examined.

For surgery it is desirable to have a well-scrubbed operating area and rigidly clean but nonsterilized instruments. Number 36 cotton thread makes satisfactory sutures, or Number 00 catgut may be used. By using

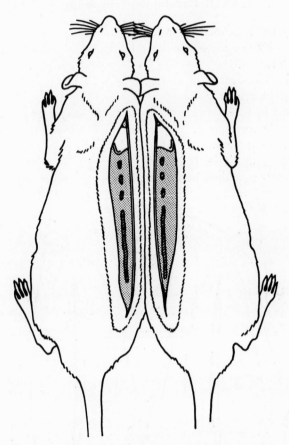

FIG. 2. Parabiosis: Body wall incisions.

ether or Nembutal anesthesia, the pair of rats are lightly anesthetized, and the hair is removed from the sides of the rats to be joined. Small animal clippers (John Oster Mfg. Company, Milwaukee, Wisconsin) are satisfactory for removing the fur. The shaved area extends from the middorsal line over the lateral body surface three-quarters of the distance to the ventral mid-line, and from the base of the ear to the base of the tail (Fig. 1). The shaved area is sterilized by washing with 70% ETOH,

Chlomine solution, or other suitable nontoxic sterilizing solution. In general it has been found most feasible to perform the castration of one partner just prior to starting the parabiosis portion of surgery, using one period of anesthesia for both operative procedures. Following castration of one partner (in our laboratory it is always the right partner),

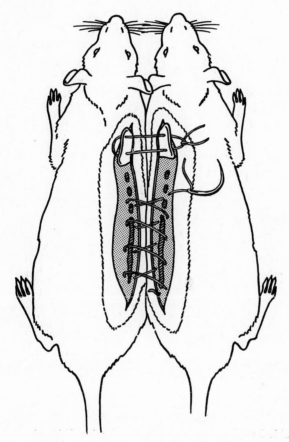

FIG. 3. Parabiosis: Placement of sutures in body walls and scapulae.

a straight-line incision is made in the skin of each rat extending from approximately 1 cm. back of the ear, to within 1 or 2 cm. of the base of the tail (Fig. 1). The abdominal wall of each rat is incised from the area ventral to the iliac bone anteriorly to the ribs, but care is taken that the diaphragm is left intact. The thin layer of muscles covering the ribs are lightly scarified; and the muscles over the scapulae (pectoralis superficialis) are cut just enough to expose the scapulae, taking care that the

larger blood vessels are left intact (Fig. 2). By using Number 36 cotton
thread the four cut edges of the abdominal walls are sewn together with a
continuous suture (Fig. 3) so that the body cavities are separate (without coelioanastomosis); the suturing is continued forward joining the
muscles over the rib region (so as to form a continuous connection be-

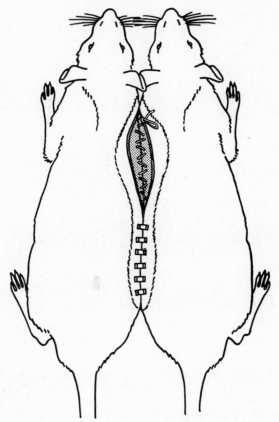

FIG. 4. Parabiosis: Placement of wound clips for dorsal skin closure.

tween the two animals thus producing a sturdier connection and permitting a greater area of vascular anastomoses). The shoulder blades are
then sutured, using Number 16 cotton thread or linen thread, by making
a loop through the scapulae (Fig. 3) and tying securely. It is urgent that
all sutures be firmly tied at the beginning and ends of sutured incisions,
and that stitches be sufficiently close together to prevent herniation, as
well as deep enough to prevent tearing out. Finally the skin incisions are
joined, using 11-mm. surgical wound clips—first over the dorsal surface

(Fig. 4); then the animals are turned on their backs and the ventral skin incisions are closed in the same manner (Fig. 5). The anterior and posterior ends of the incisions should be examined carefully to make sure there are no gaping areas; if there is a tendency for the ends of skin incisions (at neck or tail) to pull open, additional wound clips should be

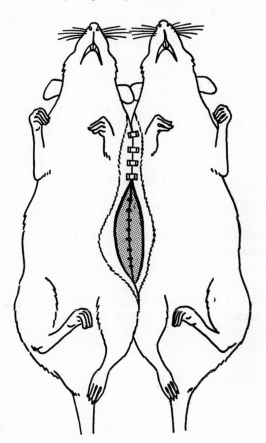

Fig. 5. Parabiosis: Ventral skin closure.

used to close the gaping incision. After the operation is completed, it is advisable to bind the base of the tails with adhesive tape, but not so tightly as to hamper circulation. The tape prevents excessive strain on the sutured area during the healing stage; the tape should be removed at the end of 3 or 4 days. The rats may be allowed to remain in parabiosis for whatever period of time is desired for the experiment; 10 days of treatment has been the usual period, with autopsy on the eleventh day although 7 days is also used (Section III, F).

For purposes of testing anti-gonadotropic activities of steroids the following pairs may be used:

Male + castrate male   ♂ ♂
Female + castrate male   ♀ ♂
Female + castrate female   ♀ ♀
Male + castrate female   ♂ ♀

If no steroid is administered to the castrate-partner of parabiotic rats during 10 days of parabiosis, the pituitary of the castrate member releases increased amounts of gonadotropin(s) which are carried to the intact member via vascular anastomoses. The increased gonadotropin(s) is sufficient to stimulate the ovaries of an intact female partner or the testes, and secondarily, the ventral prostate and seminal vesicles of an intact male partner.

III. Development of the Parabiosis Method

A. INHIBITION OF OVARIAN WEIGHT INCREASE

Parabiosis has been used to demonstrate the phenomenon of castration hypersecretion resulting in ovarian weight increase in intact females and its prevention by means of gonadal hormones. A review of the historical development and use of parabiosis for study of gonadotropic hormones was made by Finerty (1952). Early tests were made by Kallas (1930) using extracts of ovaries and by Martins and Rocha (1931a, b) using testicular extracts to prevent stimulation of the intact gonads of the intact rat when paired with a castrate partner.

1. Lack of Sex-Specificity for Steroids

a. Estrogen inhibition of gonadotropin. Meyer and Hertz (1937) first established parabiosis as a method for quantitative determination of the amount of estrogen (estrone) required to completely inhibit the post-castration hypersecretion. Assay animals are put into parabiosis at 30 days of age; one member of the pair is castrated and treatment consists of daily injections of steroid for a period of 10 days. An inhibitory dose of steroid is the smallest quantity which produces unstimulated ovaries in the intact female member of the pair. Meyer and Hertz established reliability of the method by using rats from two colonies; by using both female-castrate female and female-castrate male pairs, they determined that the estrone effects on the secretion of gonadotropin were not sex specific (Table I).

b. Androgen inhibition of gonadotropin. Later the same year Hertz

TABLE I

OVARIAN WEIGHTS OF FEMALE RATS IN PARABIOSIS WITH CASTRATED
MALE OR FEMALES GIVEN VARYING QUANTITIES OF ESTRONE[a]

Colony	No. of pairs	Sex of pairs	Amount estrone per day (μg.)	Mean ovarian weight ± S.E. (mg.)
Z¹	7	♀ ♀	0.05	24.0 ± 4.8
Z¹	6	♀ ♀	0.20	13.7 ± 1.14
Z¹	3	♀ ♀	1.00 ⎫	
Z¹	2	♀ ♀	5.00 ⎬	13.4 ± 1.13
Z¹	11	♀ ♀	None (control)	71.0 ± 12.4
Z¹	8	♂ ♀	0.05	42.5 ± 12.1
Z¹	11	♂ ♀	0.20	18.4 ± 1.7
Z¹	7	♂ ♀	1.00 ⎫	
Z¹	4	♂ ♀	5.00 ⎬	15.7 ± 1.0
Z¹	16	♂ ♀	None (control)	72.8 ± 11.4
Z²	2	♀ ♀	5.00 ⎫	
Z²	3	♂ ♀	1.00 ⎬	12.15 ± 1.0
Z²	8	♂ ♀	5.00 ⎭	
Z²	5	♀ ♀	None (control)	81.8 ± 18.3
Z²	6	♂ ♀	None (control)	85.8 ± 18.3
S¹	8	♀ ♀	0.20	14.0 ± 0.62
S¹	9	♀ ♀	None (control)	90.3 ± 10.3
S¹	10	♂ ♀	0.20	51.8 ± 11.7
S¹	7	♂ ♀	1.00	13.57 ± 0.67
S¹	8	♂ ♀	None (control)	81.2 ± 13.2

[a] From Meyer and Hertz (1937).

and Meyer (1937) tested androgens (testosterone, testosterone propionate, and dehydroandrosterone) quantitatively, for inhibition of postcastration hypersecretion of gonadotropin; testosterone was used in graded doses in both female-castrate male and female-castrate female pairs and again demonstrated the lack of sex specificity in its effect. These two papers established (1) that more steroid, both estrogenic and androgenic, is required to inhibit postcastration changes in male than in female rats, and (2) that larger quantities of androgens than estrogens are required to effect the inhibition (Table II).

c. Progesterone inhibition of gonadotropin. Continuing the studies of the influence of steroidal hormones on the secretion of gonadotropic hormones in parabiotic rats, Biddulph *et al.* (1940) used progesterone as well as estradiol and estriol to inhibit gonadotropin hypersecretion and thereby added the third class of gonadal hormones to the roster of effec-

TABLE II[a]

EFFECT OF ANDROGENS ON THE SECRETION OF GONADOTROPINS IN PARABIOTIC RATS

Androgen	Sex	Dose[b]	Total No. of pairs in group	Mean ovarian Wt. ± S.E.	Mean seminal vesicle Wt. ± S.E.	Ovarian weight distribution (mg.)[c]					
						0–20	21–34	35–54	55–94	95–144	145–224
Testosterone	♂♀	10	10	68.6 ± 13.7	12.1 ± 0.79	2	2	—	4	2	—
	♂♀	10	14	19.2 ± 4.3	—	12	—	1	1	—	—
	♂♀	30	9	29.1 ± 6.8	16.8 ± 1.04	5	1	1	1	—	—
	♂♀	30	9	16.0 ± 1.2	—	8	—	—	—	—	—
	♂♀	50	8	24.6 ± 4.2	23.0 ± 2.51	4	2	2	—	—	—
	♂♀	75	8	14.7 ± 0.90	17.3 ± 1.14	8	—	—	—	—	—
	♂♀	100	6	20.1 ± 0.95	20.0 ± 1.76	4	2	—	—	—	—
Testosterone propionate	♂♀	2	5	104.8 ± 5.19	13.6 ± 0.7	—	—	—	1	4	—
	♂♀	10	5	52.4 ± 23.2	35.0 ± 2.6	2	1	—	1	1	—
	♂♀	15	5	18.8 ± 1.07	49.8 ± 5.09	4	1	—	—	—	—
Dehydroepi-androsterone	♂♀	1000	5	56.4 ± 13.82	9.4 ± 0.17	1	1	2	2	—	—
	♂♀	3000	7	15.2 ± 1.25	52.8 ± 5.9	6	—	—	—	—	—
Control (I)	♂♀	0	13	123.8 ± 17.9	8.57 ± 0.52	2	0	0	2	3	6
	♂♀	0	10	67.0 ± 13.03	—	1	1	3	2	2	1
Control (II)	♂♀	0	16	72.8 ± 13.52	—	4	1	3	3	4	1
	♂♀	0	11	71.0 ± 12.3	—	1	2	1	4	3	1
Control (III)	♂♀	0	7	89.2 ± 15.87	—	1	—	1	—	5	—
	♂♀	0	5	81.8 ± 18.27	—	1	—	—	1	3	—
Control (IV)	♂♀	0	8	81.2 ± 13.19	—	1	—	—	6	—	1
	♂♀	0	15	90.06 ± 11.61	—	—	1	3	5	5	1
Combined controls	♂♀	0	44	92.09 ± 8.42	—	8	1	4	11	12	8
	♂♀	0	41	78.31 ± 6.55	—	3	4	7	12	13	2

[a] From Hertz and Meyer (1937).

[b] Daily dose, in μg., administered subcutaneously in 0.05 cc. corn oil.

[c] The ovarian weights of six normal rats of similar age and body weight were found to be: 14, 16, 18, 19, 20, and 21 mg., respectively, the mean being 18 ± 1.13 mg.

TABLE III[a]

The Influence of Estrogens and Progesterone on the Secretion of Gonadotropic Hormones in Parabiotic Rats

Hormone	Sex of pairs	Dose per day (µg.)	No. of pairs	Mean ovarian weight ± S.E.	Ovarian weight distribution (mg.)								
					0–20	21–34	35–49	50–64	65–79	80–94	95–109	110–124	125–214
Estriol	♀ ♀	0.1	6	38 ± 10.5	1	3			2				
		0.3	7	22 ± 5.3	6			1					
		0.5	6	14 ± 1.7	6								
		1.0	5	17 ± 2.0	3	2							
		1.5	4	13 ± 1.8	4								
		3.0	6	13 ± 0.8	6								
		4.5	5	16 ± 0.8	5								
	♀ ♂	4.5	5	86 ± 14.0				1	1	1	1	1	
		6.0	7	41 ± 11.9	3	1		1	1		1		
		8.0	7	19 ± 5.4	6				1				
		10.0	5	15 ± 0.4	5								
		15.0	4	12 ± 0.8	4								
Estradiol	♀ ♀	0.01	7	46 ± 14.9	3	1		1	1			1	
		0.0175	7	13 ± 1.8	6	1							
		0.025	6	15 ± 2.0	6								
		0.05	5	13 ± 0.4	5								
	♀ ♂	0.05	6	52 ± 15.7	2	1			1	1	1		
		0.075	6	23 ± 5.2	3	2		1					
		0.10	5	22 ± 2.3	1	4							
		0.15	5	14 ± 0.9	5								
Progesterone	♀ ♀	500	18	42 ± 8.0	8	2		3	1	3		1	
	♀ ♀	1000	8	20 ± 7.1	7				1				
		1 Rb.U.	7	17 ± 2.7	6	1							
Control (V)	♀ ♀	—	24	85 ± 10.9	1	7	2		4		1	3	6
	♀ ♂	—	15	88 ± 13.5		2	3	1		1	3	1	4
Combined controls	♀ ♀	—	59	80 ± 5.8	4	9	6	3	11	3	6	6	11
	♀ ♂	—	59	91 ± 7.1	9	3	6	2	2	9	6	6	16

[a] From Biddulph et al. (1940).

tive inhibitory steroids, at the same time establishing the low inhibitory activity of progesterone as compared to estrogens and androgens (Table III).

d. Adrenal cortical hormone inhibition of gonadotropin. Using the same parabiotic approach, Byrnes and Shipley (1950) examined the uterine-stimulating and gonadotropic-inhibiting properties of deoxycorticosterone acetate (DCA), cortisone, and two types of commercial preparations of adrenal extracts. DCA proved to be a moderate-to-weak inhibitor of gonadotropin, whereas in the maximum tolerated dose cortisone

TABLE IV

THE UTERINE STIMULATING AND GONADOTROPIC-HORMONE-INHIBITING ACTIVITY
OF ALPHA-ESTRADIOL, DEOXYCORTICOSTERONE ACETATE, COMPOUND E,
LIPO-ADRENAL CORTEX, AND ADRENAL CORTEX EXTRACT[a]

Compound	Dose per day	No. of pairs	Ovaries[b] (mg.)	Uterus[c] (mg.)
None		23	160 (110–230)	52 (32–90)
α-Estradiol	0.0032 μg.	2	146	47
	0.0065 μg.	2	122	60
	0.009 μg.	2	16	45
	0.012 μg.	3	25	51
	0.025 μg.	3	25	135
	0.050 μg.	2	29	168
DCA	250 μg.	2	133	80
	425 μg.	5	35	67
	500 μg.	2	20	77
	1000 μg.	2	23	123
	2000 μg.	1	35	110
Compound E	500 μg.	2	250	70
	2000 μg.	2	195	53
Lipo-adrenal cortex	0.5 R.U. (0.0125 cc.)[d]	2	170	45
	1 R.U. (0.025 cc.)	3	22	65
	2 R.U. (0.05 cc.)	4	20	117
	4 R.U. (0.10 cc.)	2	23	175
Adrenal cortex extract	0.625 R.U. (0.25 cc.)[d]	1	125	43
	2 R.U. (0.8 cc.)	3	118	52
	4 R.U. (1.6 cc.)	3	65	45

[a] From Byrnes and Shipley (1950).
[b] Ovaries of the left, intact partner.
[c] Uterus of the right, ovariectomized, injected partner.
[d] Original volume of the extract.

did not produce inhibition. Both commercial preparations of adrenal extracts inhibited pituitary gonadotropin secretion; the lipo-adrenal extract was more effective than the aqueous material in relation to its adrenal-cortical activity (Table IV). No attempt was made to determine the chemical nature of the inhibitory substance.

2. Ratio of Steroid for Pituitary Inhibition/Uterine Stimulation

Byrnes and Meyer (1951a) made use of the dual end points of ovarian weight decrease in intact female and uterine stimulation in the castrate partner to study the relationship between the amount of estrogen (estra-

TABLE V

THE UTERINE AND OVARIAN WEIGHTS OBTAINED IN PARABIOTIC RATS
GIVEN ESTROGEN[a]

Compound	Dose (μg./day)	No. of pairs	Average organ weights (mg.)	
			Ovaries[b]	Uterus[c]
Uninjected	—	23	160 (110–230)	52 (32–90)
α-Estradiol	0.0032	2	146	47
	0.0065	2	122	60
	0.0065	1	15	43
	0.009	2	16	45
	0.012	3	25	51
	0.020	3	20	65
	0.025	3	25	135
	0.050	2	29	168
Estrone	0.050	3	112	51
	0.075	2	30	48
	0.10	6	34	52
	0.15	3	40	56
	0.20	5	42	131
	1.00	3	31	217
Compound No. 15	5.00	2	134	75
	25.00	3	152	70
	50.00	2	22	61
	100.	3	24	65
	200.	2	30	85
	250.	2	32	138
	500.	2	29	148

[a] From Byrnes and Meyer (1951a).
[b] Ovaries of the left, intact partner.
[c] Uterus of the right, ovariectomized, injected partner.

diol, estrone, and a synthetic estrogen) required to inhibit gonadotropic hormone secretion and the amount of the estrogen required to stimulate the uterus in immature female rats. All three compounds inhibited gonadotropin hypersecretion at a lower dose than that required to produce uterine stimulation (Table V). Experimental results such as these have established the physiological validity of the experimental procedure.

3. Transfer of Steroid across Parabiotic Union

A fortunate aspect of steroid administration to one member of parabiotic rats is that transfer of injected steroid in sufficient amounts to affect the intact partner does not occur until the dose level is greater than is necessary to inhibit castration hypersecretion. Biddulph *et al.* (1941) concluded it was necessary to inject 40 times the amount of estradiol [80 × the dose of diethylstilbestrol (DES)] required to prevent gonadotropin hypersecretion before there was evidence of uterine stimulation in the non-injected partner of ovariectomized female-ovariectomized female pairs. Shipley, *et al.* (1943) made similar studies in castrate male-castrate male pairs and found that testosterone propionate was not transferred in sufficient quantities to be detected until 50 times the dose to produce gonadotropin inhibition was given. It appears that transfer of steroid between parabionts is not likely to be a problem in testing, if minimum doses of steroid necessary to produce inhibition are used.

4. Alterations in Steroid Sensitivity in Strains of Rats

It is pertinent to the data currently obtained to emphasize the change in magnitude of ovarian weight increase, and pituitary sensitivity to steroids, in the parabiotic rats over the period from 1937 to 1960. The ovarian weights of control untreated female-castrate female pairs obtained by Meyer and Hertz (1937) averaged 71.0 mg. for laboratory-grown rats, and 90.3 mg. for Sprague-Dawley rats; in 1940 Biddulph, Meyer, and Gumbreck obtained 80.0-mg. ovaries; in 1950 Byrnes and Shipley found ovarian weights which averaged 160.0 mg. in untreated pairs, but in 1959–1960 our data show the average weight of ovaries of untreated pairs to be around 200.0 mg. The ovarian weights in noncastrate female pairs in 1940 were approximately 16.0 mg. and the ovaries were composed only of follicles. At the present time noncastrate female pairs have ovaries weighing approximately 35 mg. and containing several corpora lutea (Table VI). The sensitivity of the castrate rat pituitary to estrone, testosterone, or progesterone has also evolved, so that inhibition of castration hypersecretion now requires larger daily doses than in the earlier experiments (Meyer and Hertz, 1937; Hertz and Meyer, 1937; Biddulph *et al.* 1940; Byrnes and Shipley, 1950; Byrnes and Meyer,

TABLE VI

OVARIAN WEIGHTS IN UNTREATED NONCASTRATE PARABIOTIC RATS[a]

Group	Duration of parabiosis (days)	No. of pairs	Body weight ♀ ♀ (gm.)		Intact female		Intact female	
					Ovarian weight (mg.)	Ovarian response	Ovarian weight (mg.)	Ovarian response
Noncastrate Nonlitter mates	10	10	103	106	31.2 (17.5–51.5)	Few C.L.[b] 4/10	31.8 (20.3–42.8)	Few C.L. 7/10
Noncastrate Litter mates	10	9	107	107	32.0 (24.5–46.0)	Few C.L. 4/9	31.4 (17.4–43.7)	Few C.L. 6/9
Noncastrate Litter mates	10	9	105	100	29.4 (19.0–38.8)	Few C.L. 5/9	30.3 (14.8–49.9)	Few C.L. 5/9

[a] From Shipley (1960a), unpublished data. Data obtained under Contract No. SA-43-ph-2413, Cancer Chemotherapy National Service Center, National Institutes of Health.

[b] C.L. = corpora lutea.

1951a; Byrnes et al. 1951). This appears to be due to some degree of selection for increased productivity by breeders, such as described by Fischer (1960), and referred to earlier. As a result the present colony have more potent pituitaries and mature earlier than did the original colony.

B. SIMULTANEOUS TESTS OF GONADOTROPIN SECRETION, ASSAYS OF PITUITARY CONTENT, AND CHANGES IN PERCENTAGE OF PITUITARY CELL TYPES

1. Method of Meyer, Biddulph, and Finerty (1946)

More detailed tests which made use of parabiosis technique are those of Meyer, Biddulph, and Finerty who used three methods for analysis of pituitary gonadotropic activity: (1) measurement of hormone released into the blood stream, as evidenced by ovarian weights of intact parabionts, (2) pituitary gonadotropin content, determined by biological assay, and (3) study of the cytological changes in the pituitary gland by cell counts. The results of the triple assay can be seen in Tables VII and VIII.

a. *Additive effects of two steroids given simultaneously.* Byrnes et al. (1951) extended the use of parabiotic rats to include a study of the cytological response of pituitary glands to progesterone, and to estrogen-progesterone combinations. They concluded that the effects of estrogen

TABLE VII

THE EFFECT OF OVARIECTOMY AND ESTROGEN TREATMENT ON THE AVERAGE WEIGHT
OF VARIOUS ORGANS OF IMMATURE FEMALE RATS[a]

Treatment	No. of rats	Body weight (gm.)	Ovarian weight (mg.)	Uterine weight (mg.)	Pituitary weight (mg.)
Untreated	56	114.3 ±0.9[b]	18.8 ±0.6	74.7 ±4.4	4.5 ±0.2
Ovariectomized (10 days)	58	108.6 ±1.0	—	30.3 ±1.3	5.5 ±0.2
Ovariectomized plus 0.055 µg. estradiol per day for 10 days	60	100.3 ±0.7	—	115.1 ±1.6	5.5 ±0.2
Untreated parabiotic rats: Left partner (intact)	53	89.0 ±1.1	131.3 ±6.0	—	5.1 ±0.4
Right partner (ovariectomized 10 days)	53	85.4 ±1.4	—	—	4.4 ±0.3
Estrogen-treated parabiotic rats: (0.055 µg. estradiol per day for 10 days) Left partner (intact)	51	84.0 ±1.3	16.5 ±0.5	—	3.9 ±0.2
Right partner (ovariectomized 10 days)	51	81.8 ±1.3	—	—	4.6 ±0.2

[a] From Meyer et al. (1946).
[b] Standard error.

and progesterone were additive, neither inhibiting nor potentiating the effect of the other. Table IX summarizes the inhibition of gonadotropin secretion. The pituitary cytology revealed the basophil cells rose from 6.2% in the nonovariectomized females to 15.9% in the ovariectomized parabiont; combined estradiol and progesterone therapy (0.0032 µg. estradiol and 500 µg. progesterone per day) reduced the basophils to 5.2%; 1000–1400 µg. progesterone alone reduced basophils to 6.3%.

C. REVERSAL OF CONSTANT ESTRUS IN PARABIOTIC RATS

Using adult parabiotic rats, Hill (1932, 1933) and Witschi and Levine (1934) observed that when sufficient time elapsed and the pituitary gland of the gonadectomized partner had become hypersecretory, the intact partner developed a condition of continuous estrus.

TABLE VIII

The Effect of Ovariectomy and Estrogen Treatment on Cell Types and Gonadotropic Content of the Pituitary Gland of Single and Parabiotic Female Rats[a]

Treatment	Average ovarian weight (mg.)	Pituitary assay data		Cell type analysis		
		No. of rats	Average ovarian weight (mg.)	Av. % acidophils	Av. % basophils	Av. % chromatophils
Untreated	18.8 ± 0.6[b]	15	26.0 ± 3.2	23.8 ± 0.6	6.5 ± 0.4	69.7 ± 1.0
Ovariectomized (10 days)		14	39.0 ± 6.1	23.7 ± 1.7	19.7 ± 0.4	56.6 ± 1.4
Ovariectomized plus 0.055 µg. estradiol per day for 10 days		14	77.0 ± 6.3	29.3 ± 0.7	9.7 ± 0.3	61.0 ± 0.9
Untreated parabiotic rats:						
Left partner (intact)	131.3 ± 6.0	16	11.0 ± 0.4	20.2 ± 0.3	4.0 ± 0.3	75.8 ± 0.5
Right partner (ovariectomized 10 days)		12	28.0 ± 5.0	23.6 ± 0.7	11.6 ± 0.5	64.8 ± 0.7
Estrogen-treated parabiotic rats: (0.055 µg. estradiol per day for 10 days)						
Left partner (intact)	16.5 ± 0.5	10	25.0 ± 4.6	23.9 ± 0.8	7.7 ± 0.2	68.4 ± 0.8
Right partner (ovariectomized 10 days)		13	49.0 ± 4.3	30.4 ± 0.4	9.1 ± 0.3	60.5 ± 0.4

[a] From Meyer et al. (1946).
[b] Standard error.

TABLE IX

UTERINE AND OVARIAN WEIGHTS IN PARABIOTIC RATS GIVEN ESTROGEN
AND PROGESTERONE[a]

Treatment	Dose (μg./day)	Average ovarian weight[b] (mg.)	Average uterine weight[c] (mg.)	No. of pairs
Controls		160 (110–230)	52 (32–90)	23
Estradiol	0.0032	146	47	2
	0.0065	122	60	2
	0.0065	15	43	1
	0.009	16	45	2
	0.012	25	51	3
	0.020	20	65	3
	0.025	25	135	3
	0.050	29	168	2
Progesterone	50	171	41	4
	200	158	40	7
	500	106	51	13
	750	131	62	7
	1000	41	62	7
Estradiol Progesterone	0.0032 500	41	56	12
Estradiol Progesterone	0.012 200–1000	28	137	6
Estradiol Progesterone	0.050 10–1000	21	129	8

[a] From Byrnes et al. (1951).
[b] Ovaries from the left, intact partner.
[c] Uterus from the right, ovariectomized, injected partner.

1. Method of Meyer and Biddulph (1941)

Meyer and Biddulph used the production of constant estrus as the basis for a test of steroidal inhibition of hypersecretion. Daily administration of 1, 2, or 3 μg. of estradiol to the ovariectomized partner produced, first, a period of diestrus lasting approximately 10 days in the nonovariectomized partner, followed by estrous cycles. The estrous cycles persisted as long as estradiol was administered to the castrate partner; following estrogen withdrawal estrous cycles gradually became irregular and then changed again to continuous estrus. The investigators did not develop a dose-response curve for the assay, but reported that some pairs required larger doses of estradiol to produce regular cycles than did others. This suggests that a dose-response curve could be established using the appearance of regular cycles as an end point. Apparently, a colony of adult parabiotic female-castrate females could be used repeatedly for assays. The disadvantage of the test lies in the time required to establish a constant estrus (40–50 days after parabiosis) colony of parabionts.

D. Use of Hypophysectomized Rats in Parabiosis

In another refinement of the parabiosis method, Biddulph and Meyer (1946) hypophysectomized both male and female rats and gonadectomized their parabiotic partners. The pairs were autopsied at varying intervals after parabiosis, the longest interval being 53 days. If the hypophysectomized partner was a female the ovaries were stimulated but only follicles were found in the ovaries, whereas the testes of hypophysectomized males paired with gonadectomized partners were only slightly smaller than those of normal rats and the accessory gland weights were normal. Luteinizing hormone (LH) given to the hypophysectomized female partner of each pair produced luteinization of the ovaries, indicating that insufficient LH was secreted or transferred from the gonadectomized partner to produce luteinization.

1. Method of Greep and Jones (1950)

Greep and Jones used hypophysectomized males and females paired with gonadectomized partners and confirmed the development of large ovaries composed of only follicles in hypophysectomized females but found marked growth of testes and enlarged accessory glands in the hypophysectomized male parabionts. Low dose levels of testosterone propionate given daily to the gonadectomized member of the pairs produced inhibition in the castrate partner. There was proportionately greater depression of ventral prostate and seminal vesicles than of testes weights, however, larger doses of testosterone propionate further inhibited castration hypersecretion from the injected parabiont (Table X).

The combination of gonadectomized rats and hypophysectomized rats offers the distinct advantage that it provides a means for testing inhibition of a single component of the FSH*-LH complex, as well as a method to show complete suppression of the gonadotropin hypersecretion. The disadvantages are technical ones, in that more skills are required to pre-

* FSH = follicle-stimulating hormone.

TABLE X

THE EFFECT OF TESTOSTERONE PROPIONATE ON CIRCULATING GONADOTROPIN OF THE
CASTRATE PARTNER OF CASTRATE MALE-HYPOPHYSECTOMIZED MALE PARABIONTS[a]

Dose	Parabionts	No. of pairs	Combined body weight (gm.)	Testes (mg.)	Seminal vesicles (mg.)	Ventrial prostate (mg.)
15 μg.	Castrate male				20.7	32.2
		5	155			
	Hypoph. male			879	22.0	43.2
20 μg.	Castrate male				33.0	42.2
		3	136			
	Hypoph. male			470	7.8	18.2
30 μg.	Castrate male				101.0	106.0
		2	170			
	Hypoph. male			574	14.9	16.6
Controls	Castrate male				8.9	8.8
		2	158			
	Hypoph. male			1620	189.0	140.0

[a] From Greep and Jones (1950).

pare hypophysectomized-gonadectomized pairs of rats than intact-gona-
dectomized pairs.

E. ANDROGENIC-MYOTROPHIC EFFECTS RELATED TO GONADOTROPIN INHIBITION

Following the finding that 19-nortestosterone possesses an altered
ratio of myotrophic to androgenic activity as compared to testosterone
and testosterone propionate (Hershberger et al., 1953), and that gonadotropin-inhibiting activity is retained by 19-nor compounds (Shipley,
1954), it seemed desirable to include an end point for myotrophic as well
as for androgenic and gonadotropin inhibitory effects of steroids. The
gonadotropin-inhibiting effects of 19-nor compounds has been well confirmed (Epstein et al., 1958; Lerner et al., 1959).

1. Method of Shipley and Meyer (1956)

The operative procedure used by Shipley and Meyer is the same as
that previously described using 30-day-old rats; the intact partner is a
female and the castrate member is a male rat. The castrate partner is
treated by subcutaneous or oral administration once daily, for 10 days,

with autopsy on the eleventh day. Ovarian weight and ovarian response of the intact female partner are used to gauge the degree of inhibition of castration hypersecretion; weights of ventral prostate, seminal vesicles and levator ani are used to assay the relative androgenic and myotrophic activities of the steroids. It is recommended that parabionts to be used for judging comparative myotrophic potency be of uniform size. If body weights of parabionts differ sharply from the normal range, they should be discarded from the assay. Increase in levator ani muscle weight appears to be a result of general body growth and myotrophic hormone activity; hence if the body weight of a pair of rats falls below normal for postoperative parabionts, the levator ani will be relatively smaller than in similarly treated parabionts maintaining good growth rates. Table XI includes data obtained from testing a number of steroids, some of which possessed marked myotrophic as well as anti-gonadotropin activity.

F. SEVEN-DAY MODIFICATION OF THE PARABIOSIS METHOD

The precocious maturity and increased gonadotropic potency in currently produced commercial strains of rats makes it difficult to gauge complete inhibition of gonadotropin secretion; indeed, the noncastrate female-female parabiont rats, from present-day strains parabiosed from 30 to 40 days of age, have ovaries with varying degrees of luteinization. Because of precocious maturing, increased pituitary activity, and greater convenience of a short assay, it seemed desirable to develop a method which avoids these inconveniences. From those exigencies was developed the 7-day method of assay.

1. Method of Shipley (1960a)

Parabiotic pairs of rats, either female-castrate female or female-castrate male are made using 30-day nonlitter-mate rats. Body weights are closely matched, using rats weighing 75 to 80 gm. Steroid administration is once daily for 7 days. The diluent may be oil or CMC (sodium carboxymethylcellulose) for subcutaneous administration; 0.5% tragacanth, 1% acacia, 0.9 saline or oil may be used as diluent for oral administration. Operative procedures and treatment are as previously described (Section II). Comparative data for 7 and 10 days of steroid treatment are shown in Tables XII, XIII, and XIV. Complete suppression of castration hypersecretion appears to be accomplished by lower dose levels in the 7-day test than in 10-day tests with both estrogen and androgen. The 7-day assay gives data with a sharper end point for suppression of ovarian weight and ovarian response, than the data from 10-day assays.

TABLE XI

INHIBITORS OF CASTRATION HYPERSECRETION AND MYOTROPHIC ACTIVITY
OF STEROIDS IN FEMALE-CASTRATE MALE PARABIOTIC RATS[a]

| Treatment and total dose/rat | No. of pairs | Body weight (gm.) | | Intact female ovarian weight (mg.) | Castrate male | |
		♀	♂		Ventral prostate (mg.)	Levator ani (mg.)
Controls	30	100	99	227.0	13.9	24.0
Testosterone, 0.4 mg.	30	101	102	92.3	42.7	37.1
Testosterone, 0.8 mg.	30	102	111	59.4	79.7	58.8
19-Nortestosterone, 17-ethynyl-, 0.4 mg.	5	101	96	103.7	17.7	28.6
19-Nortestosterone, 17-ethynyl-, 0.8 mg.	5	99	98	35.6	28.2	37.2
19-Nortestosterone, cyclopentanepropionate, 0.4 mg.	5	105	106	97.6	8.9	37.0
19-Nortestosterone, cyclopentanepropionate, 0.8 mg.	5	101	106	30.2	16.2	62.7
19-Nortestosterone, 17-methyl-, 0.4 mg.	10	108	106	176.8	19.0	34.0
19-Nortestosterone, 17-methyl-, 0.8 mg.	10	107	112	121.6	22.6	45.1
19-Nortestosterone, 17-methyl-, 1.2 mg.	5	107	112	82.9	26.5	36.5
19-Nortestosterone, 17-methyl-, 2.4 mg.	5	104	113	34.9	53.7	70.9
Androsterone, 0.4 mg.	5	95	90	173.6	30.5	17.5
Androsterone, 0.8 mg.	5	104	103	134.5	33.6	21.9
Δ^4-Androstene-3,17-dione, 0.4 mg.	5	100	93	175.5	29.7	19.9
Δ^4-Androstene-3,17-dione, 0.8 mg.	5	94	93	133.0	31.9	22.1
D-homotestosterone, propionate, 0.6 mg.	5	107	107	109.0	37.2	37.5
D-homotestosterone, propionate, 1.2 mg.	5	107	113	47.6	60.5	52.9
Testosterone, $2\alpha,17\alpha$-dimethyl-, 0.6 mg.	5	108	98	181.1	24.5	28.1
Testosterone, $2\alpha,17\alpha$-dimethyl-, 6.0 mg.	5	97	118	24.9	74.6	82.6
Progesterone, 0.6 mg.	10	100	100	229.8	13.4	20.2
Progesterone, 30.0 mg.	10	97	104	87.9	28.9	30.4
Progesterone, Δ^{16}-dehydro-, 0.6 mg.	5	103	92	215.1	13.3	19.9
Progesterone, Δ^{16}-dehydro-, 30.0 mg.	5	103	104	166.5	13.2	25.2

TABLE XI (Continued)

Treatment and total dose/rat	No. of pairs	Body weight ♀ (gm.)	Body weight ♂ (gm.)	Intact female ovarian weight (mg.)	Castrate male Ventral prostate (mg.)	Castrate male Levator ani (mg.)
Progesterone, 21-fluoro-, 0.6 mg.	5	99	94	222.6	13.9	20.0
Progesterone, 21-fluoro-, 30.0 mg.	5	103	104	68.7	17.3	24.0
Testosterone, 11β-hydroxy-, 17-propionate, 0.6 mg.	5	98	101	130.7	29.1	30.4
Testosterone, 11β-hydroxy-, 17-propionate, 3.0 mg.	5	95	103	37.3	68.7	58.0

[a] From Shipley (1960a), unpublished. Data obtained under Contract No. SA-43-ph-2413, Cancer Chemotherapy National Service Center, National Institutes of Health.

G. Use of Mice in Parabiosis

1. Method of Miyake and Minesita (1960)

A recently developed assay method of Miyake and Minesita uses parabiotic mice for the study of pituitary hypersecretion and its inhibition by steroids. They consider the use of mice an advantage in the relative ease and speed of parabiotic union, lower mortality than in rats and in use of nonlitter mates. The method designates use of intact female-castrate male pairs of mice; the castrate male is treated once daily for 10 days with the steroid prepared as a fine crystal suspension. The mice are sacrificed on the day following the last injection. More than 5 pairs of parabionts are used for each dose of steroid; control groups are composed of 9 to 18 pairs of animals. Anti-gonadotropin potency of a steroid is expressed as a percentage of inhibition of ovarian growth of the intact partner calculated according to the formula $100(V - C)/(V - Vi)$, where V equals ovarian weight of the intact partner in control (vehicle injected) pairs; C equals ovarian weight in compound-injected pairs, and Vi equals ovarian weights in noncastrate pairs (vehicle injected). Results obtained from tests of estrogens, androgens, and progestins (see Table XXIII of Chapter 4, this volume) correlate with that from early tests in rats. In general, the estrogens are the most active steroid inhibitors of castration hypersecretion, while androgens and progestins are markedly less active, as a rule. There are some notable exceptions, however, such as 17-

TABLE XII

COMPARISON OF 7- AND 10-DAY TREATMENT OF FEMALE-CASTRATE
FEMALE PARABIONTS[a]

| Treatment (daily dose) | Duration of parabiosis (days) | No. of pairs | Body weight ♀ ♀ (gm.) | | Intact female | | Castrate female |
					Ovarian weight (mg.)	Ovarian response	Uterine weight (mg.)
Controls	7	8	94	95	98.0 (51.6–151.0)	Few to many C.L.[b] 7 of 8	39.4 (25.8–59.6)
Estrone, 0.1 μg.	7	7	98	96	74.4 (33.5–145.3)	Few to many C.L. 5 of 7	49.2 (37.3–63.3)
Estrone, 0.5 μg.	7	7	92	92	29.5 (21.7–40.5)	Few C.L. 1 of 7	133.2 (115.4–162.8)
Estrone, 1.0 μg.	7	8	89	88	28.3 (17.8–37.4)	Follicles 8 of 8	135.9 (97.5–180.6)
Estrone, 5.0 μg.	7	8	93	89	37.0 (24.7–55.3)	Few C.L. 2 of 8	166.5 (148.6–203.4)
Estrone, 10 μg.	7	8	90	92	36.9 (18.8–58.7)	Few C.L. 1 of 8	173.7 (144.6–196.2)
Controls	10	6	102	104	212.8 (180.2–257.0)	Numerous to many C.L. 6 of 6	62.1 (35.2–113.2)
Estrone, 0.1 μg.	10	8	107	102	95.6 (24.4–160.7)	Several to numerous C.L. 7 of 8	53.7 (33.6–78.0)
Estrone, 0.5 μg.	10	8	112	115	72.7 (23.5–119.6)	Few to numerous C.L. 7 of 8	125.7 (100.6–152.4)
Estrone, 1.0 μg.	10	8	109	108	46.5 (27.7–58.4)	Few to several C.L. 6 of 8	175.4 (123.4–266.3)
Estrone, 5 μg.	10	8	104	106	47.7 (27.7–69.0)	Few to several C.L. 5 of 8	174.2 (148.4–195.8)
Estrone, 10 μg.	10	8	107	102	48.5 (26.6–72.7)	Few to several C.L. 6 of 8	201.0 (171.3–231.7)

[a] From Shipley (1960b), unpublished. Data obtained under Contract No. SA-43-ph-2413, Cancer Chemotherapy National Service Center, National Institutes of Health.
[b] C.L. = corpora lutea

TABLE XIII

INHIBITION OF OVARIAN WEIGHTS IN PARABIOTIC RATS (FEMALE-CASTRATE MALE) FOLLOWING 7-DAY TREATMENT WITH TESTOSTERONE[a]

Treatment (daily dose)	Days treated	No. of pairs	Body weight (gm.) ♀	♂	Intact female		Castrate male	
					Ovarian weight	Ovarian response	Ventral prostate	Levator ani
Controls	7	7	95	97	128.6 (100.8–155.6)	Numerous to many C.L.[b] 7 of 7	14.2 (10.1–18.2)	19.1 (15.6–22.0)
Testosterone, 40 μg.	7	7	94	92	74.3 (30.6–125.4)	Numerous to many C.L. 4 of 7	32.8 (18.7–49.2)	23.8 (16.2–29.8)
Testosterone, 80 μg.	7	7	97	99	33.0 (27.8–40.8)	Follicles	52.5 (39.2–65.5)	40.9 (24.5–51.9)
Testosterone, 160 μg.	7	7	95	102	25.2 (15.2–32.0)	Follicles	95.9 (74.8–114.3)	52.1 (44.3–64.6)
Testosterone, 320 μg.	7	7	99	101	35.5 (22.0–56.1)	Few to several C.L. 4 of 7	123.8 (84.6–153.7)	55.9 (40.2–74.0)

[a] From Shipley (1960b), unpublished. Data obtained under Contract No. SA-43-ph-2413, Cancer Chemotherapy National Service Center, National Institutes of Health.

[b] C.L. = corpora lutea.

TABLE XIV

INHIBITION OF OVARIAN WEIGHTS IN PARABIOTIC RATS (FEMALE-CASTRATE MALE) FOLLOWING 10-DAY TREATMENT WITH TESTOSTERONE[a]

Treatment (daily dose)	Days treated	No. of pairs	Body weight (gm.) ♀	♂	Intact female Ovarian weight	Ovarian response	Castrate male Ventral prostate	Levator ani
Controls	10	7	102	102	210.7 (148.9–302.8)	Numerous to many C.L.[b] 7 of 7	12.2 (11.2–14.8)	22.8 (15.2–41.8)
Testosterone, 40 µg.	10	7	106	99	179.2 (20.0–253.6)	Several to many C.L. 6 of 7	21.2 (13.7–29.8)	26.6 (13.3–46.2)
Testosterone, 80 µg.	10	7	104	104	103.2 (59.6–184.0)	Few to numerous C.L. 7 of 7	30.3 (21.0–47.6)	32.6 (17.2–51.6)
Testosterone, 160 µg.	10	7	107	119	53.9 (27.2–118.4)	Few to numerous C.L. 3 of 7	84.1 (58.8–98.0)	74.2 (56.0–85.5)
Testosterone, 320 µg.	10	6	103	117	31.1 (16.4–47.6)	Few to several C.L. 3 of 6	161.5 (138.0–199.5)	85.0 (71.5–91.0)

[a] From Shipley (1960b), unpublished. Data obtained under Contract No. SA-43-ph-2413, Cancer Chemotherapy National Service Center, National Institues of Health.

[b] C.L. = corpora lutea.

ethynyl-5(10)-estrenolone (see Table XXIII of Chapter 4, this volume). The adrenal steroids are weakly active or inactive in mice, as well as in rats (Section III, A, 2, d), in suppression of gonadotropin.

IV. Inhibition of Gonadotropin in Intact Animals by Steroid Treatment

The early work in inhibition of gonadal development by steroids has been well documented, and a complete historical review will not be made to preface the discussion of methods included here.

A. INHIBITION OF GONADAL DEVELOPMENT IN IMMATURE ANIMALS

1. Methods of Biddulph (1939)

In tests reported by Biddulph three end points were used for testing the inhibitory effects of steroids on development of gonads in newborn animals. They are outlined below:

a. Newborn male rats. Gonadal inhibition was observed in newborn male rats given daily injections of 10 μg. testosterone propionate from birth to 31 days; further treatment of the testosterone-propionate-inhibited rats for 15 days or 30 days with unfractionated sheep gonadotropin produced marked increases in testes, prostate, and seminal vesicles while only small increases were obtained in testes and accessory gland weights of rats not receiving the gonadotropin. The latter data were taken as evidence that endogenous gonadotropin production was inhibited by 10 μg. testosterone propionate per day in newborn male rats (Table XV). Treatment with 10 μg. testosterone propionate daily for periods longer than 31 days, with or without an interval between cessation of treatment and autopsy, also produced gonadal and accessory gland inhibition; however the older the animals before autopsy the less the percentage difference in treated and controls; 10 μg. testosterone propionate per day was inadequate to continue inhibition in the older (and larger) rats (Table XVI).

b. Gonadotropin inhibition. Gonadotropin inhibition was again demonstrated in male rats treated with testosterone propionate from birth to 31 days of age, then castrated at 31 days and surgically united in parabiosis with intact females (Table XVII). The rats which received 2 μg. testosterone propionate per day exhibited gonadotropic hypersecretion resulting in enlarged ovaries in the intact female; male rats pretreated with 10 μg. testosterone propionate daily before parabiosis did not pro-

TABLE XV

TESTES AND ACCESSORY WEIGHTS OF MALE RATS TREATED WITH TESTOSTERONE
PROPIONATE AND TESTOSTERONE PROPIONATE PLUS GONADOTROPIC EXTRACT[a]

No. of animals	Treatment[b]	Age at autopsy (days)	Testes weight (mg.)	Seminal vesicle weight (mg.)	Prostate weight (mg.)
2	10 μg. Tp per day from birth until 31 days	46	192	22	26
2	10 μg. Tp per day from birth until 31 days plus 100 mg. SAP per day from 31 to 46 days	46	653	44	126
5	10 μg. Tp per day from birth until 31 days	61	462	18	27
6	10 μg. Tp per day from birth until 31 days plus 100 mg. SAP per day from 31 to 61 days	61	835	104	383

[a] From Biddulph (1939).
[b] Tp = testosterone propionate; SAP = sheep anterior pituitary extract.

duce sufficient gonadotropin to stimulate the ovaries of the intact female. When parabiotic union was maintained to 36 days, stimulation was observed in only one pair out of 11 pairs tested.

c. *Testes descent.* Testes descent was found to be inhibited in newborn male rats treated daily from birth to 31 days with 10 μg. of testosterone propionate. Testes descent occurred at an average of 15.1 days in controls and 24.6 days in the treated animals. (Paradoxically, 2 μg. testosterone propionate per day hastened testes descent: average time 8.2 days.) Testes descent was further delayed until 70 to 75 days of age by periodic increases in the dose level of testosterone propionate.

2. Method of Selye (1940)

Selye treated newborn female rats daily from the day of birth with 1 mg. testosterone propionate in 0.1 cc. peanut oil, administered for 14 days by intraperitoneal injection followed by subcutaneous administration through the thirtieth day of age. Animals killed on the day following the last injection were described as showing marked uterine and ovarian atrophy; other females treated for 30 days were allowed an additional one month before autopsy. At the sixtieth day of age the vaginas were not perforated, the ovaries were poorly developed; the right ovary

TABLE XVI

TESTES AND ACCESSORY WEIGHTS OF MALE RATS INJECTED FROM BIRTH WITH 10 μg.
OF TESTOSTERONE PROPIONATE FOR VARYING PERIODS OF TIME[a]

No. of animals	Treatment	Age at autopsy (days)	Testes weight (mg.)	Mature sperm in testes	Seminal vesicle weight (mg.)	Prostate weight (mg.)
12	10 μg. Tp per day from birth until 31 days	31	71	No	27	73
11	None (controls)	31	784	No	16	68
2	10 μg. Tp per day from birth until 51 days	77	1184	Some sperm heads	75	106
2	None (controls)	77	3140	Yes	459	315
4	10 μg. Tp per day from birth until 51 days	164	1730	Yes	108	102
3	None (controls)	164	3399	Yes	1076	870
2	10 μg. Tp per day from birth until 81 days	81	1349	Yes	119	139
2	None (controls)	81	3045	Yes	693	466
3	10 μg. Tp per day from birth until 81 days	152	1977	Yes	175	221
3	None (controls)	152	3215	Yes	1039	774

[a] From Biddulph (1939).

in each case was described as not visible to the naked eye; the left ovaries averaged 6.6 mg. compared to an average of 35 mg. for control rats of the same age.

3. Method of Greene and Burrill (1940)

A method used by Greene and Burrill tested the recovery of testes after androgen-induced inhibition by treatment of groups of young male rats daily, (a) from the eleventh to the thirtieth day of life, or (b) from the thirty-first to the fiftieth day of life with 0.1 mg. testosterone propionate in 0.05 cc. peanut oil, administered by subcutaneous injection. A number of rats from each treated and each control group were examined at 31 and 51 days, respectively. Table XVIII gives the absolute

TABLE XVII

The Effect of Testosterone Propionate on the Secretion of Gonadotropic Hormone in Parabiotic Rats[a]

			Left partner		Right partner	
No. of pairs	Daily dose (μg.)	No. of days in parabiosis	Mean ovarian weight (mg.)	Pituitary weight (mg.)	Mean testes weight[b] (mg.)	Pituitary weight (mg.)
11	10	13–36[c]	16[d]	4.5	71	4.7
9	2	10	121	5.6	512	5.0
11	None	10	117	4.4	784	4.7

[a] From Biddulph (1939).

[b] Testes weights are weights at the time of castration which is 31 days of age in all cases.

[c] The average time of parabiotic union was 23 days.

[d] The weight of the ovaries of the pair which showed some stimulation was 64 mg., and follicles and corpora lutea were present.

TABLE XVIII

Immature Rats[a]

	No. of animals	Age at autopsy (days)	Body weight (gm.)	Testes weight (gm.)	Percentage inhibition
Group 1					
Treated	9	31	69 (45–86)	0.187 (0.113–0.246)	67.3
Control	9	31	64 (55–75)	0.572 (0.445–0.728)	
Group 2					
Treated	4	51	142.5 (103–172)	0.837 (0.270–1.500)	57.4
Control	4	51	138.2 (104–161)	1.966 (1.163–2.105)	

[a] From Greene and Burrill (1940).

testicular weights and the percentage inhibition of testes weights that were found.

4. Method of Shay, Gershon-Cohen, Paschkis, and Fels (1941)

Shay et al. reported administration of testosterone propionate, 1 mg. three times per week to newborn male rats, from the first day of life until sacrificed at 25 to 196 days of age. Comparison of testis weight was on the basis of mg./100-gm body weight; litter-mate rats were used as controls (Table XIX). The investigators state that on histological examina-

TABLE XIX

RATS TREATED WITH TESTOSTERONE PROPIONATE[a,b]

Litter No.	Total dosage (mg.)	Age at death (days)	Testes weight (mg./100 gm. body weight)		Increase or decrease[c] (%)
			Treated	Control	
231	9	25	290	211	+13
			213	289	−17
			236	268	−8
			258	—	—
266	24	60	260	1218	−79
			279	1350	−79
260	39	90	209	—	—
99[d]	51	86	194	752	−75
168	63	155	323	910	−65
104[d]	66	115	278	755	−64
179	65	150	281	2680	−90
148	82	192	160	650	−76
179	87	196	117	778	−84
			137	—	−82

[a] From Shay et al. (1941).

[b] Given 1 mg. three times per week from the first day of life.

[c] For calculating increase or decrease, the weight of the control testes was taken as unity. In litters with more than one control, the testes weights of the controls have been averaged and the testes of each treated animal calculated individually against the average control testes weight.

[d] These animals were treated with higher doses for some time.

tion (after Zenker-formol fixative, hematoxylin-eosin stain) at the age of 60 and 90 days no sperm heads were visible; after 155 days of treatment sperm heads were seen in some tubules but no mature spermatozoa occurred. In many tubules they observed sloughing of cells and formation of giant cells. The interstitial tissue was reduced in quantity and individual cells were pycnotic. Administration of 5 mg. testosterone propionate six times per week from the first day of life to 30 days increased testicular weight, but produced interstitial cell damage. The increased testis weight is interpreted as a direct effect of the androgen on the testes.

5. Method of Price and Ortiz (1944)

The relation of age to reactivity in the reproductive system of the rat was examined by Price and Ortiz. They included a study of responsiveness of gonads and accessory organs to testosterone propionate and to estradiol benzoate. Injections were made for a period of only 6 days beginning on the day of birth, 4, 8, 12, 20, 30, or 50 days of age; autopsy was on the day following the last injection. In female rats, 6 days of age at autopsy, the ovaries and oviducts were weighed together, and in 6-day-old males the seminal vesicles and coagulating glands were weighed together. Testosterone propionate (0.1 mg. per day) inhibited testes weights and inhibited ovarian weights except in newborn female rats (started on day of birth) and when injections were started at 20 and 30 days of age. Estradiol benzoate inhibited ovaries in females of all ages except 20 and 50 days, and inhibited testes weights in all males tested. The exceptions noted were probably due to an inadequate dose level of estrogen, which is specified as 1 R.U. (rat unit) daily.

6. Method of Leathem and Wolf (1955)

A method utilizing single injections of steroids is used by Leathem and Wolf. The assay was originally designed to use 22-day intact male rats injected subcutaneously with a single dose of the test material (Leathem, 1950) ; 72 hours later the rats were autopsied and testes, ventral prostate, and seminal vesicles were dissected out and weighed.

The 72-hour assay is extended by Leathem and Wolf (1955) to compare the effects of a single dose of 0.25 mg. estradiol benzoate with 0.25 mg. testosterone propionate, and a combination of the two given simultaneously, in immature rats, mice, hamsters, and guinea pigs. Table XX is a summary of data obtained.

All four species show suppression of testis weight in response to estradiol benzoate and to testosterone propionate given singly or in combination. The estrogen was more effective than testosterone propionate in depression of testis weight in all species. Examination of the literature has not revealed use of this method in establishment of a dose-response curve, but the test should lend itself to quantitative measurements.

7. Method of Leathem (1949)

a. Single injection in immature mice. Leathem uses both male and female mice 10 days of age, and administers the steroid in a single subcutaneous injection. Table XXI shows results obtained with testosterone. At 10 and 20 days after the single injection testes weights are suppressed

TABLE XX

INFLUENCE OF SPECIES ON THE MEAN 72-HOUR RESPONSE TO VARIOUS STEROIDS[a,b]

No. of animals	Treatment[c]	Body weight (gm.)	Testis (mg.)	Seminal vesicle (mg.)	Ventral prostate (mg.)
			Rat		
5	None	50	327	8.7	38
5	T.P.	51	273	24.9	23
5	E.B.	48	240	21.6	36
5	T.P. + E.B.	49	273	30.0	26
			Mouse		
13	None	11	76	7.6	—
20	T.P.	12	70	16.8	—
23	E.B.	12	61	8.4	—
7	T.P. + E.B.	13	73	16.0	—
			Hamster		
5	None	44	362	25.5	6.2
6	T.P.	42	216	36.5	9.7
6	E.B.	42	121	23.0	6.0
6	T.P. + E.B.	44	238	38.5	8.9
			Guinea Pig		
6	None	165	478	239	—
5	T.P.	253	340	152	—
6	E.B.	238	284	168	—
4	T.P. + E.B.	228	344	222	—

[a] From Leathem and Wolf (1955).
[b] Given in doses of 0.25 mg.
[c] T.P. = testosterone propionate; E.B. = estradiol benzoate.

in the male mice, and ovaries are suppressed in the female mice. Spermatogenesis is delayed in the male, but recovers by 30 days postinjection. In the female the ovarian weights are normal and the x-zone reappears by 30 days posttreatment.

b. *Treatment of immature mice plus recovery period.* Leathem also treats 24-day-old male mice daily for 16 days, which suppresses the reproductive system; similarly treated mice are studied at 10, 20, and 30 days after the last injection to observe the rate of recovery. Ten days after the end of treatment with stilbestrol testis weight is approximately 50% of normal, and seminal vesicles weight is only about 17% of normal weight (Table XXII). The testes do not contain spermatozoa until 20

TABLE XXI

TESTOSTERONE PROPIONATE (1 MG.) GIVEN IN ONE INJECTION TO 10-DAY-OLD MICE[a]

Treatment	Testis	Seminal vesicles	Ovary	Uterus	Adrenal x-zone	
					♂	♀
T.P. + 10 days	42	21	3.0	14	−	−[b]
Control	65	6	3.4	13	+	+
T.P. + 20 days	99	37	3.6	43	−	−
Control	134	27	4.2	35	−	+
T.P. + 30 days	147	92	6.0	66	−	+
Control	159	100	6.0	74	−	+

[a] From Leathem (1949).
[b] + = present; − = absent.

days after the last stilbestrol injection; 30 days after the last injections testes weights are still below normal values. Disappearance of the adrenal x-zone is correlated to recovery of the gonads in male mice given estrogen.

8. Method of Rubinstein and Kurland (1941)

Rubinstein and Kurland test the effects of varying doses of steroid during 10 days of treatment in rats injected either intraperitoneally or subcutaneously (with sesame oil as diluent) from 22 to 32 days of age. Litter-mate rats are used as controls. Treated and control rats are autopsied the day after cessation of treatment. Ten to sixteen rats are used at each dose level and compared to twenty nontreated control rats. To determine significance, Fisher's method for small series is used to analyze the data. Table XXIII shows results of administration of testosterone in

TABLE XXII

RECOVERY OF 24-DAY-OLD MALE MICE FOLLOWING 0.002-MG. STILBESTROL × 16[a]

Treatment	Number	Testis	Seminal vesicles	Adrenal	x-zone
S + 10 days	7	83	18	7.9	+
Control	6	178	116	5.7	−
S + 20 days[b]	7	144	114	5.0	+, −
Control	7	183	117	4.2	−
S + 30 days	7	180	220	4.5	−
Control	6	200	176	4.0	−

[a] From Leathem (1949).
[b] Five-I.U. PMS daily in recovery period hastens x-zone disappearance.

TABLE XXIII

THE EFFECT OF TESTOSTERONE PROPIONATE GIVEN SUBCUTANEOUSLY IN DOSES OF 5, 10, 20, AND 50 μg. DAILY FOR 10 DAYS (22–32 DAYS OF AGE) TO RESPECTIVE GROUPS OF MALE ALBINO RATS[a]

	Control (wt.)	5-μg. group		10-μg. group		20-μg. group		50-μg. group	
		(wt.)	(% diff.)	(wt.)	(% diff.)	(wt.)	(% diff.)	(wt.)	(% diff.)
Testes (mg.)	563.0	659.0	+17 s[b]	546.0	−3 i	450.0	−20 s	276.0	−51 s
Seminal vesicles (mg.)	22.5	29.0	+29 s	33.5	+49 s	37.0	+64 s	52.0	+131 s
Initial body weight (gm.)	30.9	33.3	+7.8 i	32.1	+3.9 i	29.1	−5.8 i	30.1	−2.6 i
Final body weight (gm.)	70.8	75.3	+6.4 i	73.8	+4.2 i	67.8	−4.2 i	67.8	−4.2 i
No. of animals	20	10		16		10		10	

[a] From Rubinstein and Kurland (1941).

[b] The significance or insignificance of differences is indicated by s or i, respectively.

TABLE XXIV

Intact Males Treated with Estradiol Benzoate[a]

Estradiol benzoate, 45 days (R.U. daily)	Treatment						Pituitary assay				
	No. of rats	Final body weight (gm.)	Testes (mg.)	Seminal vesicles (mg.)	Anterior prostate (mg.)	Pituitary (mg.)	No. of hypoph. rats	No. of Pituitaries per rat	Ovaries (mg.)		Uteri (mg.)
None	19	220	2695	340	197	6.9	5	3	101	Foll.	92
0.02	12	209	2420	294	187	7.5	2	3	47	Foll.	84
0.1	12	231	2810	380	283	8.3	2	3	50.5	Foll.	82.5
1	10	208	2170	178	80	8.3					
2	7	197	1484	150	43	8.6	1	3	38	Foll.	73
2	2	161	543	44	16	7.1					
10	10	163	226	76	7	11.1	2	3	13.6		18.8
Reference controls	10	67.7	583.6	22.7	36.4	3.3					
Recipient controls							7		12.4		17.3

[a] From Greep and Jones (1950).

daily doses of 5, 10, 20, and 50 μg. Doses of 20 and 50 μg. per day produce significantly depressed testicular weights.

9. Method of Greep and Jones (1950)

In the method of Greep and Jones intact female and male rats are treated with graded doses of steroid for 45 days. At autopsy the pituitary glands are collected and assayed in hypophysectomized female rats. All intact rats are a single strain, and are 30 days of age at the start of injections. Injections are made subcutaneously in 0.1 ml. sesame oil.

The gonadotropin content of the rat pituitaries is estimated by injections of suspensions of acetone-dried pituitary glands into female rats hypophysectomized at 24 to 25 days, with injections started 24 hours later. The total dose of acetone-dried pituitary gland is suspended in 3.5 ml. of 0.9% saline and given in seven injections over 3.5 days.

Results of injections of estradiol benzoate and testosterone propionate into male rats and assays for pituitary content are in Tables XXIV and XXV. Both steroids inhibited gonadal development in males at levels which permitted normal rates of weight gain, even though no allowances were made for a dilution effect of steroid as the rats became heavier.

10. Method of Boas and Ludwig (1950)

Comb growth in the cockerel is used by Boas and Ludwig to determine gonadotropic inhibition by estrogenic steroids. One group of chicks, 3 days of age at start of test, receives daily topical applications of the steroid (in 0.02 ml. sesame oil) to the comb. The control group receives only sesame oil (0.02 ml.). Half the animals are sacrificed after 6 days of treatment (ninth day of life) and the remainder after 15 days of treatment (eighteenth day of life). Table XXVI gives results obtained following administration of 75 μg. estradiol per day. The estradiol treatment suppresses testes weights by more than 50% following both periods of treatment; comb weight is markedly inhibited after 15 days of treatment, reflecting the functional suppression of the testes. Testosterone administration, 50 μg. per day, suppresses testis weight while stimulating comb growth; simultaneous treatment with 5, 25, 50, or 100 μg. estradiol does not interfere with the effect of testosterone on the comb. (The validity of the interpretation of inhibition of pituitary gonadotropin was established in two experiments each using four groups of chicks: (a) untreated controls, (b) estrogen treated, (c) estrogen plus gonadotropin treatment, and (d) gonadotropin treatment alone; the chicks were 3 days of age and were treated for 5 days.) Estradiol, when given, was given as 50 μg. per 0.02 ml. per day by topical application. In one experiment 30 I.U. (international unit) of pregnant mare's serum

TABLE XXV

Intact Male Rats Treated with Testosterone Propionate[a]

		Treatment					Pituitary assay				
Testosterone propionate, 45 days (μg. daily)	No. of rats	Final body weight (gm.)	Testes (mg.)	Seminal vesicles (mg.)	Anterior prostate (mg.)	Pituitary (mg.)	No. of hypoph. rats	No. of pituitaries per rat	Ovaries (mg.)		Uteri (mg.)
None	19	220	2695	340	197	6.9	5	3	101	Foll.	92
10	9	229	2510	461	302	6.6	2	3	81	Foll.	104
20	10	256	2678	417	282	8.9	2	3	76	Foll.	113
50	9	226	1220	423	249	7.8	2	3	78	Foll.	130
100	8	197	447	557	376	5.6	2	3	61	Foll.	86
Reference controls:	10	67.7	583.6	22.7	36.4	3.3					

[a] From Greep and Jones (1950).

TABLE XXVI

Comb and Testis Weights of Estrogen-Treated Chicks[a]

	Age (days)	Number of chicks	Dose	Body weight (BW) (gm.)	Comb weight (CW) (mg.)	Testis weight (mg.)	$\dfrac{CW}{BW} \times 100$
C[b]	9	8	0	86 ± 10[c]	35 ± 9	30 ± 10	43 ± 7
E[d]	9	9	75	91 ± 7	28 ± 9	13 ± 4	30 ± 8
C	18	8	0	156 ± 9	345 ± 144	61 ± 20	220 ± 87
E	18	9	75	167 ± 15	74 ± 36	26 ± 5	44 ± 19

[a] From Boas and Ludwig (1950).

[b] C = Control.

[c] S.E. = $\sqrt{\dfrac{\Sigma\Delta^2}{n(n-1)}}$.

[d] E = Estrogen-treated.

(PMS) was given daily by injection, and in another experiment the dosage was 9 I.U. PMS per day by injection. Both dose levels of exogenous gonadotropin (PMS) not only nullified the effects of estradiol on testes and comb weights, but stimulated both testis and comb to an extent equivalent to that obtained when PMS was given alone. (This method for proof of inhibition of endogenous gonadotropin by response to exogenous gonadotropin has been widely used for evidence of inhibition, and is reported here to indicate its usefulness.)

11. Method of Byrnes and Meyer (1951b)

The method of Byrnes and Meyer tests closely graded dose levels of estradiol in intact and ovariectomized immature or adolescent female rats to determine the extent to which physiological doses inhibit FSH and/or LH secretion by the pituitary gland. The immature rats are 30-day-old females (Sprague-Dawley strain) weighing 70 gm.; the 30-day-old females are described as having closed vaginas, average ovarian weights of 26 mg., and average uterine weights of 46 mg. Steroid is administered at eight different dose levels. The steroid is dissolved in corn oil and the quantity of corn oil is 0.1 cc. per day for 10 days. Controls receive corn oil alone. On the eleventh day the rats are killed with illuminating gas, and ovarian and uterine weights are determined. The ovaries are examined for corpora lutea and follicles. At the time the adolescent rats are autopsied the pituitary glands are removed and assayed for gonadotropin content. The fresh pituitaries are pooled from rats receiving a given dose level, homogenized, and suspended in saline.

ELVA G. SHIPLEY

The homogenate is injected subcutaneously twice daily for the 4.5 days into 21-day-old female rats (Holtzman strain). Each recipient rat receives the equivalent of three adolescent pituitary glands. On the sixth day the recipient rats are killed and the ovarian and uterine weights are determined. The ovaries are examined for follicles and corpora lutea. Ovariectomized females, 30 days old, are injected with the steroid at the different dose levels for 10 days to gauge uterine maintenance doses. Control ovariectomized rats receive corn oil alone. Vaginal smears are taken on the eleventh day; the rats are then killed and uterine weights are determined.

Table XXVII and Fig. 6 show the results obtained with immature

TABLE XXVII

INTACT AND OVARIECTOMIZED IMMATURE FEMALE RATS INJECTED
WITH ESTRADIOL DAILY FOR 10 DAYS[a]

Intact females				Ovariectomized females		
No. of rats	Dose (μg./day)	Ovaries (mg.)	Uterus (mg.)	No. of rats	Dose (μg./day)	Uterus (mg.)
8	None	41 (25–50)	185 (101–254)	6	None	52 (43–65)
4	0.002	36 (20–42)	176 (96–242)	6	0.01	55 (45–70)
3	0.005	26 (22–36)	156 (97–188)	8	0.02	65 (50–82)
4	0.0075	23 (21–30)	104 (83–146)	5	0.03	73 (63–80)
4	0.009	19 (12–28)	60 (55–76)	4	0.04	101 (83–114)
5	0.012	21 (18–26)	70 (64–95)	4	0.05	130 (94–151)
9	0.020	30 (22–40)	108 (94–138)			
4	0.030	16 (10–27)	120 (102–162)			
4	0.05	16 (12–30)	168 (123–285)			

[a] From Byrnes and Meyer (1951b).

rats treated with estradiol-17β. In immature rats ovarian weights were inhibited with 0.0075 to 0.012 μg. per day, and by 0.03 to 0.05 μg. per day. At the points of decline the ovaries are markedly less than normal 40-day ovarian weights and less than the 30-day ovarian starting weight.

The dose levels which inhibit gonadal size are inadequate to produce normal uterine growth; thus the doses of estradiol which produce inhibition are considered by the investigators to be well within the physiological limits, and correlated with their findings in parabiotic rats (Byrnes and Meyer, 1951a). Increased ovarian weights in rats given

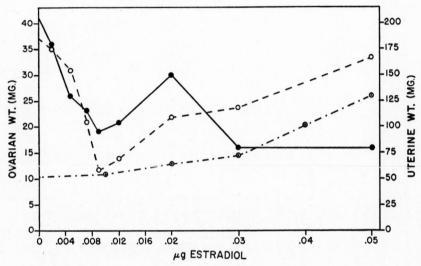

FIG. 6. The effect of estrogen on the ovarian and uterine response in intact and ovariectomized immature rats. ●——● Ovaries, ○——○ uteri of intact rats, ⊙—·—⊙ uteri of ovariectomized rats (from Byrnes and Meyer, 1951b).

0.02 μg. per day are due to increased numbers of corpora lutea. The ovarian weight stimulation in recipient assay rats correlates with the ovarian weights found in the corresponding donor rats, and verifies gonadotropin inhibition by estradiol.

12. Method of Shipley (1954)

Shipley uses four dose levels of steroids, administered subcutaneously once daily for 14 days to intact male rats 21 days of age at the start of the treatment; autopsy is on the fifteenth day. Testes, ventral prostate, seminal vesicles, and levator ani are dissected out and the weights recorded. Table XXVIII shows results of comparison of four androgenic substances, viz., testosterone, 19-nortestosterone, testosterone propionate, and 19-nortestosterone propionate. The 19-nor compounds possess myotrophic activity equivalent to their more androgenic prototype but have lost most of the accessory gland-stimulating activity (Hershberger et al., 1953). The data presented indicate that the 19-nor compounds

TABLE XXVIII

EFFECTS OF TESTOSTERONE, 19-NORTESTOSTERONE, TESTOSTERONE PROPIONATE, AND 19-NORTESTOSTERONE PROPIONATE IN 21-DAY INTACT RATS[a]

Time treated	Treatment	No. of rats	Body weight (gm.)	Ventral prostate (mg. ± S.E.)	Seminal vesicles (mg. ± S.E.)	Levator ani (mg. ± S.E.)	Testes (mg. ± S.E.)
0 time	Intact	11	47	23.5	8.3	10.8	283
14 days	Castrate	9	103	8.6	7.9	23.0	
175 μg. total dose							
14 days 12.5 μg. per day	Control	19	112	52.2 ± 4.57	23.3 ± 1.20	33.9 ± 1.33	1162 ± 18.9
	Testosterone	7	115	64.9 ± 4.84	35.7 ± 3.81	38.7 ± 2.90	1031 ± 52.4
	19-Nortestosterone	7	126	43.1 ± 2.73	17.1 ± 1.66	37.1 ± 3.35	997 ± 47.4
	Testosterone propionate	7	125	78.3 ± 3.47	53.7 ± 4.20	38.9 ± 3.42	676 ± 79.3
	19-Nortestosterone propionate	7	111	11.7 ± 1.20	11.2 ± 1.03	42.2 ± 2.84	427 ± 29.3
350 μg. total dose							
14 days 25 μg. per day	Control	19	112	52.2 ± 4.57	23.3 ± 1.20	33.9 ± 1.33	1162 ± 18.9
	Testosterone	7	118	66.5 ± 5.97	34.8 ± 3.36	33.1 ± 1.30	812 ± 29.2
	19-Nortestosterone	7	107	28.4 ± 3.17	13.6 ± 0.56	41.1 ± 2.72	540 ± 29.8
	Testosterone propionate	7	114	66.2 ± 6.65	48.7 ± 3.65	32.8 ± 1.69	393 ± 43.3
	19-Nortestosterone propionate	7	130	12.1 ± 0.68	11.9 ± 0.69	58.0 ± 2.25	416 ± 18.1
700 μg. total dose							
14 days 50 μg. per day	Control	19	112	52.2 ± 4.57	23.3 ± 1.20	33.9 ± 1.33	1162 ± 18.9
	Testosterone	6	112	50.3 ± 5.46	34.6 ± 3.13	42.3 ± 2.25	543 ± 13.2
	19-Nortestosterone	6	114	20.9 ± 2.54	13.5 ± 0.83	50.3 ± 3.12	669 ± 19.7
	Testosterone propionate	6	112	103.2 ± 5.22	105.1 ± 4.40	59.9 ± 2.68	360 ± 29.2
	19-Nortestosterone propionate	7	104	20.8 ± 2.33	26.7 ± 2.37	70.6 ± 3.48	543 ± 53.1
1400 μg. total dose							
14 days 100 μg. per day	Control	19	112	52.2 ± 4.57	23.3 ± 1.20	33.9 ± 1.13	1162 ± 18.9
	Testosterone	7	119	80.4 ± 5.22	42.0 ± 1.86	39.4 ± 1.19	805 ± 18.7
	19-Nortestosterone	7	124	75.5 ± 2.71	18.0 ± 0.32	62.8 ± 6.91	624 ± 28.7
	Testosterone propionate	7	115	146.6 ± 4.57	144.4 ± 9.84	86.3 ± 3.90	579 ± 24.6
	19-Nortestosterone propionate	7	126	53.2 ± 1.91	67.2 ± 4.08	98.1 ± 4.61	888 ± 12.0

[a] From Shipley (1954).

retain the ability to inhibit gonadotropin secretion, in spite of reduced androgenic potency.

13. Method of Beyler and Potts (1957)

Beyler and Potts use a test procedure based on modification of the rate of growth of testes of immature male rats 35 to 40 gm. body weight (age not specified) to assay gonadal inhibition. The test substance is administered once daily for 5 days. On the third day after the last injection the testes are removed, weighed, and compared with weight of testes from comparable untreated controls as well as weights of organs from control rats at the pretreatment age. The normal development rate is seen by comparing pretreatment and posttreatment controls (Table XXIX); the degree of suppression of gonads of treated

TABLE XXIX

Suppressive Effect of Ethandrostate on the Growth of Testes
of Immature Male Rat[a]

Treatment	Dose (mg./kg./day)	No. of animals	Body weight		Testicular weight (mg., mean ± S.E.)	% suppression of testicular growth[b]	Sex accessory organ weight	
			Initial	Final			Seminal vesicle (mg.)	Ventral prostate (mg.)
Controls								
Pretreatment	—	10	38	—	220 ± 10	—	5.2	18.6
Posttreatment	—	9	42	66	544 ± 22	—	8.5	33.2
Ethandrostate[c]	5.0	5	41	60	470 ± 27	23	6.4	24.5
	7.5	5	37	70	327 ± 55	67	7.0	22.5
	10.0	5	40	62	295 ± 21	77	5.6	24.2
	12.5	5	38	71	277 ± 30	82	6.7	24.1
	20.0	5	40	58	204 ± 49	105	5.4	17.2

[a] From Beyler and Potts (1957).

[b] Calculated on the basis of difference in growth of testes from treated versus untreated rats.

[c] Aqueous suspension.

rats is shown in the testicular weights and the percentage suppression of testicular growth. Repression of ventral prostate and seminal vesicle weights reflects degree of androgenicity of a test material.

14. Method of McGinty and Djerassi (1958)

McGinty and Djerassi find it feasible to use oral administration of various steroids to test inhibition of gonadotropin activity in immature (neither weight nor age given) male rats over periods of 7, 21, and 42 days; they compare testes, ventral prostates, and seminal vesicles with controls of the same age. The data (Table XXX) show the sup-

TABLE XXX

EFFECTS OF 19-NOR-17α-ETHYNYLTESTOSTERONE (NORLUTIN), OF ITS
19-NOR-17α-METHYL, -ETHYL, AND -VINYL ANALOGS, AND OF
17α-METHYLTESTOSTERONE ON SEMINAL VESICLE, VENTRAL PROSTATE,
AND TESTES WEIGHTS OF IMMATURE INTACT RATS[a]

Compound[b]	Days	Seminal vesicles (mg.)	Ventral prostate (mg.)	Testes (mg.)
Controls	7	21	45	684
19-Nor-17α-ethynyltestosterone (Norlutin)	7	25	38	315[c]
19-Nor-17α-methyltestosterone	7	77	78	612
19-Nor-17α-ethyltestosterone	7	26	45	536
19-Nor-17α-vinyltestosterone	7	20	30	315[c]
17α-Methyltestosterone	7	50	73	449
Controls	21	90	99	1954
19-Nor-17α-ethynyltestosterone (Norlutin)	21	23	25	249[c]
19-Nor-17α-methyltestosterone	21	101	94	934
19-Nor-17α-ethyltestosterone	21	35	51	793
19-Nor-17α-vinyltestosterone	21	26	34	587[c]
17α-Methyltestosterone	21	110	112	838
Controls	42	541	234	3428
19-Nor-17α-ethynyltestosterone (Norlutin)	42	46	59	1223
19-Nor-17α-methyltestosterone	42	254	149	1302
19-Nor-17α-ethyltestosterone	42	60	57	1771
19-Nor-17α-vinyltestosterone	42	176	89	2170
17α-Methyltestosterone	42	401	245	1643

[a] From McGinty and Djerassi (1958).
[b] Compounds administered 1.0 mg. daily, orally.
[c] Undescended.

pression of gonadal development by the steroids for each period of treatment. The more marked androgenicity of 17α-methyltestosterone and 19-nor-17α-methyltestosterone are reflected in ventral prostate and seminal vesicle weights which exceed those of the controls for each period of administration.

15. Method of Saunders and Drill (1958)

Graded doses of steroid are tested by Saunders and Drill for gonadotropin inhibition in immature rats, 25 days old at the start of injections, which are continued for 30 days. The results of a test using both male and female rats are summarized in Table XXXI. In the

TABLE XXXI

Effect of Daily Subcutaneous Injections of Norethynodrel on Organ Weights in Rats[a,b]

Norethynodrel daily dose (mg./kg.)	Body weight (gm.)	Testes (mg.)	Seminal vesicles (mg.)	Ventral prostate (mg.)	Ovaries (mg.)	Uterus (mg.)
			Males			
None	178 ± 9.3	2426 ± 100	118.0 ± 14.1	104.3 ± 13.7		
0.02	175 ± 6.4	2481 ± 60	108.9 ± 9.4	94.2 ± 10.4		
0.1	174 ± 8.8	1848 ± 213	80.4 ± 12.9	60.3 ± 9.9		
0.5	141 ± 6.6	273 ± 61	22.0 ± 1.1	11.8 ± 1.1		
			Females			
None	150 ± 7.7				38.5 ± 4.5	160.2 ± 18.9
0.02	146 ± 6.0				32.2 ± 4.6	157.9 ± 21.9
0.1	138 ± 5.4				26.5 ± 3.7	200.9 ± 11.2
0.5	137 ± 4.6				21.4 ± 1.7	198.6 ± 6.1

[a] From Saunders and Drill (1958).
[b] Treatment was continued from the 25th to the 55th day of age.

males the effects are most striking. At the highest dose level testicular suppression was marked; the testes weight was only 11% that of controls (body weight was suppressed by 20%). Ventral prostates and seminal vesicles were also markedly inhibited. In the treated female rats the body weight decrease was not significant; however, the decrease in ovarian weight was progressive with increasing doses and was judged significant at the two higher dose levels. Stimulation of uterine weights reflected estrogenicity of the compound.

B. Gonadal Suppression in Adolescent and Adult Rats

1. Method of Heller, Heller, and Sevringhaus (1942)

Heller, Heller, and Sevringhaus make use of the phenomenon of "compensatory hypertrophy" in unilaterally castrated female rats to test the inhibitory effects of estradiol. They use virgin female rats 6 to 8 months of age, and remove a single ovary, left or right ovary removed in alternating rats. The removed ovaries are weighed to serve as auto-controls. Steroid injections are started immediately and continued for 10 or 20 days. The daily dose of estradiol was 5 μg. in sesame oil. Control animals included: (a) unilaterally ovariectomized females without treatment, (b) normal intact females, and (c) intact females given steroid daily for 10 or 20 days. Figure 7 illustrates the ovarian

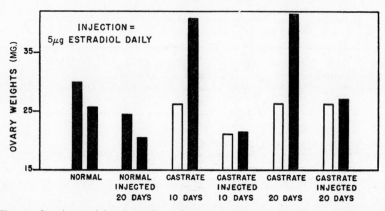

Fig. 7. Ovarian weights in unilateral castrated female rats. Solid columns indicate ovarian weights obtained at autopsy. The open columns indicate weights of the ovaries removed at operation 10 or 20 days before autopsy. In the normals, one bar represents right, and the other, left ovarian weights. From Heller *et al.* (1942).

weights obtained at autopsy and the degree to which estrogen inhibits pituitary gonadotropin hypersecretion ("compensatory hypertrophy") following partial castration.

2. Method of Lerner, Holthaus, and Thompson (1959)

Lerner, Holthaus, and Thompson tested for gonadotropin inhibition by treating intact mature male or female rats with steroids administered for 10 days. Use of testosterone propionate and 19-nortestosterone benzoate produces suppression of testes weights in treated groups. Gonad-inhibiting dose levels of 19-nortestosterone benzoate are nonstimulatory to ventral prostate and seminal vesicles; testosterone propionate produces similar degrees of gonadal suppression but is more androgenic. Dose levels of 3 and 15 mg./kg. per day inhibit ovarian weight in the adult female rat.

3. Method of Beyler and Potts (1957)

Beyler and Potts test for gonadotropin inhibition in young adult male rats weighing 170 to 190 gm. and in reproductively mature females

TABLE XXXII

The Effect of Ethandrostate on the Reproductive System of Intact Male Rats[a]

Treatment	No. of animals	Dose (mg./kg.)	Body weight (gm.)			Organ weights (mean ± S.E.)			
			Initial	Final	Δ	Pituitary (mg.)	Testes (mg.)	Seminal vesicle (mg.)	Ventral prostate (mg.)
Castrate control	10	—	176	223	+47	10.1 ± 0.4	—	42 ± 4	21 ± 0.9
Intact control	10	0	176	250	+74	7.6 ± 0.3	2805 ± 59	223 ± 10	231 ± 21
Ethandrostate (oil solution)	5	2	176	248	+72	7.8 ± 0.3	2780 ± 97	187 ± 23	164 ± 16
	5	8	180	235	+55	8.4 ± 0.3	2370 ± 50	115 ± 6	121 ± 7
	5	16	186	216	+30	10.2 ± 0.3	2510 ± 60	89 ± 20	106 ± 14
	4	20	183	209	+26	10.5 ± 0.5	2260 ± 220	66 ± 8	94 ± 9
Intact controls	6	0	191	256	+65	8.8 ± 0.4	2890 ± 77	190 ± 10	202 ± 27
Ethandrostate (aqueous suspension)	7	2	188	258	+70	8.5 ± 0.3	2870 ± 60	178 ± 10	180 ± 17
	7	4	190	256	+66	9.7 ± 0.3	3040 ± 51	142 ± 11	169 ± 11
	6	8	191	231	+40	9.8 ± 0.3	2570 ± 72	63 ± 7	76 ± 9
	6	16	188	216	+28	10.7 ± 0.6	2580 ± 59	56 ± 10	52 ± 12

[a] From Beyler and Potts (1957).

weighing 180 to 200 gm. The test material is administered once daily
6 days per week for 2 weeks. Untreated intact rats and rats which
were castrated on the first day of the test are used as controls. The
rats are sacrificed within 24 hours after the last injection. The data
in Table XXXII show changes in testicular weights, and repression of
ventral prostate and seminal vesicles in male rats. Doses of 8 and 16
mg./kg. (in aqueous suspension) reduced seminal vesicles and ventral
prostate to near-castration size, suggesting complete inhibition of gonadotropin production. The steroids are also compared on the basis of
relative doses of estrogens required to produce 50–100% castration
atrophy in male rats versus the estrogenic unit of the steroid (Table
XXXIII).

TABLE XXXIII

COMPARISON OF ETHANDROSTATE WITH PHENOLIC ESTROGENS WITH RESPECT TO
NUMBER OF ESTROGENIC UNITS OF EACH REQUIRED TO EFFECT 50 AND 100%
OF CASTRATION ATROPHY OF SEX ACCESSORY ORGANS OF MATURE MALE RAT[a]

	A	B	C	Dose ratio	
Compound	Dose required to effect 50% of castration atrophy (mg./kg./day)	Dose required to effect 100% of castration atrophy (mg./kg./day)	Calculated dose equivalent to one estrogenic unit[b] (mg./kg./day)	A:C	B:C
Estradiol-17β	0.010	0.409	0.0008 ± 0.0003[c]	13:1	512:1
Estradiol-monobenzoate	0.007	0.358	0.001 ± 0.00025	7:1	358:1
Estrone	0.019	0.522	0.009 ± 0.003	2:1	58:1
Diethylstilbestrol dipalmitate	0.148	0.481	0.037 ± 0.013	4:1	13:1
Ethandrostate					
Aqueous suspension	5.4	18.0	9.0 ± 4.5	0.6:1	2:1
Oil solution	6.6	88.0	22.0 ± 7.8	0.3:1	4:1

[a] From Beyler and Potts (1957).
[b] One estrogenic unit equals one uterine growth stimulating ED_{50}.
[c] Approximate $ED_{50} \pm$ S.E.

Ovarian changes in female rats are used to test gonadotropin inhibition in female rats. At autopsy the ovaries, uterus, adrenals, and
pituitary are removed, cleaned, and weighed. Fluid is expressed from
the uteri before weighing. Intact female rats which receive only the
vehicle serve as controls. The data in Table XXXIV show inhibitory

TABLE XXXIV

The Effect of Ethandrostate on the Reproductive System of Intact Mature Female Rats[a]

Treatment	Dose (mg./kg./day)	No. of animals	Body weight (gm.)			Organ weights (mg., mean ± S.E.)			
			Initial	Final	Δ	Ovaries	Uterus	Pituitary	Adrenal
None	—	5	180	198	+18	63.5 ± 3.9	350 ± 34	11.6 ± 0.65	52.7 ± 2.4
Ethandrostate	2	5	184	194	+10	51.1 ± 2.1	382 ± 20	10.2 ± 0.75	53.8 ± 8.4
Ethandrostate	4	5	185	198	+13	42.6 ± 2.3	383 ± 11	11.7 ± 0.80	58.2 ± 2.3
Ethandrostate	8	5	182	186	+ 4	32.3 ± 2.3	486 ± 37	13.2 ± 0.93	52.7 ± 4.3

[a] From Beyler and Potts (1957).

effects of the steroid, ethandrostate, on ovarian weights, and the low potency of its uterotrophic activity.

4. Method of McGinty and Djerassi (1958)

McGinty and Djerassi use essentially the same procedures as Beyler and Potts (Section IV, B, 3) and readily demonstrate the anti-gonadotropic action of a number of steroids by daily oral administration of from 1 to 4 dose levels for a period of 14 days to the intact mature rat. Results from use of oral administration of four steroids are shown in Table XXXV. Reduction in weight of the testes is obtained by all the

TABLE XXXV

Effect of 19-Nor-17α-ethynyltestosterone (Norlutin) and Related Compounds on Seminal Vesicle, Prostate, and Testes Weights of Adult Intact Rats[a]

Daily dose	Compound[b]	Seminal vesicles (mg.)	Ventral prostate (mg.)	Testes (mg.)
	Controls	699	291	3041
0.5 mg.	19-Nor-17α-ethynyltestosterone (Norlutin)	352	195	2960
	19-Nor-17α-ethyltestosterone	393	215	2919
	19-Nor-17α-methyltestosterone	207	198	2467
	17α-Methyltestosterone	660	303	3060
	Controls	922	245	3141
2.0 mg.	19-Nor-17α-ethynyltestosterone (Norlutin)	111	84	2248
	19-Nor-17α-ethyltestosterone	237	133	2688
	19-Nor-17α-methyltestosterone	860	232	2540
	17α-Methyltestosterone	728	269	2512
	Controls	718	254	3243
8.0 mg.	19-Nor-17α-ethynyltestosterone (Norlutin)	126	99	1821
	19-Nor-17α-ethyltestosterone	735	267	3080
	19-Nor-17α-methyltestosterone	1379	468	2885
	17α-Methyltestosterone	1329	585	2738

[a] From McGinty and Djerassi (1958).
[b] Steroids administered once daily, orally, for 14 days.

steroids tested and marked reductions in ventral prostates and seminal vesicles are also seen, except where the steroid is sufficiently androgenic to mask the inhibition by stimulating ventral prostates and seminal vesicles (Tables XXXVI and XXXVII). McGinty and Djerassi point

TABLE XXXVI

EFFECT OF 17α-ETHYNYLESTRADIOL-3-METHYL ETHER AND OF ESTRONE
AND 17α-ETHYNYLESTRADIOL ON SEMINAL VESICLE, PROSTATE,
AND TESTES WEIGHTS OF ADULT INTACT RATS[a]

Dose (μg.)	Compound[b]	Seminal vesicles (mg.)	Ventral prostate (mg.)	Testes (mg.)
	Controls	866	349	3165
200	17α-Ethynylestradiol-3-methyl ether	115	65	1792
20	17α-Ethynylestradiol-3-methyl ether	140	70	2342
12	17α-Ethynylestradiol-3-methyl ether	106	56	2323
6	17α-Ethynylestradiol-3-methyl ether	194	84	2603
100	Estrone	108	68	2157
40	Estrone	113	60	2402
10	Estrone	473	167	2927
10	17α-Ethynylestradiol	71	34	1796

[a] From McGinty and Djerassi (1958).
[b] Steroids administered once daily, orally, for 14 days.

TABLE XXXVII

EFFECT OF 19-NOR-17α-VINYLTESTOSTERONE ON SEMINAL VESICLE, PROSTATE,
AND TESTES WEIGHTS OF ADULT INTACT RATS[a]

Dose (mg.)		Seminal vesicles (mg.)	Ventral prostate (mg.)	Testes (mg.)
	Controls	677	405	3052
0.5	19-Nor-17α-vinyltestosterone[b]	413	181	2946
2.0		118	110	2483
8.0		162	149	2438

[a] From McGinty and Djerassi (1958).
[b] Steroid administered once daily, orally, for 14 days.

out the possibility that the strong anti-gonadotropic potency of 19-nor-17α-ethynyltestosterone may be due to contamination with 17α-ethynyl-estradiol-3-methyl ether.

5. Method of Saunders and Drill (1958)

Saunders and Drill test the gonadotropin-inhibiting effects of steroids by treating young adult male and female rats with subcutaneous in-

TABLE XXXVIII

EFFECTS OF DAILY TREATMENT WITH 0.5 MG. OF NORETHYNODREL PER KILOGRAM FOR 30 DAYS ON ORGAN WEIGHTS AT AUTOPSY[a]

	Body weight (gm.)	Testes (mg.)	Seminal vesicles (mg.)	Ventral prostate (mg.)	Levator ani (mg.)	Pituitary (mg.)	Adrenals (mg.)	Ovaries (mg.)	Uterus (mg.)
Males									
Initial control	251 ± 3.7	2999 ± 63	250.6 ± 8.3	242.8 ± 16.4	166.1 ± 4.3	8.13 ± 0.11	43.5 ± 1.5		
After 30-day treatment									
Control	370 ± 6.9	3381 ± 62	348.0 ± 13.2	432.3 ± 21.2	264.7 ± 10.5	10.72 ± 0.38	54.4 ± 2.2		
Norethynodrel	277 ± 5.1	1337 ± 206	82.9 ± 4.4	53.9 ± 9.4	95.7 ± 6.2	10.54 ± 0.42	70.4 ± 5.4		
After 30-day recovery									
Control	385 ± 10.3	3624 ± 108	425.5 ± 26.2	518.2 ± 31.1	315.1 ± 16.5	11.02 ± 0.26	55.3 ± 1.9		
Norethynodrel	382 ± 4.9	3141 ± 94	345.3 ± 13.6	385.3 ± 32.1	265.6 ± 12.2	11.98 ± 0.28	54.7 ± 2.3		
Females									
Initial Control	210 ± 4.0					9.37 ± 0.27	65.9 ± 4.1	81.0 ± 3.6	356 ± 23
After 30-day treatment									
Control	244 ± 3.6					11.38 ± 0.41	58.9 ± 2.0	67.0 ± 3.2	386 ± 18
Norethynodrel	227 ± 5.9					10.42 ± 0.12	48.3 ± 1.6	29.1 ± 2.3	399 ± 16
After 30-day recovery									
Control	270 ± 3.1					13.09 ± 0.40	67.0 ± 7.5	85.0 ± 5.8	429 ± 22
Norethynodrel	253 ± 5.8					11.48 ± 0.70	59.3 ± 1.7	71.4 ± 3.8	453 ± 44

[a] From Saunders and Drill (1958).

jections for 30 days and compare with rats given similar treatment but allowed a 30-day recovery period. Results of a test are summarized in Table XXXVIII. Norethynodrel inhibits gonadotropin secretion in males, as evidenced by suppression of weight of testes, ventral prostates, and seminal vesicles, but a 30-day posttreatment recovery period produces a marked degree of recovery in testes, ventral prostates, and seminal vesicles. Thirty days of treatment also inhibits ovarian weight in females; but the estrogenicity of the steroid masks inhibitory effects in the uterus. Thirty days posttreatment recovery restores the ovaries to near normal weights.

C. Reduction in Pituitary Content of Gonadotropin

1. Method of Saunders and Drill (1958)

Saunders and Drill use a brief period of treatment to test steroids for suppression of pituitary gonadotropin content. Intact adult male rats are treated daily for 5 days. The pituitaries are removed and homogenized, then injected into recipient immature female rats; one donor pituitary equivalent is given in 6 injections over a 3-day period. The weight of recipient ovaries and uteri are the criteria for inhibition. Table XXXIX contains data from a test and shows the extent of suppression of gonadotropin following 5 days of treatment.

TABLE XXXIX

Effects of Treatment of Immature Female Rats with Extracts of Pituitary Glands of Steroid-Treated Male Rats[a,b]

	Response in recipient	
Treatment of recipient	Ovaries (mg.)	Uterus (mg.)
None	15.8 ± 1.1	34.7 ± 2.1
Pituitary from control rat	84.4 ± 14.6	87.6 ± 11.0
Pituitary from norethynodrel-treated rat	32.6 ± 1.7	104.8 ± 5.5

[a] Donors were treated with 1 mg. of steroid daily for 5 days. Each recipient received a total of 1 pituitary gland over a 3-day period.
[b] From Saunders and Drill (1958).

D. Comparison of Species for Testing Gonadal Suppression by Steroids

1. Tests of Leathem and Wolf (1955)

Leathem and Wolf report the comparative effects of 20 days of injection of estradiol benzoate in several species of test animals. The animals were given varying dose levels of the estrogen: adult rats (0.1 mg.), mice (0.01, 0.025 mg.), hamsters (0.035 mg.), guinea pigs (0.166 mg.), and rabbits (0.25, 2.5 mg.) were the species and dose levels used. Table XL shows control weights of testes of the various

TABLE XL

Testis Weight in Various Species following Estradiol Benzoate for 20 Days[a]

	Control		Treated animals		
Species	No. of animals	Testis weight (mg.)	No. of animals	Daily dose (μg.)	Testis weight (mg.)
Mouse	15	205	11	10	166
			5	25	113
Hamster	10	2897	12	35	676
Rat	15	2832	8	100	848
Guinea pig	6	2766	6	166	1228
Rabbit	6	4398	5	250	3453
			2	2500	1268

[a] Modified from Leathem and Wolf (1955).

species, and gives testes weights of comparable animals following 20 days of estradiol benzoate treatment. Marked gonadal inhibition was obtained in all species after 20 days of estradiol benzoate treatment, confirming the usefulness of the five species for testing gonadal inhibition via steroid inhibition of pituitary gonadotropin.

E. Inhibition of Spermatogenesis

1. Method of Ludwig (1950)

In examining the effects of testosterone propionate on spermatogenesis, Ludwig emphasizes the dual effect of androgens on the testis. The tests are designed to demonstrate the relationship between the size of the dose of the androgen, the depressing effect on pituitary gonadotropin, and the direct stimulating effect of androgens on the testis; histological examination of the testis is used to substantiate depressed or maintained spermatogenesis.

Thirty-day-old male rats are given daily injections for 30 days; the gonads, accessory organs, and various other tissues are removed at autopsy and weighed. Fresh pituitaries are assayed in immature female rats. It is worth noting that the investigator found 1 fresh pituitary

TABLE XLI

DATA CONCERNING AVERAGE TESTIS WEIGHT AND GONADOTROPIC POTENCY OF PITUITARIES OF 30-DAY-OLD RATS INJECTED WITH DAILY DOSES OF TESTOSTERONE PROPIONATE, ESTRADIOL, OR BOTH, FOR 30 DAYS AND OF CONTROLS OF THE SAME AGE[a]

Series[b]	Testis weight			Average weights of uterus and ovaries of immature female rats used in assay of dried pituitaries of 30-day-old[d] male rats (3 pituitaries per female)					Average weights of uterus and ovaries of immature female rats used in assay of fresh pituitaries of 30-day-old[d] male rats (1 pituitary per female)				
	Organ weight (mg.)	% of body weight	% diff. from controls	No. of females	Weight of fresh pituitary (mg.)	Uterus (mg.)	Ovaries (mg.)	% of control potency	No. of females	Weight of fresh pituitary (mg.)	Uterus (mg.)	Ovaries (mg.)	% of control potency
60 Day controls	2409.5	1.183 ± 0.012		6	19.9	80.9	83.6	100	7	7.6	104.5	93.7	100
0.01–0.04 mg. T.P.	1917.2	0.944 ± 0.044	−20.20[c]	2	20.7	84.1	74.8	86.08	3	5.9	126.2	62.3	57.16
0.1 mg. T.P.	876.7	0.417 ± 0.021	−64.75[c]	7	17.8	130.0	51.0	48.42	2	7.7	109.1	47.0	36.29
1.0 mg. T.P.	1659.0	0.878 ± 0.020	−25.78	3	17.3	31.7	22.1	2.69	6	5.0	36.3	25.5	6.96
2.0 mg. T.P.	1897.2	1.006 ± 0.016	−14.96[c]	2	14.7	56.5	23.8	5.38					
3.0 mg. T.P.	1857.8	1.050 ± 0.021	−11.24[c]						6	5.1	36.0	19.1	0
4.2 μg. E.	824.4	0.450 ± 0.053	−61.96[c]										
4.2 μg. E. and 1 mg. T.P.	1763.7	0.914 ± 0.030	−22.74[c]						6	9.3	40.0	18.5	0
8.4 μg. E.	319.9	0.184 ± 0.010	−84.45[c]										
8.4 μg. E. and 1 mg. T.P.	1903.2	0.949 ± 0.035	−19.78[c]						5	5.4	37.2	23.4	4.09
30-Day-old rats	577.2	0.764 ± 0.025											
Uninjected immature female controls:									14		35.1	20.4	0

[a] From Ludwig (1950).
[b] T.P. = testosterone propionate; E. = estradiol.
[c] Statistically significant.
[d] Age at start of treatment.

equivalent to 3 acetone-dried pituitaries in the immature female recipient and, hence, altered the procedure to use fresh or fresh-frozen glands for assay. Table XLI and Fig. 8 illustrate the results obtained with testosterone propionate, estradiol, and a combination of the two steroids. The greatest depression of testis weight is in groups receiving 0.1 mg. testosterone propionate per day, yet gonadotropic potency is further reduced at the higher dose levels. Estradiol is highly effective in gonadal inhibition and in reduction of gonadotropic potency of the pituitary. The 30-day-old rats receiving 0.1 mg. testosterone propionate show de-

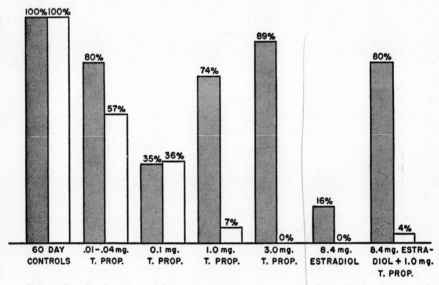

Fig. 8. Graph of testis weight and gonadotropic potency of pituitaries (expressed as per cent of control data) of 30-day-old rats used in the experiment. Shaded column: testis weight, 60-day controls = 100%. Open column: gonadotropic potency of pituitaries, 60-day controls = 100%. From Ludwig (1950).

pression of spermatogenesis; the tubules are small and the most advanced stages of spermatogenesis are secondary spermatocytes and spermatids. Estradiol inhibits spermatogenesis equivalent to 0.1 mg. testosterone propionate per day; the addition of large amounts (1.0 mg. per day) of testosterone propionate to the estradiol treatment prevents the estradiol inhibition of spermatogenesis. Interstitial tissue is markedly reduced by all doses of testosterone propionate from 0.1 mg. and up, and by estradiol; estradiol and testosterone propionate combined have effects similar to the larger doses of testosterone propionate on interstitial tissue.

Implantation of pellets of 15 or 5% testosterone propionate into one testis of rats receiving 0.1 mg. testosterone propionate per day by subcutaneous administration effectively protects the tubules of the implanted testis against decrease in size and decrease in spermatogenesis, whereas the unimplanted testis shows regression from parenteral treatment with 0.1 mg. per day of testosterone propionate, this being the dose level which inhibits gonadotropin secretion without being sufficient to sustain the seminiferous tubules and the spermatogenic process.

2. Method of Van Oordt and Basu (1960)

Van Oordt and Basu utilize *Rana temporaria* as test animals for inhibition of spermatogenesis. Pellets of steroids are implanted into the dorsal lymph sac during the first part of the cycle. Control animals are autopsied at the start and at the end of the tests. The steroid pellets are removed, freed of tissue, dried, and weighed. (The pellet causes a foreign body reaction with connective tissue capsule development— occasionally the skin perforates and the pellet is lost; such animals are discarded.) The testes and seminal vesicles are fixed in Bouin's fluid, sectioned at 7 μ and stained with hemalum-eosin. In some cases diameters of the testis tubules are measured with the aid of an ocular micrometer. The average diameter of 20 tubules (cross section) are taken for each testis measured. Frogs treated with testosterone during the first part of the cycle are without secondary spermatogonia; primary spermatogonia, spermatocytes, and spermatids seemed unaffected.

The investigators point out the effect is like that previously found following hypophysectomy in *Rana temporaria* (Van Oordt, 1956).

V. Reversal of Castration Changes in Pituitary Glands

A. ASSAY OF HORMONE CONTENT OF SERUM

1. Methods of Gans (1959a, b)

Test methods have been devised by Gans to measure the amount of gonadotropin circulating in sera of donor rats, and thereby to evaluate the effects of castration and steroid administration on gonadotropin secretion into the blood stream.

The gonadotropin of sera of gonadectomized rats treated with gonadal hormones is assayed by Gans by the following procedures. Adult castrate rats are used as donors of sera; gonadectomy is performed 3 months prior to collection of serum. Donor rats which are treated with steroids receive treatment for the last 4 weeks of the 3 months castration. Blood is collected by heart puncture; the blood is centrifuged for 10 minutes, the serum is poured off, "and the procedure repeated."

TABLE XLII

Effect of Serum from Hormone-(resp. oil-) Treated Castrated Male Rats on Uterine and Ovarian Weights of Hemispayed Hypophysectomized Rats[a]

Donor Rats Males	Recipients (Females)	Treatment	Student's t	Uterine weight (mg.)	Student's t	Student's t	Ovarian weight increase (mg.)	Student's t	No. of animals
Castrated (oil)	Hemispayed	Serum	5.2	29.5 ± 2.6		4.6	3.9 ± 0.4		30
Castrated (2 μg. estradiol benzoate)	Hemispayed	Saline	4.7	14.8 ± 0.6	3.4		2.2 ± 0.2	2.8	28
	Hemispayed	Serum		19.5 ± 0.8		0.8	2.5 ± 0.3		26
Castrated (oil)	Hemispayed	Serum	7.2	41.8 ± 5.1		2.7	4.3 ± 0.6		19
Castrated (100 μg. testosterone propionate)	Hemispayed	Saline	1.8	16.8 ± 0.5	4.0		2.6 ± 0.4	4.2	21
	Hemispayed	Serum		20.2 ± 1.7		1.7	1.7 ± 0.3		24

NOTE: Each recipient received 20-I.U. chorionic gonadotropin in addition to a daily dose of serum (resp. saline) of 2×1.0 ml. duration of the experiment: 6 days.

[a] From Gans (1959a).

Sera of similarly treated rats are pooled and preserved in the refrigerator. The steroid-treated donor rats receive twice daily injections for 4 weeks.

  a. Steroid suppression of FSH in serum. The assays for FSH content of sera use uterine weight of hemispayed hypophysectomized immature female recipient rats (30 to 35 gm. body weight; age not specified) as the criterion for FSH effects on the ovaries. All recipient hypophysectomized assay animals are given an "overdose" of chorionic gonadotropin. The investigators ascribe any differences in uterine weights of recipients as due to FSH in the donor pituitaries. Any changes in ovarian weights or ovarian histology are used as confirmatory criteria. Spayed hypophysectomized immature female rats are used as controls for the direct stimulatory effects of the serum on uterine growth; the serum is uterotrophic in castrate recipient rats, hence groups of treated castrate hypophysectomized rats are included to gauge the uterotrophic effect, but the factor responsible is not identified. Each recipient assay animal receives twice daily injections of serum for 6 days.

  Preliminary tests (Gans, 1959a) show that the serum of castrated male rats clearly stimulates uterine and ovarian weights of hemispayed recipients in excess of the direct uterotrophic effect of the serum. The administration of 2 μg. estradiol benzoate or 100 μg. testosterone propionate decreases the serum gonadotropin, as assayed in hemispayed hypophysectomized recipients (Table XLII).

  b. Steroid suppression of ICSH in serum. In a modification of the assay Gans (1959b) uses ovariectomized female donor rats, and assays the sera in nongonadectomized hypophysectomized immature male recipient rats (body weight 30 to 35 gm.) to determine interstitial cell-stimulating hormone (ICSH) content of the sera. Injections are of 1 ml. serum twice daily for 6 days. The weights of the ventral prostate, and to a lesser extent the seminal vesicles, are used as criteria for the androgen produced as a result of ICSH administration. The gonadotropin content of the serum is decreased by 2 μg. estradiol, or by 100 μg. testosterone propionate per day (Table XLIII).

B. Assay of Pituitary Content

1. Method of Finerty and Meyer (1950)

  The effect of graded dosages of estrogen upon pituitary cytology and function is tested by Finerty and Meyer using ovariectomized rats. Histological studies and gonadotropin assays are made on pituitary glands of rats ovariectomized at 31 days of age and injected from that day through 40 days of age, with graded amounts of test material. For cytological study the pituitary glands at autopsy are fixed immediately

TABLE XLIII

ICSH in Serum of Spayed Female Rats; Prostate Test[a]

Donor rats (spayed females) Daily treatment during 26–28 days	Daily treatment during 6 days	Recipients						No. of animals
		Testicles (mg.)	Student's t	Ventral prostate (mg.)	Student's t	Seminal vesicles (mg.)	Student's t	
A. 0.2-ml. oil	2 × 1 ml. serum	164 ± 6.1	A-B = 9.7 A-C = 4.7 A-D – 14.0	11.1 ± 0.5	A-B = 7.6 A-C = 4.3 A-D = 10.0	4.8 ± 0.2	A-D = 5.0 C-D = 4.2	28
B. 2 µg. estradiol benzoate in 0.2-ml. oil	2 × 1 ml. serum	92 ± 3.6	B-D = 4.0 C-D = 8.8 B-C = 4.6	5.6 ± 0.2	B-D = 3.4 C-D = 5.4 B-C = 3.3	3.8 ± 0.2		25
C. 100 µg. testesterone propionate in 0.2 ml. oil	2 × 1 ml. serum	123 ± 5.9		7.4 ± 0.5		4.5 ± 0.2		22
D.	2 × 1 ml. saline	76 ± 1.7		4.7 ± 0.2		3.6 ± 0.1		31

[a] From Gans (1959b).

in Zenker-formal, sectioned at 4 μ and stained with a modified azocarmine method described by Briseno-Castrejon and Finerty (1949). The average percentage of each cell type is estimated by differentially counting all the cells in every fifth field of a horizontal section through the middle of each gland.

The pituitary glands of four groups of treated rats are assayed for gonadotropic content. The recipient assay animals are female rats hypophysectomized at 25 days of age; injections of homogenized fresh pituitary gland tissue (total of 15 mg.) are made over 5 days, with

TABLE XLIV

THE EFFECT OF OVARIECTOMY AND ESTROGEN TREATMENT ON CELL TYPES AND GONADOTROPIC CONTENT OF THE PITUITARY GLANDS OF IMMATURE FEMALE RATS[a]

		Pituitary cell type analysis			Pituitary assay data	
Treatment	No. of rats	% Acidphils	% Basophils	% Chromophobes	No. of rats	Ovarian weight (mg.)
Untreated	10	38.9 ± 1.2[a]	6.2 ± 0.2	54.9 ± 1.2	4	13.2 ± 0.4
Ovariectomized (10 days)	10	39.1 ± 0.9	15.9 ± 0.5	45.0 ± 1.1	6	72.9 ± 9.6
Ovariectomized plus 0.025 µg. dienestrol per day for 10 days	10	44.4 ± 1.6	10.1 ± 0.5	45.5 ± 1.7	—	—
Ovariectomized plus 0.10 µg. dienestrol per day for 10 days	12	47.4 ± 1.5	5.2 ± 1.0	47.4 ± 1.2	8	74.8 ± 11.4
Ovariectomized plus 0.50 µg. dienestrol per day for 10 days	9	41.7 ± 2.7	3.1 ± 0.7	55.2 ± 3.2	—	—
Ovariectomized plus 2.0 µg. dienestrol per day for 10 days	10	35.8 ± 2.0	3.1 ± 0.6	61.1 ± 3.2	—	—
Ovariectomized plus 5.0 µg. dienestrol per day for 10 days	5	31.2 ± 1.0	0.9 ± 0.3	67.9 ± 1.0	11	28.6 ± 2.2
Uninjected assay controls					16	9.9 ± 0.4

[a] From Finerty and Meyer (1950).
[b] Standard error.

autopsy on the thirty-first day of life. Results obtained with dienestrol, 0.025 to 5.0 μg. per day, are shown in Table XLIV. The postcastration rise in percentage of basophil cells is inhibited by 0.10 μg. dienestrol per day, with further reductions in basophil cell counts at higher dose levels. Assays of donor pituitaries in hypophysectomized female rats shows that gonadotropic content is not reduced by 0.10 μg. per day, but is reduced in donor rats given 5.0 μg. dienestrol per day.

2. Method of Mortimore, Paulsen, and Heller (1951)

Mortimore, Paulsen, and Heller use castrated adult female rats to examine the effects of steroids on hypophyseal gonadotropin content. The rats are of the Sprague-Dawley strain, and weigh 200 to 260 gm. at the time of ovariectomy. Prior to castration they are shown to have regular estrus cycles, by daily vaginal smear examination. The injections of steroids are given subcutaneously every 12 hours for 16½ days, and are started 24 to 48 hours postcastration. Daily vaginal smears are continued during treatment. At autopsy 24 hours after the last injection, organs are weighed and the anterior pituitary glands are frozen until used for assay. The assay for pituitary content is according to the method of Jungck, Maddock, and Heller (1947) using 24-day-old female rats (Sprague-Dawley strain), and injecting one donor pituitary completely dispersed in 6 cc. of water, into each recipient rat at the rate of 1 cc. twice daily for 3 days. Of the steroids tested pregnenolone, 17α-hydroxyprogesterone, acetoxytestosterone, and 1,4-androstadiene-3,17-dione exhibit some degree of effectiveness in decreasing gonadotropin content of ovariectomized rat pituitaries. These results can be compared to the effects of estrololactone and estrone shown in Table XLV. Estrololactone partially inhibits the castration increase in gonadotropin at 100 and 1000 μg. per day, whereas 10-μg. estrone per day completely prevents the castration increase in potency over the intact control female rat pituitaries.

3. Method of Breneman and Mason (1951)

The influence of androgen on pituitary gonadotropin content of birds is the basis of an assay by Breneman and Mason who use single-comb White Leghorn chicks, caponized at 5 days of age. The chicks are housed in battery brooders; the number of birds in each cage are kept approximately equal, and the position of the birds in the batteries are rotated to eliminate possible differences in lighting or temperature. Subcutaneous injections of steroid in 0.1 ml. of sesame oil daily are begun on the tenth day and continued through the thirty-ninth, with autopsy on the fortieth day. Intact males and control capons receive

TABLE XLV

ESTROGENIC AND PITUITARY ACTIVITY OF ESTRONE AND ESTROLOLACTONE INJECTED INTO ADULT FEMALE CASTRATED RATS[a]

Compound	Daily dose for 16½ days (μg.)[b]	No. of rats	Vaginal cytology	Thymus weight (mg.)	Uterine weight (mg.)	Anterior pituitary weight (mg.)	Vagina open	Uterus weight (mg.)	Ovary weight (mg.)
			Castrated female donor rats				Anterior pituitary recipient rats		
Estrololactone	10	3	Anestrus	665	136	9.4	+	130	88
	100	4	Estrus	544	245	9.8	+	88	74
	1000	4	Estrus	250	442	10.6	+	114	45
Estrone	1	4	Estrus	380	410	11.3	+	97	102
	10	3	Estrus	152	667	14.0	−	75	17
	100	4	Estrus	74	613	13.8	−	48	12
	200	4	Estrus	82	690	14.6	−	41	10
Uninjected castrated controls	0	15	Anestrus	480	147	9.5	+	95	81
Uninjected intact controls	0	4	Cycling	245	398	9.0	+	138	17.3
Uninjected intact recipient controls	—	15	—	—	—	—	—	24	13

[a] From Mortimore et al. (1951).
[b] Each donor rat was injected twice daily.

TABLE XLVI

ANALYSIS OF PITUITARIES[a]

| Donors | | | | Assay | | | Gonad | | Chicks units[b] per pituitary |
Series	No.	Daily treatment	Pituitary average (mg.)	Series	No.	Treatment	Range	Weight average	
A	10	♂ + Sesame oil	6.50	A'	16	4 mg. of A	7.8–21.3	13.25 ± 0.99	6.29
B	9	♂ + 0.5 μg. T.P.[c]	6.80	B'	15	4 mg. of B	7.9–21.2	12.25 ± 1.09	5.71
C	9	♂ + 1.0 μg. T.P.	6.30	C'	14	4 mg. of C	8.7–17.9	12.53 ± 0.81	5.51
D	10	♂ + 5.0 μg. T.P.	5.50	D'	13	4 mg. of D	6.3–18.0	11.47 ± 1.06	4.07
E	10	♂ + 10.0 μg. T.P.	5.10	E'	12	4 mg. of E	7.5–20.7	14.13 ± 1.16	5.49
F	8	♂ + 50.0 μg. T.P.	4.10	F'	8	4 mg. of F	3.7– 7.7	5.14 ± 0.45	—
G	14	♂ + Sesame oil	4.60	G'	15	4 mg. of G	5.4–14.7	10.13 ± 0.75	2.62
H	12	♀ + Sesame oil	4.10	H'	10	4 mg. of H	5.2–14.8	7.84 ± 0.88	1.15
				I	18	Water	3.7– 8.0	5.63 ± 0.29	—

[a] From Breneman and Mason (1951).
[b] A net increase of 35% over the control represents one chick unit.
T.P. = testosterone propionate.

the sesame oil without testosterone propionate. Pullets are not injected. Comb measurements are made on the tenth, twenty-first, twenty-sixth, thirty-first, thirty-fifth, and fortieth days for determination of a comb factor (Height × Length mm./2). At autopsy, combs are carefully dissected by cutting parallel to the head; comb weights are recorded. The comb factor and the weight are measures of androgenic effects. The anterior lobe of the pituitary is removed, and the glands from each series are placed in a moist chamber and weighed as a group. The pituitaries are stored in acetone and at the time of assay are dried, ground in a mortar, taken up in distilled HOH, and injected on the basis of 4 mg. equivalent of fresh gland in 1 cc. of water. For pituitary assay the total dose is given in 5 injections spaced at 12-hour intervals beginning at 18 hours posthatching. The recipient chicks are kept in shipping boxes without food or water during the injection period and are autopsied 12 hours after the final injection. This method of assay, which utilizes testis weight of the chick to estimate the amount of gonadotropins, was suggested by Byerly and Burrows (1938) and previously used by Breneman (1945), at which time the chick unit was established as the amount of gonadotropin required to produce a net increase of 35% over the control recipient comb weight.

The data in Table XLVI show results of administration of 0.5, 1.0, 5.0, 10.0, and 50.0 µg. of testosterone propionate per day. Gonadotropin content of capon pituitaries is inhibited to below that of normal intact cockerels when the daily dose is 50 µg.; 10 µg. or less has little effect on the assayable gonadotropin content. No gonadotropin is found in the pituitaries of capons treated with 50 µg. testosterone propionate per day.

4. Method of Greep and Jones (1950)

Greep and Jones use both male and female rats, castrated at 30 days of age and treat them for 45 days by subcutaneous injection of estrogen or androgen; the diluent is 0.1 ml. sesame oil per injection. The pituitary glands of the donor rats are acetone dried, ground, and suspended in 0.9% saline, so that each recipient hypophysectomized female rat receives the total dose of pituitary in 3.5 ml. saline in 7 injections over 3.5 days. Autopsy is on the morning after the last injection. Pituitaries of both male and female castrated donor rats given either estradiol benzoate or testosterone propionate in adequate doses contain less gonadotropin than postcastration controls; the hormone contents are not readily compared however, since a dose of 3-treated rat pituitaries is compared to the effect of a single pituitary from an untreated castrated rat (Tables XLVII and XLVIII).

TABLE XLVII

CASTRATED MALE RATS TREATED WITH ESTRADIOL BENZOATE OR TESTOSTERONE PROPIONATE[a]

Treatment	No. of rats	Treated group Final body weight (gm.)	Seminal vesicles (mg.)	Ventral prostate (mg.)	Pituitary (mg.)	Pituitary assay No. of hypoph. rats	No. of pituitaries per rat	Ovaries (mg.)	Uteri (mg.)
Estradiol benzoate, 45 days (R.U. daily)									
None	8	201	12.5	7.7	11.2	3	1	158 C.L.[b]	89
0.02	7	208	19.3	7.9	11.9	2	3	96 C.L.	100
0.1	9	219	15.1	6.0	11.8	2	3	106 C.L.	116
0.5	10	203	16.3	7.3	12.3	2	3	89 C.L.	111
1	12	189	22.5	7.2	10.3	2	3	60 C.L., foll.	109
3	9	154	49.5	7.4	6.9	2	3	70 Foll.	95
Recipient controls						7		12.4	17.3
Testosterone propionate, 45 days (µg. daily)									
None	8	201	12.5	7.7	11.2	3	1	158 C.L.	89
10	10	200	165	165	8.6	2	3	97 C.L.	101
50	8	197	357	241	7.6	1	3	71 C.L.	103
100	9	223	382	323	6.8	2	3	81 Foll.	87
Recipient controls						7		12	17

[a] Modified from Greep and Jones (1950).
[b] C.L. = corpora lutea.

TABLE XLVIII

SPAYED RATS TREATED WITH ESTRADIOL BENZOATE OR TESTOSTERONE PROPIONATE[a]

	Treated group				Pituitary assay			
Treatment	No. of rats	Final body weight (gm.)	Uteri (mg.)	Pituitary (mg.)	No. of hypophys-ectomized rats	No. of pituitaries per rat	Ovaries (mg.)	Uteri (mg.)
Estradiol benzoate, 45 days (R.U. daily)								
None	13	173	23	8.7	12	1	70.4 C.L.[b]	92.3
0.2	10	156	74	7.4	2	3	38.8 Foll.	86
1	11	174	173	9.1	1	3	22.5 Foll.	69
5	10	137	197	10.4				
							Recipient controls	
					7		12.4	17
Testosterone propionate, 45 days (μg. daily)								
None	13	173	23.0	8.7	12	1	70.4 C.L.	92.3
10	11	178	23.7	7.8	3	3	119.7 1 Foll. 2 C.L.	83.7
50	13	195	45.2	7.3	3	3	49.1 Foll.	102.0

[a] Modified from Greep and Jones (1950).
[b] C.L. = corpora lutea.

5. Method of Hoogstra and Paesi (1957)

Hoogstra and Paesi assayed the effects of steroids on FSH content of pituitaries of gonadectomized and intact male and female rats (weighing about 200 gm.) by means of an "overdose" of chorionic gonadotropin to all recipient hypophysectomized immature male rats (30–35 gm.). The gonadectomized donor animals are untreated for 2 months, then treated with steroid twice daily for 1 week by subcutaneous injection. At autopsy the hypophyses of each group of rats are pooled, homogenized with an all-glass homogenizer and extracted with saline. The "extracts" are injected twice daily for 1 week in hypophysectomized male rats; the hypophysis and one testis are removed on the day preceding the first day of treatment. All recipients also receive 20 I.U. chorionic gonadotropin daily, with the intention of "overcoming all errors due to differences of ICSH content of the extracts." On the eighth day following hypophysectomy, the rats are autopsied, and the remaining testis is removed and weighed. Increase in weight of the single testis is used as the measure of FSH content of the donor pituitaries. In the data presented estradiol reduces the gonadotropic potency of the pituitaries. (Note: Two points should be made regarding this type of assay: (1) The well-known synergistic effects of FSH and LH may produce variable increases as a result of differing proportions of FSH and LH, even though 20 I.U. of chorionic gonadotropin have been given as an "overdose." (2) One week of steroid treatment is probably inadequate to reverse castration changes of 2 months standing. In addition, it would be helpful in evaluating the results, to have testes weights from hypophysectomized untreated recipient rats, and recipient hypophysectomized rats given only 20 I.U. of chorionic gonadotropin.)

6. Method of Paesi, de Jongh, and Croes-Buth (1959)

Tests of Paesi, de Jongh, and Croes-Buth were designed to determine and to separate the effects of a low dose of testosterone propionate on the FSH and ICSH content of pituitaries of intact and gonadectomized male and female rats. Donor rats receive either solvent (oil), or steroid daily in two subcutaneous injections of 0.1 ml. each. The period of treatment is 4 weeks, but the length of the castration period is not specified. FSH is determined by the testicular weight increase in hemicastrated hypophysectomized male recipient rats receiving an "overdose of ICSH" (chorionic gonadotropin, 20 I.U. per rat). The testis removed at time of hypophysectomy serves as control testis weight. For ICSH measurements the recipient rats are immature hypophysectomized male rats; the final prostate weights serve as criteria for ICSH content.

TABLE XLIX

THE INFLUENCE OF 0.1 MG. TESTOSTERONE PROPIONATE DAILY ON THE ICSH CONTENT OF HYPOPHYSES FROM INTACT AND GONADECTOMIZED, MALE AND FEMALE RATS[a]

| Donors | | | Recipients (hypophysectomized immature males) | | | | | | | |
Kind of animal	Treatment (4 weeks)	No. of hypophyses administered as an extract (total dose)	Number	Initial weight (gm.)	Weight increase (gm.)	Tail length increase (mm.)	Ventral prostate (mg.)	Seminal vesicles (mg.)	Thyroid (mg.)	Adrenal (mg.)
Intact females	Solvent	0.8	15	32.5	13.9 ± 0.98 $\}t = 1.8$	13.8 ± 0.8 $\}t = 2.1$	15.9 ± 1.0 $\}t = 2.8$	6.9	8.9	7.2
	T.P.[b]	0.8	16	33	16.8 ± 1.3	15.7 ± 0.49	11.8 ± 1.1	6.6	7.9	8.3
Intact males	Solvent	0.8	29	33	14.6	14.5	18.2 ± 0.75 $\}t = 2.9$	7.8	7.1	6.5
	T.P.	0.8	28	34	13.8	14.6	14.8 ± 0.78	7.3	7.1	6.4
Spayed females	Solvent	0.2	21	33	7.0 ± 1.04 $\}t = 1.9$	10.8	21.2 ± 0.4	9.1	5.4	6.0
	T.P.	0.2	19	33	10.0 ± 1.27	10.9	20.4 ± 1.6	8.8	5.2	7.4
Castrate males	Solvent	0.2	16	33	15.9 ± 1.0 $\}t = 2.8$	13.7	23.0 ± 1.7	11.1	6.0	7.0
	T.P.	0.2	16	32.5	11.5 ± 1.27	13.7	21.3 ± 1.5	10.4	4.9	6.2
Untreated control recipients			4	33.5	10.0	8.5	4.3	5.3	6.9	8.2

a From Paesi et al. (1959).
b T.P. = testosterone propionate.

TABLE L

THE INFLUENCE OF 0.1 MG. TESTOSTERONE PROPIONATE DAILY ON BODY WEIGHT AND VARIOUS ORGAN WEIGHTS OF INTACT AND GONADECTOMIZED MALE AND FEMALE RATS[a]

Treatment (4 weeks):	Intact females			Spayed females			Intact males			Castrated males		
	Solvent	T.P.[b]	t	Solvent	T.P.	t	Solvent	T.P.	t	Solvent	T.P.	t
Number:	66	66		43	48		48	56		66	63	
Body weight at beginning of treatment (gm.):	222	222		271	274		283	286		258	259	
Weight increase during treatment (gm.):	22.2 ± 2.1	37.6 ± 2.0	4.9	14.4 ± 2.4	18.3 ± 2.2		31.0 ± 3.6	27.0 ± 3.1		64.6 ± 3.6	49.5 ± 3.6	3.0
Ovaries (mg.):	73.0 ± 2.4 (64)	35.5 ± 2.3 (62)	2.4									
Uterus (mg.):	448 ± 19 (64)	216 ± 8.5 (63)		102 ± 6.4 (28)	143 ± 8.4 (30)	3.8						
Testes (gm.):							2.60 ± 0.23 (36)	1.96 ± 0.22 (43)	5.3			
Ventral prostate (mg.):							227 ± 14.7 (40)	260 ± 12.5 (46)	1.72	19 (8)	229 ± 12.3 (8)	
Seminal vesicles (mg.):							439 ± 30	560 ± 21	3.4	68 (8)	567 ± 54 (8)	
Adrenals (mg.):	63.4 ± 1.9 (48)	49.9 ± 1.5 (48)	5.3	53.7 ± 2.3 (28)	45.6 ± 1.7 (30)	2.85	43.2 ± 1.9 (36)	43.4 ± 1.8 (43)		54.3 ± 4.0 (8)	46.9 ± 4.8 (8)	1.2
Thyroid (mg.):	32.4	31.2		33.2 ± 1.5 (28)	31.5 ± 1.8 (29)		39.0 (37)	37.6 (42)		37.5 ± 3.8 (8)	33.8 ± 2.8 (8)	
Anterior lobe of hypophysis (mg.):	10.6 ± 0.23 (49)	8.9 ± 0.23 (63)	5.3	10.8 (42)	10.1 (47)		7.2 ± 0.16 (49)	6.8 ± 0.18 (55)		11.6 ± 0.33 (49)	10.4 ± 0.29 (51)	2.8

[a] From Paesi et al. (1959).
[b] T.P. = testosterone propionate.

The pituitary "extracts" are injected subcutaneously, twice daily for 7 days. At the dosage given testosterone propionate (100 μg. per day) decreased the ICSH content of intact male and intact female pituitaries, but not that of castrate rat pituitaries (Table XLIX). The doses of steroids were probably inadequate to reverse completely postcastration hypersecretion.

Upon examination of the ovarian weights of the intact females and the testes of the intact male rats, it becomes apparent that inhibition of gonadotropin occurs following testosterone propionate treatment; ovarian weights are reduced by more than 50% and testes weights by approximately 25% (Table L). Since testosterone propionate is stimulatory on ventral prostate and seminal vesicles, and uterotrophic in the castrate female, it is not possible to judge the inhibitory effects macroscopically in castrate animals.

VI. Inhibition of Luteinizing Hormone Activity of the Pituitary

The physiological control of FSH and LH secretion from the pituitary gland has been the subject of many investigations; however, specificity of control has not yet been delineated. A few of the varied tests devised to show the inhibitory aspect of steroid action on the luteinizing hormone are reported here. There is insufficient evidence in results obtained from use of these tests to rule out inhibition of FSH as well, but by reason of showing the obvious effects of steroids in prevention of corpora lutea formation or function, we believe it is justifiable to include the assays under the classification of anti-luteinizing tests.

A. ANTI-LUTEINIZATION IN INTACT ANIMALS

1. Method of Astwood and Fevold (1939)

a. *Pseudopregnant rats.* Astwood and Fevold devised assays to determine the inhibitory activity of progesterone against luteinizing hormone by utilizing rats made pseudopregnant by electrical stimulation of the cervix. It had been determined previously that electrical stimulation to the cervix during pseudopregnancy does not prolong pseudopregnancy, and it was postulated that the progesterone produced in the pseudopregnant rat prevented secretion of LH. The investigators use normal adult female rats whose vaginal smears indicate they are cycling regularly. Control rats are normal adult females in which the cervixes are stimulated with a "strong faradic current"; in the test reported, 63 of 65 control females became pseudopregnant as shown by vaginal smears. Ten cycling females were treated for 3 days with 1.5 mg. (total) progesterone followed by electrical stimulation. After electrical stimulation 9 of 10 became pseudopregnant. Administration of 4 mg. progesterone per day for 3 or 4 days followed by electrical stimulation led to pseudopregnancy in only 2 of 11 rats; pseudopregnancy was prevented in 9 of 11 rats.

b. *FSH-primed rats.* As an additional test for the effectiveness of progesterone as inhibitor of luteinizing hormone, Astwood and Fevold administer a purified FSH to immature female rats 21 to 29 days of age at a dose level of 0.25 R.U. per day for periods of 4, 7, or 10 days. The dose level of FSH is sufficient to produce stimulated ovaries in

TABLE LI

INHIBITION OF LUTEINIZATION BY PROGESTERONE[a]

Age at start	Days treated	Daily dose of progesterone (mg.)	No. of rats	Ovary weights (mg.)	Per cent luteinized	
					Partial	Complete[b]
23	4	0.0	4	42.3	25	0
		0.5	2	32.2	0	0
23	7	0.0	4	48.6	75	0
		0.5	2	28.0	0	0
21	7	0.0	6	39.2	17	17
		0.25	6	25.7	0	0
		0.5	5	25.2	0	0
28	7	0.0	4	176.0	100	100
		0.1	5	129.0	80	60
		0.25	5	112.2	100	20
		0.5	5	56.8	20	0
25	10	0.0	3	97.7	67	67
		0.1	5	110.4	100	40
		0.5	5	47.0	60	20
		1.0	3	42.3	0	0
Hypophysectomized						
29	10	0.0	8	79.6	0	0
		0.5	7	78.0	0	0
Normal controls						
		0.0	10	130.0	100	90

[a] From Astwood and Fevold (1939).
[b] Complete luteinization refers to the typical "mulberry" ovaries with many corpora lutea. Each animal received 0.25 R.U. of purified FSH daily in 2 doses.

which corpora lutea are formed via LH from the rat's own pituitary. In rats receiving treatment with progesterone in addition to FSH, the luteinization is partially or completely inhibited as shown in Table LI. No corpora lutea are formed in hypophysectomized females given FSH, supporting the conclusion that progesterone inhibits the release of LH in the nonhypophysectomized rats.

2. Method of Burdick and Emerson (1939)

Burdick and Emerson produce repression and resorption of the corpora lutea of early pregnancy by testosterone propionate. Mated mice are used, and the first subcutaneous injections are given 10 to 14 hours after finding the vaginal plug. Two dose levels of testosterone propionate are used, 5 or 0.25 mg. per day; autopsies are performed 4 to 10 days after mating. Five milligrams testosterone propionate per day cause corpora lutea to become corpora albicans and to hasten their resorption; the corpora are barely discernible after 8 days of injections, and the ovaries are decreased in size.

Similar treatment for 8 days with 0.25 mg. testosterone propionate per day results in small and degenerated corpora lutea, but less regression of ovarian size. Resorption of corpora lutea is not as rapid with 0.25 mg. per day, but the final change is as definite; temporary sterility is established with both treatments. Dose-response curves have not been established but the investigators suggest resorption of corpora lutea in pregnant mice as a means of assay.

3. Method of Junkmann (1957)

Junkmann uses progestins to inhibit the luteinization produced in immature rats by estrogen. For the assay he uses immature female rats weighing 50 to 55 gm. (age not specified) and reports that 8 of 9 female rats given 10 μg. of estradiol valerate in a single subcutaneous injection had an average of 5.8 corpora lutea when autopsied 1 week later. In rats which received 10-mg. progesterone daily in addition to the estrogen, only 1 animal out of 10 developed a single corpus luteum, i.e., 0.1 corpus luteum per animal (Fig. 9). When the dose of progesterone was reduced to 1 mg. per day, 3 of 9 rats produced corpora lutea, an average of 0.9 corpus luteum per animal. When 17α-hydroxyprogesterone caproate was given in a single injection of 10 mg. together with a single injection of estradiol valerate, 1 of 10 rats produced 2 corpora lutea, an average of 0.2 corpus luteum per animal. A dose of 1 mg. of 17α-hydroxyprogesterone caproate was less effective, permitting an average of 3 corpora lutea per rat. The data suggest that the assay might be used as a quantitative measure of anti-luteinizing activity of steroids. Gleason

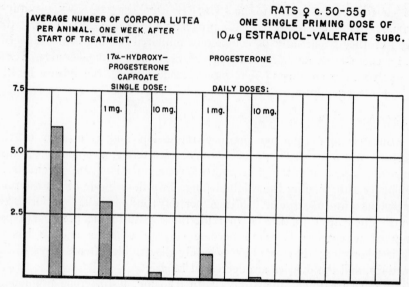

FIG. 9. Formation of corpora lutea in the rat after administration of progesterone or 17α-hydroxyprogesterone caproate. From Junkmann (1957).

and Parker (1959) used the Junkmann technique in examining anti-luteinizing effects of two derivatives of progesterone, purported to have long-acting progestational effects; each of the compounds was given to a group of rats in a single injection equivalent to 10 mg. of progesterone; progesterone was given to other rats once daily; all test animals including controls, received 10 µg. estradiol valerate in a single intramuscu-

TABLE LII

ANTI-LUTEINIZING EFFECT OF PROGESTERONE PREPARATIONS[a]

Treatment	Average number of corpora lutea per animal[b]	
	8 days	14 days
Control	5.4	—
Progesterone[c]	0.2	—
17α-Hydroxyprogesterone-17-heptanoate[d]	2.3	3.0
17α-Hydroxyprogesterone-17-heptanoate-3-benziloyl hydrazone[d]	1.3	4.1

[a] From Gleason and Parker (1959).
[b] Ten animals were used in each group.
[c] One milligram daily injected subcutaneously.
[d] Single subcutaneous injection equivalent to 10 mg. progesterone.

lar injection at the start of the test. The test animals were immature
female rats 50 ± 5 gm. body weight (neither age nor strain of rats
was specified); the results obtained are in Table LII. Progesterone,
daily, and the 17α-hydroxy ester of progesterone or its hydrazone given
in a single injection were all inhibitors of luteinization.

4. Method of Shipley (1960b)

Junkmann's method for anti-luteinizing effects of steroids has been
reinvestigated by Shipley. The first tests were designed to determine the
preferable age and weight of a standard strain of rats for use in estrogen
stimulation of corpora lutea formation. The rats are of the Holtzman
strain; 21-day-old females of that strain weigh 50 to 55 gm., and it
seemed desirable to examine that group since 50- to 55-gm. rats had
been specified for the Junkmann assay. In addition to 21-day-old rats,
Shipley tested 24-, 27-, 30-, 33-, and 35-day-old female rats. The Junkmann procedure was used, injecting 10 μg. estradiol valerate in a single
injection, and progesterone as daily subcutaneous injections in sesame
oil for 7 days, with autopsy on the day following the last injection. The
data are in Table LIII. No corpora lutea were obtained in either group
of rats 21 days of age at the start of the test. In rats receiving only
estradiol valerate at 24 days of age, only 1 corpus luteum was found in
1 of 6 rats; in rats similarly treated, except that progesterone was given
daily, no corpora lutea were found. In rats, of the other age groups,
receiving only estradiol valerate fewer corpora lutea were found than in
control rats receiving no estrogen; progesterone further inhibited corpora
lutea formation in the 27- to 35-day-old females. On the basis of these
data, the 35-day-old female (Holtzman strain) was selected as test animal. An assay with varying dose levels of progesterone and Provera (6α-
methyl-17α-hydroxyprogesterone acetate) is shown in Table LIV. Both
compounds are effective inhibitors of corpora lutea formation under the
conditions of this assay. On the basis of these data it appears that
estrogen in the dose administered cannot be counted on to increase corpora
lutea formation in the strain of rats used. Nevertheless, it can be clearly
shown in 27- to 35-day-old female rats, of the Holtzman strain, that
progestational compounds administered once daily for 7 days inhibit
corpora lutea formation. It is recommended that in testing for anti-
luteinizing effects of steroids, the strain of rat to be used be pretested to
determine the most suitable age and/or weight for use in the assay. If
this is done inhibition of luteinization can be shown in female rats of
suitable age, without the priming administration of estrogen. Estradiol
valerate per se under the conditions described can inhibit luteinization.

TABLE LIII

INHIBITION OF LUTEINIZATION IN OVARIES OF INTACT FEMALE RATS (IMMATURE)
BY ADMINISTRATION OF PROGESTERONE[a]

Age (days) at start	Treatment[b]	No. of rats	Final body weight	No. of rats with C.L.[c]	Total No. of C.L.	Average No. of C.L.
21	Estradiol valerate	6	82	0	0	0
21	Estradiol valerate + progesterone	5	90	0	0	0
24	Estradiol valerate	6	99	1	1	0.17
24	Estradiol valerate + progesterone	5	104	0	0	0
27	Estradiol	6	119	3	21	3.5
27	Estradiol + progesterone	5	118	1	1	0.2
27	Controls (untreated)	10	111	3	22	2.2
27	Progesterone	10	111	0	0	0
27	Estradiol valerate	10	103	2	4	0.4
27	Estradiol valerate + progesterone	10	104	0	0	0
30	Controls	7	120	4	34	4.85
30	Progesterone	8	118	0	0	0
30	Estradiol valerate	7	105	2	2	0.3
30	Estradiol valerate + progesterone	8	113	0	0	0
33	Controls	7	126	6	44	6.3
33	Progesterone	9	128	0	0	0.0
33	Estradiol valerate	7	114	3	5	0.71
33	Estradiol valerate + progesterone	8	118	2	2	0.25
35	Controls	7	130	6	60	8.5
35	Progesterone	9	133	2	24	2.7
35	Estradiol valerate	7	127	7	38	5.4
35	Estradiol valerate + progesterone	8	121	2	3	0.38

[a] From Shipley (1960b).

[b] Estradiol valerate was given in a single intramuscular injection, 10 μg./0.1 ml. sesame oil. Progesterone treatment was 1.0 mg. per day, subcutaneous injection in 0.1 ml. sesame oil.

[c] C.L. = corpora lutea.

TABLE LIV

PROGESTERONE AND PROVERA AS INHIBITORS OF CORPORA LUTEA FORMATION
IN 35-DAY-OLD RATS[a]

| Treatment | Daily dose (mg.) | No. of rats | Body weight (gm.) | | Ovary weight (mg.) | No. of rats with C.L.[b] | Total No. of C.L. | Average No. of C.L. |
			Initial	Final				
Controls		15	95	133	39.4	14	121	8.1
Progesterone	0.125	9	95	130	31.1	6	46	5.1
	0.25	8	94	135	34.7	5	31	3.9
	0.50	8	94	132	31.0	1	11	1.4
	1.00	7	93	131	25.2	1	12	1.7
	2.00	8	93	131	22.1	0	0	0.0
6α-Methyl-	0.025	8	95	132	34.4	5	46	5.8
17α-acetoxy-	0.05	7	94	134	28.8	1	13	1.9
progesterone	0.10	8	92	134	21.7	0	0	0.0
(Provera)	0.20	8	92	129	24.2	0	0	0.0
	0.40	8	94	135	23.0	0	0	0.0

[a] From Shipley (1960b).
[b] C.L. = corpora lutea.

B. REPRESSION OF LUTEINIZATION IN OVARIAN AUTOGRAFTS

1. Method of Mardones, Bruzzone, Iglesias, and Lipschutz (1951)

Mardones, Bruzzone, Iglesias, and Lipschutz (1951), and Mardones, Iglesias, and Lipschutz (1956), use intrasplenic ovarian autografts in castrated guinea pigs to test anti-luteinizing activity of steroids. The test is based on the results of earlier investigations from the same laboratory (Barahona et al., 1950; Iglesias et al., 1950). The test animals are castrate female guinea pigs, with one ovary implanted in the spleen. Two weeks after castration and transplantation of an ovary, a pellet of estradiol is implanted subcutaneously (to permit formation of corpora lutea in the grafted ovary) and a pellet of pure steroid, or of steroid mixed with cholesterol, is implanted subcutaneously to test its efficacy as an inhibitor of luteinization. The absorption of steroid per day is calculated by dividing total loss of weight of the recovered pellet by the number of days implanted, on the assumption of nonselective absorption of the steroid in the mixture. The animals are autopsied 60 days after grafting (45 days after steroid implantation). The spleen is fixed in Bouin's and the section containing the graft is cut with a razor into thin slices. Representative slices are used for microscopical ex-

TABLE LV

EIGHTY-NINE CASTRATED GUINEA PIGS WITH INTRASPLENIC OVARIAN AUTOGRAFTS[a]

Group	Progestational potency[c]	Estradiol per day (μg.)	Progestational steroid per day (μg.)	No. of animals Total (n)	No. of animals With corpora lutea (n₁)	Corpora lutea Average per animal[d] (x)	Corpora lutea Average of largest diameters,[e] (mm.) (y)	Corpora lutea Coefficient of luteinization (xy)	No. of pellets of progestational steroid per animal
O[b]	—	26–28	0	30	27	1.50	1.60	2.40	0
	1		Progesterone						
Ia[b]		25–52	8–15(12)	18	9	1.40	1.06	1.48	½–1, 40%
Ib[b]		31–54	16–23(20)	10	3	0.80	0.91	0.73	½, 40%
Ic		33–74	22–58(40)	8	0	0	0	0	½, 40%
	4–8		19-Norprogesterone						
IIa		41–78	2–4(3)	9	1	0.11	0.45	0.05	½, 20%
IIb		35–89	12–23(19)	9	0	0	0	0	½, 40%
	2–3		Δ¹¹-Dehydroprogesterone						
IIIa		44–73	10–13(11)	9	3	0.44	1.70	0.75	1, 40%
IIIb		26–64	34–74(42)	11	0	0	0	0	3, 40%
	about 1/33–1/10[f]		11-Ketoprogesterone						
IV		47–53	29–55(41)	6	2	0.50	1.23	0.62	1, 40%
	about 1/33–1/12[f]		11β-Hydroxyprogesterone						
V		40–77	33–66(47)	9	1	0.11	1.70	0.19	2, 40%

VI	11α-Hydroxyprogesterone	>1/12[a]	30–73	22–63(43)	19	14	1.40	1.50	2.10	½, 40%
VIIa[b]	Ethynyltestosterone	1/10	34–64	150–208(173)	10	10	1.70	1.21	2.06	8–12, pure
VIIb[b]			21–37	458–967(728)	4	3	0.75	1.69	1.27	20, pure
VIII	11-Ketoprogesterone	about 1/33–1/10	31–80	494–688(560)	8	0	0	0	0	2, 80%

NOTE: Pellets of estradiol, of progesterone, and of five different progesterone derivatives have been implanted subcutaneously; 72 experiments from former work[b] have been added for comparison.

[a] From Mardones et al. (1956).

[b] Taken for comparison from Table 1 in Mardones et al. (1951).

[c] See Tullner and Hertz (1953); Meystre et al. (1948); Ingle et al. (1953); Byrnes et al. (1953).

[d] Sum of corpora lutea of the group divided by n.

[e] Sum of the largest diameters of the group divided by n.

[f] Various tests: (a) Astwood test (formation and maintenance of deciduoma in traumatized uterus of pseudopregnant rat)—less than 8% the activity of P; (b) copulatory reflex in estrogen-primed ovariectomized guinea pigs—about 3% the activity of P; (c) Corner-Allen test with rabbit uterus—4 to 10% the activity of P (Byrnes, 1953).

[g] No reaction in Astwood test with the 12 fold of P (Byrnes et al., 1953).

amination. The number of corpora lutea are counted and the diameter of each corpus luteum is measured; each animal is characterized by its largest corpus luteum diameter. A coefficient of luteinization is determined by multiplying the average number of corpora lutea per animal by the average of the largest diameter per animal. Mardones *et al.* (1951) found progesterone, deoxycorticosterone, and to a lesser extent, ethynyl testosterone and vinyl testosterone, effective inhibitors of luteinization. Mardones and co-workers (1956) extended the series to include a number of progesterone derivatives (Table LV). Progesterone, 19-norprogesterone, and Δ^{11}-dehydroprogesterone inhibit corpora lutea formation at relatively low absorption levels; 11-ketoprogesterone completely inhibits corpora lutea formation but the indicated absorption is much greater than for the other highly inhibitory compounds. Figueroa and Lipschutz (1957) modified the method to the extent that the guinea pigs are autopsied at 2 weeks postimplantation of steroids instead of 45 days as in the earlier method. Using the modified procedure, they confirm the effects of progesterone, DOC, 11β-hydroxyprogesterone, and 11-ketoprogesterone inhibition of corpora lutea in autografts of ovarian tissues in spleen of guinea pigs, and report that 17α-hydroxyprogesterone, compound S, hydrocortisone, and cortisone do not show anti-luteinizing potency.

2. Method of Desclin (1959)

Desclin ovariectomizes female rats at 45 days of age, and makes an autograft of one ovary into the spleen. If the rats are untreated the ovarian graft becomes fully luteinized; daily administration of 1 μg. estradiol benzoate for 1 month permits development of normal appearing follicles, regularly suppressing luteinization. The result is attributed to suppression of elaboration and liberation of luteinizing hormone from the pituitary. The same result is obtained when testosterone propionate is given in doses of 50 to 100 μg. per day. Administration of smaller doses (0.25–0.30 μg.) of estradiol benzoate daily does not inhibit all luteinization; some follicles are present between corpora lutea and are without thecal luteinization; at the lower doses some corpora lutea show vacuolation and the interstitial tissue is suppressed. (Adhesions were noted in only 5 of 35 animals.)

VII. Inhibition of Ovulation

Ovulation is generally regarded as being a product of the functioning of the pituitary gland via elaboration and release of gonadotropic hormones; therefore it is a suitable end point for a test for the inhibition of gonadotropic hormones.

A. Inhibition of Induced Ovulation

The fact that the female rabbit is an induced ovulator has made the animal eminently suitable for studies in inhibition of ovulation. Ovulation and corpora lutea formation occur only after suitable stimulation of coitus.

1. Method of Zondek and Sklow (1941)

The tests of Zondek and Sklow utilize electrical stimulation of the central nervous system (Marshall and Verney, 1936) to induce secretion of gonadotropin in the rabbit with resulting ovulation, formation of corpora lutea, and progestational transformation of the uterine mucosa. In the electrical stimulation method one electrode is introduced into the rectum, the other, a long needle, is placed subcutaneously on the spinal process of the lumbar vertebrae; an alternating current of 30 volts is used. Stimulation for 3 seconds is carried out twice with an interval of 7 seconds; this is repeated 1 hour later. Marshall and Verney obtained corpora lutea in 66% of their rabbits, and Zondek and Sklow report 62.5%. Using the method of electrical stimulation following treatment of rabbits with single or multiple doses of estradiol benzoate, or multiple injections of testosterone propionate, Zondek and Sklow were able to inhibit ovulation and corpora lutea formation as judged by absence of either corpora lutea or progestational mucosa. The minimal dose for estradiol was 0.5 mg. given in a single injection 8 hours prior to electrical stimulation; the minimal dose for testosterone was 10 mg., which was given over 5 days with electrical stimulation on the sixth day.

2. Method of Pincus and Chang (1953)

The effectiveness of progesterone in inhibition of ovulation in the mature rabbit has been reaffirmed by Pincus and Chang, using both subcutaneous and intravaginal routes of administration. In their method the treated female is mated at suitable intervals following treatment. Proof of ovulation is obtained at laparotomy 24 hours after mating by "the presence of corpora lutea in the ovaries." A single subcutaneous injection of 30 mg. of progesterone inhibits ovulation for as long as 24 days. Intravaginal doses of 1 to 30 mg. of progesterone inhibit ovulation when rabbits are bred 24 hours later. 17α-Hydroxyprogesterone (2 mg.) administered intravaginally prevents ovulation; ethynyl testosterone administered orally inhibits ovulation in proportion to dose, over the range of 2 to 10 mg. 17-Methylprogesterone is effective subcutaneously or intravaginally, but is ineffective orally. Neither 11α-hydroxyprogesterone nor a series of compounds which are reduction products of progesterone are effective as inhibitors of ovulation.

3. Method of Pincus, Chang, Zarrow, Hafez, and Merrill (1956)

In a modification of the previous test, Pincus, Chang, Zarrow, Hafez and Merrill utilize post-partum female rabbits which are treated with the test steroid 24 hours prior to mating to a fertile male. Laparotomy is performed 24 hours after mating to determine the presence or absence of ovulation points on the ovary. (The previous report of Pincus and Chang (1953) had shown that 1 to 2 mg. of progesterone will inhibit ovulation in estrous rabbits.) In the data presented in Table LVI the range of dosage and percentage of ovulations show the suitability of

TABLE LVI

The Effects of Certain 19-Nor-steroids on Ovulation
in the Postpartum Rabbit[a,b]

Compound	Dosage	No. of animals	Per cent ovulating
Vehicle	—	62	82 ± 4.88
17α-Ethynyl-19-nortestosterone	0.1	4	50
	0.25	4	0
	0.5	8	0
	2.0	4	0
	10.0	4	0
	5.0 (oral)	4	0
17α-Ethynyl-5(10)estren-17β-ol-3-one	0.1	5	40
	0.2	5	40
	1.0	5	0
	5.0 (oral)	5	20
	10.0 (oral)	5	40
17α-Ethyl-19-nortestosterone	0.2	4	25
	1.0	5	20
	5.0	5	0
	10.0 (oral)	5	40
17α-Methyl-19-nortestosterone	0.1	4	50
	0.5	4	25
	2.0	4	0
	5.0 (oral)	3	33

[a] From Pincus et al. (1956).
[b] All by subcutaneous injection unless otherwise noted.

the method for testing inhibitors of ovulation when given either by subcutaneous or oral administration.

Essentially the same test procedure has been used by Elton and Edgren (1958) in examination of the anti-ovulatory effects of 17α-(2-methallyl)-19-nortestosterone, except they specify use of multiparous rabbits (without the specification of post-partum). Their results are to be seen in Table LVII. One pertinent observation is made by Elton

TABLE LVII

INHIBITION OF COPULATION-INDUCED PITUITARY GONADOTROPIN RELEASE IN MULTIPAROUS RABBITS 24 HOURS FOLLOWING A SINGLE INJECTION OF SC-9022 OR PROGESTERONE[a]

Compound	Dose (mg./rabbit)	No. treated	No. accepting male	No. ovulating after copulation	Per cent failing to ovulate
Oil	—	12	12	12	0
Progesterone	0.5	6	4	2	50
	1.0	9	4	0	100
SC-9022[b]	0.01	6	5	5	0
	0.05	6	5	4	20
	0.1	13	4	1	75
	0.5	13	7	1	86
	1.0	10	2	0	100

[a] From Elton and Edgren (1958).
[b] 17α(2-Methallyl)-19-nortestosterone.

and Edgren (1958) to the effect that both progesterone and 17α-(2 methallyl)-19-nortestosterone decreases the number of females which will accept males. This effect of progesterone and other anti-ovulatory steroids has been observed by other investigators (Shipley, unpublished; Sawyer and Everett, 1959).

4. Method of Sawyer and Everett (1959)

In examining effects of progesterone on ovulation Sawyer and Everett use three methods for inducing ovulation in multiparous rabbits: (a) mating with a buck; (b) glass-rod stimulation of the vagina, or (c) intravenous copper acetate, as 1 ml. of 1% solution buffered with sodium acetate.

Progesterone is administered in oil at a dosage of 2 mg.; estradiol benzoate is used only if indicated to increase receptivity, and is generally given on days 1 and 2, 0.1 mg. per day, followed by progesterone on day 3. The investigators find estrogen priming facilitates mating or artificial stimulation; the rabbit is considered to be in estrus if its vaginal orifice is bright pink. Evidence of ovulation is finding of ruptured follicles 48 hours after attempted stimulation; histologically confirmed luteinization in hemorrhagic or cystic follicles is also accepted as positive evidence of pituitary activation.

Mating or intravenous copper acetate within 4 hours after injection of progesterone stimulates ovulation; however 24 hours after treatment with progesterone, 7 of 21 (33%) estrous (or estrogen-primed) rabbits would not accept the male, and 10 of 14 (73%) failed to ovulate; 10 of 10 (100%) estrogen-progesterone-treated females failed to ovulate after receiving artificial vaginal stimulation under these conditions, and 8 of 17 (47%) estrogen-primed rabbits were not ovulated by copper acetate 24 hours after progesterone treatment. These figures are compared to 7% failure to breed in the control group.

B. Suppression of Ovulation in Spontaneously Ovulating Animals

It is generally less feasible to use rats and mice in anti-ovulation tests than rabbits, because of the desirability to recover ova in these species as proof of ovulation. However, a number of such tests have been devised. Burdick and Whitney (1941) describe visualization of tubal ova in mice and Everett (1947) in rats.

1. Method of Everett (1948)

Everett (1947) kills the rats with illuminating gas, removes the ampullae and mounts them in physiological saline under a cover slip. The thin walls of the ampullae allow identification of granulosa cell masses and ova the first day after ovulation. Everett (1948) has established actual ovulation time in his 4-day cyclic rats as in progress by 1:10 A.M. and completed by 2:30 A.M. the night following proestrus. Histological appearance of new corpora lutea from 5-day cyclic rats at corresponding times led him to conclude ovulation in 5-day cyclic rats occurs at a similar time. Everett (1948) finds that 1 mg. progesterone on the first day of diestrus in 4-day cyclic rats inhibits ovulation for 1 day in 75% of the rats, and 1.5 mg. inhibits 100% of the rats. If progesterone (1.5 mg.) is given on day 1 and on day 2 of diestrus, ovulation is delayed for 2 days (Fig. 10).

2. Method of Austin and Bruce (1956)

In tests designed to determine the effect of continuous estrogen administration in rats and mice, Austin and Bruce administer stilbestrol in drinking water. The stilbestrol is made into a stock solution of

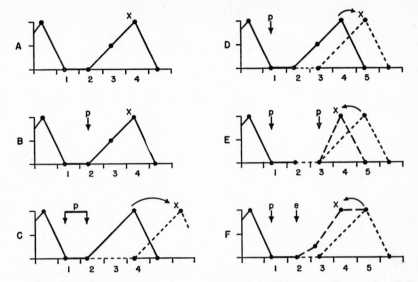

Fig. 10. The 4-day cycle and its experimental modifications. Two units of the ordinate represent a full estrous smear. Time in days is indicated on the abscissa, each unit representing 24 hours (midnight to midnight). Days of the cycle are numbered progressively beginning on the first day of diestrus. Ovulation time is represented by X.

A. The standard 4-day cycle, ovulation occurring 1:00 to 2:30 A.M. early in day 4.

B. Progesterone (p) injected on the second day does not accelerate ovulation and vaginal changes.

C. 1.5 mg. of progesterone (p) on days 1 and 2 of diestrus retards the cycle 2 days.

D. 1.5 mg. of progesterone (p) on day 1 of diestrus retards ovulation and vaginal estrus about 24 hours. This is an "artificial" 5-day cycle, now indicated by the numbering below the abscissa.

E. In such an artificial 5-day cycle, additional progesterone on day 3 of diestrus advances ovulation time and vaginal cornification about 24 hours (contrast with Fig. 10, C).

F. In the artificial 5-day cycle estrogen (e) on the second day of diestrus advances ovulation time 24 hours.

5 µg./ml. and diluted as required for drinking water. (The amounts ingested were estimated to be about 65, 22, 8.5, 2.6, and 1.0 µg. per rat per day; and 5.6, 2.3, 0.8, or 0.08 µg. per mouse per day. The ranges were calculated as 325 to 5 µg./kg. for rats and 224 to 3 µg./kg. for mice.) The test solution is administered for 7 to 14 days prior to cohabitation with males. The males of necessity have access to the estrogen solution; hence the males are replaced at 4- to 5-day intervals to avoid the effects of estrogen. Vaginal smears are obtained once each day. Within 36 hours after finding a vaginal plug or sperm the female is killed;

TABLE LVIII

INCIDENCE OF OVULATION AND SPERMATOZOON ON PENETRATION IN RATS
ON DIFFERENT LEVELS OF STILBESTROL INTAKE[a]

Stilbestrol (μg./rat/day)	No. of rats	Rats with eggs	Total eggs	Mean eggs per ovulation	Penetrated eggs		Eggs with >2 sperm	
					No.	%	No.	%
65.0	9	0	0	0	0	0	0	0
22.0	6	0	0	0	0	0	0	0
8.5	14	2	15	7.5	15	100	5	33
2.6	10	8	74	9.3	74	100	15	20
1.0	7	7	76	10.9	69	91	6	9
None	12	12	137	11.4	125	91	26	21

[a] From Austin and Bruce (1956).

the ovaries are fixed in Bouin's, sectioned, and stained with hematoxylin and eosin, and used as confirmation of presence or absence of ovulation. The eggs are removed from the Fallopian tubes by dissection under normal saline and are examined fresh with the phase microscope. The number of rats or mice with eggs, the total and mean number of eggs ovulated, the number of eggs penetrated by sperm, and the number of eggs with more than 2 sperm are recorded. Tables LVIII and LIX give results obtained by Austin and Bruce in rats and in mice. Graded responses in inhibition of ovulation are obtained in rats at levels above 1 μg. ingested per day, with no ovulations at levels of 22 and 65 μg. per day. There is some reduction in numbers of eggs ovulated in treated rats,

TABLE LIX

INCIDENCE OF OVULATION AND SPERMATOZOON ON PENETRATION IN MICE
ON DIFFERENT LEVELS OF STILBESTROL INTAKE[a]

Stilbestrol (μg./mouse/day)	No. of mice	Mice with eggs	Total eggs	Mean eggs per ovulation	Penetrated eggs		Eggs with >2 sperm	
					No.	%	No.	%
5.6	18	1	3	3	3	100	0	0
2.3	19	3	20	6.7	5	25	0	0
0.8	20	16	142	8.9	122	86	33	27
0.08	16	15	146	9.7	134	92	22	16
None	19	19	185	9.7	139	75	18	13

[a] From Austin and Bruce (1956).

further supporting the inhibitory effect of estrogen on ovulation. In mice a graded response is also obtained, but at the highest dose level administered, 1 of 18 mice ovulated 3 eggs. In the mice ingesting 2.3 μg. per day both the percentage of mice ovulating and the average number of ova per ovulation are slightly higher; 0.8 μg. per day permits 75% ovulation, and 0.08 μg. per day allows 94% ovulation, and the normal number of eggs per ovulation. The results indicate suitability of the method for testing orally active inhibitors of ovulation, if the steroids do not prevent mating.

VIII. Inhibition of Fertility by Steroids

A few methods which have been used to test anti-fertility are presented. It is known that a large number of steroids inhibit gonadotropin, and that a number of the well-known compounds inhibit fertility via suppression of gonadotropins. Methods for testing anti-fertility are presented, however, with the awareness that there are many stages in reproductive physiology at which a substance might interfere with fertility without pituitary involvement. If anti-fertility effects are to be interpreted in terms of inhibition of gonadotropin, some additional evidence such as depressed ovarian development in the female, or regression of testis and/or failure of spermatogenesis in the male seems desirable.

PREVENTION OF MATING

1. Method of Huffman (1941)

Huffman tested anti-reproductive activity of steroids in female rats by daily administration to females caged with known fertile males. No litters were born to any of 19 females during the period of treatment with 2 mg. testosterone per day; estrus also ceased during androgen administration. Following cessation of treatment estrus returned to normal, and after caging with the same males as before healthy litters were born.

2. Method of Wilson and Wilson (1943)

Wilson and Wilson tested the inhibition of reproductive capacity in male rats by treatment with testosterone propionate over a period of 28 days, starting treatment at day of birth, 5, 10, 15, and 20 days of age. The total doses of testosterone propionate were as shown in Table LX. The androgen was administered three times a week for 4 weeks. Untreated controls of comparable ages were raised under identical conditions. When the rats reached ages ranging from 125 to 190 days (4 to 5 months of posttreatment), reproductive capacity was subjected to three tests.

TABLE LX

WEIGHTS OF TESTES, PROSTATE GLANDS, AND SEMINAL VESICLES[a]

Age when treated (days)	Total dose (mg.)	No. of animals	Testes (mean, S.E.) (mg./100 gm. body weight)	Prostate glands (mean, S.E.) (mg./100 gm. body weight)	Seminal vesicles (mean, S.E.) (mg./100 gm. body weight)
1–28	0.75	2	605 ± 50.9	90 ± 19.8	46 ± 2.8
1–28	1.50	2	329 ± 28.3	40 ± 14.9	32 ± 12.0
1–28	36.0	4	472 ± 16.5	67 ± 10.5	36 ± 4.5
5–33	36.0	4	827 ± 66.0	139 ± 20.5	117 ± 15.5
10–38	36.0	4	870 ± 47.5	208 ± 34.5	133 ± 14.0
15–43	36.0	1	805	195	153
20–48	36.0	3	908 ± 15.0	278 ± 27.7	183 ± 12.1
Control		6	847 ± 22.4	311 ± 21.6	183 ± 10.6

[a] From Wilson and Wilson (1943).

a. *Fecundity.* Ten males treated by Wilson and Wilson from day of birth through 28 days, were caged with 2 normal females of proven fertility. Only 1 male sired a litter during the period.

b. *Sexual potency.* Eight males treated by Wilson and Wilson from birth through 28 days, and 11 males from groups treated at older ages were also tested. Each male was housed with 2 or 3 females known to have regular estrous cycles; daily vaginal smears were obtained from the females. When sperm were found in a vaginal smear the male was credited with successful mating and the female was isolated for verification of pregnancy. The occurrence of estrus without sperm was recorded as failure for the male; in this manner each male was given six or more opportunities to inseminate females. The results are presented in Table LXI. Testosterone treatment from birth to 28 days rendered 7 of 8 males sexually impotent, when tested 4 to 5 months later. The later the treatment was initiated the less permanent the inhibition of sexual potency. When testosterone propionate was given from the twentieth to the forty-eighth day of life, the sexual potency 4 to 5 months later approached normal, but the difference in the means was statistically significant.

c. *Libido.* Inhibition of sexual drive was tested in 16 male rats of the treated series and in 8 control rats by direct observation of mounting activity with females in which receptivity was induced by treatment with 25 R.U. of estradiol benzoate, followed 48 hours later by 0.4 mg. progesterone. Male rats were allowed 5 days to become acclimated to individual cages; a receptive female was placed in the cage for 15 minutes and the number of mounts (with pelvic thrusts) was recorded per period;

TABLE LXI

SEXUAL POTENCY OF ANDROGEN-TREATED MALE RATS WITH NORMAL ESTROUS
FEMALES AND LIBIDO WITH RECEPTIVE FEMALES[a]

Animal (No.)	Total dose (mg.)	Sexual potency		Libido	
		No. of estrous periods	No. of inseminations	No. of 15-minute test periods	Mean number of mounts per period
Treated from birth to 28 days of age					
29a	0.75	6	0	11	<1
29b	0.75	6	4	11	8.1
28a	1.5	6	0	11	6.6
28b	1.5	6	0	11	0
1a	36.0	9	0	11	<1
1b	36.0	6	0	13	1.9
2a	36.0	7	0	11	0
2b	36.0	6	0	12	<1
Treated from the 5th to 33rd day of age					
13a	36.0	6	2	11	13.5
13b	36.0	8	0	11	<1
14a	36.0	6	3		
14b	36.0	9	0		
Treated from the 10th to the 38th day of age					
15a	36.0	13	5	11	4
15b	36.0	6	4	11	2.2
16a	36.0	11	3		
16b	36.0	10	0		
Treated from the 15th to the 43rd day of age					
17a	36.0	7	4	11	6.5
Treated from the 20th to the 48th day of age					
18a	36.0	6	5	11	10.5
18b	36.0	6	5	11	5.4
18c	36.0			11	4.4
Control					
1		6	6	5	9
2		6	6	8	19.1
3		7	6	10	11.2
4		8	7	11	14.3
5				11	17.4
6				11	12.9
7				20	16.6
8				22	14.5

[a] From Wilson and Wilson (1943).

5 or 6 different females were used in one evening per male rat; after 1 week the entire test was repeated; thus each male was observed for a total of 11 such 15-minute periods. The average number of mounts per period was calculated and used as an index of libido. The data (Table LXI) show that libido was markedly reduced in all treated males, probably as a result of reduced androgen production, secondary to reduced gonadotropic hormone secretion.

After studying reproductive capacity the males were killed and the testes, ventral prostate, and seminal vesicles were removed and weighed. A smear of ejaculate was collected and examined for motile spermatozoa at time of sacrifice. The majority of treated rats ejaculated semen containing motile sperm, however the ejaculate was scanty and frequently did not coagulate. Treatment from first day of life resulted in decreased testis and accessory organ weights. If treatment was begun at 5 days of age or later testis weight was normal, although accessory weights were decreased with treatment started prior to 20 days of age (Table LXI).

3. Method of Saunders (1958)

Female rats are used by Saunders to test graded doses of steroids as inhibitors of reproductive capacity. Adult females (about 3 months of age) are treated daily for 35 days with subcutaneous injections of steroids in oil; on the fifth day of treatment each 2 females are housed with a normal untreated male. The males are rotated at weekly intervals and cohabitation is maintained throughout the treatment period and for an additional 5 months, or until the females become gravid. Estrone, progesterone, and testosterone propionate are used as standard steroids. An additional eight steroids were tested in comparison with the standards. Table LXII shows the percentage of fertile matings which occurred during the 5 months following cessation of treatment. Estrone and 3-(6-methoxy-2-naphthyl)2,2-dimethylpentanoic acid proved to be the most potent inhibitors of fertility on the basis of 100% inhibition of fertile matings during the period of treatment. Estrone (0.1 mg. per day) and norethynodrel (5.0 mg. per day) produced the highest percentages of nonfertile matings during the recovery periods (Table LXII). The method offers the advantage of measuring both the acute effects and the prolonged aftereffects on reproductive capacity, with the disadvantage of being an extremely long-term experiment if carried 5 months beyond the expiration of treatment.

4. Method of Pincus, Chang, Zarrow, Hafez, and Merrill (1956)

a. Single injection or short period of treatment. Pincus, Chang, Zarrow, Hafez, and Merrill express the opinion that the significant indicator

TABLE LXII

EFFECT OF VARIOUS STEROIDS ON FERTILE MATINGS[a]

Compound	Daily dose (mg./kg.)	No. of rats	First fertile matings (%)				Not fertile (%)
			During treatment	Days after treatment			
				1–30	31–60	61–150	
Oil	—	100	91	9	—	—	—
Estrone	0.005	10	60	20	10	10	—
	0.01	7	0	71	0	29	—
	0.02	10	0	90	10	—	—
	0.05	10	0	80	10	—	10
	0.1	17	0	35	6	12	47
Testosterone propionate	0.1	9	78	22	—	—	—
	0.2	10	10	80	10	—	—
	0.5	9	0	67	22	—	11
	1.0	8	0	63	37	—	—
Progesterone	0.2	10	70	30	—	—	—
	1.0	10	60	40	—	—	—
	2.0	10	20	70	—	10	—
	5.0	10	0	0	40	40	20
3-(6-Methoxy-2-naphthyl)2,2-dimethylpentanoic acid (Vallestril)	0.005	10	30	40	30	—	—
	0.01	8	0	100	—	—	—
	0.02	7	0	56	44	—	—
	0.05	4	0	50	25	25	—
	0.1	9	0	33	44	—	22
17α-Ethynyl-17-hydroxy-5(10)-estren-3-one (norethynodrel)	0.1	10	80	20	—	—	—
	0.2	10	0	90	—	—	10
	0.5	20	0	100	—	—	—
	5.0	10	0	0	30	20	50
17α-Ethyl-19-nortestosterone (Nilevar)	0.005	10	70	30	—	—	—
	0.1	20	50	45	5	—	—
	0.2	19	42	37	11	—	—
	1.0	10	0	80	10	—	10
	5.0	8	0	50	25	13	12
Diethylaminoethyl-O-methyl-podocarpate (SC-4956)	1.0	10	60	30	10	—	—
	5.0	11	64	36	—	—	—
17α-Methyl-4,5-dihydro-19-nortestosterone (SC-6583)	5.0	10	0	70	20	10	—

TABLE LXII (Continued)

Compound	Daily dose (mg./kg.)	No. of rats	First fertile matings (%)				
			During treatment	Days after treatment			Not fertile (%)
				1–30	31–60	61–150	
16α-Methylestriol-	0.1	10	100	—	—	—	—
3-methyl ether	0.2	20	95	5	—	—	—
(SC-6924)	0.5	20	70	10	5	15	—
	1.0	8	25	63	12	—	—
	10.0	5	0	80	—	20	—
17α-(1-Methallyl)-	0.2	10	90	10	—	—	—
19-nortestosterone	0.5	10	40	60	—	—	—
(SC-8117)	1.0	9	11	89	—	—	—
	2.0	9	0	89	—	11	—
17α-(2-Methallyl)-	0.1	10	90	10	—	—	—
19-nortestosterone	0.2	10	90	10	—	—	—
(SC-9022)	0.5	10	20	70	10	—	—
	1.0	10	0	90	10	—	—

NOTE: Period in which first fertile mating occurred in female rats treated daily for 5 days before and 30 days after placing with males.

[a] From Saunders (1958).

of anti-fertility effect is the latent period between cohabitation with males and the mating which results in pregnancy. The steroids are administered to mature breeding female rats which are placed with fertile males at the time of initial (or only) administration. Table LXIII shows the effects of a number of steroids administered in various dose levels, and under various dosage regimes, on delay in pregnancy, numbers of corpora lutea, numbers of normal embryos, per cent of ova which fail to implant, and the percentage of fetal degeneration. Examination of the data from use of 17α-ethynyl 19-nortestosterone and of 17α-ethynyl-5(10)estren-17β-ol-3-one indicates the method is suitable for quantitative measurement of inhibitors of fertility.

b. Prolonged treatment. Pincus, Chang, Zarrow, Hafez, and Merrill also test the effects of prolonged oral administration of a steroid on fertility; adult female rats are treated every other day for 70 days; the dose is administered by stomach tube. At 18 days of treatment the rats are divided into two groups; one group is housed with males at 18 days and the other group is housed with males at 39 days, while treatment continues for 70 days. Cohabitation continues until pregnancy occurs. Control females (given oil solvent) were similarly caged with males at

TABLE LXIII

The Effects of 19-Nor-steroids on Mating and Pregnancy in the Rat[a]

Compound	Dosage regime	Dose (mg.)	No. of rats	Days between cohabitation and successful mating	Average No. of corpora lutea	Average No. of normal embryos	Per cent ova failing to implant	Fetal degeneration (% total embryos)
Control	—	—	50	4.7 ± 0.57	12.2 ± 0.41	9.4 ± 0.37	9.0	6.9
I 17α-Ethynyl-19-nortestosterone	S.I.[b]	10	11	38.3 ± 3.12[e]	13.6 ± 1.19	8.6 ± 0.94	10.0	29.7
	S.F.[c]	10	12	9.3 ± 1.48[e]	13.4 ± 0.87	11.6 ± 1.22	11.7	2.8
	S.F.	25	11	16.3 ± 1.96[e]	12.7 ± 0.73	11.1 ± 0.96	10.1	2.4
	F2X2[d]	5	11	17.5 ± 1.50[e]	14.4 ± 1.11	12.1[f] ± 0.68	13.9	2.2
II 17α-Ethynyl-5(10)estren-17β-ol-3-one	S.I.	1	12	13.7 ± 1.43[e]	15.6[f] ± 1.21	11.8 ± 0.97	15.5	10.8
	S.I.	2	12	21.8 ± 2.04[e]	14.0 ± 0.78	11.3 ± 0.51	8.3	12.3
	S.I.	5	12	17.8 ± 1.67[e]	11.7 ± 0.66	10.3 ± 0.65	3.6	8.9
	S.F.	2	10	10.4 ± 3.39	14.7[f] ± 0.80	12.2 ± 1.30	15.6	1.6
	S.F.	5	12	16.5 ± 2.66[e]	13.1 ± 0.77	9.6 ± 0.95	12.1	16.7
	F2X2	2	12	16.3 ± 1.16[e]	12.7 ± 0.54	10.3 ± 1.17	8.6	11.5
III 17α-Ethyl-19-nortestosterone	F2X2	1	10	9.2 ± 2.61	12.8 ± 0.49	11.6 ± 0.65	6.5	3.5
		5	10	9.5 ± 1.96[e]	11.6 ± 1.09	10.3 ± 1.09	11.0	2.6

[a] From Pincus et al. (1956).
[b] S.I. = single subcutaneous injection.
[c] S.F. = single feeding.
[d] F2X2 = feeding twice a week for 2 weeks.
[e] Values differ significantly from the control.
[f] Significantly higher than control value.

18 days and 39 days after treatment was initiated. Records were kept of individual times of conception; the difference in the total period of cohabitation and days of treatment during cohabitation of treated rats is considered the length of sterility due to treatment (Table LXIV). Vaginal

TABLE LXIV

THE EFFECTS OF THE ORAL ADMINISTRATION OF 17-ETHYNYLESTRENEOLONE UPON THE REPRODUCTIVE BEHAVIOR OF ADULT FEMALE RATS[a]

Type of animal	No.	Total dosage (mg.)	Caged with males after	Latent period to conception (days)	Sterile period following medication (days)
Control	4	—	18 days	28 ± 1.63	—
Experimental	4	70	18 days	78 ± 0.91	26
Control	5	—	39 days	7.4 ± 0.71	—
Experimental	4	70	39 days	59.5 ± 4.85	28.5

NOTE: Each experimental animal received 2 mg. in oil by stomach tube every other day, each control animal received an equal amount of the oil solvent every other day.

[a] From Pincus *et al.* (1956).

smears are taken daily; mating may take place at various times without pregnancy resulting from the early matings.

REFERENCES

Astwood, E. B., and Fevold, H. L. (1939). *Am. J. Physiol.* **127**, 192.

Austin, C. R., and Bruce, H. M. (1956). *J. Clin. Endocrinol. and Metabolism* **13**, 276.

Barahona, M., Bruzzone, S., and Lipschutz, A. (1950). *Endocrinology* **46**, 407.

Beyler, A. L., and Potts, G. O. (1957). *Endocrinology* **60**, 519.

Biddulph, C. (1939). *Anat. Record* **73**, 447.

Biddulph, C., and Meyer, R. K. (1946). *Proc. Soc. Exptl. Biol. Med.* **63**, 92.

Biddulph, C., Meyer, R. K., and Gumbreck, L. G. (1940). *Endocrinology* **26**, 280.

Biddulph, C., Meyer, R. K., and Gumbreck, L. G. (1941). *J. Exptl. Zool.* **88**, 17.

Boas, N. F., and Ludwig, A. W. (1950). *Endocrinology* **46**, 299.

Breneman, W. R. (1945). *Endocrinology* **36**, 190.

Breneman, W. R., and Mason, R. C. (1951). *Endocrinology* **48**, 752.

Briseno-Castrejon, B., and Finerty, J. C. (1949). *Stain Technol.* **24**, 103.

Bunster, E., and Meyer, R. K. (1933). *Anat. Record* **57**, 339.

Burdick, H. O., and Emerson, B. B. (1939). *Endocrinology* **25**, 913.

Burdick, H. O., and Whitney, R. (1941). *Am. J. Physiol.* **132**, 405.

Byerly, T. C., and Burrows, W. H. (1938). *Endocrinology* **22**, 366.

Byrnes, W. W. (1953). Private communication.

Byrnes, W. W., and Meyer, R. K. (1951a). *Endocrinology* **48**, 133.

Byrnes, W. W., and Meyer, R. K. (1951b). *Endocrinology* **49**, 449.

Byrnes, W. W., and Shipley, E. G. (1950). *Proc. Soc. Exptl. Biol. Med.* **74**, 308.

Byrnes, W. W., Meyer, R. K., and Finerty, J. C. (1951). *Am. J. Physiol.* **164**, 26.

Byrnes, W. W., Stafford, R. O., and Olson, K. J. (1953). *Proc. Soc. Exptl. Biol. Med.* **82**, 243.

Desclin, L. (1959). *Ann. endocrinol. (Paris)* **20**, 222.

Elton, R. L., and Edgren, R. A. (1958). *Endocrinology* **63**, 464.

Epstein, J. A., Kupperman, H. S., and Cutler, A. (1958). *Ann. N.Y. Acad. Sci.* **71**, 560.

Everett, J. W. (1947). *Endocrinology* **41**, 364.

Everett, J. W. (1948). *Endocrinology* **43**, 389.

Figueroa, S., and Lipschutz, A. (1957). *Endocrinology* **61**, 657.

Finerty, J. C. (1952). *Physiol. Revs.* **32**, 277.

Finerty, J. C., and Meyer, R. K. (1950). *Endocrinology* **46**, 494.

Fischer, R. (1960). Personal communication.

Gans, E. (1959a). *Acta Endocrinol.* **32**, 362.

Gans, E. (1959b). *Acta Endocrinol.* **32**, 373.

Gleason, C. H., and Parker, J. M. (1959). *Endocrinology* **65**, 508.

Greene, R. R., and Burrill, M. W. (1940). *Endocrinology* **26**, 516.

Greep, R. O., and Jones, I. C. (1950). *Recent Progr. in Hormone Research* **5**, 197.

Heller, C. G., Heller, E. J., and Sevringhaus, E. L. (1942). *Endocrinology* **30**, 309.

Hershberger, L. G., Shipley, E. G., and Meyer, R. K. (1953). *Proc. Soc. Exptl. Biol. Med.* **83**, 175.

Hertz, R., and Meyer, R. K. (1937). *Endocrinology* **21**, 756.

Hill, R. T. (1932). *J. Exptl. Zool.* **63**, 203.

Hill, R. T. (1933). *Endocrinology* **17**, 414.

Hoogstra, M. J., and Paesi, F. J. A. (1957). *Acta Endocrinol.* **24**, 353.

Huffman, J. (1941). *Endocrinology* **29**, 77.

Iglesias, R., Lipschutz, A., and Rojas, G. (1950). *Endocrinology* **46**, 414.

Ingle, D. J., Beary, D. F., and Purmalis, A. (1953). *Endocrinology* **53**, 221.

Jungck, E. C., Maddock, W. O., and Heller, C. G. (1947). *J. Clin. Endocrinol. and Metabolism* **7**, 1.

Junkmann, K. (1957). *Recent Progr. in Hormone Research* **13**, 389.

Kallas, H. (1930). *Klin. Wochschr.* **9**, 1345.

Leathem, J. H. (1949). *Trans. N.Y. Acad. Sci. Ser. II*, **11**, 239.

Leathem, J. H. (1950). *Trans. N.Y. Acad. Sci. Ser. II*, **12**, 234.

Leathem, J. H., and Wolf, R. C. (1955). *Mem. Soc. Endocrinol. No. 4*, 220.

Lerner, L. J., Holthaus, F. J., Jr., and Thompson, C. R. (1959). *Endocrinology* **64**, 1010.

Ludwig, D. J. (1950). *Endocrinology* **46**, 453.

McGinty, D. A., and Djerassi, C. (1958). *Ann. N.Y. Acad. Sci.* **71**, 500.

Mardones, E., Bruzzone, S., Iglesias, R., and Lipschutz, A. (1951). *Endocrinology* **49**, 817.

Mardones, E., Iglesias, R., and Lipschutz, A. (1956). *Endocrinology* **58**, 212.

Marshall, F. H. A., and Verney, E. D. (1936). *J. Physiol.* **86**, 327.

Martins, R., and Rocha, A. (1931a). *Compt. rend. soc. biol.* **106**, 510.

Martins, R., and Rocha, A. (1931b). *Endocrinology* **15**, 421.

Meyer, R. K., and Biddulph, C. (1941). *Am. J. Physiol.* **134**, 141.

Meyer, R. K., and Hertz, R. (1937). *Am. J. Physiol.* **120**, 232.

Meyer, R. K., Biddulph, C., and Finerty, J. C. (1946). *Endocrinology* **39**, 23.

Meystre, C., Tschopp, E., and Wettstein, A. (1948). *Helv. Chim. Acta* **31**, 1463.

Miyake, T., and Minesita, T. (1960). *Advance Abstr. 1st Intern. Congr. Endocrinol., Copenhagen.*

Mortimore, G. E., Paulsen, C. A., and Heller, C. G. (1951). *Endocrinology* **48**, 143.

Paesi, F. J. A., de Jongh, S. E., and Croes-Buth, S. (1959). *Acta Endocrinol.* **30**, 259.

Pincus, G., and Chang, M. C. (1953). *Acta Physiol. Latinoam.* **3**, 177.

Pincus, G., Chang, M. C., Zarrow, M. X., Hafez, E. S. E., and Merrill, A. (1956). *Endocrinology* **59**, 695.

Price, D., and Ortiz, E. (1944). *Endocrinology* **34**, 215.

Rubinstein, H. S., and Kurland, A. A. (1941). *Endocrinology* **28**, 495.

Saunders, F. J. (1958). *Endocrinology* **63**, 561.

Saunders, F. J., and Drill, V. A. (1958). *Ann. N.Y. Acad. Sci.* **71**, 516.

Sawyer, C., and Everett, J. W. (1959). *Endocrinology* **65**, 644.

Selye, H. (1940). *Endocrinology* **27**, 657.

Shay, H., Gershon-Cohen, J., Paschkis, K. E., and Fels, S. S. (1941). *Endocrinology* **28**, 485.

Shipley, E. G. (1954). Unpublished data.

Shipley, E. G. (1960a). Unpublished data.

Shipley, E. G. (1960b). Unpublished data.

Shipley, E. G., and Meyer, R. K. (1956). Unpublished data.

Shipley, E. G., Meyer, R. K., and Biddulph, C. (1943). *Am. J. Physiol.* **140**, 230.

Tullner, W. W., and Hertz, R. (1953). *Endocrinology* **52**, 195.

van Oordt, P. G. W. J. (1956). Thesis. University of Utrecht, Utrecht, The Netherlands.

van Oordt, P. G. W. J., and Basu, S. L. (1960). *Acta Endocrinol.* **33**, 103.

Wilson, J. G., and Wilson, H. C. (1943). *Endocrinology* **33**, 353.

Witschi, E., and Levine, W. T. (1934). *Proc. Soc. Exptl. Biol. Med.* **32**, 101.

Zondek, B., and Sklow, J. (1941). *Endocrinology* **28**, 923.

Chapter 6

Androgens and Anabolic Agents

RALPH I. DORFMAN

I. Introduction

Androgens by definition are substances which possess characteristic biological activity affecting the secondary sex characters of various male animals. Traditionally, androgens have been assayed by the comb response in the fowl and on the seminal vesicles and prostate of the rodent. It is the purpose of this section to deal with the techniques employed, their sensitivity, and their reproducibility.

Within the past few years there has been increased interest in the nitrogen-retaining activity of androgens and related steroids as therapeutic agents in certain debilitating diseases. The original demonstration that steroids can produce this effect in the castrated dog is credited to Kochakian (1937) and Kochakian and Murlin (1935, 1936), and Kenyon *et al.* (1938, 1944) first observed this relationship in humans. The effect of various steroids on nitrogen retention in various species has been reviewed (Dorfman and Shipley, 1956). Eisenberg and Gordan (1950) suggested that the ability of a steroid to retain nitrogen was correlated with its ability to stimulate the levator ani muscle. The property of steroids to cause nitrogen retention and to stimulate the levator ani muscle, also called the anabolic action, is not necessarily correlated with the action of the compound on the mammalian androgen indicators, the seminal vesicle and prostate. Methods for the evaluation of this anabolic action are included in this chapter.

II. Surgical Procedures

Since the methods to be described are concerned primarily with capons and castrated rats, the surgical procedures are given below.

A. Caponizing

White or Brown Leghorn cockerels are usually employed because of their relatively high sensitivity to androgens and because they are usually readily available. The cockerels are operated upon at approximately 6 weeks of age, but with care the operation can be conveniently done as early as 1 to 2 weeks of age. The 6-week-old animals are fasted for 24 hours before surgery, while 1- to 2-week-old cockerels need be fasted for only 6 to 8 hours.

After fasting, the animals are anesthetized with ether and placed on their sides. The incision is made between the last 2 ribs, the muscle layer divided, and the incision pulled apart with small retractors. The testis is found close to the mid-line of the posterior abdominal wall, alongside the vena cava. The capsule enclosing the testis is cut and the gonad removed. It is imperative to remove the testis intact as fragments left behind usually are vascularized and persist, giving rise to incompletely caponized animals. The incision is closed by sewing. The second testis is removed in a similar fashion on the other side.

Even if great care is taken to remove the testis, some animals will show comb growth subsequent to operation. These animals, called slips, are not suitable for assay purposes and must be discarded.

B. Castration in the Rat

Under ether anesthesia, an incision is made in the tip of the scrotum large enough to permit the removal of the testis. A single ligature is placed around the internal spermatic vessels, the deferential vessels, and the ductus deferns. The testis and epididymis are removed. The incision is closed by a suture or by means of a wound clip (Griffith and Farris, 1942).

III. Bird Methods

A. CAPON COMB GROWTH

Most workers using the capon comb test have employed the White or Brown Leghorn capon. The English game bantam has been found to be a relatively reactive breed, but the heavier breeds are reported to be less reactive. The Plymouth Rock capon has been shown to be one-fifth as sensitive as the Brown Leghorn (Callow and Parkes, 1935). The relative sensitivity of various breeds will be discussed further under comments on the use of the chick's comb for androgen assay.

1. Injection

a. Method of Gallagher and Koch (1935). The method consists in determining the growth of the capon's comb after 5 daily intramuscular injections of the unknown and in comparing the comb response with that found for a standard preparation of crystalline material under the same experimental conditions.

The bioassay method may be employed in 1 of 2 different ways. The first consists essentially in using the original design of Gallagher and Koch (1935). In working with most urines the preferred standard is androsterone, since the greater part of the activity in human urines is due to this androgen. An exception to this is the urine from subjects with adrenal cortical tumors, where dehydroisoandrosterone makes up the bulk of the active androgens. In the original work of Gallagher and Koch (1935), the standard was a highly purified bull testis preparation, and a "characteristic curve" was determined. Testosterone or other suitable androgen could be used.

Another design consists in running two concentrations of unknown in parallel with two concentrations of the standard, according to the design of Bliss (1944). This method is illustrated in Section III A, p. 285.

At the beginning of an assay the sum of the length plus height $(L + H)$ of each individual comb is determined by measurement with a millimeter rule placed directly on the comb. It is often of value to record the exact barble used for the determination of the height. The capons are injected intramuscularly, daily, for 5 consecutive days. The daily dose is contained in 1 ml. of olive or corn oil. Twenty-four hours after the last injection the combs are remeasured and the growth of the comb expressed as the sum $(L + H)$ in millimeters. If the first method is used, the mean $L + H$ increment of 8 capons is referred to the standard curve and the unitage in international units (I.U.) or milligrams of the reference substance read directly from the dose-response curve. If the second method is used, the relative potency of unknown and standard is calculated according to the method of Bliss (1944). Factors which must be considered are as follows.

(1) The initial comb size is of importance; for every millimeter difference in the initial length (from 57 mm.) of the comb, a correction of 0.17 mm. of comb growth may be used.

(2) The body weight of capons has only an insignificant effect on growth of comb.

(3) The unknown and standard should be run under identical light conditions.

(4) Before a capon is used again for an assay, it is usually necessary to wait about one month to allow sufficient time for regression of the comb.

Gallagher and Koch (1935) found a mean error of 22.6% when the unknown was run in parallel with a standard, and groups of 16 to 25 capons were used for both the unknown and the standard.

b. *Method of Greenwood* et al. (*1935*). Greenwood *et al.* (1935) have employed the Brown Leghorn capon for the assay of androgens in a manner similar to that of Gallagher and Koch (1935). At the beginning of the experiment the length and height of the combs are measured with a millimeter rule. The hormone, in 0.2 ml. of oil, is injected once daily into the pectoral muscle. At the end of 3 or 5 days, depending on the individual experiment, the combs are remeasured and the response is determined as the difference in length and height of the comb between the pre- and post-injection measurements.

TABLE I

THE RESPONSE OF THE CAPON'S COMB TO ANDROSTERONE[a]

Type test (days)	Total dose (mg.)	No. of capons	Comb growth $L + H$ (mm. $\pm$ S.E.)[a,b]
3	0.3	5	0.6 ± 0.59
	0.6	5	1.8 ± 0.20
	1.2	5	5.4 ± 0.75
	2.4	5	7.8 ± 1.15
	4.8	5	9.8 ± 0.73
5	0.5	5	2.8 ± 1.34
	1.0	5	6.2 ± 0.85
	2.0	5	10.6 ± 1.03
	4.0	5	15.4 ± 1.11
	8.0	5	17.4 ± 0.80

[a] Data of Greenwood *et al.* (1935).
[b] S.E. is the standard error of the mean.

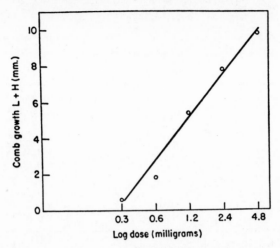

FIG. 1. Capon's comb response to androsterone injected daily for 3 days (Greenwood *et al.*, 1935).

Table I and Figs. 1 and 2 illustrate the comb response after the 3- and 5-day injection periods, respectively. When the data of Greenwood *et al.* (1935) are plotted as the logarithm of the dose versus response, a linear function was realized for both the 3- and 5-day tests. This being the case, the slopes were calculated and the index of precision (λ) determined. For the 3-day test the slope (b) was 8.09 and λ was equal to 0.189, while for the 5-day test $b = 12.72$, and $\lambda = 0.180$.

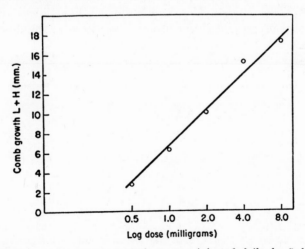

FIG. 2. Capon's comb response to androsterone injected daily for 5 days (Greenwood *et al.*, 1935).

TABLE II

THE RESPONSE OF THE CAPON'S COMB TO ANDROSTERONE
BY INJECTION[a]

(Three Injections)

Total dose (I.U.)	No. of capons	Mean comb growth $L + H$ (mm. $\pm$ S.E.)
0.75	10	1.70 $\pm$ 0.23
1.50	10	2.75 $\pm$ 0.23
3.00	8	3.25 $\pm$ 0.43
4.50	9	4.11 $\pm$ 0.41
6.00	9	5.11 $\pm$ 0.33
7.50	10	6.05 $\pm$ 0.57
9.00	9	7.33 $\pm$ 0.46

[a] Data of Emmens (1939).

c. *Method of Emmens* (*1939*). Emmens (1939) has studied the capon's comb growth response to androsterone in the Brown Leghorn. The method is similar to that of Gallagher and Koch (1935). Brown Leghorn cockerels are caponized at 6 weeks of age and used at 6 to 9 months of age. The hormone is administered daily in 0.1 ml. of oil for 5 consecutive days. Comb measurements are done before treatment and 24 hours after the last injection by the method already described (see Section III A, p. 277).

Tables II and III present the data of Emmens (1939) concerning the response of the comb to androsterone after 3 and 5 days of injections, respectively. The data at 3 or 5 days do not fit a linear relationship when the response is plotted against the logarithm of the dose (Fig. 3),

TABLE III

THE RESPONSE OF THE CAPON'S COMB TO ANDROSTERONE
BY INJECTION[a]

(Five Injections)

Total dose (I.U.)	No. of capons	Mean comb growth $L + H$ (mm. $\pm$ S.E.)
1.25	10	3.15 $\pm$ 0.32
2.50	10	4.50 $\pm$ 0.36
5.00	8	5.81 $\pm$ 0.43
7.50	9	7.77 $\pm$ 0.63
10.00	9	9.44 $\pm$ 0.47

[a] Data of Emmens (1939).

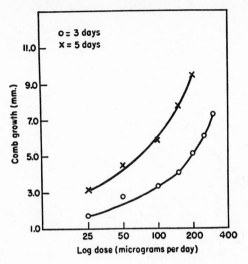

FIG. 3. Capon's comb response to androsterone injected daily for 3 and 5 days, respectively (Emmens, 1939).

but when the data are plotted as logarithm of dose versus logarithm of response, a linear relationship is found (Fig. 4). Making use of this latter relationship, the values of the slope have been calculated and the index of precision λ determined. In the 3-day test the slope was 0.568 and $\lambda = 0.197$, while in the 5-day test, the slope was 0.404 and $\lambda = 0.280$.

Table IV illustrates the estimated errors as calculated by Emmens (1939). Both the 3- and 5-day tests are considered.

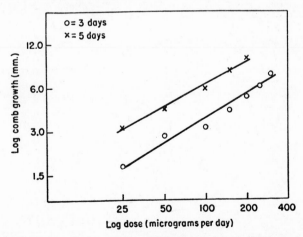

FIG. 4. Capon's comb response to androsterone injected daily for 3 and 5 days, respectively. Data plotted on basis of log-dose-log response (Emmens, 1939).

TABLE IV

ESTIMATED ERRORS AT DIFFERENT COMB GROWTH LEVELS AND THE STANDARD ERROR OF THE ESTIMATE OF THE DAILY DOSE OF A TEST PREPARATION EXPRESSED AS A PERCENTAGE OF THE ESTIMATE, ASSUMING THE DOSE-RESPONSE LINES TO BE ACCURATELY KNOWN[a]

	Estimated Errors						
Comb growth $L + H$ (mm.)	Average standard errors of response, approximate (pooled data from 3- and 5-day tests)			Standard error of estimate of daily dose (%)			
				3-Day		5-Day	
	(σ)	(σ_m) 5 Birds	(σ_m) 10 Birds	5 Birds	10 Birds	5 Birds	10 Birds
2	0.75	0.35	0.25	41.0	30		
4	1.10	0.50	0.35	17.5	12	31	21
6	1.40	0.70	0.45	14.5	10	19	12.5
8	1.75	0.85	0.60	12.5	8.5	15.5	10.5
10	2.10	1.00	0.70			13.5	9.0

[a] From Emmens (1939).

TABLE V

THE RESPONSE OF THE CAPON'S COMB TO INJECTED ANDROSTERONE BY METHOD OF GALLAGHER AND KOCH[a,b]

Total dose (μg.)	No. of birds	Mean comb growth (mm. ± S.E.)
50	15	1.20 ± 0.37
100	15	1.53 ± 0.43
150	14	2.44 ± 0.46
200	15	3.75 ± 0.48
250	14	3.33 ± 0.48
300	16	5.08 ± 0.42
500	16	6.50 ± 0.59
500	14	7.67 ± 0.50
500	15	7.98 ± 0.74
700	16	7.80 ± 0.77
1000	16	8.66 ± 0.96
1500	16	11.91 ± 0.77
2000	16	13.41 ± 0.95
2500	15	14.51 ± 1.14
5000	14	18.83 ± 1.02

[a] Data of McCullagh and Cuyler (1939).
[b] Corrected for 57-mm. comb size.

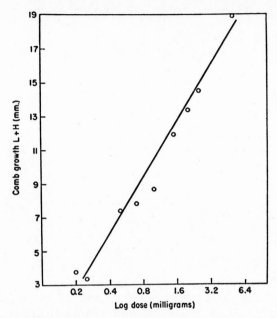

Fig. 5. Capon's comb response to androsterone injected daily for 5 days (McCullagh and Cuyler, 1939).

d. Method of McCullagh and Cuyler (1939). The method is similar to that of Gallagher and Koch (1935). The pooled results are represented in Table V and Fig. 5. The total dose of androsterone ranges from 50 to 5000 μg. administered over a 5-day period. Between 200 and 5000 μg., a linear relationship of the log dose to response was found. From these data a slope of 10.52 and λ = 0.271 was found.

2. Inunction

a. Method of Emmens (1939). White or Brown Leghorn capons may be used. The hormone dissolved in oil is applied daily for 3 days to the capon's comb; 0.1 ml. of oil solution is used each day. Before treatment is started the combs are measured with a millimeter rule and again 24 hours after the last inunction (see Section III A, p. 277). The response length (L) plus height (H) is determined by the difference between the two measurements.

The data are those of Emmens which have been calculated by the simplified design of Bliss (1944). Table VI and Fig. 6 present the response of the capon's comb to a total dose of from 1.2 to 4.8 μg. of androsterone. Table VII presents the results of 4 theoretical assays using a total of 20 animals, 10 on the standard and 10 on the unknown. Since the unknown

TABLE VI

THE RESPONSE OF THE CAPON'S COMB TO ANDROSTERONE
ADMINISTERED BY INUNCTION[a]

(Three Daily Inunctions)

Total dose androsterone (μg.)	No. of capons	Comb response $L + H$ (mm. ± S.E.)
1.2	10	2.55 ± 0.60
2.4	10	5.30 ± 0.55
3.6	10	5.80 ± 0.78
4.8	10	7.05 ± 0.32

[a] Data of Emmens (1939).

and standard are identical, the actual potency ratio is 100%. In the 4 tests the determined potency ratio varied from 92 ± 34 to 130 ± 10. In only one instance were the slopes of the unknown and standard significantly different. The index of precision λ varied from 0.108 to 0.360 with a mean of 0.184 ± 0.063.

b. Method of McCullagh and Cuyler (1939). This method is essentially the same as described under Gallagher and Koch (1935) except for the application of the androgen solution directly to the capon's comb. McCullagh and Cuyler (1939) have been able to demonstrate a log dose-

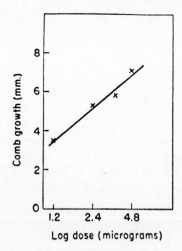

FIG. 6. Capon's comb response to androsterone inuncted daily for 3 days (Emmens, 1939).

TABLE VII

THE ASSAY OF ANDROSTERONE BY THE CAPON COMB INUNCTION METHOD
OF EMMENS (1939)[a]

$N = 5$
High dose of standard = High dose of unknown
Low dose of standard = Low dose of unknown
standard = unknown

Dosage level (μg.)	b	λ	t	Potency ratio (% ± S.E.)
0.4; 0.8	9.33	0.108	1.215	130 ± 16
0.4; 1.2	6.88	0.360	0.684	92 ± 34
0.4; 1.6	7.50	0.186	0.875	97 ± 19
0.8; 1.6	5.83	0.079	2.610	119 ± 22

[a] Based on the data of Emmens (1939).

response curve which is a straight line from a total dose of 2 to 80 μg. of androsterone.

The androgen is dissolved in sesame oil so that the total dose is contained in 1 ml. of solution. Each day for 5 consecutive days, 0.2 ml. of the androgen solution is applied evenly over the whole comb.

Table VIII presents the influence of androsterone by inunction on the

TABLE VIII

THE RESPONSE OF THE CAPON'S COMB TO ANDROSTERONE
ADMINISTERED BY INUNCTION[a]

Total dose of androsterone (μg.)	No. of capons	Mean comb growth (mm. ± S.E.)
2.0	15	1.0 ± 0.37
4.0	15	2.0 ± 0.43
7.0	15	2.53 ± 0.55
10.0	15	4.27 ± 0.52
20.0	15	7.93 ± 0.64
50.0	15	12.87 ± 0.67
100.0	15	14.33 ± 0.80

[a] Data of McCullagh and Cuyler (1939).

capon's comb. The total dose ranged from 2 to 100 μg. Between the limits of 7 and 50 μg. an excellent agreement was found for a linear relationship

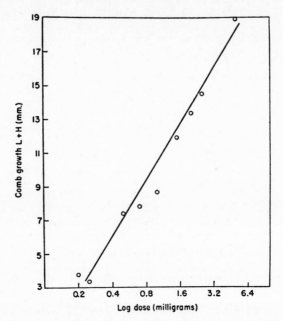

Fɪɢ. 7. Capon's comb response to androsterone inuncted daily for 5 days (McCullagh and Cuyler, 1939).

between the logarithm of the dose and the response (Fig. 7). The slope over this range was found to be 30.3 and $\lambda = 0.0763$.

B. CHICK COMB GROWTH

1. General Remarks

The early studies of Ruzicka (1935), Burrows *et al.* (1936), Dorfman and Greulich (1937), and Frank and Klempner (1937) indicated the advisability of using the chick's comb as the test object for androgen assays. Ruzicka (1935) painted the chick's comb with a 0.5% solution of androsterone in oil each day for a period of several weeks, and obtained large increases in comb area. He did not, however, study this reaction quantitatively. Frank and Klempner (1937) applied the androgens in oil solutions directly to the base of the comb of White Leghorn chicks. Applications were begun on the sixth day after hatching and were repeated on 10 successive days. The animals were sacrificed and the comb weights were determined on the day following the last application. These workers were able to evoke a definite response with as little as 20 μg. of androsterone. Burrows and his co-workers (1936) injected both androsterone and testosterone either into the base of the chick's comb or into the breast muscles and found that both of these androgens stimulated comb growth. In all the studies mentioned the response is the weight of the comb, which perhaps represents an advantage over the less exact methods of measurement of the size of the capon's comb. However, the capon comb method has the advantage that each animal serves as its own control, since comb measurements are made before and after hormone administration.

2. Relative Reactivity of the Comb of Various Breeds of Chicks to Androgens (Dorfman, 1948b)

It has been known for some time that various breeds of fowl differ as to their practicability for use in androgen assays when the comb is used as the test organ. The reactivity of 3 breeds of chicks to testosterone propionate has been studied. The hormone was administered by direct application to the comb. This procedure should rule out variations in the metabolism or inactivation of the hormone in the body. In these experiments we are dealing only with the direct stimulation and the local inactivation of the hormone at the site of the comb.

The 3 breeds of chicks studied were the White Leghorn, the Rhode Island Red, and the Barred Rock. The animals were kept in a thermostatically controlled brooder and were fed chick starting mash and water exclusively. The chicks were 2 to 3 days of age at the beginning of the experiment. The total dose of testosterone propionate was contained in 0.35 ml. of corn oil and administered once daily for 7 days. Fivehundredths of a milliliter of the hormone solution was dropped on the comb from a 1-ml. tuberculin syringe fitted with a No. 24 hypodermic needle. Twenty-four hours after the last hormone application the animals were killed, and body weight and comb weights were determined. The animals were autopsied at 9 to 10 days of age. The comb responses are expressed as the ratio of the comb weight in milligrams to the body weight in grams. Body weights did not vary significantly.

The dosage range of testosterone propionate investigated varied from 2 to 20,480 μg. for the White Leghorn male and female chicks, and 40 to 20,480 μg. for the Rhode Island Red and Barred Rock breeds (Table IX).

No significant difference was found in the comb ratios between male and female untreated chicks for any of the 3 breeds studied, but a significant difference in comb ratios was found between animals of different breeds. White Leghorn chicks showed the largest combs, the Barred Rocks the smallest, and the combs of the Rhode Island Reds were intermediate. This order of comb size of control chicks was true for both the males and females.

On the basis of the minimal quantity of testosterone propionate

TABLE IX

The Relative Reactivity of the Combs of White Leghorn, Rhode Island Red, and Barred Rock Chicks to Testosterone Propionate When Administered by Direct Application to the Comb

| Breed of chick | Amount administered (μg.) | No. of chicks | | Ratio = $\dfrac{\text{comb (mg.)}}{\text{body weight (gm.)}}$ ± S.E. | |
		M	F	M	F
White Leghorn	0	62	56	0.38 ± 0.01	0.36 ± 0.01
	2	13	6	0.46 ± 0.04	0.43 ± 0.06
	5	28	34	0.55 ± 0.02	0.47 ± 0.02
	10	32	31	0.63 ± 0.03	0.52 ± 0.02
	20	18	45	0.65 ± 0.04	0.67 ± 0.02
	40	36	51	0.77 ± 0.05	0.69 ± 0.02
	80	46	38	1.03 ± 0.05	0.91 ± 0.05
	160	29	36	1.53 ± 0.10	1.54 ± 0.09
	2560	25	13	1.74 ± 0.07	1.74 ± 0.15
	5120	12	12	1.88 ± 0.15	1.98 ± 0.15
	20,480	8	13	1.89 ± 0.22	1.82 ± 0.16
Rhode Island Red	0	47	29	0.25 ± 0.01	0.23 ± 0.01
	40	14	11	0.33 ± 0.01	0.33 ± 0.02
	80	13	11	0.36 ± 0.03	0.40 ± 0.04
	160	9	14	0.48 ± 0.05	0.49 ± 0.05
	640	9	16	0.85 ± 0.10	0.82 ± 0.10
	1280	15	10	0.91 ± 0.07	0.87 ± 0.09
	2560	32	21	0.92 ± 0.05	1.03 ± 0.07
	5120	11	12	1.14 ± 0.07	1.03 ± 0.08
	20,480	—	19	—	1.10 ± 0.08
Barred Rock	0	26	37	0.21 ± 0.01	0.20 ± 0.01
	40	13	10	0.25 ± 0.02	0.22 ± 0.02
	80	12	13	0.23 ± 0.02	0.29 ± 0.02
	160	9	14	0.36 ± 0.04	0.32 ± 0.02
	640	12	17	0.54 ± 0.03	0.55 ± 0.03
	1280	11	15	0.61 ± 0.02	0.63 ± 0.04
	2560	24	31	0.85 ± 0.01	0.82 ± 0.04
	5120	9	15	0.97 ± 0.09	1.07 ± 0.08
	20,480	12	10	1.01 ± 0.11	1.02 ± 0.07

needed to produce a 20% increment in comb ratio, the male White Leghorns were 15 times as sensitive as the Rhode Island Reds and 20 times as sensitive as the Barred Rocks. Similarly, the female White Leghorn combs were 10 times as sensitive as those of the Rhode Island Reds, and 20 times those of the Barred Rocks.

The comparative sensitivities of the combs of the 3 breeds were evaluated by selecting portions of the log dose-response curves where the

TABLE X

THE MAXIMUM SLOPES OF COMB RESPONSE ATTAINABLE BY RHODE ISLAND RED
AND BARRED ROCK CHICKS[a]

(Logarithm Dose-Response)

Breed of chicks	Sex	Dosage levels of testosterone propionate (μg.)	Total No. of animals	Slope ($b \pm$ S.E.)
White Leghorn[a]	M	20; 40; 80	100	0.677 ± 0.107
	F	10; 20; 40; 80	165	0.357 ± 0.023
Rhode Island Red	M	80; 160; 640	31	0.545 ± 0.026
	F	80; 160; 640	41	0.485 ± 0.110
Barred Rock	M	640; 1280; 2560	47	0.537 ± 0.101
	F	640; 1280; 2560; 5120	78	0.484 ± 0.110

[a] The White Leghorn comb response curve was taken where the slope was not significantly different from that of the other breeds.

slopes of all 3 breeds were not significantly different, and by using the displacement of the curves as another measure of the relative sensitivity of the various breeds (Table X and Fig. 8). Under these conditions and expressing the sensitivity of the male White Leghorn chick comb as 100%,

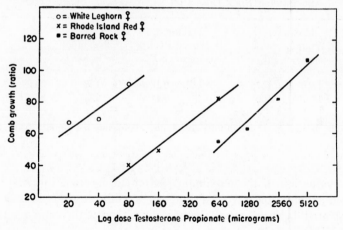

FIG. 8. Comb responses of three breeds of female chicks to testosterone propionate (Dorfman, 1948b).

the sensitivity of the Rhode Island Red was found to be 10% and that of Barred Rock 1.8%. In the female chicks the relative comb sensitivities were similarly: White Leghorn, 100%; Rhode Island Red, 8.9%; and Barred Rock 1.8% (Table XI).

TABLE XI

RELATIVE SENSITIVITY OF VARIOUS BREEDS TO TESTOSTERONE PROPIONATE AS
MEASURED BY AMOUNT OF HORMONE NECESSARY TO PRODUCE SIMILAR SLOPES

	Males		Females	
Breed of animals	Sensitivity in % of White Leghorn	Error range $(P = 0.95)$	Sensitivity in % of White Leghorn	Error range $(P = 0.95)$
White Leghorn	100	0	100	—
Rhode Island Red	10.0	$+32; -25$	8.9	$+48; -33$
Barred Rock	1.8	$+23; -19$	2.0	$+33; -25$

A third criterion of sensitivity of the combs to androgen was the maximum slope attainable using a log dose-response relationship for at least 3 points. No significant difference in maximum slope was found for the Rhode Island Red and Barred Rock chick combs, but the White Leghorns showed a significantly greater slope (Table XII and Fig. 9).

TABLE XII

COMPARISON OF MAXIMUM SLOPES ATTAINED BY REGRESSION OF WHITE LEGHORN
AND BARRED ROCK COMBS ON TESTOSTERONE PROPIONATE[a]

Sex	Maximum White Leghorn (slope[b] ± S.E.)	Maximum Barred Rock (slope ± S.E.)	Total No. of chicks	t	P
M	1.215 ± 0.147	0.537 ± 0.101	158	3.027	0.01
F	1.361 ± 0.100	0.484 ± 0.110	223	8.240	0.01

[a] Rhode Island Red maximum slopes not significantly different from those of Barred Rock.

[b] Derived from 40-, 80-, and 160-μg. doses of testosterone propionate.

An evaluation of the maximum percentage increase in comb size by androgen stimulation revealed that no significant difference could be demonstrated between the 3 breeds for either male or female chicks (Table XIII).

3. Method of Frank et al. (1942)

The method was devised by Frank et al. (1942) and studied by Dorfman (1948a). Using it, Klempner et al. (1942) have shown that in 24 determinations of androsterone in the dosage range of 20 to 40 μg., the mean error was 13%, and in 39 determinations over the range of 10 to

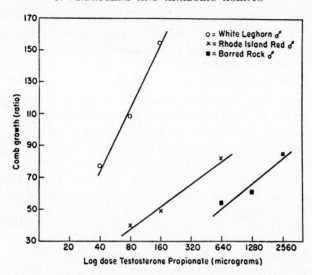

FIG. 9. Comb responses of three breeds of male chicks to testosterone propionate (Dorfman, 1948b).

50 μg., the mean error was 24.6%. In another study (Dorfman, 1948a) the results of Klempner *et al.* (1942) were confirmed. In the latter study, in the range of 20 to 40 μg., a mean error of 12% was found, and in the range of 10 to 40 μg., a mean error of 24% was found.

White Leghorn chicks should be used at 2 to 3 days of age. Mixed pullets and cockerels are used. The animals should be kept in a brooder with a thermostatic control. It is well to keep the temperature between 88° and 96°F.

The total dose of material to be administered to each chick is dissolved in 0.35 ml. of sesame oil; 0.05 ml. of oil is administered daily for 7 days, starting when the animals are 2 to 3 days of age. The material is

TABLE XIII

COMPARATIVE MAXIMUM COMB RATIOS ATTAINED BY THREE BREEDS OF CHICKS
AFTER APPLICATION OF TESTOSTERONE PROPIONATE

| | Males | | Females | | Mean increase |
Breed of chick	Control ratio	Maximum increase (%)	Control ratio	Maximum increase (%)	male and female (%)
White Leghorn	0.38	395	0.36	415	405
Rhode Island Red	0.25	357	0.23	364	361
Barred Rock	0.21	344	0.20	426	385

dropped on the comb by means of a 1-ml. tuberculin syringe fitted with a fine hypodermic needle. An attempt is made to apply the oil solution slowly so that spreading to the head feathers is minimized. Twenty-four hours after the last application of androgen solution, the chicks are autopsied (8–9 days of age).

Body weights are determined at the time of the first application of the androgens, and again at autopsy along with weight of comb and sex of the animal. The combs are removed by two longitudinal incisions along the base of the comb at its juncture with the scalp. The incisions are extended vertically down to the skull. The comb is freed from the skull and the base is touched lightly on a towel to remove blood from the cut surface. The comb is weighed quickly, on a suitable torsion balance, to avoid drying.

Calculations:

Activity equivalent to 100 μg. of androsterone per chick

$$= \frac{1.061(\Sigma W) - 0.0043(\Sigma W^2) - 0.397(\Sigma B_i) - 0.267(\Sigma B_t) + 14.75_m + 18.54N_f)}{100(N_m + N_f)}$$

where ΣW = the sum of the comb weights, expressed in milligrams

ΣW^2 = the sum of the squared comb weights

ΣB_i = the sum of the initial body weights, expressed in grams

ΣB_t = the sum of the terminal body weights, expressed in grams

N_m = the number of male chicks used in the assay

N_f = the number of female chicks used in the assay.

4. Method of Dorfman (1948a) (Inunction)

a. Testosterone propionate. The assay of testosterone propionate can be carried out by a chick comb method using the details of age of chicks, volume of oil, time of hormone application to comb, and determination of the comb weight as described in Section III B, p. 287. The experimental design and calculations are different.

The design of Bliss (1944) is employed, using 2 concentrations of the standard and 2 concentrations of the unknown. The total concentration of testosterone propionate used for each animal should be in the range of 20 to 160 μg. Within the range of 20 to 160 μg., using 32 animals on the standard and 32 animals on the unknown, errors in the determination of the potency ratio are lower than 38% at $P = 0.95$.

The response of the male and female White Leghorn chick comb to testosterone propionate is presented in Table XIV. In Table XV the data have been considered by the method of Bliss (1944). A linear relationship was found when the logarithm of the dose was plotted against the logarithm of the response, and the data are calculated on this basis.

TABLE XIV

THE RESPONSE[a] OF THE CHICK COMB TO TESTOSTERONE PROPIONATE

5 μg.		10 μg.		20 μg.		40μg.		80 μg.		160 μg.	
S♂	U♂	S♂	U♂	S♂	U♂	S♂	U♂	S♂	U♂	S♂	U♂
0.45	0.48	0.38	0.98	0.44	0.51	1.10	0.96	1.33	1.13	2.46	2.16
0.51	0.52	0.56	0.73	0.58	0.69	0.67	1.10	1.10	1.31	1.62	1.38
0.63	0.68	0.53	0.84	1.13	0.50	0.81	0.80	0.97	1.30	1.60	2.71
0.67	0.50	0.75	0.71	1.02	0.56	0.81	0.89	1.17	0.77	1.30	3.21
0.75	0.62	0.66	0.67	0.58	0.41	1.37	1.52	1.64	1.34	1.15	1.13
0.48	0.67	0.66	0.53	0.55	0.59	0.90	0.61	1.55	1.48	1.25	2.00
0.69	0.59	0.42	0.68	0.82	0.69	0.71	0.45	1.11	1.46	1.72	1.17
0.50	0.47	0.77	0.56	0.76	0.44	0.63	1.08	1.48	1.11	1.23	1.91
S♀	U♀	S♀	U♀	S♀	U♀	S♀	U♀	S♀	U♀	S♀	U♀
0.43	0.37	0.43	0.61	0.63	0.83	0.36	0.64	0.76	1.15	0.85	1.53
0.32	0.32	0.38	0.41	0.68	0.84	1.68	0.69	0.92	1.42	2.03	1.09
0.53	0.58	0.54	0.55	0.57	0.69	0.46	0.93	0.96	0.88	2.65	1.63
0.37	0.67	0.56	0.55	0.55	0.73	0.69	0.89	0.84	0.51	0.89	1.60
0.45	0.62	0.80	0.48	0.92	0.82	0.78	0.73	0.82	1.16	2.12	2.05
0.39	0.37	0.43	0.36	0.66	0.51	0.84	1.69	1.34	1.20	2.76	2.66
0.67	0.49	0.51	0.49	0.58	0.43	0.82	0.97	0.96	1.13	1.59	1.98
0.47	0.38	0.49	0.42	0.65	0.53	0.86	0.76	0.76	1.21	1.14	1.90

NOTE: S = standard; U = unknown.

[a] Response expressed as ratio of comb weight in milligrams to body weight in grams.

TABLE XV

ASSAY OF TESTOSTERONE PROPIONATE BY DIRECT COMB APPLICATION

$$\frac{\text{High dose of standard}}{\text{Low dose of standard}} = \frac{\text{High dose of unknown}}{\text{Low dose of unknown}}$$

Standard = Unknown
(log dose = log response)

N (half ♂ half ♀)	Dosage levels (μg.)	b	λ	t	Potency ratio (% ± S.E.)	Error range $P = 0.95$ (%)
16	40; 160	0.5025	0.277	0.318	128 ± 21	−27; +38
12	40; 160	0.5000	0.322	1.835	129 ± 24	−31; +46
16	20; 80	0.4115	0.229	0.805	87 ± 14	−27; +38
12	20; 80	0.3729	0.329	0.785	95 ± 20	−35; +54
16	80; 160	0.5908	0.205	1.445	111 ± 13	−21; +26
16	20; 40	0.3848	0.369	0.694	102 ± 23	−38; +56

TABLE XVI

RESPONSE OF THE MALE CHICK'S COMB TO TESTOSTERONE
ADMINISTERED BY APPLICATION[a,b]

Total amount administered (μg.)	No. of chicks	Comb ratio ± S.E.
0	62	38 ± 1
50	33	84 ± 4
100	32	112 ± 5
200	34	136 ± 7

[a] Seven days.
[b] Dorfman (1960).

In each instance, 2 dose levels of both the unknown and standard were considered. The number of animals in each group in 3 cases was 16 (8 males and 8 females), and 12 (6 males and 6 females) in the other comparisons.

At the level of 40 to 160 μg. for groups of 16 (total animals, 64) an error range of −28 to +38% was found as compared to an error range of −31 to +46% for groups of 12 (total animals, 48). In a second instance where groups of 16 to 12 were compared at the 20- and 80-μg.

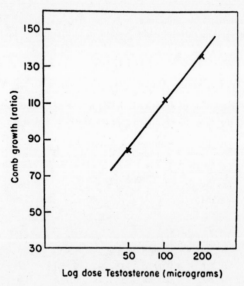

FIG. 10. Chick's comb response to inuncted testosterone (Dorfman, 1960).

levels, an error range of -7 to $+38\%$ was found for the groups of 16, while the groups of 12 showed an error range of -35 to $+54\%$ ($P = 0.95$).

The highest error range of the potency ratio was found at the levels of 20 and 40 μg., although 16 animals were used at each dose level. This error range was from -38 to $+56\%$.

No significant difference was found in the slopes of the unknown and standard. The t values ranged from 0.318 to 1.835.

b. Testosterone. Testosterone was assayed by the same procedure used for testosterone propionate. A linear relationship was found between the logarithm of the dose and the response. The simplified design was employed (Bliss, 1944).

Table XVI and Fig. 10 illustrate the response of the male chick's comb to the direct application of testosterone. The assay is illustrated in Table XVII. The actual potency ratio was 1. The potency ratios

TABLE XVII

Assay of Testosterone by Direct Comb Application[a]

$$\frac{\text{High dose of standard}}{\text{Low dose of standard}} = \frac{\text{High dose of unknown}}{\text{Low dose of unknown}}$$

Standard = Unknown
$N = 15$

Dosage levels (μg.)	b	λ	t	Potency ratio $\pm$ S.E.
50; 100	105	0.238	0.145	92 $\pm$ 13
100; 200	87	0.415	1.510	124 $\pm$ 30
100; 200	137	0.251	1.840	94 $\pm$ 11
100; 200	102	0.360	1.160	102 $\pm$ 16
100; 200	86	0.408	0.684	129 $\pm$ 32

[a] Dorfman (1960).

varied from 0.92 to 1.29 in 5 different runs. No significant differences in the slopes of the unknown and standard were found.

c. Androsterone. Valle *et al.* (1947) have studied the chick comb method by direct application of androsterone. Two-day-old white Leghorn male chicks are placed in brooders at a temperature of 32° to 37°C. They are fed *ad libitum* bread and milk plus a dry food consisting of corn meal, 50%; rice bran 20%; wheat bran, 15%; meat meal, 10%; and bone meal, 5%. Beginning with the third day of life and continuing for 7 consecutive days, 0.05 ml. of oil solution of the hormone is applied to the comb. Twenty-four hours after the last hormone application the animals are killed and the combs removed by the method of Frank *et al.* (1942), described in Section III B, p. 287. Animals which gained less than 2 gm. during the experimental period were discarded.

Table XVIII illustrates the results using androsterone by direct ap-

TABLE XVIII

THE RESPONSE OF THE MALE CHICK'S COMB TO ANDROSTERONE BY APPLICATION

Expt. No.	Dosage (μg.)	No. of chicks	Mean comb weight (mg.)	Variance	Slope	Sigma slope
A	15.0	20	46.7	267.95		
	22.4	20	53.1	272.77	42.264	11.54
	33.5	19	62.0	699.82		
	50.0	18	68.3	408.86		
B	15.0	18	41.9	247.62		
	22.4	14	49.0	218.30	41.685	10.56
	33.5	16	56.3	261.76		
	50.0	16	63.7	652.37		
C	15.0	14	55.2	305.41		
	22.4	16	60.9	389.34	41.516	11.42
	33.5	16	67.3	360.17		
	50.0	12	77.2	599.61		
D	15.0	17	42.5	204.34		
	22.4	20	48.9	253.78	55.975	10.04
	33.5	14	64.0	384.08		
	50.0	18	70.0	408.50		
E	50.0	17	78.8	606.74		
	75.0	16	91.8	797.63	115.114	16.14
	112.0	18	118.1	949.14		
	168.0	16	136.1	794.86		

[a] Valle *et al.* (1947).

plication. In experiments A through D low concentrations (15–50 μg.) of androsterone were applied. Under these conditions a mean slope of 44.1 ± 3.68 was found and a mean value of $\lambda = 0.424 \pm 0.033$ was calculated. Between 50 and 168 μg. of androsterone, a steeper slope of 115.114 was found and a correspondingly more favorable value of 0.244 for λ.

5. *Method of Munson and Sheps (1958) (Inunction)*

This method is the most sensitive described for the chick's comb and has a useful range of 0.35 to 5.6 μg. of androsterone total dose. This high sensitivity is due to the use of absolute alcohol as the vehicle, a small volume of vehicle, and, as in the other chick comb methods, the use of a sensitive breed of chicks. One disadvantage is the fact that the total dose of any unknown material must be soluble in 0.07 ml. of absolute ethanol. The mean index of precision (λ) was established as 0.34 with a standard deviation of 0.056. This means that with 40 chicks on the standard and 20 on the unknown that the minimum standard error of a potency estimate is 24%.

For the assay single-comb White Leghorn cockerels were received on the day of hatching and the following day distributed randomly into groups of equal size. The cages and corresponding groups of chicks are numbered consecutively, and the treatments assigned by formal randomization. The solutions are applied to the comb once daily for 7 days. For this a 0.01-ml. micropipet fitted with bulbs made from rubber tubing is employed. Inunction is starting either on day of hatching or the following day.

To reduce the incidence of diarrhea the chicks are fed only cracked corn for the first 2 days. The diet is then changed to a mixture of equal amounts of corn and starting mash together with grit. Food is removed on the evening of the seventh day. The following morning the chicks are killed with ether, one group at a time. Combs are removed with a sharp No. 10 Bard-Parker scalpel, blotted on filter paper to remove blood, and weighed to the nearest 0.5 mg. For statistical calculations, the results are expressed as:

$$100 \times \log \frac{\text{Comb weight in mg.}}{\text{Body weight in dg.}}$$

Typical results obtained with the method of Munson and Sheps (1958) are illustrated in Fig. 11 showing excellent agreement in response to androsterone in two consecutive experiments.

6. Method of Dorfman (1948) (Injection)

Testosterone propionate dissolved in corn oil is injected subcutaneously once daily for 5 consecutive days, starting 4 days after hatching. Male White Leghorn chicks are used. The daily dose is contained in 0.1 ml. of oil. Twenty-four hours after the last injection the chicks are killed with chloroform, and the comb and body weights determined. The combs are removed as described in Section III B, p. 287. The response is expressed as 100 times the ratio of the comb weight in milligrams to the body weight in grams. A linear relationship is found when the logarithm of dose is plotted against the response.

The results of three tests using the simplified design are shown in Table XIX. The actual potency ratio was 1. Potency ratios of 0.92 ± 0.20,

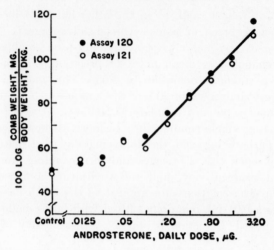

FIG. 11. Comb response to androsterone in two consecutive experiments (Munson and Sheps, 1958).

1.20 ± 0.20, and 1.02 ± 0.17 were found. The slopes of the standards and unknowns did not differ significantly. The measure of precision, λ, was 0.374, 0.276, and 0.275.

TABLE XIX

ASSAYS OF TESTOSTERONE PROPIONATE BY INJECTION[a]

$$\frac{\text{High dose of standard}}{\text{Low dose of standard}} = \frac{\text{High dose of unknown}}{\text{Low dose of unknown}}$$

$$\text{Standard} = \text{Unknown}$$
$$N = 15$$

Dosage level (mg.)	b	λ	t	Potency ratio % ± S.E.)
0.5; 1.0	47.5	0.374	1.278	92 ± 20
1.0; 2.0	83.9	0.276	0.106	120 ± 20
0.5; 2.0	66.2	0.275	1.865	102 ± 17

[a] Dorfman (1960).

7. Method of Dorfman (1960) (Oral Administration)

The hormone is mixed thoroughly with a standard chick starting mash in a mechanical mixer. White Leghorn cockerels are fed this mixture for 10 days starting at 2 to 3 days of age. The chicks are killed with chloroform, at which time comb and body weights are determined. The removal of the combs is described in Section III B, p. 287. The response is represented as 100 times the ratio of the comb weight in milligrams to the body weight in grams. A linear relationship exists between the logarithm of the dose and the response.

TABLE XX

THE RESPONSE OF THE MALE CHICK'S COMB TO
METHYLTESTOSTERONE ADMINISTERED ORALLY[a,b]

Concentration of androgen in food (mg./kg.)	No. of chicks	Comb ratio ± S.E.
0	32	42 ± 2
5	23	112 ± 8
10	23	157 ± 11
20	20	188 ± 14
40	19	251 ± 17

[a] Ten days on diet.
[b] Dorfman (1960).

The response of the chick's comb to orally administered methyltestosterone is shown in Table XX. Table XXI shows the results of the assay using the simplified design (Bliss, 1944).

TABLE XXI

THE ASSAY OF METHYLTESTOSTERONE ADMINISTERED ORALLY
TO MALE CHICKS[a]

$$\frac{\text{High dose of standard}}{\text{Low dose of standard}} = \frac{\text{High dose of unknown}}{\text{Low dose of unknown}}$$

Standard = Unknown
(log dose = response)
$N = 10$

Dosage levels (mg./kg.)	b	λ	t	Potency ratio (% ± S.E.)
5; 10	151	0.315	1.060	129 ± 30
5; 20	122	0.404	0.266	121 ± 35
30; 40	207	0.326	0.650	83 ± 20

[a] Dorfman (1960).

C. Sparrow's Bill (Pfeiffer et al., 1944)

Androgens cause blackening of the bill of the English sparrow. Thus, the male in the winter months has an ivory-colored bill, and as the testis function increases in the spring the bill blackens. This blackening is due to the increased concentration of androgen resulting from the increased testicular function, and has been suggested for the assay of androgens but as yet has not been adapted to quantitative assay. Some of the results of Pfeiffer et al. (1944) are presented to illustrate the potentialities of the method.

English sparrows (*Passer domesticus*) were trapped as immature birds in summer. The males were castrated and females were used as intact animals in the fall of the year. The animals were housed in wire cages measuring $3 \times 3 \times 4$ feet. A dry mixture of finely cracked grain and poultry growing mash was fed along with an ample supply of fresh water. In the experiments presented in Tables XXII, XXIII, and XXIV, some animals received the hormone by direct application to the breast; others received the hormone subcutaneously; while still others received the hormone by direct application to the bill. The hormone was given intramuscularly in 0.05 ml. of sesame oil per day, or was applied to the skin in the breast region in absolute alcohol. The local bill reaction was produced by placing one drop of an absolute alcohol solution on one side of the bill from a No. 22 hypodermic needle fitted to a 1-ml. tuberculin syringe.

Table XXII presents the response of the Sparrow's bill to testosterone propionate administered intramuscularly. A total of 100 μg. administered over 10 days produced 100% responses in both castrated males and

TABLE XXII

The Response of the Sparrow's Bill to Testosterone Propionate
Administered Intramuscularly[a]

Daily dose (μg.)	No. of birds and sex[b]	No. of days	Animals responding (%)
2.5	4 ♀	10	0
5.0	4 ♀	10	0
10.0	4 ♀	10	100
2.5	3 ♂	10	0
5.0	3 ♂	10	67
10.0	3 ♂	10	100

[a] Pfeiffer et al. (1944).
[b] ♂ = castrate males.

TABLE XXIII

THE RESPONSE OF THE SPARROW'S BILL TO TESTOSTERONE PROPIONATE
APPLIED TO THE SKIN OF THE BREAST[a]

Daily dose (μg.)	No. of birds and sex	No. of days	Animals responding (%)
2.0	3 ♀	25	33
4.0	5 ♀	25	60
8.0	4 ♀	15	75

[a] Pfeiffer et al. (1944).

normal females. A total of 50 μg. in the same period of time produced blackening in 2 of 3 castrated males. The application of the hormone to the skin in the breast area was not particularly effective (Table XXIII). However, direct application of androgens, either androsterone or testosterone, was the most sensitive test yet described. A total of 1 μg. of testosterone administered in 16 divided doses produced positive

TABLE XXIV

THE RESPONSE OF THE SPARROW'S BILL TO TESTOSTERONE AND ANDROSTERONE
APPLIED LOCALLY[a]

Androgen	Daily dose (μg.)	No. of birds and sex[b]	No. of days	Animals responding (%)
Testosterone	0.5	5 ♀	10	60
	1.0	2 ♀	10	100
	2.0	2 ♀	10	100
	0.063	6 ♂	16	67
	0.125	3 ♂	10	100
	0.250	4 ♂	10	100
Androsterone	0.25	4 ♀	10	100
	0.50	4 ♀	10	100
	1.00	4 ♀	10	100
	3.30	4 ♀	10	100
	6.60	4 ♀	10	100
	13.30	3 ♀	10	100
	0.063	5 ♂	16	100
	0.125	5 ♂	10	60
	0.250	10 ♂	10	100

[a] Pfeiffer et al. (1944).
[b] ♂ = castrate males.

responses in 4 of 6 castrated males, and a similar dose of androsterone produced 100% of positive responses in 5 castrated males (Table XXIV).

D. Additional Bird Methods

In addition to the methods already described, reports on the use of the capon's comb by injection have been made by Ruzicka *et al.* (1934), Tschopp (1935), Butenandt and Tscherning (1934), and Dingemanse *et al.* (1931). Various methods using the direct comb application of androgens have been described by Dessau (1935, 1937), Voss (1937), Fussganger (1934), Oesting and Webster (1938), Mussio Fournier *et al.* (1940). Courrier and Jost (1939) have published studies on the use of the chick comb method.

IV. Mammalian Assays

A. Method of Mathieson and Hays (1945)

The standard and unknown should be run simultaneously at each of two concentrations so that the ratio of the high dose to the low dose of both unknown and standard is equal to 4. For this purpose the high dose will be taken as the material supplied, whereas the low dose will be prepared by diluting the material supplied in 1 part plus 3 parts of corn oil.

Rats are castrated between the ages of 26 to 29 days and weighing 40 to 75 gm. The animals are used between 2 to 12 weeks after castration at which time the animals are divided into 4 groups, each group containing 21 castrated animals.

Each castrated rat receives 0.2 ml. of a solution containing either the unknown or the standard. The solutions are injected subcutaneously using a 1-ml. tuberculin syringe fitted with a 24-gauge needle. Seventy-two hours after the administration of the test material the rats are killed and the body weights determined. The ventral surface is opened to expose the male accessory organs and bladder. Two lateral incisions are made to permit easy access to the seminal vesicles. With a pair of forceps and curved iridectomy scissors, each of the vas deferens is cut and the seminal vesicles and prostate removed by incision at a point near the base of the bladder. The tissue is dipped in physiological saline and placed on a cork board under a dissecting microscope. The coagulating glands are teased from the seminal vesicle and the latter incised at a point nearest the ejaculatory ducts. The seminal vesicles

TABLE XXV

THE ASSAY OF TESTOSTERONE PROPIONATE USING THE RESPONSE
OF THE SEMINAL VESICLES OF THE CASTRATED MALE RAT[a]

$$\frac{\text{High dose (Unknown)}}{\text{Low dose (Unknown)}} = \frac{\text{High dose (Standard)}}{\text{Low dose (Standard)}}$$

N	b	s	λ	t	Potency ratio (% ± S.E.)	Theoretical potency ratio (%)
11	19.6	5.38	0.296	0.105	63 ± 13	80
11	20.7	5.26	0.255	1.078	80 ± 14	80
11	17.1	5.63	0.329	0.990	95 ± 22	100
11	21.4	4.68	0.218	0.679	109 ± 16	100
11	23.6	5.00	0.212	1.822	98 ± 14	120
11	18.7	4.75	0.254	0.493	133 ± 30	120

are again immersed in saline, dried on blotting paper for a few seconds, and weighed to the nearest 0.5 mg.

The results are listed in Table XXV. Previously, Mathieson and Hays (1945) reported two assays using a solution of testosterone propionate containing 10 mg. of the hormone ester per milliliter. They found 10.72 ± 1.83 and 9.26 ± 1.74, respectively.

B. DATA OF CALLOW AND DEANESLY (1935)

The data of Callow and Deanesly (1935) are shown in Tables XXVI and XXVII. Table XXVI illustrates the response of the seminal

TABLE XXVI

THE RESPONSE OF THE PREPUBERALLY CASTRATED RAT ACCESSORY GLANDS
TO ANDROSTERONE[a,b]

Total dose of androsterone (mg.)	No. of rats	Seminal vesicles (mg.)	Prostate (mg.)
3.5	5	9	44
6.0	6	14	64
10.0	5	32	112
15.0	5	17	129
20.0	5	26	129
28.0	5	46	394

[a] Ten-day treatment.
[b] Callow and Deanesly (1935).

vesicles and prostate to androsterone in prepuberally castrated rats treated daily for 10 days. Table XXVII presents data on the seminal vesicle and prostate response of the postpuberally castrated rat to androsterone.

TABLE XXVII

THE RESPONSE OF THE POSTPUBERALLY CASTRATED RAT ACCESSORY GLANDS TO ANDROSTERONE[a,b]

Total dose of androsterone (mg.)	Mean body weight (gm.)	Weight of seminal vesicles (mg.)	Weight of prostate (mg.)
0	165	51	55
7.0	157	122	291
14.0	155	204	429
28.0	167	431	577

[a] Fourteen days of injection; 5 animals per group.
[b] Callow and Deanesly (1935).

Postpuberal rats weighing 130 to 155 gm. were castrated and injected with androsterone in arachis oil for 14 consecutive days. Twenty-four hours after the last injection the animals were sacrificed. The prepuberally castrated animals were operated at 35 to 70-gm. body weight, usually between 40 to 50 gm. These castrates were treated once daily with the hormone dissolved in 0.1 ml. of arachis oil for 10 consecutive days. Twenty-four hours after the last injection the animals were sacrificed.

The entire reproductive tract was dissected free of fat, fixed in Bouin's fluid, and transferred to 70% alcohol. The prostrates and seminal vesicles were dissected carefully, drained thoroughly, and weighed.

C. ANDROGEN-ANABOLIC ASSAYS

Eisenberg and Gordan (1950) suggested that the effect of steroids on the levator ani muscle of the castrated rat is a reasonable indicator of protein-anabolic activity. They pointed out that this myotrophic effect is distinct from the androgenic effect and that whereas the muscle is stimulated by pituitary growth hormone, the seminal vesicle does not respond to this treatment. A further argument in favor of this view has been the fact that the levator ani muscle of the castrated rat continues to grow in the absence of the gonads (Sakamoto et al., 1951.

There is no universal agreement, however, that the levator ani muscle actually measures true anabolic activity of steroids. Some investigators rather feel that this muscle is just another tissue that has a relatively high sensitivity to androgens (Nimni and Geiger, 1957). These workers point out the androgens and anabolic steroids are able to stimulate the levator ani even on a protein-free diet which cannot support somatic growth. In spite of this argument, however, the relative potency of a compound on the levator ani has been shown to correlate, at least roughly, with the ability of the compound to retain nitrogen and promote growth in normal individuals and patients suffering from debilitating diseases. In this section levator ani anabolic tests will be presented.

1. Method of Eisenberg and Gordan (1950)
(Modified by Saunders and Drill, 1957)

Male rats 23–25 days of age were castrated and 3 weeks later the test compounds, dissolved in corn oil, were intramuscularly injected once daily for 7 consecutive days. The volume of corn oil was 0.1 ml. per day. One day after the last injection the animals were sacrificed and the seminal vesicles, ventral prostates, and levator ani muscles were removed and weighed. The evaluation of the relative anabolic or myotrophic effect of a steroid was judged by its ability to stimulate the levator ani in relation to its ability to stimulate the "pure" androgen indicators, the seminal vesicles, and the prostate.

2. Method of Hershberger et al. (1953)

This method has the advantage over that of the Eisenberg and Gordan (1950) procedure in that the time is decreased from a period of 30 days to 7 days. Male rats 21 days of age were castrated and placed on a stock diet. Beginning on the day of surgery, the animals were injected subcutaneously once daily with the test compounds dissolved in oil for 7 consecutive days. One day after the last injection the animals were sacrificed and the levator ani, ventral prostate, and seminal vesicles were dissected and weighed. In evaluating steroids for possible use as anabolic agents, Hershberger et al. (1953) suggested the use of the levator ani-ventral prostate ratio which was defined as the ratio of the increase in levator ani weight divided by the increase in ventral prostate weight. Thus the larger the ratio of a given compound the more likely the compound may be a therapeutically valuable agent. The authors did not calculate levator ani-seminal vesicle ratios because the seminal vesicles are less sensitive to small doses than the prostate and are believed to be affected more by non-androgenic steroids.

Some typical data of Hershberger et al. (1953) are presented in

TABLE XXVIII

INFLUENCE OF TESTOSTERONE AND RELATED STEROIDS ON THE SEMINAL VESICLES, VENTRAL PROSTATE, AND LEVATOR ANI OF THE CASTRATED RAT[a]

Compound administered	Total dose (mg.)	No. of rats	Tissue weight (mg. $\pm$ S.E.)		
			Seminal vesicle	Ventral prostate	Levator ani
0	0	25	9.7 $\pm$ 0.4	7.0 $\pm$ 0.3	12.2 $\pm$ 0.5
Testosterone	0.35	6	35.3 $\pm$ 1.8	14.7 $\pm$ 0.9	20.4 $\pm$ 2.3
	0.70	8	46.5 $\pm$ 4.6	17.8 $\pm$ 1.3	21.9 $\pm$ 2.0
	1.4	11	48.4 $\pm$ 2.3	27.4 $\pm$ 2.3	23.7 $\pm$ 1.0
	1.75	8	63.5 $\pm$ 4.5	38.2 $\pm$ 5.5	28.8 $\pm$ 0.9
19-Nortestosterone	0.7	5	19.7 $\pm$ 2.5	12.1 $\pm$ 1.7	21.6 $\pm$ 0.5
	1.4	11	20.7 $\pm$ 1.8	12.5 $\pm$ 0.6	24.5 $\pm$ 2.0
	2.1	5	27.5 $\pm$ 5.1	14.4 $\pm$ 1.1	28.1 $\pm$ 2.2
Androsterone	0.67	3	69.9 $\pm$ 8.9	7.6 $\pm$ 0.5	15.5 $\pm$ 0.5
	1.75	6	93.0 $\pm$ 3.7	11.2 $\pm$ 0.5	16.6 $\pm$ 1.3
	3.5	6	109.4 $\pm$ 4.1	13.8 $\pm$ 0.7	15.4 $\pm$ 2.0

[a] Herschberger et al. (1953).

Table XXVIII. Differences in the levator ani-ventral prostate ratios for the different compounds are indicated in these data. Androsterone at the total dose of 1.75 mg. had a ratio of 0.05 while 19-nortestosterone had a ratio of 1.1 at a dose level of 1.4 mg. Testosterone at a dose level of 1.4 mg. had an intermediate ratio of 0.30.

3. Data of Dorfman (1960)

The method used in this study is based on that described in Section IV C, p. 305, derived from the Hershberger et al. (1953) test, and consists in the use of 21-day-old, 40 to 55-gm. rats, which were castrated on the twenty-first to twenty-fourth day of life. The test compounds were injected subcutaneously once daily for 10 consecutive days starting on the day of surgery. The vehicle is the aqueous suspending medium (Section I B, p. 709) and the daily dose was contained in 0.5 ml. of the solution. At autopsy, body, ventral prostate, seminal vesicle, and levator ani weights were determined to the nearest 0.5 mg.

Typical data are presented in Table XXIX for the seminal vesicle, ventral prostate, and the levator ani responses to testosterone. This method has an over-all λ value for the seminal vesicle, ventral prostate, and levator indicators in the range of 0.137, 0.162, and 0.171, respectively.

TABLE XXIX

THE RESPONSE OF THE CASTRATED RAT TO SUBCUTANEOUS INJECTION
OF TESTOSTERONE—10-DAY TEST[a]

Total dose testosterone (mg.)	No. of rats	Mean tissue weight (mg. ± S.E.)		
		Seminal vesicle	Ventral prostate	Levator ani
0	42	11.5 ± 0.45	12.2 ± 0.58	29.0 ± 1.08
0.3	42	11.7 ± 0.58	18.8 ± 1.15	29.4 ± 0.84
0.6	46	21.8 ± 1.00	35.5 ± 1.49	34.2 ± 1.25
1.2	44	57.7 ± 3.69	71.9 ± 2.49	49.8 ± 1.60
2.4	39	101.0 ± 3.52	103.7 ± 3.30	62.2 ± 1.15

[a] Dorfman (1960).

Attempts to increase the precision of the assay by extending the number of treatment days was not particularly successful, although the time was extended up to 30 days (Dorfman, 1960).

The method may also be practiced by gavage, but the 10-day test period is inferior to a 20-day administration period. By using the latter conditions, a preliminary estimate of the index of precision (λ) was, for seminal vesicles 0.191 (0.137–0.272), for the ventral prostate 0.282 (0.192–0.417), and for the levator ani 0.218 (0.140–0.363).

D. NITROGEN RETENTION METHODS—ANABOLIC ACTIVITY

1. Method of Stafford et al. (1954)

These workers have suggested a method involving the measurement of nitrogen excretion in the castrated rat fed a liquid diet and in nitrogen balance. The method was not recommended for strictly quantitative work, but by the use of three indices some estimate of the relative potencies of two compounds can be made. These indices include the "greatest daily retention" which is defined as the difference between the lowest daily N value after beginning of treatment and the preinjection mean. The second index "total N retention" is the sum of the differences between the preinjection excretion and the daily values during the retention period, and the third index is the "number of days in the retention period." This last index is the period between the last day on which N was equal to or higher than the preinjection average, and the last day before two consecutive values equal to or higher than the preinjection average were obtained.

The method of Stafford et al. (1954) consists in castration of 25-day-

TABLE XXX

Composition of Liquid Diet[a]

Component	Amount
Cell flour	180 gm.
Salt mixture No. 2	120 gm.
(Nutritional Biochemicals, Cleveland, Ohio)	
Brewer's yeast	300 gm.
Casein	480 gm.
Starch	600 gm.
Dextrin	570 gm.
Sucrose	600 gm.
Water	3300 ml.
Corn oil	570 ml.
Cod liver oil	30 ml.
Wheat germ oil	30 ml.
Vitamin K, 0.5% in cottonseed oil	30 ml.

[a] Stafford et al. (1954).

old rats which were kept untreated for 67 days (average weight of 300 gm.). During the initial period the animals were kept on a stock diet, but at 67 days they were changed to a liquid diet—forced feeding regime (see Table XXX). At the start, the rats received 10 ml. per day and this was increased to 26 ml. per day. Steroid treatment was started 24 days after the 26-ml. per day level had been attained and continued for 30 days. The steroids were administered once daily in 0.1 ml. cottonseed oil. Twenty-four-hour urine specimens were collected

TABLE XXXI

Influence of Testosterone Propionate (TP) and Nortestosterone Cyclopentylpropionate (NC) or Nitrogen (N) Excretion in the Castrated Rat[a]

Compound administered	Daily dose (mg.)	No. of rats	Total N retained (mg.)	No. of days in retention period	Greatest single retention (mg.)
TP	0.25	5	398	16	44
	1.00	5	604	20	73
NC	0.5	4	507	16	54
	2.0	5	483	16	60

[a] Stafford et al. (1954).

three times weekly and analyzed for total nitrogen. Results of a typical experiment are presented in Table XXXI.

2. Nitrogen Retention in the Monkey (Stucki et al., 1960)

A method for the assay of anabolic steroids in the monkey (*Macaca mulatta*) had been suggested by Stucki *et al.* (1960). A linear dose-response curve was established over the range of 50 to 400 μg. of fluoxymestrone (9α-fluoro-11β-hydroxy-17α-methyltestosterone) per kilogram per day using the end point of nitrogen retention expressed as total N retained per day during the treatment period. A balanced twin cross-over assay was found to be satisfactory with an efficiency calculated to be 1.5–2.0. The authors point out that at least for one compound, fluoxymestrone, the effective dose found for the monkey on a kilogram basis was comparable to that previously established for humans for the same steroid.

E. ADDITIONAL MAMMALIAN METHODS

A variety of investigators have reported on the use of the rodent for androgen assay. These include Tscherning (1936), Butenandt and Hanisch (1935), Morato Manaro (1940), Deanesly and Parkes (1936), Miescher *et al.* (1936, 1937), Korenchevsky *et al.* (1935), Ruzicka and Rosenberg (1936), Fischer (1938), Loewe and Voss (1931), Dirscherl *et al.* (1936), Masson *et al.* (1942), Selye and Albert (1942), and Korenschevsky and Dennison (1936).

V. Summary of Methods

Tables XXXII, XXXIII, and XXXIV summarize the characteristics of various methods for the assay of androgens. In these tables the androgen, the relationship, the duration of the test, the slope (*b*), the index of precision (λ), and the sensitivity are recorded.

Table XXXII deals with those methods involving administration of the hormone by injection and measuring the response by the growth of the capon's comb. The 3-day tests appear to have an accuracy equivalent to that of the 5-day tests. Thus, using the method of Greenwood *et al.* (1935) (3), the value of λ was 0.189 for the 3-day test and 0.180 for the 5-day test. The difference is not significant. By using the test of Emmens (1939), λ actually was smaller for the 3-day test. For the 5-day test the sensitivity appears to be in the range of 0.2 to 0.3 mg. androsterone.

TABLE XXXII

SUMMARY OF ANDROGEN METHODS

(Capon's Comb—Intramuscular Injection)

Material	Relationship	Duration of test (days)	Slope (b)	Index of precision (λ)	Sensitivity (mg.)	Reference
Androsterone	Log dose-comb growth	3	8.09	0.189	0.3	Greenwood et al. (1935)
Androsterone	Log dose-comb growth	5	12.72	0.180	0.5	
Androsterone	Log dose-log comb growth	3	0.568	0.197	0.075	Emmens (1939)
Androsterone	Log dose-log comb growth	5	0.404	0.280	0.125	
Androsterone	Log dose-comb growth	5	10.52	0.271	0.200	McCullagh and Cuyler (1939)

The use of the inunction technique results in a method approximately 50 times as sensitive as the injection method (Table XXXIII). The precision of the local method is at least as great as the injection method, or greater. The method of McCullagh and Cuyler (1939) showed the low value of λ equal to 0.076. Thus, in using a design consisting of 10 animals on the unknown and 10 on the standard, an accuracy of −15 to +17 at $P = 0.95$ could be expected.

TABLE XXXIII

SUMMARY OF ANDROGEN METHODS

(Capon's Comb—Inunction)

Material	Relationship	Duration of test (days)	Slope (b ± S.E.)[a]	Index of precision (λ ± S.E.)	Sensitivity (mg.)	Reference
Androsterone	Log dose-comb growth	3	7.37 ± 0.74	0.184 ± 0.063	1.2	Emmens (1939)
Androsterone	Log dose-comb growth	5	30.3	0.076	7.0	McCullagh and Cuyler (1939)

TABLE XXXIV

SUMMARY OF ANDROGEN METHODS

(Chick's Comb)

Material	Route	Relationship	Duration of test (days)	Slope ($b \pm$ S.E.)	Index of precision ($\lambda \pm$ S.E.)	Sensitivity	Reference
Testosterone propionate	Application	Log dose–comb weight	7	0.461 ±0.035	0.289 0.026	20 µg.	Dorfman (1948a, 1960)
Testosterone	Application	Log dose–comb weight	7	103 ± 9	0.334 ±0.038	50 µg.	Dorfman (1960)
Testosterone propionate	Subcutaneous injection	Log dose–comb weight	5	65.9 ±10.5	0.308 ±0.033	500 µg.	Dorfman (1960)
Methyltestosterone	Oral	Log dose–comb weight	10	160 ±25	0.348 ±0.028	5 mg. Kilo food	Dorfman (1960)
Androsterone	Application	Log dose–comb weight	7	44.1 ±3.68	0.424 ±0.033	15 µg.	Valle et al. (1947)
Androsterone	Application	Log dose–comb weight	7	115.1	0.244	50 µg.	Munson and Sheps (1958)
Androsterone	Application	Log dose– log comb ratio	7	29.5	0.34	0.35 µg.	Munson and Sheps (1958)

The chick comb methods, although more convenient than the capon methods, have a lower precision. These are summarized in Table XXXIV.

REFERENCES

Bliss, C. I. (1944). *J. Am. Statist. Assoc.* **39**, 479.

Bliss, C. I., and Cattell, Mc. K. (1943). *Ann. Rev. Physiol.* **5**, 479.

Bülbring, E. (1935). *Quart. J. Exptl. Physiol.* **111**, 1.

Burrows, W. H., Byerly, T. C., and Evans, E. I. (1936). *Proc. Soc. Exptl. Biol. Med.* **35**, 60.

Butenandt, A., and Hanisch, G. (1935). *Z. physiol. Chem., Hoppe-Seyler's* **237**, 75.

Butenandt, A., and Tscherning, K. (1934). *Z. physiol. Chem., Hoppe-Seyler's* **229**, 167, 185.

Callow, R. K., and Deanesly, R. (1935). *Biochem. J.* **29**, 1424.

Callow, R. K., and Parkes, A. S. (1935). *Biochem. J.* **29**, 1414.

Courrier, R., and Jost, A. (1939). *Compt. rend. soc. biol.* **130**, 1515.

Deanesly, R., and Parkes, A. S. (1936). *Biochem. J.* **30**, 291.

Dessau, F. (1935). *Acta Brevia Neerl. Physiol., Pharmacol., Microbiol.* **5**, 94.

Dessau, F. (1937). *Acta Brevia Neerl. Physiol., Pharmacol., Microbiol.* **7**, 1.

Dingemanse, E., Freud, J., Kober, S., Laqueur, E., Luchs, A., and Munch, A. W. P. (1931). *Biochem. Z.* **231**, 1.

Dirscherl, W., Kraus, J., and Voss, H. E. (1936). *Z. physiol. Chem., Hoppe-Seyler's* **241**, 1.

Dorfman, R. I. (1948a). *Endocrinology* **42**, 1.

Dorfman, R. I. (1948b). *Endocrinology* **42**, 7.

Dorfman, R. I. (1960). Unpublished data.

Dorfman, R. I., and Greulich, W. W. (1937). *Yale J. Biol. and Med.* **10**, 79.

Dorfman, R. I., and Shipley, R. A. (1956). "Androgens, Biochemistry, Physiology, and Clinical Significance," 590 pp. Wiley New York.

Eisenberg, E., and Gordan, G. S. (1950). *J. Pharmacol. Exptl. Therap.* **99**, 38.

Emmens, C. W. (1939). *Med. Research Council (Brit.) Special Rept. Ser.* **234**, 1.

Fischer, A. (1938). *Rev. franç. endocrinol.* **16**, 1.

Fisher, R. A. (1934). "Statistical Methods for Research Workers." Oliver & Boyd, London.

Frank, R. T., and Klempner, E. (1937). *Proc. Soc. Exptl. Biol. Med.* **36**, 763.

Frank, R. T., Klempner, E., Hollander, F., and Kriss, B. (1942). *Endocrinology* **31**, 63.

Fussgänger, R. (1934). *Med. Chem. Abhandl. Med.-Chem. Forschungsstatten I. G. Farbenindustrie A. G.* **2**, 201.

Gallagher, T. F., and Koch, F. C. (1935). *J. Pharmacol. Exptl. Therap.* **55**, 97.

Greenwood, A. W., Blyth, J. S. S., and Callow, R. K. (1935). *Biochem. J.* **29**, 1400.

Griffith, J. Q., and Farris, E. J. (1942). "The Rat in Laboratory Investigation," p. 395. Lippincott, Philadelphia, Pennsylvania.

Hershberger, L. G., Shipley, E. G., and Meyer, R. K. (1953). *Proc. Soc. Exptl. Biol. Med.* **83**, 175.

Irwin, J. O. (1937). *J. Roy. Statist. Soc.* **4**, 1.

Kenyon, A. T., Knowlton, K., and Sandiford, I. (1944). *Ann. Internal. Med.* **20**, 632.

Kenyon, A. T., Sandiford, I., Bryan, A. H., Knowlton, K., and Koch, F. C. (1938). *Endocrinology* **23**, 135.

Klempner, E., Hollander, F., Frank, R. T., and Kriss, B. (1942). *Endocrinology* **31**, 71.

Kochakian, C. D. (1937). *Endocrinology* **21**, 750.

Kochakian, C. D., and Murlin, J. R. (1935). *J. Nutrition* **10**, 437.

Kochakian, C. D., and Murlin, J. R. (1936). *Am. J. Physiol.* **117**, 642.

Korenchevsky, V., and Dennison, M. (1936). *Biochem. J.* **30**, 1514.

Korenchevsky, V., Dennison, M., and Simpson, S. L. (1935). *Biochem. J.* **29**, 2131.

Loewe, S., and Voss, H. E. (1931). *Med. Klin.* (*Munich*) **27**, 1719.

Masson, G., Borduas, A., and Selye, H. (1942). *Rev. can. biol.* **1**, 57.

Mathieson, D. R., and Hays, H. W. (1945). *Endocrinology* **37**, 275.

McCullagh, D. F., and Cuyler, W. K. (1939). *J. Pharmacol. Exptl. Therap.* **66**, 379.

Miescher, K., Wettstein, A., and Tschopp, E. (1936). *Biochem. J.* **30**, 1970.

Miescher, K., Kagi, H., Scholz, C., and Wettstein, A. (1937). *Biochem. J.* **294**, 39.

Morato Manaro, J. (1940). *Arch. clin. e inst. endocrinol., Fac. med.* (*Montevideo*) **1**, 343.

Munson, P. L., and Sheps, M. C. (1958). *Endocrinology* **62**, 173.

Mussio Fournier, J. C., Albrieux, A. S., and Prego, L. (1940). *Arch. clin. e inst. endocrinol. Fac. med.* (*Montevideo*) **1**, 332.

Nimni, M. E., and Geiger, E. (1957). *Proc. Soc. Exptl. Biol. Med.* **94**, 606.

Oesting, R. B., and Webster, B. (1938). *Endocrinology* **22**, 307.

Pfeiffer, C. A., Hooker, C. W., and Kirschbaum, A. (1944). *Endocrinology* **34**, 389.

Ruzicka, L. (1935). *Bull. soc. chim. France* **5**, 1497.

Ruzicka, L., and Rosenberg, H. P. (1936). *Helv. Chim. Acta* **19**, 357.

Ruzicka, L., Goldberg, M. W., and Meyer, J. (1934). *Helv. Chim. Acta* **18**, 210.

Sakamoto, W., Gordan, G. S., and Eisenberg, E. (1951). *Proc. Soc. Exptl. Biol. Med.* **76**, 406.

Saunders, F. J., and Drill, V. A. (1957). *Proc. Soc. Exptl. Biol. Med.* **94**, 646.

Selye, H., and Albert, S. (1942). *Proc. Soc. Exptl. Biol. Med.* **49**, 361.

Stafford, R. O., Bowman, B. J., and Olson, K. J. (1954). *Proc. Soc. Exptl. Biol. Med.* **86**, 322.

Stucki, J. C., Forbes, A. D., Northam, J. I., and Clark, J. J. (1960). *Endocrinology* **66**, 585.

Tscherning, K. (1936). *Angew. Chem.* **49**, 11.

Tschopp, E. (1935). *Klin. Wochschr.* **14**, 1064.

Valle, J. R., Henriques, S. B., and Henriques, O. B. (1947). *Endocrinology* **41**, 335.

Voss, H. E. (1937). *Klin. Wochschr.* **16**, 769.

Chapter 7

Anti-Androgenic Substances

RALPH I. DORFMAN

I. Introduction

Substances possessing anti-androgenic activity are of practical as well as theoretical interest. Systemically active compounds may be of enormous benefit for women suffering from certain types of hirsutism and men suffering from androgen-dependent prostatic tumors. Local use of anti-androgenic compounds could also be of use in women with hypertricosis, in prevention of certain types of male baldness, for the inhibition of facial hair growth in men, and for the treatment and/or prevention of acne in young men and women.

Studies on inhibition of androgens have been reviewed (Dorfman and Shipley, 1956). The following compounds have been reported to possess anti-androgenic activity: estrone, estradiol-17β, and progesterone (Mühlbock, 1938a,b; Hoskins and Koch, 1939); 3-p-methoxyphenyl-4-methyl-7-hydroxycoumarin (Gley et $al.$, 1936); methylcholanthrene (Hertz and Tullner, 1947); 17-ethynyl-19-nortestosterone (Dorfman, 1959; Dorfman and Dorfman, 1960; Dorfman and Stevens, 1960); 2-acetyl-7-oxo-1,2,3,4,4a,5,6,7,9,10,10a-dodecahydrophenanthrene (Ro2-7239) (Randall and Selitto, 1958; Dorfman, 1959; Dorfman and Stevens, 1960); 11α-hydroxyprogesterone (Byrnes et $al.$, 1953); and A-norprogesterone (Lerner et $al.$, 1960).

Two types of anti-androgen bioassays have been used, those involving the capon's or chick's comb and those involving mammalian androgen indicators, usually the seminal vesicles and prostate. A relatively large number of substances, particularly progestational agents, are anti-androgenic on the comb tests, while anti-androgenic substances are limited to a relatively few compounds. Ro 2-7239 and A-norprogesterone are active in both the fowl and mammalian tests, and the latter compound is unique in that it can produce 100% inhibition of the testosterone stimulation of the comb. This chapter will discuss the various tests that have been described and implied.

II. Chick Comb Methods

A. INUNCTION

Two bioassay methods have been described in this group, one which consists in the admixture of the androgen with the food while the test compound is administered by direct inunction to the comb, and another procedure which consists in the single injection on day one of the assay of a long-acting androgen and the daily comb inunction of the test compound.

1. Androgen Fed—Test Compound Inuncted
(Dorfman and Dorfman, 1960)

This method employs 1- to 3-day-old male or female White Leghorn chicks which are housed in a heated brooder maintained at 80°F. Testosterone is incorporated into the finely ground chick starting mash at a concentration of 80 mg. per kilogram of food. The chicks are placed on this diet on day one. The test compound is dissolved in corn oil (or sesame oil) so that the total dose is contained in 0.35 ml. of the vehicle. Each day for 7 days 0.05 ml. of the oil solution is inuncted on the comb. Control chicks receive only the vehicle. Twenty to twenty-four hours after the last inunction the combs are removed and, after blotting the cut edge, weighed rapidly to the nearest 0.5 mg. Body weights are also determined. The results may be expressed in absolute comb weights or as the ratio of milligrams of comb per gram of body weight.

Typical results using progesterone and norethisterone (17α-ethynyl-19-nortestosterone) are presented in Table I. The unstimulated comb in animals of this age usually have comb ratios of the order of 0.30 to 0.38.

2. Androgen Injected—Test Compound Inuncted (Dorfman, 1959)

This method employs 1- to 3-day-old male or female White Leghorn chicks which are housed in a heated brooder maintained at 80°F. A single dose of 0.5 mg. of testosterone enanthate contained in 0.5 ml. of corn (or sesame) oil is injected on the first day of the assay. The test

TABLE I

THE INHIBITORY EFFECT OF PROGESTERONE AND NORETHISTERONE INUNCTED ON THE
COMBS OF TESTOSTERONE (INCORPORATED IN FOOD[a]) STIMULATED CHICKS[b]

Steroid inuncted	Total dose (mg.)	No. of chicks	Mean comb ratio ± S.E.
0	0	396	1.75 ± 0.02
Progesterone	0.5	61	1.54 ± 0.05
	1.0	211	1.41 ± 0.03
	2.0	216	1.38 ± 0.03
	4.0	63	1.15 ± 0.04
Norethisterone	0.1	138	1.40 ± 0.03
	0.2	97	1.35 ± 0.03
	0.4	77	1.19 ± 0.04
	0.8	56	1.25 ± 0.06
	1.6	43	1.21 ± 0.04

[a] All chicks received testosterone in their food, 80 mg. per kilogram.
[b] Dorfman and Dorfman (1960).

compound is dissolved in oil so that the total dose is contained in
0.35 ml. of the vehicle. Each day for 7 days 0.05 ml. of the oil solution
is inuncted on the comb. Control groups receive only the vehicle. Twenty
to twenty-four hours after the last inunction the combs are removed and,
after blotting the cut edge, weighed rapidly to the nearest 0.5 mg.

TABLE II

THE INHIBITORY EFFECT OF NORETHISTERONE AND RO 2-7239 INUNCTED ON THE
COMBS OF TESTOSTERONE ENANTHATE (INJECTION[a]) STIMULATED CHICKS[b]

Compound inuncted	Total dose (mg.)	No. of chicks	Mean comb ratio ± S.E.
0	0	24	1.08 ± 0.07
Norethisterone	0.25	22	0.93 ± 0.04
	0.5	21	0.92 ± 0.04
	1.0	23	0.85 ± 0.04
Ro 2-7239	0.1	17	0.97 ± 0.034
	0.2	17	0.92 ± 0.04
	0.4	17	0.73 ± 0.06
	1.6	13	0.74 ± 0.04

[a] All chicks received 0.5 mg. of testosterone enanthate on first day.
[b] Dorfman (1959).

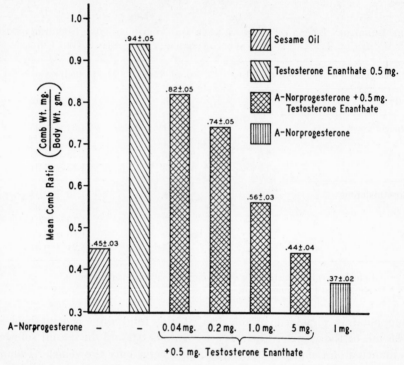

FIG. 1. Anti-androgenic activity of *A*-norprogesterone on testosterone-induced chick comb growth (Lerner *et al.*, 1960).

Body weights are also determined. The results may be expressed in absolute comb weights or as the ratio of milligrams of comb per gram of body weight.

Typical results using this method involving the injection of the androgen and inuncting the test compound are illustrated in Table II and Fig. 1.

B. INJECTION

Androgen Fed—Test Compound Injected
(Dorfman and Dorfman, 1960)

This method employs 1- to 3-day-old male or female White Leghorn chicks which are housed in a heated brooder maintained at 80°F. Testosterone is incorporated into the finely ground chick starting mash at a concentration of 80 mg. per kilogram of food. The chicks are placed on this diet on day one. The test compound is dissolved in corn (or sesame) oil so that the total dose is contained in 0.7 ml. of the vehicle.

Each day for 7 days 0.1 ml. of the oil solution is injected subcutaneously. Control chicks receive only the vehicle. Twenty to twenty-four hours after the last injection the combs are removed and, after blotting the cut edge, weighed rapidly to the nearest 0.5 mg. Body weights are also determined. The results may be expressed in absolute comb weights or as milligrams of comb per gram of body weight.

A study using this method is presented in Table III and indicates

TABLE III

THE INHIBITORY EFFECT OF PROGESTERONE AND NORETHISTERONE (INJECTION) ON THE COMBS OF TESTOSTERONE (IN FOOD[a])-STIMULATED CHICKS[b]

Steroid injected	Total dose (mg.)	No. of chicks	Mean comb ratio ± S.E.
0	0	195	1.38 ± 0.03
Progesterone	0.5	101	1.31 ± 0.05
	1.0	123	1.37 ± 0.05
	2.0	119	1.13 ± 0.05
Norethisterone	4.0	9	0.92 ± 0.09

[a] All chicks received testosterone in their food, 80 mg. per kilogram.
[b] Dorfman and Dorfman (1960).

that both progesterone and norethisterone are active by the injection route, but relatively less active than by the inunction method.

III. Mammalian Methods

Ro 2-7239 and A-norprogesterone consistently inhibit the action of androgens on the seminal vesicles, prostate, and levator ani. Randall and Selitto (1958) demonstrated that a 1:1 ratio of testosterone to Ro 2-7239 produced inhibitory effects on all three tissues in the castrated rat. The method employed by this group is described below.

A. INJECTION

1. Castrated Rat—Injection (Randall and Selitto, 1958)

Albino male rats weighing 70 gm. were castrated under ether anesthesia. Starting one day after surgery, the rats were injected once daily with 0.15 mg. of testosterone propionate in sesame oil (volume not specified). The test compound was also dissolved in sesame oil and injected subcutaneously daily for 7 days at a separate site. Twenty-four hours after the last injection the rats were sacrificed, at which time body, seminal vesicles, and levator ani weights were determined.

The anti-androgenic activity of Ro 2-7239 by this method is illustrated in Fig. 2. The stimulating total dose of testosterone of 1.05 mg.

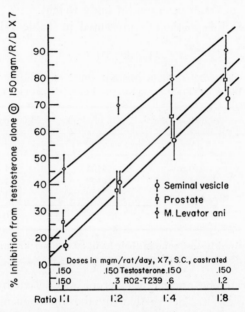

FIG. 2. Anti-androgenic activity of Ro 2-7239 in the castrated rat (Randall and Selitto, 1958).

caused weight increases of 565% in the seminal vesicles, 365% in the prostate, and 105% in the levator ani muscle. When the ratio of testosterone to Ro 2-7239 was 1 to 8, inhibitions of 70 to 90% were observed. Some typical data using this method are illustrated in Table IV dealing with the anti-androgenic activity of A-norprogesterone.

2. Castrated Rat—Injection (Dorfman and Stevens, 1960)

Rats, 26 to 28 days of age, were castrated and, starting on the same day, were injected subcutaneously once daily with 0.5 ml. of an aqueous suspension of testosterone (2 mg./3.5 ml.) for 7 days. The test compound was also placed in aqueous suspension and the rats received 0.5 ml. per day for 7 days starting with the day of surgery. The aqueous suspending medium consisted of sodium chloride (0.9%), polysorbate 80 (0.4%), carboxymethylcellulose (0.5%), and benzyl alcohol (0.9%). One day after the last injection the rats were sacrificed and the weights of the

TABLE IV

The Anti-Androgen Activity of *A*-norprogesterone in the Castrated Rat[a,b]

Total dose of A-norprogesterone (mg.)	Total dose of testosterone propionate (μg.)	No. of rats	Mean tissue weight (mg. ± S.E.)		
			Seminal vesicle plus coagulating gland	Ventral prostate	Levator ani
0	0	42	11.2 ± 0.3	11.3 ± 0.3	21.6 ± 0.7
0	175	42	52.7 ± 1.7	58.1 ± 1.8	31.2 ± 0.9
7	0	6	11.1 ± 0.7	11.6 ± 0.8	22.3 ± 2.3
35	0	4	8.6 ± 0.2	12.6 ± 1.5	18.9 ± 1.4
7	175	6	38.6 ± 3.6	36.2 ± 1.7	29.0 ± 2.0
35	175	4	24.6 ± 1.2	31.9 ± 1.7	20.3 ± 1.3
175	175	3	13.1 ± 0.5	13.1 ± 2.3	17.3 ± 1.6

[a] Seven-day assay.
[b] Lerner *et al.* (1960).

body, seminal vesicles, prostate, and levator ani determined. By using this method, it was possible to demonstrate a statistically significant interference with the peripheral action of testosterone (Table V).

TABLE V

The Inhibition of the Action of Testosterone by Ro 2-7239[a]

Testosterone injected (mg.)	Ro 2-7239 injected (mg.)	No. of rats	Mean tissue ratio ± S.E.		
			Seminal vesicle	prostate	Levator ani
0	0	7	0.05 ± 0.005	0.07 ± 0.007	0.24 ± 0.031
2	0	7	0.94 ± 0.058	0.96 ± 0.072	0.67 ± 0.045
2	50	7	0.68 ± 0.053	0.65 ± 0.031	0.57 ± 0.026

[a] Dorfman and Stevens (1960).

B. Castrate Rat—Gavage (Dorfman and Stevens, 1960)

This method can be practiced precisely as described for the castrate rat (Section III, A, 2) except that the test compound is administered by gavage instead of by subcutaneous injection. A typical experiment is presented in Table VI using a total dose of 2.4 mg. of testosterone and a total dose of 100 mg. of Ro 2-7239. In this study, inhibition was only found on the prostrate end point.

TABLE VI

THE INHIBITION OF THE ACTION OF TESTOSTERONE BY RO 2-7239[a]

Testosterone injected (mg.)	Ro 2-7239 by gavage (mg.)	No. of rats	Mean tissue ratio ± S.E.		
			Seminal vesicle	Prostate	Levator ani
0	0	8	0.10 ± 0.007	0.16 ± 0.009	0.21 ± 0.013
2.4	0	9	1.03 ± 0.075	1.24 ± 0.082	0.40 ± 0.017
2.4	100	10	0.97 ± 0.087	0.98 ± 0.062	0.43 ± 0.017

[a] Dorfman and Stevens (1960).

IV. Comments

The methods now available and presented in this chapter for assessing anti-androgenic activity are qualitative tests. As best they can establish an approximate rank order of activity of test compounds based on minimum amounts of material necessary to produce a statistically significant peripheral interference with the action of androgens. The tests can also define the maximum anti-androgenic activity attainable with a given compound. The method suffers from the fact that usable dose-response relationships cannot be established, making it impossible to calculate true errors of potency ratios.

The chick comb methods, particularly the one involving the single injection of testosterone enanthate and the inhibition attained by direct inunction of the test compound, are reasonably reliable and reproducible but indicate activity for many compounds which do not show similar anti-androgenic activity in the mammalian tests. These tests, because of their simplicity and economy, can serve as a convenient screening type assay with the thought that any compound showing a positive effect on the chick comb should be studied further in a rat test. At the present time the recommended methods include the chick comb method (Dorfman, 1960) and the three mammalian tests.

Ro 2-7239 and A-norprogesterone are effective anti-androgenic substances in both the chick comb and mammalian tests. Ro 2-7239, at certain doses, also exhibits a low order of androgenic activity and is perhaps the first known nonsteroidal androgen (Dorfman, 1960; Dorfman and Stevens, 1960). A-Norprogesterone seems to possess only anti-androgenic activity (Lerner et al., 1960).

References

Byrnes, W. W., Stafford, R. O., and Olson, K. J. (1953). *Proc. Soc. Exptl. Biol. Med.* **82,** 243.

Dorfman, R. I. (1959). *Endocrinology* **64,** 463.

Dorfman, R. I. (1960). *Science* **131,** 1096.

Dorfman, R. I., and Dorfman, A. S. (1960). *Acta Endocrinol.* **33,** 308.

Dorfman, R. I., and Shipley, R. A. (1956). "Androgens, Biochemistry, Physiology and Clinical Significance," p. 133. Wiley, New York.

Dorfman, R. I., and Stevens, D. F. (1960). *Endocrinology* **67,** 394.

Gley, P., Mentzer, C., Delors, J., Molho, D., and Millon, J. (1946). *Compt. rend. soc. biol.* **140,** 748.

Hertz, R., and Tullner, W. W. (1947). *J. Natl. Cancer Inst.* **8,** 121.

Hoskins, W. H., and Koch, F. C. (1939). *Endocrinology* **25,** 266.

Lerner, L. J., Bianchi, A., and Borman, A. (1960). *Proc. Soc. Exptl. Biol. Med.* **103,** 172.

Mühlbock, O. (1938a). *Acta Brevia Neerl. Physiol. Pharmacol. Microbiol.* **8,** 50.

Mühlbock, O. (1938b). *Acta Brevia Neerl. Physiol. Pharmacol. Microbiol.* **8,** 142.

Randall, L. O., and Selitto, J. J. (1958). *Endocrinology* **62,** 693.

Chapter 8

Corticoids

Ralph I. Dorfman

I. Introduction

Corticoids may be defined as a class of organic compounds biosynthesized in the adrenal or produced synthetically in the laboratory which correct some or all of the adverse effects caused by the removal of the adrenal gland. The biological action of these substances which have been studied for their possible use as bioassay procedures include life maintenance, influence on electrolyte balance, protection in the adrenalectomized animal against changes in environmental temperature, external pressure, toxins, chemical poisons, infection, trauma, influence on carbohydrate and protein metabolism, and changes in formed elements of the blood and their ability to inhibit inflammation. All these physiological actions, in essence, represent the adverse changes that occur when animals are deprived of adrenocortical secretions. This chapter will treat those tests which have been found to be most efficient.

Some representative corticoids are indicated in Fig. 1. Cortisol and corticosterone are the principal corticoids produced in the adrenal and are highly effective with respect to carbohydrate and protein metabolism; they possess only minimum effects on electrolyte balance. Aldosterone is

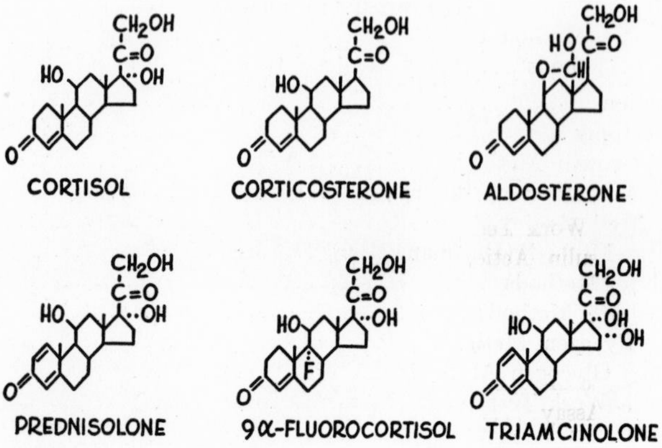

FIG. 1. Representative corticoids.

the most active naturally occurring corticoid that influences electrolyte balance and possesses a low carbohydrate and protein activity. The other three corticoids are more active variants of cortisol with certain unique properties. Prednisolone is some four times as active as cortisol in various carbohydrate and anti-inflammatory tests, whereas 9α-fluorocortisol is some nine times more active. This fluorinated steroid is uniquely active as a sodium-retaining substance and even more effective as a potassium excretor. Triamcinolone is also a synthetic laboratory corticoid where the introduction of the 16α-hydroxy group appears to have prevented the 9α-fluoro groups from exhibiting its high electrolyte effect while the molecule still possesses a relative intense glycogenic action.

II. Adrenalectomy

The majority of the assay methods described in this chapter use adrenalectomized rats and mice. Since similar operative procedures are employed in both species, a description of adrenalectomy in the rat is presented. The method is that of Grollman (1941) and is depicted in Figs. 2 and 3, reprinted from Grollman's publication.

animals appear normal in every respect a few minutes after the operation.

III. Survival-Growth Methods

A. DRAKE—METHOD OF BÜLBRING (1937)

Bülbring (1937) has described a method using the bilaterally adrenalectomized drake. Drakes weighing 1.4 to 1.9 kg. are operated upon, using ether-chloroform anesthesia, and are immediately injected with the test material once hourly for 20 hours. The method has not been

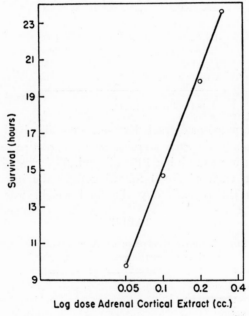

FIG. 4. Response of the adrenalectomized drake to adrenal cortical extract (Bülbring, 1937).

extensively used; however, from the original data it can be seen (Fig. 4) that a linear relationship exists between the logarithm of the dose and the response using an adrenal cortical extract. The slope was 17.48 and λ, the index of precision, was found to be 0.215 ± 0.036 (Bülbring, 1937; Bliss and Cattell, 1943).

B. Rat Methods

1. Method of Grollman (1941)

Young male rats at the age of 20 days were placed on the diet described in Table I for 10 days. Then all animals weighing 50 gm. or more were bilaterally adrenalectomized. A few hours after the operation the animals were weighed and injected subcutaneously with graded

TABLE I

DIET FOR ADRENALECTOMIZED RATS[a]

Constituent	Amount (gm.)
Yellow corn meal	2280
Powdered whole milk	1000
Linseed oil meal	480
Casein	150
Alfalfa meal	60

[a] Grollman (1941).

quantities of hormone or extract. Extracts were dissolved either in saline or 10% ethanol, while such steroids as deoxycorticosterone were dissolved in a mixture containing 10% ethanol, 20% propylene glycol, and 80% water. On each of the 6 following days the injections were repeated and on the seventh day the final weight was recorded. The

TABLE II

THE BODY WEIGHT RESPONSE OF ADRENALECTOMIZED RATS
TO DEOXYCORTICOSTERONE ACETATE[a,b]

Total dose of deoxycorticosterone acetate (mg.)	No. of rats	Mean body growth in 6 days (gm. ± S.E.)[c]
0.24	6	All died
0.36	6	3.8 ± 2.6 (1 dead)
0.60	8	17.4 ± 2.3
0.90	9	21.6 ± 1.2
1.50	6	24.8 ± 1.8

[a] Rats injected daily for 6 consecutive days.
[b] S.E. = standard error of the mean.
[c] Olson et al. (1944a).

mean weight gain was calculated from the initial and final weights of the individuals in the assay group. All animals surviving more than 2 weeks after the cessation of injections were not considered in the calculations of potency. Adrenal cortical remnants and accessory tissues were found in such surviving rats. Table II (Fig. 5) illustrates the results

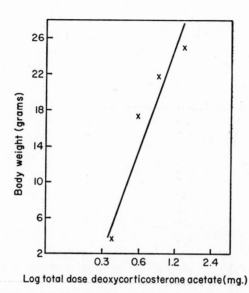

FIG. 5. Weight response of adrenalectomized rats to deoxycorticosterone acetate (Olson *et al.*, 1944a).

published by Olson *et al.* (1944a) following the use of this method for deoxycorticosterone acetate (DCA). The log dose-response relationship for this method is linear. The slope is 33.16 and λ has been estimated to be 0.154. The method is sensitive to 360 μg. of DCA.

One difficulty of this method as pointed out by Olson *et al.* (1944a) is the fact that, at least in the dosage range studied, the slopes of adrenal cortical extract were significantly different from that found with DCA. This may be due not so much to the difference in activity of this pure compound and the mixture in the extract as to the fact that the deoxycorticosterone was used in the form of acetate. Thus, the acetate had a prolonged action compared with the more fleeting activity of the aqueous extract.

2. *Method of Cartland and Kuizenga (1936)*

Male albino rats are bilaterally adrenalectomized at 28 days of age. The animals are injected daily for 10 to 20 days, as the case may be, for the individual experiments. Body weights are determined at the start and the end of the test period, and the gain in weight calculated for each animal.

Tables III and IV illustrate the growth response of adrenalectomized

TABLE III

THE GROWTH RESPONSE OF 28-DAY-OLD MALE ADRENALECTOMIZED RATS
TO ADRENAL CORTICAL STEROIDS[a]

Compound	Amount per day (μg.)	No. of rats	Mean body weight gain in 10 days (gm. ± S.E.)
Corticosterone	50	3	4 ± 2.0
	67	5	10.0 ± 2.8
	100	15	10.5 ± 1.4
	125	9	7.8 ± 2.2
	250	10	17.7 ± 2.1
Cortisol	50	5	11.2 ± 1.1
	100	5	19.0 ± 2.2
	200	5	24.4 ± 3.8
Cortisone	67	10	12.3 ± 1.4
	156	5	16.2 ± 0.9
	312	5	22.8 ± 1.8

[a] Injected daily for 10 days.

TABLE IV

THE GROWTH RESPONSE OF 28-DAY-OLD MALE ADRENALECTOMIZED RATS
TO ADRENAL CORTICAL STEROIDS[a]

Compound	Amount per day (μg.)	No. of rats	Mean body weight gain in 10 days (gm. ± S.E.)
Corticosterone	100	5	15.6 ± 4.4
	250	9	36.0 ± 3.2
Cortisol	50	5	15.6 ± 4.9
	100	7	31.7 ± 6.5
Cortisone	200	5	41.6 ± 5.8
	100	10	18.9 ± 3.1
	125	6	22.0 ± 4.9
	156	5	25.8 ± 2.2
	312	5	33.6 ± 2.5

[a] Injected daily for 20 days.

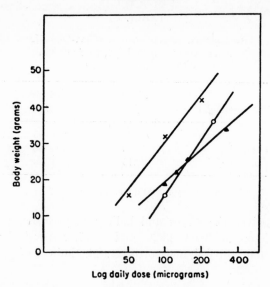

Fig. 6. Weight response of adrenalectomized rats to adrenocortical steroids (Kuizenga, 1949).

KEY: O = corticosterone; X = cortisol; ▲ = cortisone.

rats to varying doses of corticosterone, cortisol, and cortisone during 10- and 20-day test periods, respectively (Kuizenga, 1949). The relationship of log dose to response was found to be linear in each case (Fig. 6). Table V gives the slopes of the three steroids in the 10-day

TABLE V

THE PRECISION OF THE GROWTH METHOD OF ASSAY[a]

Compound	Slope (b)	Index of precision (λ)
Corticosterone	21.19	0.279
Cortisol	21.96	0.246
Cortisone	13.21	0.287

[a] Injected daily for 10 days.

test. The slopes for corticosterone, cortisol, and cortisone were 21.19, 21.96, and 13.21, respectively. Also tabulated is λ, the index of precision. These values varied from 0.246 to 0.287. Specifically, the use of 20 animals on the unknown run simultaneously with 20 animals on the standard will result in a determination of the potency ratio with an error range of −33 to +48 at $P = 0.95$.

TABLE VI

The Growth Response of 28-Day-Old Male
Adrenalectomized Rats to Adrenal
Cortical Steroids[a]

Compound	Slope (b)	Index of precision (λ)
Corticosterone	49.63	0.195
Cortisol	43.20	0.328
Cortisone	28.15	0.309

[a] Injected daily for 20 days.

Table VI gives the slopes and indices of precision for the 20-day tests. Here slopes of 49.63, 43.20, and 28.15, respectively, were found for corticosterone, cortisol, and cortisone. The indices of precision varied from 0.195 to 0.328.

TABLE VII

The Relative Activity of Adrenal Cortical Steroids and an
Adrenal Extract on the Basis of a Growth Method[a,b]

Material	No. of animals	Slope (b)	Relative potency	Error range, P = 0.95 (%)		t
Cortisone	26	28.2	100	—	—	—
Cortisol	18	43.2	219	−34;	+51	0.365
Corticosterone	14	49.6	108	−32;	+47	1.263

[a] Twenty-day test.
[b] Cartland and Kuizenga (1936).

Table VII summarizes the relative activity of the three steroids by the 20-day growth test. Cortisone was chosen as the standard. No departure from parallelism was found, with t values of 0.365 and 1.263 for the studies on cortisol and corticosterone, respectively.

3. Method of Tolksdorf et al. (1956)

A method of studying the influence of corticoids on life maintenance similar to the previously described methods of Grollman (1941) and Cartland and Kuizenga (1936) was employed by Tolksdorf et al. (1956). Male rats 50–70 gm. in weight were adrenalectomized and injected subcutaneously once daily for 14 days. The test compounds were suspended in 1 part ethanol and 9 parts 50% aqueous propylene glycol. The animals subsisted on Purina Lab Blox and tap water. Those animals which survived more than three weeks following the last injection and which showed normal growth rates were eliminated on the probability that they had functional adrenal tissue. Table VIII lists some typical data on the influence of various corticoids.

TABLE VIII

THE INFLUENCE OF CORTICOIDS ON THE SURVIVAL OF ADRENALECTOMIZED, IMMATURE MALE RATS[a]

Compound administered	Daily dose (mg.)	No. of rats	Mean survival (days ± S.E.)
0	0	5	8.2 ± 1.59
Deoxycorticosterone acetate	0.045	17	9.4 ± 0.81
	0.090	18	13.7 ± 1.02
	0.180	13	21.5 ± 1.20
Cortisol	0.12	10	13.0 ± 1.12
	0.24	11	14.9 ± 0.70
	0.48	11	19.5 ± 0.58
Prednisolone	0.015	9	8.0 ± 0.97
	0.03	10	10.3 ± 1.24
	0.06	9	14.1 ± 1.94
	0.12	7	15.6 ± 1.29

[a] Tolksdorf et al. (1956).

C. MOUSE METHOD (DORFMAN, 1960)

Male Swiss mice (6–9 gm.) are bilaterally adrenalectomized under ether anesthesia. Animals subjected to excessive trauma usually die within 24 hours. Those alive the day following the operation are injected subcutaneously with the hormone dissolved in 0.05 ml. of corn oil. The injections are continued for 10 successive days. The diet consisted of commercial dog chow (Purina) with no supplementation and with tap water to drink.

Table IX illustrates the response to 12.5, 25, 50, 100, and 400 μg. of DCA. Increasing the dosage from 100 to 400 μg. produced no further increase in the percentage of surviving animals. Extensive critical studies of this method are yet to be made (Dorfman, 1960).

TABLE IX

THE RESPONSE OF THE MALE IMMATURE ADRENALECTOMIZED MOUSE
TO DEOXYCORTICOSTERONE ACETATE[a]

Daily dose of deoxycorticosterone acetate (μg.)	Total number of animals	Number alive on the 10th day	Per cent of animals alive
0	36	29	19
12.5	20	14	30
25	25	14	44
50	37	22	41
100	36	27	81
400	10	8	80

[a] Mice injected daily for 10 days.

IV. Electrolyte Methods

The activity of adrenocortical hormones with respect to sodium and potassium metabolism was for a long time assessed by employing the adrenalectomized dog (Hartman et al., 1931; Olson et al., 1944a, b). This method suffered from the fact that relatively large amounts of active material were required for significant results, and further, from the great difficulty and expense of obtaining sufficient assay animals for precise bioassays. In 1947 Dorfman et al. suggested the use of the change in radiosodium excretion in adrenalectomized male rats as a sensitive indicator of electrolyte metabolism. It was found in these studies that the sensitivity of the test could be greatly enhanced by subjecting the test animals to a relatively high sodium load. It was possible to detect 0.98 μg. of DCA in a 6-hour test employing 35 μg. of sodium chloride per gram body weight as the sodium load.

These results were extended to include the influence of various adrenocortical steroids and related compounds on sodium and potassium metabolism, and the comparative activities of various adrenocortical steroids (Dorfman, 1949a, b).

Cortisol was studied at three concentrations. It was found that this compound was inactive at 25 μg. At the 50-μg. level, a distinct increase in sodium excretion occurred. At the 200 μg. dose level, neither sodium retention nor excretion could be demonstrated. Other steroids studied including 11-dehydrocorticosterone acetate at 100 μg. and corticosterone at 400 μg. were inactive. Testosterone and estradiol-17β, even at concentrations as high as 2 mg., were inactive in the 6-hour radiosodium test (Dorfman, 1949b). With a potassium load equivalent to 200 μg. of potassium chloride per gram body weight, it was shown that as little as 10 μg. of DCA caused a significant increase in radio-potassium excretion.

These early studies have since been confirmed and the method extended and simplified by Spencer (1950), Deming and Luetscher (1950), and Marcus *et al.* (1952) who used flame photometry instead of the radioactive technique. Kagawa *et al.* (1952) used a chemical determination of sodium. Marcus *et al.* (1952) and Simpson and Tait (1952) did studies of both the sodium and the potassium excretion.

Deoxycorticosterone acetate at various concentrations was administered to groups of adrenalectomized rats by Marcus *et al.* (1952), and the change in urine volume and the sodium and potassium excretion were studied. The urine volume decreased as the concentration of hormone was increased from 2.4 to 120 μg. A corresponding decrease in sodium excretion was also noted. At 2.4 μg., a slight retention (9%) of sodium was found which increased to a 78% retention when the higher dose of 60 μg. was employed. The potassium concentration in the urine showed an inverse picture. At 2.4 μg. of DCA the increase in potassium excretion was 12%, and this increased to 51% when the DCA was 120 μg. These workers studied the effect of additional adrenocortical steroids on potassium excretion. Deoxycorticosterone acetate, at all dosage levels studied, produced retention of sodium and increased excretion of potassium. This was also true when an adrenocortical extract (Upjohn) was administered. When 11-dehydrocorticosterone was studied, retention of sodium was found at the 10-μg. level, whereas no change in potassium excretion could be demonstrated. When the dosage level of 11-dehydrocorticosterone was increased to 50 and 200 μg., no sodium retention could be demonstrated, but the increase in potassium excretion at these higher dosage levels was highly significant. This phenomenon of no sodium-retaining activity but distinct effects on the potassium excretion was also observed when corticosterone at dosage levels varying from 50 to 400 μg. and cortisone at dosage levels of 10 and 50 μg. were employed. Cortisone at the level of 200 μg. produced increased excretion of both sodium and potassium. Cortisol produced no effect at the 10- and 50-μg. dose levels whereas a 200-μg. level caused only an increased excretion of potassium.

Simpson and Tait (1952) measured both urinary sodium and potassium and introduced the concept of using the sodium-to-potassium ratio as an index of electrolyte activity of corticoids. The lowering of the ratio of these two electrolytes was dependent on the logarithm of the dose of DCA in the range of 0.8 to 4 μg. of hormone. The slopes of the responses of adrenocortical extract as well as various active corti-costeroids were found to be linear and parallel to the reference substance DCA. This standard curve could be used for bioassays. In this test, progesterone, estradiol, and testosterone were found to be inactive.

TABLE X

COMPARISON OF ELECTROLYTE METHODS

Test animal (wt. range, gm.)	Method of analysis of Na changes	Hours of urine collection	Sensitivity of DCA, (μg.)	λ	Reference
Adrex.[a] male rats (110–130)	Radioactive Na	6	1	0.287	Dorfman *et al.* (1947)
Adrex. female rats (150)	Flame photometer Na	5	1		Deming and Luetscher (1950)
Adrex. male rats (150–175)	Flame photometer Na	4	2.4	0.252	Marcus *et al.* (1952)
Adrex. male rats (30–40)	Radioactive Na/K	2	0.8	0.300	Simpson and Tait (1952)
Adrex. male rats (150–155)	Chemical Na determination	2	1	0.256	Kagawa *et al.* (1952)
Adrex. male Swiss mice (25)	Flame photometer Na	6	0.5		Spencer (1950)

[a] Adrex. = adrenalectomized.

Table X summarizes the six different methods that have been suggested for the assay of adrenocortical extracts with respect to their electrolyte metabolic activity. This table indicates the test animal that has been employed, including the weight range, the method of analysis of sodium changes, the hours of urine collection, the least amounts of DCA required to give a significant response, and finally lambda (λ), the measure of the precision of the assay. It should be remembered that the smaller the value of λ the more precise is the bioassay technique. In the four methods that have been calculated with respect to λ, it is interesting that the maximum variation in this value is from 0.252 to 0.300. In other words, these four methods have approximately the same degree of reproducibility. Further it may be noted that it is not necessary to use the radioactive isotopes, but that other techniques are sufficiently sensitive such as flame photometric determination of the electrolytes or even chemical determinations. Although Simpson and Tait (1952) and Kagawa *et al.* (1952) have employed 2-hour collections, their error range is not significantly different from those employing the 6-hour collection periods. When adrenalectomized mice were employed, as was the case in Spencer's experiments (1950), the same high order of sensitivity was found. In this set of data, however, although the investigator presented a good dose-response curve, not enough data were presented to calculate the value of λ or to evaluate the reproducibility of this particular modification.

A detailed discussion of the bioassay of aldosterone by J. F. and S. A. S. Tait has appeared in Volume I of this series.

V. Carbohydrate Methods

A. RAT GLYCOGEN METHODS

1. Method of Olson et al. *(1944a)*

Male albino rats, 60–75 days of age and weighing 145–185 gm., are bilaterally adrenalectomized under ether anesthesia (see p. 326). They are placed on the high protein diet described in Table XI and are

TABLE XI

DIET FOR ADRENALECTOMIZED RATS[a]

Constituent	Per cent
Casein	58.0
Dried brewer's yeast	6.0
Sucrose	8.5
Lard	19.0
Hawk-Oser (1931) salt mixture	4.0
Calcium carbonate	1.0
Cod-liver oil	1.0
Cereal cellulose	2.0
Cystine	0.3
Choline chloride	0.2
	100.0

[a] Olson *et al.* (1944a).

given 1% sodium chloride in their drinking water until the morning of the fourth postoperative day. The animals are fasted for 24 hours until the morning of the fifth postoperative day. The drinking water is removed and the injections are started. The hormone in saline or 10% ethanol is administered in 4 equally divided doses at 2-hour intervals. Two hours after the last injection, 1.5 ml. of a 1% solution of sodium amytal is injected intraperitoneally. One-half of the left lateral lobe of each liver is removed and dropped into a tared, tapered 50-ml. centrifuge tube containing 2.0 ml. of cold 30% KOH (Cori, 1932). The samples are quickly weighed, placed in a boiling-water bath, and the tissue is digested. The glycogen is isolated and hydrolyzed by the method of Good *et al.* (1933). The reducing substances are de-

TABLE XII

GLYCOGEN DEPOSITION IN ADRENALECTOMIZED RATS[a]

Steroid	Total dose (mg.)	No. of rats	Mean liver glycogen deposition (% ± S.E.)
Corticosterone	0.39	4	0.44 ± 0.08
	0.47	4	0.52 ± 0.10
	0.58	4	0.84 ± 0.06
	0.62	3	0.72 ± 0.11
	0.94	4	1.15 ± 0.09
	1.15	4	1.40 ± 0.17
	1.24	4	1.39 ± 0.19
11-Dehydrocorticosterone	0.39	5	0.66 ± 0.09
	0.42	5	0.47 ± 0.05
	0.79	6	1.00 ± 0.09
	0.87	9	1.29 ± 0.08
	1.16	5	1.40 ± 0.18
	1.74	7	1.98 ± 0.16
Cortisone	0.33	4	0.79 ± 0.13
	0.39	6	0.61 ± 0.12
	0.39	5	0.61 ± 0.08
	0.66	5	1.10 ± 0.15
	0.77	6	1.05 ± 0.10
	0.79	5	1.31 ± 0.13
	1.27	5	1.72 ± 0.16
Cortisol	0.44	4	0.73 ± 0.07
	0.54	4	1.22 ± 0.05
	0.72	4	1.28 ± 0.14
	0.88	4	1.80 ± 0.10
	0.93	6	1.85 ± 0.16
	1.08	4	2.09 ± 0.17

[a] Olson *et al.* (1944b).

termined with reagent 50 by the method of Shaffer and Somogyi (1933).

Table XII lists the influence of various steroids on the deposition of liver glycogen in the adrenalectomized rat. The data are those of Olson *et al.* (1944b). The four steroids studied were corticosterone, 11-dehydrocorticosterone, cortisol, and cortisone. Table XIII lists the

TABLE XIII

THE LINEAR REGRESSION COEFFICIENTS FOR VARIOUS ADRENAL CORTICAL STEROIDS[a]

Steroid	$a \pm$ S.E.	$b \pm$ S.E.	t
Corticosterone	1.24 ± 0.05	2.06 ± 0.29	
11-Dehydrocorticosterone	1.37 ± 0.05	2.14 ± 0.21	0.23
Cortisone	1.46 ± 0.05	1.91 ± 0.27	0.37
Cortisol	1.95 ± 0.05	3.29 ± 0.41	2.45

[a] Olson *et al.* (1944b).

linear regression coefficients for the four steroids which influence glycogen deposition. On the basis of these data the relative activities of the various steroids were calculated and are presented in Table XIV. Cortisone was chosen as the standard. On this basis corticosterone was found to be 75% as active as the standard, and 11-dehydrocorticosterone

TABLE XIV

THE RELATIVE ACTIVITIES OF ADRENAL CORTICAL COMPOUNDS EXPRESSED
IN TERMS OF CORTISONE[a]

Compound	No. of animals	Slope (b)	Potency ratio (%)	Error, $P = 0.95$ (%)
Cortisone	36	1.82	100	—
Corticosterone	23	1.88	75	−16 to +20
Cortisol	26	3.20	—	—
11-Dehydrocorticosterone	37	2.05	88	−13 to +16

[a] Olson *et al.* (1944b).

had a relative activity of 88%. The fourth steroid, cortisol, was found to have a slope significantly greater than the standard ($t = 2.45$), and therefore, the relative potency was not calculated. Olson *et al.* (1944a) have used this method to assay the potency of adrenal cortical extracts in terms of corticosterone. Five such extracts had slopes not significantly different from the standard, cortisone.

TABLE XV

THE PRECISION OF THE METHOD OF OLSON *et al.* (1944a, b)

Compound	Slope (b)	Index of precision	Sensitivity (μg.)
Corticosterone	2.06	0.112	300
11-Dehydrocorticosterone	2.14	0.126	300
Cortisone	1.91	0.141	300
Cortisol	3.29	0.077	300

Tables XIV and XV illustrate the precision of the Olson *et al.* (1944a) method for the various steroids studied. The index of precision, λ, varied from 0.077 to 0.141. If we consider the mean value of λ, we find that the use of 10 animals on the unknown and 10 on the standard should result in an accuracy of -21 to $+26\%$ at $P = 0.95$ for the determination of the potency ratio. When the number of animals is doubled, that when a total of 40 animals are used, the error range at $P = 0.95$ is -15 to $+18\%$.

2. *Method of Pabst* et al. (*1947*)

The method is based on the ability of certain adrenal cortical hormones to cause glycogen deposition in the fasting adrenalectomized male albino rat and is based on the work of Olson *et al.* (1944a, b). The actual data utilized in this assay are those of the latter workers who made them available to the author for this evaluation.

Male albino rats of the Sprague-Dawley strain weighing 140–160 gm. were maintained on a Purina dog chow diet. They were bilaterally adrenalectomized under ether anesthesia. After the operation the animals were placed on a high protein diet (see Table XI). Tap water containing 1% sodium chloride was used as drinking water. After a 24-hour fast, between the fourth and fifth postoperative days, the crystalline hormones dissolved in cottonseed oil were injected subcutaneously in 4 divided doses at 2-hour intervals. The volume of oil varied from 0.18 to 0.25 ml. per injection. Between $1\frac{1}{2}$ and $2\frac{1}{2}$ hours after the last injection the animals were anesthetized with 0.75 ml. of a 2% solution of cyclopal sodium administered intraperitoneally. The entire liver was removed for analysis of the glycogen content.

The liver was blotted on absorbent paper to remove the surface blood and immediately placed in 30% KOH. Approximately 2 ml. of the potassium hydroxide solution was used for each gram of liver. Complete digestion of the liver was accomplished by heating it for 30 to 40 minutes on the steam bath. The method of Good *et al.* (1933)

with modifications was employed. Absolute alcohol was used for precipitation of the glycogen. Hydrolysis of the glycogen was accomplished
by adding 2.5 ml. of normal H_2SO_4 and autoclaving the solution for
15 minutes at 15 lb. Glucose determinations were done by the modified
iodometric copper method of Shaffer and Somogyi (1933), using reagent
50 containing no KI. Results in Table XVI express the liver glycogen
content in glucose equivalents in per cent.

TABLE XVI

LIVER GLYCOGEN DEPOSITION IN THE FASTING ADRENALECTOMIZED MALE RAT
TREATED WITH ADRENAL CORTICAL HORMONES[a,b]

Hormone	Dose (mg.)	Liver glycogen (% ± S.E.)	Standard deviation
Corticosterone	0.35	0.45 ± 0.07	0.21
	0.50	0.87 ± 0.08	0.26
	0.71	0.95 ± 0.09	0.30
	1.00	1.28 ± 0.07	0.23
11-Dehydrocorticosterone	0.35	0.25 ± 0.03	0.08
	0.50	0.48 ± 0.05	0.17
	0.71	0.87 ± 0.09	0.29
	1.00	1.34 ± 0.08	0.26
Cortisol	0.125[c]	0.45 ± 0.07	0.20
	0.250	0.98 ± 0.09	0.27
	0.350	1.25 ± 0.08	0.27
	0.500	1.68 ± 0.08	0.25
	0.710	1.82 ± 0.11	0.35
	1.000	2.22 ± 0.14	0.43
Cortisone	0.25	0.77 ± 0.07	0.22
	0.35	0.71 ± 0.09	0.29
	0.50	1.37 ± 0.07	0.21
	0.71	1.54 ± 0.10	0.32
	1.00	1.74 ± 0.06	0.20

[a] Ten animals per group.
[b] Pabst et al. (1947).
[c] Nine animals in this group.

Figure 7 illustrates the linear relationship which exists between
the logarithm of the dose and the response using the deposition of liver
glycogen in the fasting adrenalectomized male rat as the end point.
Table XVII presents the relative potency of four adrenal cortical
steroids when the method of Pabst et al. (1947) is used. Cortisone was
chosen as the standard, and no departure from parallelism of slope

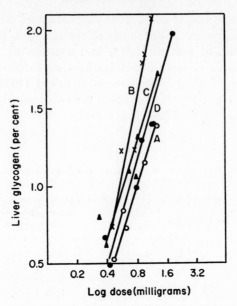

FIG. 7. Liver glycogen response of adrenalectomized rats to adrenocortical steroids (Pabst *et al.*, 1947).

KEY: A = corticosterone; B = cortisol; C = cortisone; D = 11-dehydrocorticosterone.

was found for the four steroids studied. Corticosterone and 11-dehydrocorticosterone were 54 and 48% as active as the standard, whereas cortisol had a relative potency of 155% of the standard.

The method of Pabst *et al.* (1947) was analyzed by the 2 × 2 design of Bliss (1944a, b). This can be employed since the following conditions hold:

TABLE XVII

THE RELATIVE POTENCIES OF VARIOUS ADRENAL CORTICAL STEROIDS EXPRESSED IN TERMS OF THE ACTIVITY OF CORTISONE[a]

Compound	No. of rats	$b \pm$ S.E.	Potency ratio (%)	Error, $P = 0.95$ (%)	t
Cortisone	50	1.848 ± 0.191	100	—	—
Corticosterone	40	1.677 ± 0.183	54	$-13; +15$	0.602
11-Dehydrocorticosterone	40	2.229 ± 0.251	48	$-10; +12$	1.202
Cortisol	59	1.963 ± 0.131	155	$-12; +14$	0.005

[a] Pabst *et al.* (1947).

1. The response is a linear function of the logarithm of the dose.

2. Two concentrations of unknown, and two of standard, are employed so that the following relationship is established.

$$\frac{\text{High dose of standard}}{\text{Low dose of Standard}} = \frac{\text{High dose of unknown}}{\text{Low dose of unknown}}$$

When these conditions are met the calculations for slope (b), index of precision (λ), potency ratio, and error range of the potency ratio are simplified. The parallelism of the slopes of unknown and standard are measured by t.

TABLE XVIII

THE ASSAY OF 11-DEHYDROCORTICOSTERONE

$$\frac{\text{High dose of standard}}{\text{Low dose of standard}} = \frac{\text{High dose of unknown}}{\text{Low dose of unknown}}$$

Standard = Unknown

$N = 5$

Dosage levels (µg.)	b	λ	t	Potency ratio (% ± S.E.)
1000; 500	286	0.088	0.934	93 ± 9
710; 500	256	0.096	0.625	107 ± 11
1000; 710	318	0.089	1.350	98 ± 9
710; 350	203	0.106	0.935	107 ± 12
500; 350	151	0.095	0.328	99 ± 10
1000; 350	217	0.093	0.906	91 ± 9

TABLE XIX

THE ASSAY OF CORTISONE

$$\frac{\text{High dose of standard}}{\text{Low dose of standard}} = \frac{\text{High dose of unknown}}{\text{Low dose of unknown}}$$

Standard = Unknown

$N = 5$

Dosage levels (µg.)	b	λ	t	Potency ratio (% ± S.E.)
1000; 710	116	0.209	1.090	84 ± 19
1000; 500	123	0.158	0.598	110 ± 16
1000; 350	227	0.090	1.125	93 ± 9
710; 500	111	0.281	1.039	87 ± 27
710; 350	270	0.108	0.122	85 ± 10
500; 350	430	0.046	1.468	103 ± 5

TABLE XX

THE ASSAY OF CORTICOSTERONE

$$\frac{\text{High dose of standard}}{\text{Low dose of standard}} = \frac{\text{High dose of unknown}}{\text{Low dose of unknown}}$$

Standard = Unknown

$N = 5$

Dosage levels (μg.)		b	λ	t	Potency ratio (% ± S.E.)
1000;	710	226	0.108	0.650	110 ± 11
1000;	500	139	0.163	0.395	103 ± 17
1000;	350	183	0.239	0.153	109 ± 25
710;	500	54	0.355	1.320	125 ± 51
710;	350	167	0.136	0.430	118 ± 16
500;	350	273	0.084	0.684	100 ± 9

TABLE XXI

THE ASSAY OF CORTISOL

$$\frac{\text{High dose of standard}}{\text{Low dose of standard}} = \frac{\text{High dose of unknown}}{\text{Low dose of unknown}}$$

Standard = Unknown

$N = 5$

Dosage levels (μg.)		b	λ	t	Potency ratio (% ± S.E.)
1000;	710	271	0.103	2.240	125 ± 16
1000;	500	180	0.151	1.388	159 ± 38
1000;	350	214	0.128	3.520	112 ± 10
1000;	250	207	0.142	3.195	144 ± 22
1000;	125	193	0.163	1.965	137 ± 23
710;	250	208	0.136	0.519	105 ± 15
710;	500	100	0.302	0.298	124 ± 44
710;	350	215	0.139	1.122	84 ± 12
500;	250	235	0.118	0.368	117 ± 15
500;	350	282	0.082	2.550	96 ± 8
500;	125	204	0.102	1.158	111 ± 11
350;	250	184	0.120	2.190	83 ± 11
350;	125	177	0.131	1.482	85 ± 12
250;	125	174	0.142	1.248	107 ± 16

Tables XVIII through XXI illustrate the use of this simplified design when a total of 20 animals, 10 on the unknown and 10 on the standard, was employed. In each case the unknown and standard were the same and the theoretical potency ratio was 100%. The ratio of the high dose to the low dose varied. When 11-dehydrocorticosterone was employed in six trials the potency ratio found varied from 93 to 107%. In no instance was a significant difference in slopes of unknown and standard found. The standard error of the potency ratio varied from ±9 to ±12%. These data are presented in Table XVIII.

Tables XIX and XX illustrate the use of a total of 20 animals, using the hormones cortisone and corticosterone, respectively. No significant differences in slopes were found in either case. In the studies using cortisone, potency ratios of 84 to 110% were found, as compared to the theoretical value of 100%. The standard error of the potency ratio varied from ±5 to ±27% in six trials. With corticosterone (Table XX) the potency ratio varied from 100 to 125%. In five of the six trials the standard error of the potency ratio varied from ±9 to ±25%, but in one trial the value was ±51%.

Cortisol was studied in a similar manner over the dosage ranges of 125 to 1000 μg. per animal (Table XXI). In five of the fourteen trials significant differences in slopes of unknown and standard were found. In five trials over the dosage range of 125 to 500 μg. per animal, the potency ratio varied from 83 to 117%. The standard error of the potency ratio varied from ±8 to ±15%. In eight trials, when the dosage levels of 710 and 1000 μg. were employed for either the high dose, low dose, or both, the potency ratio varied from 84 to 159%, and the standard error of the potency ratio varied from ±10 to ±44%. Thus, the more reliable assay range appeared to be between 125 and 500 μg.

Table XXII summarizes the data on the precision of the Pabst *et al.* (1947) method. The indices of precision varied from 0.095 ± 0.002 to 0.149 ± 0.031. Thus, the method has a precision similar to that found for the Olson *et al.* (1944b) method.

TABLE XXII

THE PRECISION OF THE METHOD OF PABST *et al.* (1947)

Compound	Slope (b)	Index of precision (λ)	Sensitivity (μg.)
11-Dehydrocorticosterone	239 ± 25	0.095 ± 0.002	350
Cortisone	213 ± 51	0.149 ± 0.031	350
Corticosterone	198 ± 23	0.146 ± 0.024	125
Cortisol	203 ± 12	0.140 ± 0.014	125

3. Method of Stafford et al. (1955)

Male Sprague-Dawley rats, 140–160 gm., were adrenalectomized and placed on a stock laboratory diet and 1% NaCl solution as drinking water. On the morning of the fourth postoperative day food was withdrawn and the following morning the fasting-adrenalectomized rats received a single subcutaneous injection of the test compound suspended in 0.5 ml. of an aqueous mixture of 0.5% carboxymethylcellulose, 0.4% Tween 80, 1.5% benzyl alcohol, and 0.9% sodium chloride. Seven hours after treatment the animals were anesthetized by intraperitoneal injection of a 1% solution of sodium cyclopal. The livers were removed and dropped into hot 30% KOH and digested. The glycogen was estimated by the Seifter and Dayton method (1949).

Some typical results dealing with the relative potencies of corticoids and the expected limits of error are illustrated in Table XXIII.

TABLE XXIII

THE RELATIVE POTENCIES OF VARIOUS CORTICOIDS BY A RAT LIVER GLYCOGEN METHOD USING A SINGLE INJECTION[a]

Expt. No.	Steroid	Total dose (mg.)	No. of rats	Mean liver glycogen (%)	Relative potency (limits of error at $P = 0.95$) cortisol = 1
1	Cortisol	0.3	5	0.6	
		0.6	4	1.2	
		0.9		2.1	
	Prednisolone	0.1	5	1.0	
		0.2	4	1.1	
		0.3	5	1.7	2.8 (2.6–3.1)
2	Cortisol	0.3	5	0.6	
		0.6	5	1.4	
		0.9	4	1.9	
	9α-Fluoro-prednisolone acetate	0.005	5	0.6	
		0.010	5	1.4	
		0.015	4	1.5	53.0 (47.6–59.2)
	9α-Fluoro-cortisol acetate	0.025	5	0.08	
		0.050	5	1.5	
		0.075	4	1.8	12.6 (11.4–13.9)

[a] Stafford et al. (1955).

4. Method of Chart et al. (1955)

Twenty-one-day-old rats of the Holtzman strain weighing 50–55 gm. were accustomed to laboratory conditions for a 2-day period on Rockland or Purina Rat diet and tap water. Following this period the ani-

mals were bilaterally adrenalectomized and given 5% Cerelose in a
0.9% NaCl solution for drinking water. On the evening of the second
postoperative day, food was removed and on the morning of the third
postoperative day the saline drinking water was removed, the test
compounds in 0.1 ml. of corn oil were injected subcutaneously and
the rats placed in individual cages. Six hours after injection the animals were weighed, sacrificed by cervical dislocation, and the entire liver
was removed and transferred to a hot solution of 30% KOH for digestion. The liver glycogen concentration was determined and the values
expressed as glucose per 100 gm. body weight.

The method as described had a sensitivity of 10 μg. of cortisone as
indicated in Table XXIV. The calculated average coefficient of variation

TABLE XXIV

LIVER GLYCOGEN DEPOSITION IN ADRENALECTOMIZED IMMATURE RATS[a]

Dose of cortisone (μg.)	No. of rats	Liver glycogen (mg./100 gm. B.W. $\pm$ S.E.
0	25	0.68 $\pm$ 0.74
10	12	2.52 $\pm$ 0.33
30	13	9.69 $\pm$ 0.93
50	17	13.8 $\pm$ 1.1
100	18	22.6 $\pm$ 1.1
200	18	28.7 $\pm$ 2.2
300	19	39.4 $\pm$ 1.7

[a] Chart et al. (1955).

of 30.5% agrees well with that calculated for the method of Olson et al.
(1944a, b) [29.5%] and Pabst et al. (1947) [23.3%].

B. MOUSE GLYCOGEN METHODS

Three groups of workers have studied the liver glycogen response of
the adrenalectomized mouse to adrenal cortical steroids (Venning et al.,
1946; Eggleston et al., 1946, and Dorfman et al., 1946a). The methods
are essentially of two types. The first, such as that of Venning et al.
(1946), depends upon the deposition of glycogen in the depleted liver of
the fasting-adrenalectomized mouse. The methods employed by Eggleston
et al. (1946) and Dorfman et al. (1946a) use the fasting-adrenalectomized mouse and depend on protecting the fall in liver glycogen. Examples of these two methods will be discussed in detail.

1. Method of Venning et al. (1946)

It is important to use a single strain of mice. Two days before adrenal-ectomy the mice are placed on the McCollum diet (Table XXV) which contains 26% protein and 52% carbohydrate. The male mice (20–25 gm.) are bilaterally adrenalectomized and kept at a constant temperature of

TABLE XXV

MᴄCᴏʟʟᴜᴍ Dɪᴇᴛ Uꜱᴇᴅ ɪɴ ᴛʜᴇ
Mᴏᴜꜱᴇ Gʟʏᴄᴏɢᴇɴ Mᴇᴛʜᴏᴅꜱ

Constituent	Per cent
Whole wheat flour	67.5
Casein	15.0
Whole milk powder	10.0
Butter	5.0
Calcium carbonate	1.5
Sodium chloride	1.0

76°F. The animals receive a solution of 0.9% NaCl containing 5% glu-cose for drinking water on the first postoperative day. On the morning of the second postoperative day, 0.9% NaCl solution is used for drinking water. At 5:00 P.M. on the third postoperative day, the food is removed. On the fourth postoperative day a total of 7 subcutaneous injections are given at 9:15 A.M., 10:00 A.M., 10:45 A.M., 11:30 A.M., 12:30 A.M., 1:30 P.M., and 2:30 P.M. The total volume injected is 1.4 ml. The solution con-sists of the hormone in 10% ethanol to which 70 mg. of glucose has been added for each 1.4 ml. of solution. At 3:30 P.M., 1 hour after the last injection, the animals are weighed and anesthetized with sodium amytal (0.2 ml. of a 1.8% solution). The livers are removed and placed in 4 ml. of hot 30% KOH in a 15-ml. graduated centrifuge tube. After digestion, the glycogen is precipitated by the addition of 1.2 volumes of 95% ethanol. The tubes are heated until the mixture just begins to boil, cooled in an ice bath, and centrifuged. The supernatant liquid is poured off, and the tubes are allowed to drain. The sides of the tubes are washed with 0.5 ml. of ethanol and again allowed to drain. Final traces of ethanol are removed by heating the tubes in a hot-water bath for a few minutes. After hydrolysis of the glycogen, the glucose is determined by the method of Good *et al.* (1933). The glycogen is expressed as milligrams of liver glucose per 100 gm. of body weight.

Table XXVI illustrates the influence of 11-dehydrocorticosterone and cortisone on the deposition of liver glycogen. The relationship is linear

TABLE XXVI

THE INFLUENCE OF ADRENAL CORTICAL STEROIDS ON THE DEPOSITION
OF LIVER GLYCOGEN IN THE FASTING-ADRENALECTOMIZED MOUSE[a]

Compound	Total amount administered (μg.)	No. of mice	Mean liver glycogen (mg./100 gm. ± S.E.)
0	0	34	4.1 ± 0.5
11-Dehydrocorticosterone	40	8	42 ± 4.8
	80	8	69 ± 7.9
	160	9	94 ± 7.1
Cortisone	10	8	33 ± 3.2
	10	8	35 ± 2.5
	20	8	61 ± 2.0
	20	8	63 ± 4.4
	40	8	91 ± 7.5
	50	8	102 ± 7.8

[a] Method of Venning *et al.* (1946).

when the response is plotted against the logarithm of the dose. The method is sensitive enough to detect about 10 μg. of cortisone and about 40 μg. of 11-dehydrocorticosterone. Further, the indices of precision for the assay of these two compounds was calculated and found to be 0.137 and 0.222, respectively.

2. Method C of Eggleston et al. (1946)

Male mice (18–24 gm.) are bilaterally adrenalectomized under sodium pentobarbital anesthesia. The animals receive 0.25 ml. of Upjohn's aqueous adrenal cortical extract and are placed in a constant temperature room at 78°F. The animals are placed on the McCollum diet (see p. 349) and normal saline drinking water. At 4:30 P.M. on the fourth day after operation, the animals receive 0.4 ml. of Upjohn's aqueous adrenal cortical extract. At 8:30 A.M. the following morning hourly injection of the test material is begun. For each subcutaneous injection the animals received 0.05 ml. of oil solution. Seven hourly injections are made. One-half hour after the last injection, the animals are weighed and killed by snapping their necks. The livers are quickly removed and dropped into 5.0 ml. of hot 30% KOH, in a graduated 50-ml. centrifuge tube. The liver glycogen is determined by the method of Good *et al.* (1933) using the sugar reagent of Shaffer-Hartman and Somogyi No. 2 (Peters and Van Slyke, 1932). The results are expressed as milligrams of glucose per 10 gm. of body weight (Table XXVII).

TABLE XXVII

THE LIVER GLYCOGEN RESPONSES OF ADRENALECTOMIZED MICE
TO CORTISONE USING METHODS C AND D[a]

Amount (μg.)	Method D	Method C
	Fermentable sugar (mg./10 gm. B.W. $\pm$ S.E.)	Glycogen (mg./10 gm. B.W. $\pm$ S.E.)
0	2.8	0.7 $\pm$ 0.6
0.5		1.6 $\pm$ 0.03
1.0		2.0 $\pm$ 0.08
2.5		5.0 $\pm$ 0.7
5.0	6.4 $\pm$ 0.4	6.0 $\pm$ 0.6
10.0	11.0 $\pm$ 0.2	9.3 $\pm$ 1.0
12.5		11.1 $\pm$ 1.5
20.0	19.2 $\pm$ 0.8	12.0 $\pm$ 1.0
25.0		13.3 $\pm$ 0.7
40.0	24.8 $\pm$ 1.0	

[a] From Eggleston et al. (1946).

3. Method D of Eggleston et al. (1946)

The animals are killed as in method C. The livers are removed and dropped into a graduated Pyrex centrifuge tube containing 10 ml. of N H_2SO_4. After digesting and cooling the liver 0.8 ml. of 40% NaOH and sufficient N NaOH are added to bring the solution to the first pink color with phenolphthalein. The proteins are precipitated by the method of Somogyi (1930) and the sugar is analyzed as described under method C. Five milliliters of the supernatant are transferred to a graduated 15-ml. centrifuge tube containing 5 ml. of washed and centrifuged Fleischmann's baker's yeast. The suspension is thoroughly mixed and allowed to stand at room temperature for 1 hour. The tube is centrifuged and 2 ml. of the supernatant fluid is taken for the determination. The total fermentable sugar is calculated by subtracting the nonfermentable reducing substances from the total reducing substances. The results are expressed as total fermentable sugar per 10 gm. of body weight.

Method D, which is less sensitive than C, has a precision about 10 times that of C.

Table XXVII illustrates the influence of cortisone on the deposition of liver glycogen. Method D is sensitive to 5 μg. and has a precision of $\lambda = 0.114$.

4. Summary of Mouse Glycogen Methods

The use of the adrenalectomized mouse for adrenal cortical hormone carbohydrate activity is summarized in Table XXVIII. In the main,

TABLE XXVIII

ADRENALECTOMIZED MOUSE GLYCOGEN METHODS FOR THE ASSAY
OF ADRENAL CORTICAL HORMONES

Compound	Slope (b)	Index of precision (λ)	Sensitivity (μg.)	Reference
Cortisone (method D)	21.04	0.114	5	Eggleston et al. (1946)
Cortisone	95.9	0.137	10	Venning et al. (1946)
11-Dehydrocorticosterone	86.1	0.222	40	
Cortisone	22.23	0.158	10	Dorfman et al. (1946a)

these methods compare favorably as to precision with the rat methods presented previously (see p. 339). Nissim (1952) has suggested that it is of value to calculate the coefficients of variation for the mouse glycogen assays so that independent evaluations can be made for the method and for the suitability of the strain of animals.

C. MUSCLE WORK TEST

The muscle work test for the assay of adrenal cortical steroids has been intensively studied by Ingle (1944b). The method is based upon the fact that muscular responsiveness is lost within a few hours following removal of the adrenal glands and that the work ability of the muscle can be maintained by the administration of suitable adrenal cortical extracts or pure compounds. Since the 11-oxygenated steroids are quite active and compounds such as deoxycorticosterone are practically without activity, it appears that the principal effect is on carbohydrate metabolism. The test is therefore included in this section together with the glycogen methods.

1. Method of Ingle (1944b)

For details and apparatus the reader is referred to the original description (Ingle, 1944b). An abstract of the significant points in the method follows. Male rats, 180 ± 2 gm. in weight, are adrenalectomized and nephrectomized. The animal is fixed to a board and the gastrocnemius muscle stimulated, weakly at first; then the stimulus is gradually increased until a standard intensity, which is known to be optimal for sustaining the contraction of the muscle, is reached. Subcutaneous injection of the hormones in oil (0.5 ml. per dose) is done at the beginning, and again 6 hours later. Adrenal cortical extracts are injected in aqueous ethanol solution (1.0 ml. per dose). Stimulation is continued until the muscle ceases to contract or for a period of 24 hours. The total number of contractions is recorded by means of a mechanical counter and is used as the index of efficiency.

2. Results and Conclusions

Table XXIX presents a typical set of data on the muscle work test using the adrenalectomized-nephrectomized rat and the hormone corti-

TABLE XXIX

THE INFLUENCE OF CORTISONE ON THE MUSCLE WORK
OF THE ADRENALECTOMIZED-NEPHRECTOMIZED RAT[a]

Total dose (mg.)	No. of rats	Muscle work (Number of revolutions ± S.E.)
0	25	4000
0.16	45	9439 ± 415
0.20	45	11296 ± 342
0.25	45	12982 ± 382

[a] Ingle (1944a).

sone. Over the dosage range (0.16–0.25 mg.) of hormone, the relationship is linear when the logarithm of the dose and response is considered. The slope over this range is 18,250 and λ is 0.140.

Using this test Ingle and Kuizenga (1945) compared the relative

TABLE XXX

THE RELATIVE ACTIVITY OF ADRENAL
CORTICAL COMPOUNDS ON A
MUSCLE WORK TEST[a]

Compound	Relative activity (%)
Cortisone	100
Cortisol	160
11-Dehydrocorticosterone	32
Corticosterone	46

[a] Data of Ingle and Kuizenga (1945).

activity of four different adrenal cortical steroids. If cortisone is considered the standard (100%) as in Table XXX, cortisol has a relative potency of 160%, 11-dehydrocorticosterone a value of 32%, and corticosterone 46%.

D. ANTI-INSULIN ACTION

This method described by Jensen and Grattan (1940) has not been studied in sufficient detail to judge its value. Attempts to adapt the method for quantitative work in the author's laboratory indicated that at least under the conditions used the method was too variable for precise assays.

VI. Thymolytic Assay Methods

A. MOUSE METHODS

1. Method of Santisteban and Dougherty (1954)

These investigators reported the relative thymolytic potency of various corticoids using adrenalectomized female CBA mice 10 weeks of age (18.2 ± 0.5 gm.). The steroids were suspended in aqueous solution and were administered intraperitoneally 20–24 hours after surgery in eight divided doses at 12-hour intervals. The mice were sacrificed on the fifth day 12 hours after the last injection. The index of precision varied widely from 0.037 to 0.407. Cortisone, corticosterone, and 11-dehydrocorticosterone were reported to be 36, 24, and 18% as active as cortisol.

2. Method of Dorfman et al. (1959)

Brown female mice (C57) were adrenalectomized under ether anesthesia at 24 days of age. The steroids were injected subcutaneously in 0.1 ml. of an aqueous suspension on the day of surgery and again on the following day. One day after the last injection the mice were sacrificed and body and thymus weights were determined. Results were expressed as milligrams of thymus per gram of body weight. The index of precision was of the order of 0.26 and the sensitivity about 0.1–0.2 mg. of cortisol.

B. RAT METHODS

1. Method of Stephenson (1954, 1956)

This method employs weanling Wistar strain adrenalectomized rats 21–25 days of age and weighing 35–45 gm. The corticoids were injected subcutaneously three times daily at 9 A.M., 1:30 P.M., and 5 P.M. for 2 days, and the glands were removed approximately 16 hours after the last injection. A low dose (5 mg. per kilogram, in corn oil) was selected which produced about a 25–35% involution of the thymus gland, while the high dose (twice the low dose) usually produced a 50–60% involution. In some assays a 10% ethyl alcohol in saline solvent was used.

Table XXXI summarizes the relative potencies of various corticoids

TABLE XXXI

INFLUENCE OF VEHICLE ON THE RELATIVE POTENCIES OF CORTICOIDS ADMINISTERED
BY SUBCUTANEOUS INJECTION[a]

Corticoid	Corn oil		10% Ethyl alcohol in saline	
	Relative potency	Fiducial limits ($P = 0.95$)	Relative potency	Fiducial limits ($P = 0.95$)
Cortisol	1		1	
Cortisone	0.65	0.59–0.70	0.59	0.45–0.77
Prednisone	2.96	2.59–3.39	4.12[b]	3.28–5.68
Prednisolone	4.28	4.26–5.33	5.40[b]	4.72–6.19

[a] Stephenson (1956).
[b] Significant difference ($P = 0.05$).

determined by this method when corn oil or 10% ethyl alcohol in saline were employed as solvents. Stephenson (1956) pointed out that the potencies of cortisol relative to cortisone and that of prednisolone relative to prednisone did not differ significantly when the two vehicles were used, but that the activity of prednisone and prednisolone relative to cortisol was significantly higher when the corticoids were administered in the alcohol-saline vehicle.

2. Method of Shewell (1957)

Since Bruce et al. (1952) had demonstrated that the stress of handling and injecting young rats up to 10–12 days of age was insufficient to produce thymic atrophy, Shewell suggested the use of these young rats for the quantitative assay of corticoids. The method as described employed litter-mate nestling rats of a hooded strain approximately 10 days of age and weighing initially 12–15 gm. Litters containing 8 rats were chosen and allocated to the various groups so that any one litter was represented in each experimental group. One rat of each litter served as an untreated control, one as the vehicle-injected control, and 6 were treated with test compounds. The steroids were injected with the test compounds in 0.1 ml. of a saline suspension once daily for 3 days; the rats were autopsied on the fourth day. The thymus gland was removed and weighed on a torsion balance. Typical assays using this method are presented in Table XXXII.

TABLE XXXII

ASSAY OF CORTICOIDS BY THYMIC INVOLUTION IN THE NESTLING RAT[a]

Corticoid	Relative potency, cortisone = 1	5% Confidence limits
Cortisol	2.4	1.9–3.0
9α-Chlorocortisol	3.4	1.8–6.3
9α-Fluorocortisol	5.3	4.2–6.5
Prednisone	9.9	6.6–14.6
9α-Fluroprednisolone	13.2	9.8–17.0

[a] Shewell (1957).

3. Method of Ringler and Brownfield (1960)

This modification of the thymolytic assay utilizes the intact immature female rat (40–60 gm.) and the steroid was administered in 0.2 ml. of a carboxymethlycellulose vehicle in one subcutaneous injection. Thymus weights were determined 48 hours after the single injection. When highly active corticoids were studied the index of precision of the bioassay was judged to be about 0.23.

4. Method of Dorfman et al. (1961a)

This thymolytic assay employed male albino rats 22–24 days of age which were adrenalectomized and placed on a stock diet and saline. The test compounds were suspended in an aqueous solution with Tween 80 so that the total dose was contained in 0.2 ml. of vehicle. A volume of 0.1 ml. was injected once on the day of surgery and once the following day. One day later the animals were sacrificed and body and thymus weights determined. The response was expressed as the ratio of the thymus weight in milligrams to the body weight in grams. Table XXXIII lists a series of assays in which the slopes of the unknown and standard were not significantly different and the index of precision varied from 0.15 to 0.24.

This thymolytic assay was also extended to a 6-day test which is similar to the 2-day assay described above except that the granuloma was not being considered. Typical data are presented in Table XXXIV and λ varied within a narrow range from 0.14 to 0.19.

TABLE XXXIII

BIOASSAY OF CORTICOIDS BY A THYMIC INVOLUTION METHOD (TWO-DAY TEST)[a]

Test steroid (No. of rats)	Standard steroid (No. of rats)	Combined slope (b_c)	Index of precision (λ)	Potency ratio $(\% \pm \text{S.E.})$
Cortisol acetate (25)	Cortisol (31)	−2.48	0.15	45 ± 4.1
Cortisol acetate (29)	Cortisol (31)	−2.34	0.24	47 ± 6.7
Cortisol acetate (33)	Cortisol (33)	−2.14	0.22	54 ± 6.8
9α-Fluorocortisol (63)	Cortisol (64)	−2.25	0.20	360 ± 30
Δ⁶-Dehydrocortisol (34)	Cortisol (36)	−2.28	0.24	84 ± 11

[a] Dorfman *et al.* (1961a).

TABLE XXXIV

BIOASSAY OF CORTICOIDS BY A THYMIC INVOLUTION METHOD (SIX-DAY TEST)[a]

Test steroid (No. of rats)	Standard steroid (No. of rats)	Combined slopes (b_c)	Index of precision (λ)	Potency ratio $(\% \pm \text{S.E.})$
Prednisolone acetate (30)	Cortisol acetate (33)	−1.55	0.15	354 ± 32
Prednisolone acetate (48)	Cortisol acetate (48)	−2.22	0.14	502 ± 35
Prednisolone acetate (44)	Cortisol acetate (40)	−2.09	0.19	553 ± 50
Δ⁶-Dehydrocortisol acetate (32)	Cortisol acetate (48)	−2.59	0.18	31 ± 3
Δ⁶-Dehydrocortisol acetate (38)	Cortisol acetate (38)	−2.99	0.16	49 ± 4

[a] Dorfman *et al.* (1961b).

5. Combined Thymolytic and Liver Glycogen Deposition Test of Ringler et al. (1959)

Ringler *et al.* (1959) have described a combined thymolytic-liver glycogen deposition assay in adrenalectomized rats. Immature male rats of the Sherman strain, weighing 40–60 gm., were bilaterally adrenalectomized and maintained with Purina Lab Chow and drinking fluid containing 1% NaCl. Twenty-four hours after surgery the test compounds in

0.2 ml. of an aqueous suspending medium (Perrine *et al.*, 1959) were injected subcutaneously or, alternatively, the rats were treated by gavage. The test compounds were administered once daily for 2 additional days. The rats were fasted for 15 hours prior to and 7 hours after the last injection. Livers were removed under sodium pentobarbital anesthesia and rapidly placed in 30% potassium hydroxide. Thymi were removed and weighed on a torsion balance. Liver glycogen was determined by the method of Seifter *et al.* (1950). Typical data are presented in Table XXXV for both the orally administered (gavage) and the injected corticoids.

TABLE XXXV

THE INFLUENCE OF CORTICOIDS ON THE THYMUS GLAND AND LIVER GLYCOGEN IN THE ADRENALECTOMIZED MALE RAT[a]

Route	Material administered	Total dose (mg.)	Liver glycogen (mg./gm. $\pm$ S.E.)	Thymus weight (mg./100 gm. B.W. $\pm$ S.E.)
Subcutaneous injection	0	0	2.03 $\pm$ 0.12	407 $\pm$ 18
	Cortisol	0.2	7.37 $\pm$ 0.82	302 $\pm$ 21
		0.4	12.82 $\pm$ 0.88	215 $\pm$ 16
		0.7	26.83 $\pm$ 2.78	124 $\pm$ 7
		1.0	54.60 $\pm$ 4.23	83 $\pm$ 5
	Triamcinolone	0.025	6.52 $\pm$ 0.81	341 $\pm$ 15
		0.05	11.80 $\pm$ 1.05	284 $\pm$ 11
		0.1	35.07 $\pm$ 5.63	184 $\pm$ 13
		0.2	68.60 $\pm$ 3.04	94 $\pm$ 4
Gavage	0	0	2.10 $\pm$ 0.20	390 $\pm$ 21
	Cortisol	0.5	4.24 $\pm$ 1.11	274 $\pm$ 18
		1.0	6.52 $\pm$ 0.86	211 $\pm$ 21
		2.0	16.06 $\pm$ 1.86	137 $\pm$ 15
		4.0	21.77 $\pm$ 6.97	123 $\pm$ 8
		8.0	28.51 $\pm$ 4.22	88 $\pm$ 4

[a] Ringler *et al.* (1959).

VII. Anti-Inflammatory Methods

A. SYSTEMIC ASSAYS

1. Method of Dulin (1955)—Meyer et al. (1953)

Male rats, 150–170 gm., were adrenalectomized under sodium pentobarbital anesthesia. Two nonsterile cotton dental pellets (6–8 mg.) were implanted in the mid ventro lateral subcutaneous connective tissue at the time of adrenalectomy. On the day of implantation the test steroids in aqueous suspension were injected subcutaneously in 0.2 ml. of vehicle consisting of 0.5% carboxymethylcellulose, 0.4% Tween 80, 1.5% benzyl alcohol, and 0.9% NaCl. These injections were continued once daily for a total of 7 days. Twenty-four hours after the last injection the animals were sacrificed, the cotton pellets together with the accumulated granuloma were removed, dried at 60°C. for 24 hours, and weighed. The original weight of the cotton pellet was subtracted from the total dry weight.

Typical results using this method are given in Table XXXVI.

TABLE XXXVI

ANTI-INFLAMMATORY EFFECTS OF TYPICAL CORTICOIDS[a]

Expt. No.	Steroid	Total dose (mg.)	No. of rats	Mean dry granuloma weight (mg. $\pm$ S.E.)	Relative potency, cortisol = 1
A	0	0	20	14.41 $\pm$ 0.77	
	Cortisol	0.2	17	9.97 $\pm$ 0.46	
		1.0	16	6.47 $\pm$ 0.34	
	9α-Fluoroprednisolone acetate	0.01	20	9.91 $\pm$ 0.46	
		0.05	19	7.90 $\pm$ 0.47	14
B	0	0	7	13.40 $\pm$ 0.47	
	Cortisol	0.2	7	9.80 $\pm$ 1.25	
		1.0	6	6.32 $\pm$ 0.29	
	9α-Fluorocortisol acetate	0.025	7	10.74 $\pm$ 0.34	
		0.125	8	6.05 $\pm$ 0.44	7.3
C	0	0	10	12.20 $\pm$ 0.49	
	Cortisol	0.2	8	10.10 $\pm$ 0.65	
		1.0	9	5.70 $\pm$ 0.42	
	Prednisolone acetate	0.06	10	10.00 $\pm$ 0.77	
		0.30	10	6.20 $\pm$ 0.50	3.1

[a] Dulin (1955).

2. Method of Singer and Borman (1956)

Male rats, 120–150 gm. in weight, were adrenalectomized and a cotton pellet 5–7 mg. in weight (made from nonsterile unbleached cotton, which was rolled into a ball with the fingers) was inserted subcutaneously

TABLE XXXVII

THE ANTI-INFLAMMATORY ACTIVITY OF CORTISONE AND CORTISOL ACETATE[a]

Steroid administered	Total dose (mg.)	No. of rats	Mean granuloma dry weight (mg.)
0	0	20	25.5
Cortisone acetate	1.2	19	17.0
	3.6	20	12.5
	10.8	18	10.2
Cortisol acetate	0	29	25.1
	1.2	20	20.4
	3.6	20	13.5
	10.8	19	10.0

[a] Singer and Borman (1956).

through the incision used for the surgery. The animals are fed a normal stock diet, and 1% NaCl was included in the drinking water throughout the experiment. The test compounds were suspended in an aqueous medium and injected subcutaneously once a day, starting with the day of surgery and continuing for a total of 4 consecutive days. The aqueous suspensions were prepared by grinding the test compounds in a mortar and passing through a 200-mesh screen. This finely divided material was suspended in a solution of 0.04% Tween 80, 0.7% NaCl, 0.9% benzyl alcohol, and 0.5% carboxymethylcellulose. Twenty-four hours after the last injection the rats were sacrificed and the granuloma removed. The dry granuloma was heated at 80°C. overnight and the initial weight of the cotton pellet was subtracted from the total dry weight. A typical assay is indicated in Table XXXVII in which cortisone acetate and cortisol

TABLE XXXVIII

THE RELATIVE POTENCY OF VARIOUS CORTICOIDS USING THE
ANTI-INFLAMMATORY TEST OF SINGER AND BORMAN (1956)

Steroid	Relative potency, cortisol acetate = 1	95% Confidence limits
9α-Fluorocortisol acetate	13.2	8.7 –20.0
9α-Fluorocorticosterone acetate	2.7	1.8 – 4.0
Corticosterone	0.32	0.24– 0.44
Progesterone	<0.04	—
Deoxycorticosterone acetate	<0.04	—

acetate were studied. These two steroids were active and of about the same order by this test. The relative potency of other compounds related to these steroids with the calculated error at the 95% confidence limits are presented in Table XXXVIII.

3. Method of Robert and Nezamis (1957)

Selye (1953) reported a granuloma pouch technique for the study of inflammation. The basic principles were incorporated into a method described in detail by Robert and Nezamis. This method depends essentially upon the irritant properties of croton oil which is introduced into a pouch made by injecting air subcutaneously into the middle of the back of the animal. The anti-inflammatory agent may be assayed by direct introduction into the pouch or by systematic administration. Evaluation of an anti-inflammatory agent may be assayed by direct introduction into the pouch or by systematic administration. Evaluation of anti-inflammatory activity of a compound is judged by the volume of fluid contained in the pouch at autopsy. This is measured by making a cut in the skin and emptying the fluid directly into a graduated cylinder. By systemic administration the sensitivity of the test as reported by Robert and Nezamis (1957) was about 0.7 mg. of cortisol.

B. LOCAL ASSAY

1. Method of Hershberger and Calhoun (1957)

This method was primarily designed to assay steroids for their prolonged anti-inflammatory activity by local administration.

Male Sprague-Dawley rats weighing 170–200 gm. were adrenalectomized and maintained on Rockland Rat Diet and saline. During the first postoperative day the saline was supplemented with 5% glucose. Cotton pellets (No. 3 from Richmond Dental Cotton Company, Charlotte, North Carolina) 5–8 mg. in weight were impregnated with 0.03 ml. of an acetone solution of the test compound and the acetone was removed by spontaneous evaporation. One day after surgery 4 pellets were implanted into the loose subcutaneous connective tissue of the pectoral and dorsolateral neck regions. Each animal was implanted with 2 pellets which served as controls and 2 pellets impregnated with the test compound. The pellets averaged 6 mg. Six days after implantation the pellets were removed, dried to constant weight at 72°C., and weighed to the nearest 0.1 mg.

The relative potencies of certain corticoids and the fiducial limits are presented in Table XXXIX.

TABLE XXXIX

THE RELATIVE POTENCY OF CORTICOIDS BY A LOCAL ANTI-INFLAMMATORY TEST[a]

Steroids	Relative potency, cortisol acetate = 1	Fiducial limits 95%
9α-Chloro-21-deoxycortisone	2.57	1.85–3.52
9α-Chloro-21-deoxycortisol	0.63	0.45–0.87
9α-Fluoro-21-deoxycortisol	0.34	0.25–0.47

[a] Hershberger and Calhoun (1957).

VIII. Stress Tests

These tests include the cold test, the Everse-de Fremery test, the swim test, the typhoid toxin test, and the animal restraint test. The cold test has been studied in the greatest detail.

COLD TESTS

Hartman *et al.* (1931) demonstrated a significant difference in the sensitivity of normal and adrenalectomized rats exposed to low environmental temperatures and showed that the resistance of adrenalectomized rats can be increased by the administration of adrenal cortical extracts. This phenomenon was adapted to the assay of adrenal cortical steroids by Selye and Schenker (1938), Venning *et al.* (1944), and Vogt (1943). Dorfman *et al.* (1946 b, c) have made an extensive study of the cold test as a means of assaying adrenal cortical hormones. The adrenalectomized mouse was not found to be satisfactory. Reasonable accuracy was found by using the operated rat.

1. *Method of Dorfman* et al. (*1946b, c*)

Albino rats, 22–24 days of age and weighing between 35 and 52 gm., were bilaterally adrenalectomized in one stage under ether anesthesia. The experiments were run between 12 and 24 hours after operation. At this time the animals received the hormone either by injection or by stomach tube and were immediately placed in a wide-mouth fruit jar (1 pint size) containing a sheet of filter paper for bedding. The animals were transferred to a cold room kept at 5°C. and were observed at half-hour intervals until they had all died.

Death was considered to have occurred in these studies when the animals had no visible respiration, showed low body temperature, and on stimulation showed no responsive movements.

TABLE XL

THE COLD-PROTECTING RESPONSE OF 11-DEHYDROCORTICOSTERONE ACETATE (SYNTHETIC AND ISOLATED) IN ADRENALECTOMIZED RATS[a,b]

Dosage (μg.)		No. of adrenalectomized rats	Survival (hours ± S.E.)
Synthetic	Isolated		
0	0	10	9.7 ± 0.68
40	0	10	10.7 ± 0.88
80	0	10	11.9 ± 0.97
160	0	10	13.5 ± 1.17
320	0	10	15.4 ± 0.74
0	40	10	9.8 ± 0.81
0	80	10	11.3 ± 1.23
0	160	11	11.9 ± 0.90
0	320	11	14.2 ± 0.92

[a] Temperature 47° ± 1° F.
[b] Dorfman (1949c).

It is imperative to run the unknown and standard simultaneously. In some runs the response decreases enormously. This happens about 1 out of every 3 trials, and seems to be independent of the weight of the animals, previous stress, or any other known factor. This of course reduces the value of the test enormously.

2. Results and Conclusions

Table XL illustrates the response of adrenalectomized rats exposed to low temperature when treated with two different samples of 11-dehydrocorticosterone acetate. This represents a run under favorable conditions. Table XLI shows an example of the use of the cold test method

TABLE XLI

THE ASSAY OF 11-DEHYDROCORTICOSTERONE ACETATE USING A COLD PROTECTION TEST

$$\frac{\text{High dose of synthetic sample}}{\text{Low dose of synthetic sample}} = \frac{\text{High dose of isolated sample}}{\text{Low dose of isolated sample}}$$

$$N = 10$$

Dosage level (μg.)	b	λ	t	Potency ratio (% ± S.E.)
40; 80	10.8	0.379	0.276	74 ± 22
160; 320	15.5	0.187	0.410	72 ± 11
40; 160	8.1	0.337	0.333	50 ± 14
80; 320	11.4	0.291	0.119	76 ± 16

employing the experimental design and calculations of Bliss (1944a, b). In each case the unknown and standard were significantly different as to slopes, and the index of precision, λ, varied from 0.276 to 0.410. The mean slope for the four trials was 11.5 ± 1.5, and the mean value of λ was 0.299 ± 0.072.

Table XLII lists the relative activities of various adrenal cortical

TABLE XLII

RELATIVE POTENCIES OF ADRENAL CORTICAL
STEROIDS ON THE BASIS OF A COLD TEST
EXPRESSED AS THE PERCENTAGE OF THE
ACTIVITY OF CORTISONE

Compound	Relative potency (%)
Cortisone	100
11-Dehydrocorticosterone	33
Corticosterone	9
11-Deoxycorticosterone acetate	8

steroids in the cold test. When the potency of cortisone is set at 100%, 11-dehydrocorticosterone has a relative potency of 33%, corticosterone, 9%, and 11-deoxycorticosterone acetate, 8%.

REFERENCES

Bliss, C. I. (1944a). *Science* **100**, 577.
Bliss, C. I. (1944b). *J. Am. Statist. Assoc.* **39**, 479.
Bliss, C. I., and Cattell, M. (1943). *Ann. Rev. Physiol.* **5**, 479.
Bruce, H. M., Parkes, A. S., and Perry, W. L. M. (1952). *Lancet* **1**, 790.
Bülbring, E. (1937). *J. Physiol. (London)* **89**, 64.
Cartland, G. F., and Kuizenga, M. H. (1936). *Am. J. Physiol.* **117**, 678.
Chart, J. J., Shipley, E. G., and Meyer, R. K. (1955). *Proc. Soc. Exptl. Biol. Med.* **90**, 127.
Cori, G. T. (1932). *J. Biol. Chem.* **96**, 259.
Deming, Q. B., and Luetscher, J. A., Jr. (1950). *Proc. Soc. Exptl. Biol. Med.* **73**, 171.
Dorfman, R. I. (1949a). *Proc. Soc. Exptl. Biol. Med.* **70**, 732.
Dorfman, R. I. (1949b). *Proc. Soc. Exptl. Biol. Med.* **72**, 395.
Dorfman, R. I. (1949c). *Ann. N.Y. Acad. Sci.* **50**, 551.
Dorfman, R. I. (1960). Unpublished experiment.
Dorfman, R. I., and Dorfman, A. S. (1960). Unpublished experiment.
Dorfman, R. I., Ross, E., and Shipley, R. A. (1946a). *Endocrinology* **38**, 178.
Dorfman, R. I., Shipley, R. A., Ross, E., Schiller, S., and Horwitt, B. N. (1946b). *Endocrinology* **38**, 189.
Dorfman, R. I., Shipley, R. A., Schiller, S., and Horwitt, B. N. (1946c). *Endocrinology* **38**, 165.

Dorfman, R. I., Potts, A. M., and Feil, M. (1947). *Endocrinology* **41**, 464.

Dorfman, R. I., Dorfman, A. S., and Laubach, G. (1959). *Proc. Soc. Exptl. Biol. Med.* **100**, 63.

Dorfman, R. I., Dorfman, A. S., Agnello, E. J., Figdor, S. K., and Laubach, G. D. (1961a). *Acta Endocrinol.* **37**, 343.

Dorfman, R. I., Dorfman, A. S., Agnello, E. J., Figdor, S. K., and Laubach, G. D. (1961b). *Acta Endocrinol.* **37**, 577.

Dulin, W. E. (1955). *Proc. Soc. Exptl. Biol. Med.* **90**, 115.

Eggleston, N. M., Johnston, B. J., and Dobriner, K. (1946). *Endocrinology* **38**, 197.

Good, C. A., Kramer, H., and Somogyi, M. (1933). *J. Biol. Chem.* **100**, 485.

Grollman, A. (1941). *Endocrinology* **29**, 855.

Hartman, F. A., Brownell, K. A., and Crosby, A. A. (1931). *Am. J. Physiol.* **98**, 674.

Hershberger, L. G., and Calhoun, D. W. (1957). *Endocrinology* **60**, 153.

Ingle, D. J. (1944a). *Endocrinology* **34**, 191.

Ingle, D. J. (1944b). "Physiology and Chemistry of Hormones." American Association for the Advancement of Science, Washington, D. C.

Ingle, D. J., and Kuizenga, M. H. (1945). *Endocrinology* **36**, 218.

Jensen, H., and Grattan, J. F. (1940). *Am. J. Physiol.* **128**, 270.

Kagawa, C. M., Shipley, E. G., and Meyer, R. K. (1952). *Proc. Soc. Exptl. Biol. Med.* **80**, 281.

Kuizenga, M. H. (1949). Personal communication.

Marcus, F., Romanoff, L. P., and Pincus, G. (1952). *Endocrinology* **50**, 286.

Meyer, R. K., Stucki, J. C., and Aulsbrook, K. A. (1953). *Proc. Soc. Exptl. Biol. Med.* **84**, 624.

Nissim, J. A. (1952). *J. Endocrinol.* **8**, x.

Olson, R. E., Jacobs, F. A., Richert, D., Thayer, S. A., Kopp, L. J., and Wade, N. J. (1944a). *Endocrinology* **35**, 430.

Olson, R. E., Thayer, S. A., and Kopp, L. J. (1944b). *Endocrinology* **35**, 464.

Pabst, M. L., Sheppard, R., and Kuizenga, M. H. (1947). *Endocrinology* **41**, 55.

Perrine, J. W., Bortle, L., Heyder, E., Partridge, R., Ross, E. K., and Ringler, I. (1959). *Endocrinology* **64**, 437.

Peters, J. P., and Van Slyke, D. D. (1932). "Quantitative Clinical Chemistry," Vol. 2, p. 466. Williams & Wilkins, Baltimore, Maryland.

Ringler, I., and Brownfield, R. (1960). *Endocrinology* **66**, 900.

Ringler, I., Bortle, L., Heyder, E., Monteforte, A., Perrine, J., and Ross, E. (1959). *Proc. Soc. Exptl. Biol. Med.* **102**, 628.

Robert, A., and Nezamis, J. E. (1957). *Acta Endocrinol.* **25**, 105.

Santisteban, G. A., and Dougherty, T. F. (1954). *Endocrinology* **54**, 130.

Seifter, S., and Dayton, S. (1949). *Federation Proc.* **8**, 249.

Seifter, S., Dayton, S., Novic, B., and Muntwyler, E. (1950). *Arch. Biochem.* **25**, 191.

Selye, H. (1953). *Recent Progr. in Hormone Research* **8**, 117.

Selye, H., and Schenker, V. (1938). *Proc. Soc. Exptl. Biol. Med.* **39**, 518.

Shaffer, P. A., and Somogyi, M. (1933). *J. Biol. Chem.* **100**, 695.

Shewell, S. (1957). *British J. Pharmacol.* **12**, 133.

Simpson, S. A., and Tait, J. F. (1952). *Endocrinology* **50**, 150.

Singer, F. M. S., and Borman, A. B. (1956). *Proc. Soc. Exptl. Biol. Med.* **92**, 23.

Somogyi, M. (1930). *J. Biol. Chem.* **86**, 655.

Spencer, A. G. (1950). *Nature* **166**, 32.

Stafford, R. O., Barnes, L. E., Bowman, B. J., and Meinzinger, M. M. (1955). *Proc. Soc. Exptl. Biol. Med.* **89,** 371.

Stephenson, N. R. (1954). *Can. J. Biochem. and Physiol.* **32,** 689.

Stephenson, N. R. (1956). *Can. J. Biochem. and Physiol.* **34,** 253.

Tolksdorf, S., Battin, M. L., Cassidy, J. W., MacLeod, R. M., Warren, F. M., and Perlman, P. L. (1956). *Proc. Soc. Exptl. Biol. Med.* **92,** 207.

Venning, E. H., Hoffman, M. M., and Browne, J. S. L. (1944). *Endocrinology* **35,** 49.

Venning, E. H., Kazmin, V. E., and Bell, J. C. (1946). *Endocrinology* **38,** 79.

Vogt, M. (1943). *J. Physiol. (London)* **102,** 341.

PART III

Protein Hormones and Related Hormones and Substances

Chapter 9

Epinephrine and Norepinephrine

FRED ELMADJIAN

I. Introduction

Considerable progress has been made in the past decade in the understanding of the nature of biosynthesis (Hagen and Welch, 1956; Goodall and Kirshner, 1957), secretion (Dunér, 1953; Folkow and von Euler, 1954; Goldfien and Ganong, 1958), excretion (von Euler and Hellner, 1951; Elmadjian *et al.*, 1958), and metabolism (Schayer, 1951; Armstrong and McMillan, 1957; Axelrod, 1957; Resnick *et al.*, 1958; Goodall *et al.*, 1959) of epinephrine (E) and norepinephrine (NE), as well as the mapping of the distribution of these neurohormones in the nervous system (Vogt, 1954; von Euler, 1958). These advances were made possible by the introduction of methods of assay, both biological and physical, for resolving some of the qualitative and quantitative aspects of the principal problems relating to catechol amines. Assay methods in the past were principally used for standardization of pharmaceutical preparation of adrenal medullary extracts, and the understanding of physiological aspects relating to chemical mediation of nerve impulse.

Parallel assays by different methods and the study of patterns of response of tissues and organs have given valuable data (Cannon and Rosenblueth, 1937; Tainter and Luduena, 1950). These studies focused attention on qualitative differences of certain sympathetic stimulations and preparations of adrenal medullary extracts and epinephrine. These qualitative aspects were clarified (Holtz *et al.*, 1947; von Euler, 1946) with the final identification of E and NE as the principal neurohormones of the sympathicoadrenal system (Auerbach and Angell, 1949; Goldenberg *et al.*, 1949).

A number of excellent reviews have appeared, covering aspects of measurement of E and NE in biological material (Munch, 1931; Blaschko, 1950; West, 1950; Persky, 1955; von Euler, 1956; Gaddum and Holzbauer, 1957), and more recently at the "Symposium of Catechol Amines" (1959).

This chapter contains an evaluation of methods for the extraction and separation of N and NE in biological materials and a discussion of bioassay methods for the quantitation of these compounds.

II. Extraction and Separation

The choice of the extraction method and procedure of separation depends on the nature of biological material to be processed, on the concentration of E and NE present, and on the technique of measurement to be applied, i.e, bioassay or physical. Adrenal tissue presents no special problems, since acid-alcohol or trichloroacetic acid extraction yields an extract which is suitable for direct bioassay or colorimetric determination (von Euler, 1950). Heart or nerve tissue extracts require the additional use of alumina for selective adsorption of catechols (Shaw, 1938). Extraction of free E and NE from tissues may also be achieved by extraction of aqueous mixtures of homogenized tissue saturated with sodium chloride with n-butanol (Shore and Olin, 1958). Urine and plasma require the use of column chromatography or ion exchange resins for selective adsorption and separation of catechols. Paper chromatography also yields satisfactory separation of E and NE in 1-μg. amounts.

Organic solvents may be used to advantage if free catechol is not essential to the study. Transformation of E and NE to their respective lutines, (ethylenediamine) EDA conjugates, and formation of acetylation derivatives offer various advantages. Lutines may be extracted quantitatively with isobutanol from aqueous mixtures. The same is true of fluorescent derivatives of EDA (Cohen, 1959; Weil-Malherbe and Bone, 1954). Ethyl acetate and methylene chloride offer quantitative extraction of acetylation derivatives of E and NE (Welsh, 1955). Finally, since E and NE are metabolized to the extent of 95% or better, and the principal metabolite for both substances is vanilmandelic acid (VMA), extraction for phenolic acid and chromatography may be applied for estimation of E and NE excretion (Armstrong and McMillan, 1957).

A. Solvents

Adrenal tissue may be extracted, after mincing, with 2–3 volumes of acid-alcohol at room temperature (von Euler, 1950). Occasional stirring for about one hour is followed by filtration or centrifugation. The filtrate or supernatant fluid (free of solids) is then evaporated *in vacuo* to a convenient volume. Fats may be removed with ether. Care should be taken to make certain that the final preparation is solvent-free and adjusted to pH 4.0. Trichloroacetic acid (5%) at 5–10 volumes to 1 of tissue may be used in the same manner as acid-alcohol (von Euler, 1950). The acid may be removed with repeated ether extraction. Removal of interfering substances may be achieved with the use of fuller's earth or pharmacologic agents, such as atropine and antihistamines, when bioassay is contemplated. Such extracts may be further purified by column chromatography by treatment with alumina or ion exchange resins, or paper chromatography.

Tissues in general may be extracted by homogenizing in 2 volumes of 0.01 N HCl, saturating a 5–10 cc. aliquot with NaCl, and extracting the mixture with 10 volumes of *n*-butanol (Shore and Olin, 1958). A convenient volume is centrifuged off after the mixture is shaken for one hour, and the butanol is re-extracted with a small volume of 0.01 N HCl (about 5 cc.) after adding 70 cc. of heptane. The addition of heptane lowers the solubility of the amines in butanol, allowing the amines to pass again into the aqueous phase. This method has been used for extraction of brain tissue, and the final extract is estimated by the trihydroxyindole (THI) method.

If the free catechol amines are not essential to the final estimation, prior treatment of urine with alkali, resulting in transformation to respective lutines, allows one to use isobutanol as the extract solvent. Recovery of lutines from aqueous media is quite efficient with isobutanol, and less so with ethyl acetate (Cohen, 1959). Isobutanol is also employed in the last step in extracting EDA conjugates (Weil-Malherbe and Bone, 1952, 1954).

Ethyl acetate or methylene chloride will extract quantitatively acetylated E and NE (Welsh, 1955). The compounds formed are O^3, O^4, N-triacetyl derivatives of the respective amines. This procedure is the basis for assay in the U.S. Pharmacopeia XVI method. Radioisotope dilution techniques may also be applied with the acetylation procedure (Hagopian *et al.*, 1961).

B. Alumina

The quantitative adsorption of E and NE on aluminum hydroxide was first utilized for purposes of blood extraction (Shaw, 1938). Freshly precipitated alumina was initially shaken with the mixture at pH 4.0 removing certain interfering substances, but leaving behind the catechol amines. The latter were then adsorbed to the second portion of alumina with the solution kept at pH 8.5. The alumina was then dissolved in acid. This method was utilized for use with tissue extracts and with urine (von Euler, 1946; von Euler and Hellner, 1951), with various modifications. The primary extract of the tissue with acid-alcohol or trichloroacetic acid was treated with alumina forming freshly precipitated aluminum hydroxide in the extract. Aluminum sulfate added to the extract was followed with NaOH, forming a precipitate, and this was brought to pH 8.5. The alumina was centrifuged off and dissolved in concentrated sulfuric acid. The salts were then precipitated by addition of 4 volumes of acetone:alcohol (1:1). The organic solvents were removed by evaporation *in vacuo,* leaving the extract ready for bioassay. Another procedure is the use of alumina by the "batch" method, involving the addition of a given weight of alumina to the mixture to be extracted (von Euler and Orwén, 1955). The adsorbed amines were eluted with dilute sulfuric acid or acetic acid. The application of this method of extraction for final measurement, either by bioassay or fluorometry, has been somewhat less than satisfactory (Diller, 1957; Weil-Malherbe, 1959).

Results of the "batch" method indicated interference by calcium and potassium when used with rat colon and uterus preparations. The method involving nascent precipitation and subsequent elution in concentrated sulfuric acid gives better results (von Euler and Hellner, 1951). Column chromatographic techniques are preferred, especially when small amounts of amines are involved; this is true of urine (von Euler and Lishajko, 1959), as well as blood plasma extracts (Weil-Malherbe and Bone, 1954). In general, the column for blood requires a 5 mm. bore and a 23 cm. height, and for urine, a 10 mm. bore and a 15 cm. height. One-half gram of alumina is required for blood and 1 gm. for urine; 0.2 N acetic acid may be used for elution in both blood and urine methods.

Elution with acetic acid or oxalic acid is preferred because this procedure will not elute catechol acids which are the interfering substances when fluorometry is to be applied. Sulfuric acid, concentrated or diluted, elutes all catechols. Precautions for the preparation of blood or urine should be carefully carried out before using alumina adsorption for best results. Acetate buffer at pH 4.0 will elute only amines, while catechol

acids and dopa [3-(3,4-dihydroxyphenyl)alanine] will also be eluted with
acetic acid.

C. ION EXCHANGE

Various ion exchange resins have been used successfully for the separation of catechol amines. IRC-50 was first used (Bergstrom and Hansson, 1951); Dow-X (Hagen and Welch, 1956) and Zeo-Karb 225 (Weil-
Malherbe and Bone, 1957) have also proven useful.

The procedure using Amberlite IRC-50 is suitable for separation of
as little as 20 μg. of material (Kirshner and Goodall, 1957). Amberlite
IRC-50 is buffered at a pH of 6.1 and the preparation of the resin is
completed when the mixture remains constant for about one hour of continuous stirring; it is ready for use after it is dried in air. Extractions
are prepared by homogenizing fresh adrenal glands in 10% trichloroacetic acid. After filtration, the trichloroacetic acid is removed by extraction with ether. With reduction of the volume *in vacuo*, the pH is adjusted
to 6.1 and an aliquot of this solution is used for chromatography. Elution
from the column is achieved with ammonium acetate buffer at a pH
of 6.0. The compounds eluted from this column are in the order: dopa,
followed by E, NE, and, finally, hydroxytyramine. Various factors effect
the separation of E, NE, and hydroxytyramine from Amberlite IRC-50.
The resolution of E, NE, and hydroxytyramine decreases with columns
shorter than 30 cm. Increased resolution with columns 40 cm. long, or
longer, does not justify the additional time necessary for fractionation.
The separation of these catechol amines is also dependent on the pH of
the resin and of the eluant. Increasing the pH of the resin to 6.6 greatly
enhances the separation of E from NE, but decreases the separation of
NE from hydroxytyramine. Decreasing the pH of the resin below 6.0
increases the resolution of hydroxytyramine and the NE fractionation,
but decreases the separation of E from NE. Changing the pH of the
eluant buffer will cause similar shifts in the resolving capacity of the
resin. An increase in the ionic strength of the eluant buffer will increase
the rate at which the compounds migrate down the column. The increased
resolution obtained with buffers of concentrations less than 0.4 M are
again not sufficient to compensate for the increased time required for
the fractionation.

D. PAPER CHROMATOGRAPHY

Paper chromatography was first applied to the separation of E and
NE by using phenol aqueous acid system (James, 1948). Other paper

chromatographic systems used are butanol:water:acetic acid and butanol:dilute hydrochloric acid. Locating the E and NE on paper has been accomplished by exposing the paper to various reagents: potassium ferricyanide (James, 1948), potassium iodate (Shepherd and West, 1951), and β-naphthoquinone-4-sulfonate (Glazko and Dill, 1951). When larger amounts than 2 μg. are present, rough quantitative estimations may be made by spraying the paper with potassium ferricyanide and ferric sulfate and comparing the size of the spots. With suitable precautions, amounts smaller than 2 μg. may be eluted from the paper with acid ethanol and directly estimated by bioassay.

A number of precautions are necessary to delineate various interfering substances (Vogt, 1959). With the phenol dilute acid system, dopamine and histamine lie between the E and NE which are, respectively, located at R_f 0.5 and 0.2. Furthermore, the presence of such hormones as the pituitary substances and substance P (5-hydroxytryptamine) should be eliminated, and this may be done easily because the latter substances run very close to the solvent front. Isoprenoline which has many of the biologic characteristics of E in bioassay, has an R_f of 0.7. Separation of these interfering substances may be achieved by two-dimensional paper chromatography (Schumann, 1956), using phenol and butanol solvents containing hydrochloric acid. In the butanol system, dopamine runs faster than either E or NE.

Two-dimensional paper chromatography is utilized in the identification and estimation of 3-methoxy-4-hydroxy mandelic acid (vanilmandelic acid: VMA) which is a metabolite of both E and NE. The first solvent system used is that of isopropyl alcohol, ammonia, and water. The first phase is run in this system at 25°C. for about 15 hours; the second phase of the chromatographic separation is carried out in benzene:propionic acid:water system. Detection of phenolic acids is accomplished by the use of diazotized sulfanilic acid or p-nitroaniline (Armstrong and McMillan, 1957). Quantitative estimation of VMA is accomplished by comparing the density of the color produced by standard concentrations of VMA. Normal range of values in terms of micrograms per milligrams of creatinine is 1.5 to 3.5. VMA excretion by patients with surgically confirmed pheochromocytoma ranged from 9.0 to 90.0 (Armstrong and McMillan, 1959).

Analysis for VMA has been extended with the use of high-voltage electrophoresis separation of urinary ethyl acetate extracts of phenolic acids. After separation, color development was achieved with p-nitroanaline and the colored spot eluted from paper and subsequently read on a Beckman spectrophotometer at 520 mμ (von Studnitz, 1960).

Normal values obtained were comparable to those previously reported (Armstrong and McMillan, 1959).

III. Bioassay

A basic requirement of a bioassay method for E and NE is that the biologically active form should not be accompanied by any contaminant which may influence the quantitative aspects of the assay. Preparation of the biologic material requires utmost care, since losses may occur in its activity from very small changes in chemical structure. The principal bioassay methods for E and NE are listed in Table I, with

TABLE I[a]

COMPARATIVE SENSITIVITY OF BIOASSAY METHODS

Methods of assay (biological)	Amount (ng.)[b] required for each test[c]	
	Adrenaline	Noradrenaline
Cat's blood pressure	200	100
Rat's blood pressure (C_6)	50	3
Rat's blood pressure (pithed)	7	5
Rat's uterus (2-ml. bath)	0.1	15
Rabbit's ear (perfused)	0.5	1
Rabbit's ear (Armin and Grant, 1955)	0.002	—
Rabbit's gut (10-ml. bath)	40	40
Fowl rectal cecum (2-ml. bath)	2	50

[a] From Gaddum and Holzbauer (1957).

[b] 1 ng. = 1 nanogram = 10^{-6} mg.

[c] The amount required for an accurate bioassay would be 5 to 10 times the amounts given in this table.

the minimum effective dose depicting the relative sensitivity of each method.

Advocates of bioassay and chemical assay methods have not as yet come to any agreement over the best method of assay. When methods give approximately the same values, it is apparent that the one that can be done the most rapidly, and that employs the least specialized personnel, is preferred. In general, chemical assay methods have this advantage. When low concentrations of catechol amines are to be measured, the bioassay methods seem well established.

As seen in Table I, the various bioassay methods have varying degrees of sensitivity for E and NE and no one method is sufficient for measuring mixtures of these catecholamines. For quantitative determinations of mixtures. it is necessary to use a combination of bioassays. Von Euler (1950) has made excellent use of cat blood pressure, combined with hen rectal cecum bioassays. The rat colon has been used in conjunction with the rat uterus and the most sensitive assay—the rat blood pressure and the rat uterus have been used by Vogt and her colleagues (1954).

Bioassay may be conveniently classified, based upon general techniques used: whole animal; perfusion techniques; and *in vitro* methods, as follows.

A. WHOLE ANIMAL

Cat blood pressure has been a useful method from the inception of the studies on biological assays of adrenal extracts (West, 1950), using the unanesthetized cat to a great extent (von Euler, 1950). An adult cat is given 25–45 mg. per kilogram of Nembutal, intraperitoneally, followed by an intramuscular injection of ergotamine tartrate at a dose of 0.15 mg. per kilogram, and finally 2.0 mg. per kilogram of atropine, subcutaneously. An antihistamime is also given, such as Antergan—10.0 mg. per kilogram, intramuscularly.

In a cat weighing 2 kg., adequate blood pressure responses may be obtained with 0.05–0.10 μg. of NE given intravenously by way of the femoral vein. Qualitative differences in the shape of blood pressure responses between E and NE can be observed and, quantitatively, NE is usually twice as potent as E. The responses of the extracts are compared with suitable standards. Mixtures of E and NE require an additional assay for E determinations.

Rat blood pressure has also been successfully employed (Landgrebe *et al.*, 1946; Crawford and Outschoorn, 1951). This method is not much of an improvement in terms of sensitivity over the cat blood pressure method, but it does have the advantage of a more accessible animal for testing. The sensitivity of the preparation is increased by pretreatment with hexamethonium, anesthetizing with Nembutal. The rats used weighed more than 150 gm. and were injected intraperitoneally with nembutal in the dose of 4–5 mg./100 gm., followed by 10–20 mg. per kilogram hexamethonium, subcutaneously. In addition to increasing the sensitivity of the preparation, this treatment also stabilizes the blood pressure. Amounts as small as 5 ng. (nanogram = 10^{-6} mg.) of NE are measurable by this preparation. The one disadvantage appears to be the short-lived nature of this sensitivity (Vogt, 1954). If the spinal cord is destroyed, hexamethonium is unnecessary (Holzbauer and Vogt, 1956).

B. Perfusion Methods

Perfusion techniques employing frog heart and frog blood vessels have been used in the past (West, 1950). A more useful and potentially promising method for E is that of perfusion of the rabbit ear. This method is capable of measuring 0.002 ng. of E (Armin and Grant, 1955). The early rabbit ear perfusion technique (Page and Green, 1948) may be replaced by a more simple method (Gaddum, 1950). This method, which is quite suitable for E and NE, consists of perfusing the ear at room temperature by connecting the arterial cannula with rubber tubing to a reservoir filled with perfusion fluid at a height of 20 cm. above the ear. In order to have the rate of flow constant, the fluid surface area should be large. A Mariotte bottle is not recommended. The cannula may be placed in the central artery of the ear, or the carotid artery may be cannulated in a decapitated rabbit and perfusion initiated before clotting occurs. All branches of the carotid artery, especially that of the ear, are then tied. Various modifications of this method with suitable recording devises have been described (Gaddum, 1950; Armin and Grant, 1955; Savini, 1956).

C. *In Vitro* Methods

The earlier technique of using rabbit intestines, suspended in a bath of oxygenated Tyrode's solution at 35–36°C., is used less often, because of the development of more sensitive techniques, such as those using the hen's rectal cecum and the rat colon and rat uterus preparations. The rabbit aorta-strip method is also used for certain clinical purposes, where differentiation of E and NE are not necessary, i.e., diagnosis of pheochromocytoma (Helmer and Sanders, 1957; Ewer et al., 1959).

The hen's rectal cecum has been used extensively by von Euler in conjunction with the cat blood pressure method for the measuring of mixtures of E and NE (Barsoum and Gaddum, 1935). One- or two-year-old chickens of either sex give the best results. After the chick is decapitated and bled, the rectal cecum is carefully dissected out on both sides of the rectum. The portion, approximately 3–4 cm. in length, next to the cecum is used as the test preparation. Care should be taken against contamination by the intestinal contents. Tyrode's solution is used in the bath with half its usual potassium content, and the bath is aerated with 5% CO_2 and O_2. Sensitivity of this preparation to E and NE increases during the first 10 minutes, but then remains constant for hours. The activity ratio of E to NE remains unchanged throughout the course of a single experiment. There is variability from preparation to preparation, ranging from 5 to 80. Since the muscle is very sensitive to acid, extracts used for testing should not be lower in pH than 4.0. Difficulty is encountered in the preparation of standard solutions which may be rapidly inactivated if the pH is 5.0 or higher. Care is recommended in keeping all tubing clean, since toxins produced by bacterial growth may produce irreversible relaxation and paralysis of the preparation.

The rat colon and rat uterus methods have also been used in the assay of mixtures of E and NE (Gaddum and Lembeck, 1949; Gaddum, 1950). Several features of these assays recommend them for research purposes: The rat as a laboratory animal requires little cost and space, and both catechol amines may be assayed on the same species. This method consists of testing the sample on the rat colon for NE, and on the rat uterus for E. The bioassay is based on quantitative inhibition and the catechol amine assay, on contractions induced in the uterus *in vitro* in a 2-cc. bath with acetylcholine. The inhibitions of E and NE are approximately equal when tested on the colon at room temperature, but when tested on the uterus, E is 100 times more potent than NE. The colon assay may be used when rapid estimates of total NE and E are desired.

1. *Rat Uterus*

One of the more sensitive and specific tests for E is the rat uterus test (Jalon *et al.*, 1945). The principal value of this method lies in the fact that E is approximately 100 times as sensitive as NE on the preparation. An adult rat having a vaginal smear of +2 or +3 is preferable. The animal should not have been pregnant for at least 4 weeks. Another method for preparing for bioassay involves the injecting of 50 mg. of stilbestrol into virgin rats (80–150 gm.) the day before the assay (Diller, 1957). It is preferable to use the uterus as soon as possible after excising it from the animal, but it may be used up to 24 hours if kept at 4°C. One horn of the uterus is suspended in a small bath (2 cc. capacity) with one end attached, by means of a thread loop, to a wire fastened on a rubber stopper which covers the bottom of the bath. The other end is looped and attached to a heart lever and adjusted so that the tension is adequate to indicate contraction and relaxation of the muscle. This may be accomplished by using wax to weight the lever. Readings are made on a kymograph. A smoke drum or writing ink may be used. If the temperature is kept at 30°C., a greater ratio of sensitivity to E/NE is achieved. The range may increase from 75 to 300. The reservoir of the bath consists of a modified Locke solution, having the following percentage composition: sodium chloride—0.9; potassium chloride—0.42; calcium chloride—0.006; sodium bicarbonate—0.05; glucose—0.05. Oxygen is bubbled slowly through the bath ensuring adequate mixing. When plasma is being assayed, it is recommended that the reservoir be saturated with oxygen, but bubbling of oxygen will cause frothing and overflow (Gaddum, 1950). The rate of bubbling for the experiment should be kept constant. The muscle preparation is treated with acetylcholine, so that a minimum dose is achieved for maximal contraction. This amount may differ from preparation to preparation and is standardized by using a solution of acetylcholine (10 μg./cc.) preferably beginning with minimum concentrations. After achieving a base line of contraction for acetylcholine, standard doses of E of 1 and 2 ng. are used to quantify the inhibition by the catechol amines of the acetylcholine contractions. One nanogram is added to the well and exactly 1 minute later, acetylcholine is added and the inhibition of the contraction so observed is computed as a percentage. After emptying the well, and exactly 1 minute later, acetylcholine is added and the contraction is brought back to the base line. Exactly 1 minute after the contraction and the emptying of the well, 2 ng. of E are added and 1 minute afterward, acetylcholine is placed in the well. When large doses of E are added to the well, it may take several contractions of acetylcholine to bring the base line back to normal. An assay may be performed by using 2 concentrations of the standard and 2 concentrations of the unknown for comparison purposes (Gaddum and Lembeck, 1949). Sensitivity of the uteri may be increased with a number of compounds of which dibenzyline appears to be the best (Holzbauer and Vogt, 1955). As small an amount as 0.1 ng. of E may be detected in this manner. Interference may be observed by the presence of 5-hydroxytryptamine (Gaddum, 1959), as well as oxytocin. The presence of Ca and K ions above certain concentrations which may occur in urine extracted with the direct alumina adsorption method has also been reported to interfere (Diller, 1957).

2. Rat Colon

The technique used on the rat uterus may be modified for use of the rat colon. At room temperature, E and NE are of equal sensitivity. When a piece of the colon is stored for 24 hours at 4°C., in moist air after removal from the rat, it becomes more sensitive to NE than E (Gaddum, 1950). A portion of the descending colon (approximately

4 cm.) is used; this tissue may be distinguished by the diagonal strips observed on the surface. Spontaneous movements of muscle may be reduced by lowering the temperature of the bath. At room temperature, a length as long as 25 cm. is often suitable. Lower concentrations of calcium (0.003%) are used in the colon preparation. The amount of acetylcholine necessary for the contraction is about twice that required for uterine contractions.

An automatic apparatus is described (Gaddum and Lembeck, 1949) for applying the standards and unknowns to the well, and emptying and filling the well with the modified Locke solution. In view of the instability of acetylcholine, carbachol is used in the automatic device.

REFERENCES

Armin, J., and Grant, R. T. (1955). *J. Physiol. (London)*, **128,** 511.
Armstrong, M. D., and McMillan, A. (1957). *Federation Proc.* **16,** 146.
Armstrong, M. D., and McMillan, A. (1959). *Pharmacol. Revs.* **11,** 394.
Auerbach, M. E., and Angell, E. (1949). *Science* **109,** 537.
Axelrod, J. (1957). *Science* **126,** 400.
Barsoum, G. S., and Gaddum, J. H. (1935). *J. Physiol. (London)* **85,** 1.
Bergstrom, S., and Hansson, H. (1951). *Acta Physiol. Scand.* **22,** 87.
Blaschko, H. (1950). *In* "The Hormones" (G. Pincus and K. V. Thimann, eds)., Vol. 2, p. 601. Academic Press, New York.
Cannon, W. B., and Rosenblueth, A. (1937). *In* "Autonomic Neuro-effector Systems" Macmillan, New York.
Cohen, G. (1959). *Pharmacol. Revs.* **11,** 269.
Crawford, T. B., and Outschoorn, A. S. (1951). *Brit. J. Pharmacol.* **6,** 8.
Diller, W. F. (1957). *Arch. intern. pharmacodynamie* **114,** 92.
Dunér, H. (1953). *Acta. Physiol. Scand.* **22,** 161.
Elmadjian, F., Hope, J. M., and Lamson, E. T. (1958). *Recent Progr. in Hormone Research* **14,** 513.
Ewer, R. W., Aikins, J. A., Hefferman, B. T., and Lennon, E. J. (1959). *J. Clin. Endocrinol. and Metabolism* **19,** 1037.
Folkow, B., and von Euler, U. S. (1954). *Circulation Research* **2,** 191.
Gaddum, J. H. (1950). *Methods in Med. Research* **3,** 116.
Gaddum, J. H. (1959). *Pharmacol. Revs.* **11,** 241.
Gaddum, J. H., and Holzbauer, M. (1957). *Vitamins and Hormones* **15,** 151.
Gaddum, J. H., and Lembeck, F. (1949). *Brit. J. Pharmacol.* **4,** 401.
Glazko, A. J., and Dill, W. A. (1951). *Nature* **168,** 32.
Goldenberg, M., Faber, M., Alston, E. J., and Chargaff, E. C. (1949). *Science* **109,** 534.
Goldfien, A., and Ganong, F. (1958). *Federation Proc.* **17,** 56.
Goodall, M., and Kirshner, N. (1957). *J. Biol. Chem.* **226,** 213.
Goodall, M., Kirshner, N., and Rosen, L. (1959). *J. Clin. Invest.* **38,** 707.
Hagen, P., and Welch, A. D. (1956). *Recent Progr. in Hormone Research* **12,** 27.
Hagopian, M., Dorfman, R. I., and Gut, M. (1961). *Anal. Biochem.* **2,** 387.
Helmer, O. M., and Sanders, R. M. (1957). *J. Lab. Clin. Med.* **50,** 737.

Holtz, P., Credner, K., and Kroneberg, G. (1947). *Arch. exptl. Pathol. Pharmakol., Naunyn-Schmiedeberg's* **204**, 228.

Holzbauer, M., and Vogt, M. (1955). *Brit. J. Pharmacol.* **10**, 186.

Holzbauer, M., and Vogt, M. (1956). *J. Neurochem.* **1**, 8.

Jalon, P. G. de, Bayo, J. B., and Jalon, M. G. de, (1945). *Farmacoterap. actual (Madrid)* **2**, 313.

James, W. O. (1948). *Nature* **161**, 851.

Kirshner, N., and Goodall, McC. (1957). *J. Biol. Chem.* **226**, 202.

Landgrebe, F. W., Facaulay, M. H., and Waring, H. (1946). *Proc. Roy. Soc. Edinburgh* **B62**, 202.

Munch, J. C. (1931). *In* "Bioassays" pp. 567-599. Williams & Wilkins, Baltimore, Maryland.

Page, I. H., and Green, A. A. (1948). *Methods in Med. Research* **1**, 123.

Persky, H. (1955). *Methods of Biochem. Anal.* **2**, 57.

Resnick, O., Wolfe, J. M., Freeman, H., and Elmadjian, F. (1958). *Science* **127**, 1116.

Savini, E. C. (1956). *Brit. J. Pharmacol.* **11**, 313.

Shaw, F. H. (1938). *Biochem. J.* **32**, 19.

Schayer, R. W. (1951). *J. Biol. Chem.* **189**, 301.

Schumann, H.-J. (1956). *Arch. exptl. Pathol. Pharmakol., Naunyn-Schmiedeberg's* **227**, 566.

Shepherd, D. M., and West, G. B. (1951). *Brit. J. Pharmacol.* **6**, 665.

Shore, P. A., and Olin, J. S. (1958). *J. Pharmacol Exptl. Therap.* **122**, 295.

"Symposium on Catechol Amines" (1959). (O. Krayer, ed.). Williams & Wilkins, Baltimore, Maryland.

Tainter, M. L., and Luduena, F. P. (1950). *Recent Progr. in Hormone Research* **5**, 3.

Vogt, M. (1954). *J. Physiol. (London)* **123**, 451.

Vogt, M. (1959). *Pharmacol. Revs.* **11**, 249.

von Euler, U. S. (1946). *Acta. Physiol. Scand.* **11**, 168.

von Euler, U. S. (1950). *Methods in Med. Research* **3**, 131.

von Euler, U. S. (1956). *In* "Noradrenaline" C. C Thomas, Springfield, Illinois.

von Euler, U. S. (1958). *Recent Progr. in Hormone Research* **14**, 483.

von Euler, U. S., and Hellner, S. (1951). *Acta Physiol. Scand.* **22**, 161.

von Euler, U. S., and Lishajko, F. (1959). *Acta Physiol. Scand.* **45**, 122.

von Euler, U. S. and Orwén, I. (1955). *Acta Physiol. Scand.* **33**, Suppl. 118, 1.

von Studnitz, W. (1960). *Scand. J. Clin. & Lab. Invest.* **12**, Suppl. 48, 1.

Weil-Malherbe, H. (1959). *Pharmacol. Revs.* **11**, 278.

Weil-Malherbe, H., and Bone, A. D. (1952). *Biochem. J.* **51**, 311.

Weil-Malherbe, H., and Bone, A. D. (1954). *Biochem. J.* **58**, 132.

Weil-Malherbe, H., and Bone, A. D. (1957). *Biochem. J.* **67**, 65.

Welsh, L. H. (1955). *J. Am. Pharm. Assoc. Sci. Ed.* **44**, 507.

West, G. B. (1950). *In* "Hormone Assay" (C. W. Emmens, ed.), pp. 91-107. Academic Press, New York.

Chapter 10

Thyroidal Substances

C. W. Turner and B. N. Premachandra

I. Introduction

Some of the older methods of assay of thyroidal substances, such as altering the energy metabolism or influencing body weight reported in the previous edition (Reineke and Turner, 1950), are now recognized as rather insensitive methods. In the same category there are methods based upon replacement therapy of thyroidectomized or goitrogen-treated animals.

Methods based upon the process of maturation, metamorphosis, or metabolism of amphibian tadpoles still find favor with some investigators. Similarly, the maintenance of the thyroid-pituitary balance in goitrogen-treated animals would continue to serve as a useful assay method were it not for the introduction of I^{131} techniques which can be used without sacrifice of the animals.

These methods fall into two types, namely, depression of thyroidal-I^{131}

uptake resulting from the depression of thyroid-stimulating hormone (TSH) secretion by thyroxine, and the depression of thyroidal-I^{131} release rate by thyroxine used in the technique for estimating the thyroxine secretion rate. Both methods depend upon the action of thyroxine in blocking release of TSH. However, as pointed out by Turner et al. (1959), many factors influence the uptake of I^{131} and great variations in per cent uptake are noted in individual animals.

On the other hand, the blockage of thyroidal-I^{131} release by thyroxine, when goitrogens are fed to block the recycling of I^{131}, is subject only to rate of TSH secretion and corresponding thyroxine secretion rate. By using L-thyroxine secretion rate as a standard, the comparative biological activity of its analogs may be determined.

Since the older methods are discussed in the previous review (Reineke and Turner, 1950), emphasis will be given to methods described since that time and modifications of the older methods which increase their sensitivity.

II. Thyroidal Substances

A. CHEMISTRY OF THYROXINE, DERIVATIVES, AND ISOMERS

The chief hormone of the thyroid gland is L-thyroxine. The free acid can be converted into a mono- and di-(Na or K) salt of thyroxine. Thyroxine can be converted to the monosodium salt by heating with 0.1 N sodium carbonate in which it is soluble and then precipitating by chilling the solution to 0°C. This salt contains 63.46% iodine.

The disodium salt of thyroxine is formed by dissolving thyroxine in NaOH. It is readily soluble and more so in 50% alcohol. By raising the alcohol to 80%, the disodium salt precipitates out as colorless glistening leaflets. This salt contains 61.69% iodine.

D-Thyroxine is not naturally occurring. It is produced in solution of L-thyroxine by a process of racemization in which equal amounts of D- and L-thyroxine come into equilibrium in an alkaline solution, as in its extraction from hydrolyzates of thyroglobulin or thyroprotein (see Fig. 1).

The thyroxine available earlier was DL-thyroxine whether extracted from the thyroid gland or synthesized. More recently synthetic L-thyroxine became available and is now the usual standard of reference.

In addition to L-thyroxine, the presence of 3,5,3'-triiodo-L-thyronine has been demonstrated in the thyroid glands of humans, rats, and domestic fowls and in the blood of man, rat, sheep, horse, calf, and fowl.

Thus, in addition to thyroxine, triiodothyronine must be considered a thyroid gland hormone. The relative proportions of the two hormones

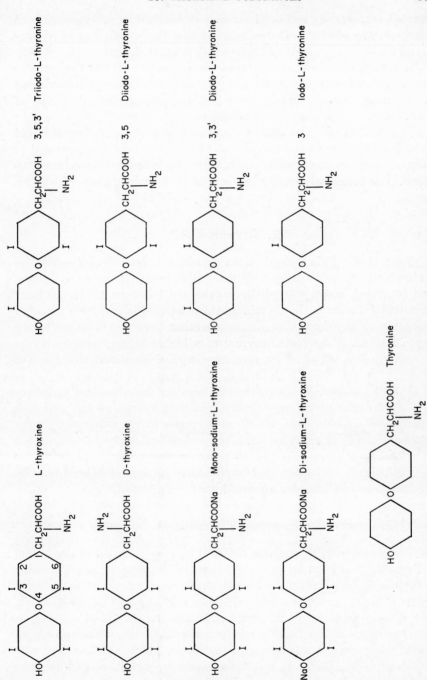

FIG. 1. Structure of thyroxine with its mono- and disodium salts and deiodinated derivatives.

secreted concurrently has not been well established in various species at this time. Preliminary evidence indicates that the contribution of triiodothyronine may be as high as 10–20% (Taurog *et al.*, 1956).

It will be noted that triiodothyronine is the first step in the metabolism of thyroxine by deiodination, a process which probably is carried on stepwise: diiodo, iodo, and finally to thyronine. The biological activity of these compounds will be considered later.

The oxidative deamination of the alanine side chain of thyroxine and related compounds to the acetic acid analogs has been demonstrated *in vivo*. In addition, the propionic and butyric acid analogs have been prepared. The biological activity of some of these preparations will be reported.

B. Thyroid, U.S.P.

Thyroid, U.S.P. is defined as the thyroid glands of domesticated animals which are used for food by man; it is free from connective tissue and fat, dried, and powdered. It contains not less than 0.17% nor more than 0.23% iodine in the thyroid combination and is free from iodine in inorganic or any form of combination other than that peculiar to the thyroid gland. A desiccated thyroid of a higher iodine content may be brought to this standard by admixture with a desiccated thyroid of a lower iodine content or with lactose, NaCl, starch, or sucrose.

The Pharmacopœia Internationalis requires that thyroid glands contain not less than 0.2% organically combined iodine and not less than 0.045% and not more than 0.055% of thyroxine iodine. Standard methods for determining organically combined iodine and thyroxine iodine are described.

Methods of extraction and purification of thyroglobulin from the thyroid glands of domestic animals have been reported.

C. Synthetic Thyroprotein (Thyroactive Iodinated Casein)

The synthesis of thyroactive material by the iodination of casein and subsequent treatment to produce oxidative coupling of diiodotyrosine molecules in the protein has made available a relatively inexpensive source of thyroxine-like material (Reineke and Turner, 1942, 1945, 1946). The thyroxine content of thyroprotein has been a subject of study since its synthesis. On the basis of early work using the *n*-butanol-soluble iodine as an index, it was estimated that about 3% thyroxine was present (Reineke *et al.*, 1945). It was later shown by Friedberg and Reineke (1952) that hydrolyzed thyroprotein contained at least 10 iodinated compounds including mono- and diiodotyrosine, diiodo- and triiodothyronine as well as thyroxine. It was then shown by Reineke (1954), by a radio-active isotope dilution technique in a group of 7 preparations, that thyro-protein which showed an estimated 3.24% thyroxine in the butanol-soluble fraction contained 1.04% true thyroxine.

The earlier studies using the higher estimated thyroxine content of thyroprotein indicated very low oral absorption. However, in using the value of 1.0% true thyroxine, the oral effectiveness of thyroprotein, thy-roglobulin, and L-thyroxine in ruminant animals is comparable.

In the literature the commercial name, Protamone, is frequently used.

D. L-Thyroxine as a Standard

The availability of L-thyroxine in a highly purified form serves as an excellent standard in all biological assays. Since this is the form in which thyroxine is secreted by the thyroid gland and, further, is the form present in thyroprotein, the administration of L-thyroxine gives the biological equivalent of normal thyroidal hormone secretion. The iodine content is 65.5%.

E. Comparison of L-, D-, and DL-Thyroxine

Many studies have been conducted to determine the relative biological activity of these compounds (see reviews of Reineke and Turner, 1950; Selenkow and Asper, 1955a). All bioassays show the L-isomer to be more active. Some investigators report D-thyroxine to be completely inactive, others indicate potency of 1/10 to 1/3 that of L-thyroxine. Griesbach et al. (1949) reported that the smallest dose of DL-thyroxine which would prevent the development of pituitary basophilia in the rat was 2.3 μg./100 gm. body weight, L-thyroxine, 1.5 μg., and D-thyroxine, 5 μg. Thus, the D-isomer was considered 0.3 as effective as the L-isomer. Tabachnick et al. (1956) reported the mouse anoxia assay indicated that sodium L-thyroxine was 7 times more potent than sodium D-thyroxine. It was noted that L-thyroxine was still effective 96 hours after the last injection, whereas D-thyroxine was no longer effective.

Money et al. (1959), using the I^{131} blocking activity in rats as the index of activity, reported that D-thyroxine was 50% as effective, and DL-thyroxine only 40% as effective as L-thyroxine. Gilliland (1959) re-ported that the thyroids of 100-gm. male rats given 0.1% methylthiou-racil in the drinking water were increased 3 times at 14 days. Rats given 5 μg. per day of L-thyroxine in addition were normal, whereas those given an equal amount of the D-isomer were as large as those on thiouracil alone. Plamondon *et al.* (1958) compared L- and DL-thyroxine activity in rats by the antigoiter method. A dose of 2.6 μg. L-thyroxine/100 gm. body weight maintained normal thyroid weight. The corresponding level of DL-thyroxine was 3.5 μg./100 gm. body weight.

Tapley and Cooper (1956a, b) reported studies *in vitro* which indicated that L- and D-thyroxine were equally active in uncoupling oxidative phosphorylation and in altering the morphology of the mitochondria. Recently, Tapley *et al.* (1959) suggested that the difference in the biological activity of the two isomers might be due to the difference in the rate of metabolism of the two compounds. In male Wistar rats the $T_{1/2}$ of D-thyroxine was 14 hours in comparison to the $T_{1/2}$ of L-thyroxine of 42 hours.

In *in vitro* experiments, Larson *et al.* (1959) showed that rat kidney slices deiodinated L-thyroxine to L-triiodothyronine, but that D-thyroxine was not similarly deiodinated. Further, with kidney mitochondrial enzyme system D-thyroxine was unaltered while L-thyroxine was actively converted to tetraiodothyroacetic acid. They suggest that failure of D-thyroxine to undergo these transformations may account for its metabolic inactivity.

F. COMPARISON OF THYROXINE AND TRIIODOTHYRONINE

Barker (1955) presented a summary of comparison of biological activity of these compounds in various species.

1. Rat

Pitt-Rivers (1953), using the goiter prevention test in rats, reported in a first test that L-triiodothyronine was 3 times more active, and in a later test, 5 times more active than equimolecular amounts of L-thyroxine. D-Triiodothyronine was reported to have 7% of the activity of the L-isomer and DL-triiodothyronine 59% of the activity of the L-isomer. Gemmill (1953) reported that thyroxine and triiodothyronine, on a molar basis, had comparable activity in inhibiting the cupric-ion-catalyzed oxidation of ascorbic acid and in stimulating the oxidation of succinate by rat heart homogenates. Both compounds increased the metabolism of normal rats to the same degree.

Heming and Holtkamp (1953) reported antigoitrogenic tests in rats showed L-triiodothyronine to be about 3.5 times as active as L-thyroxine on a molar basis. In thyroidectomized rats, L-triiodothyronine was not less than 3.5 times as active as L-thyroxine in calorigenic effect.

Anderson (1954) compared the action of DL-thyroxine and L-triiodothyronine on the release of thyroidal-I[131] in rats. The latter compound was 5 to 10 times as active as the former. DL-Thyroxine appeared to exert a more prolonged effect than L-triiodothyronine when doses of similar potency were compared.

Barker (1956) studied the oxygen consumption of tissues from injected rats. Triiodothyronine was found 4 times more active than thyroxine by this criterion.

Walker (1957) studied the skeletal maturation-promoting activity in new-born rats. It was observed at various levels that L-triiodothyronine had twice the skeletogenic effect of L-thyroxine at equimolar doses. The effect of triiodothyroacetic acid was slightly greater than, and the tetra-analog only $\frac{1}{2}$ that, of thyroxine.

Duncan and Best (1958) reported L-triiodothyronine to be 3 times as active as L-thyroxine on an equal molar basis by the goiter-prevention technique.

Enneker et al. (1958) reported that 5 μg./100 gm./day of either thyroxine or triiodothyronine was able to reduce the thyroid size of rats treated with perchlorate. However, 1 μg./100 gm./day of triiodothyronine reduced thyroid size without raising the lowered metabolism.

Plamondon et al. (1958) reported that L-thyroxine prevented goiter in rats at levels of 2.6 μg./100 gm. body weight, whereas L-triiodothyronine prevented goiter at a level of 0.42 μg./100 gm. body weight. DL-Triiodothyronine was equally as effective as the L-isomer. Thus these isomers are 6 times as active as L-thyroxine.

Stasilli et al. (1959) reported that L-triiodothyronine was 8 times more potent than L-thyroxine (sodium pentahydrate) both by the goiter prevention and calorigenic assay. Money et al. (1959) compared L-thyroxine and L-triiodothyronine in their capacity to supress I^{131} uptake by the rat thyroid. L-Triiodothyronine was 3 times as effective as L-thyroxine, whereas DL-triiodothyronine was $\frac{3}{4}$, 3,5-diiodo-L-thyroxine $\frac{1}{3}$, 3,3'-diiodo-DL-thyronine equal, and 3-iodo-DL-thyronine $\frac{1}{2}$ as effective.

Larson and Albright (1958) suggested that L-thyroxine-I^{131}, when injected intravenously, remained largely within the vascular compartment, whereas L-triiodothyronine-I^{131} very rapidly left the intravascular compartment and reached relatively high concentrations in kidney, liver, heart, and muscle. It was suggested that their biological differences might be related to the extent of their incorporation into the cell.

2. Mouse

Gemmill (1953) reported that triiodothyronine was slightly more active than L-thyroxine by the anoxia test in mice. In contrast, Anderson (1954) reported that triiodothyronine was at least 5 times as active as DL-thyroxine by this test in mice.

3. Rabbit

Brown-Grant (1955) compared the biological activity of L-thyroxine and L-triiodothyronine in the rabbit by the thyroxine secretion rate method of blocking the release of thyroidal-I^{131}. By this comparison the relative potencies were 1:1.29.

4. Tadpole

Shellabarger and Godwin (1954) reported that DL-triiodothyronine was 3.8 times as effective as DL-thyroxine in shortening the length of *Rana clamitans* tadpoles during a 10-day immersion period.

Bruice *et al.* (1954) reported that L-triiodothyronine was 4.2 times more active than L-thyroxine in reducing the width of the tail-fin of *Rana catesbiana* larva.

Money *et al.* (1958), using *Rana pipiens* tadpoles, reported that L-triiodothyronine was 5 times more active biologically than L-thyroxine.

5. Man

The comparative effectiveness of L-thyroxine and L-triiodothyronine in the elevation of metabolic rate in myxedema has been determined (Gross *et al.*, 1952). L-Triiodothyronine has been reported to be 3 to 5 times more potent than L-thyroxine in myxedema whether by single injection (Asper *et al.*, 1953) or multiple injections (LaRoche and Rapin, 1953; Deltour and Bekaert, 1953) although no appreciable difference is found between the two compounds if considered in terms of the over-all response (Blackburn *et al.*, 1953; Rawson *et al.*, 1953).

6. Fowls

Gilliland and Strudwick (1953) used equimolecular amounts of L-thyroxine and L-triiodothyronine in blocking TSH secretion in the chick pituitary. After uptake of I^{131}, the effectiveness of the two compounds was measured by the radioactivity retained after 3 days. At two levels, the L-triiodothyronine was shown to be more effective in preventing I^{131} release.

Shellabarger (1955) reported that 3.0 μg. per day of L-triiodothyronine and 3.0 μg. of L-thyroxine had equal effects upon the weight of thyroid glands of chicks fed 0.1% thiouracil for 10 days. Newcomer (1957) reported that L-thyroxine and L-triiodothyronine were of equal potency in influencing feather length, oxygen consumption rate, heart rate, and suffocation time in thiouracil-treated chicks. Thyroxine was more potent in respect to the antigoitrogenic action.

Mellen and Wentworth (1959) administered equimolar amounts of

L-thyroxine and L-triiodothyronine to baby chicks which also received 0.1% thiouracil in the diet. The antigoitrogenic activity of thyroxine was greater than triiodothyronine. Five-week-old chicks were tested for the thyroxine secretion rate equivalent which involves blockage of TSH secretion. Again the amount of thyroxine required to equal the secretion rate was less than of triiodothyronine.

Newcomer and Barrett (1960) determined the oxygen uptake of surviving ventricular myocardium of chicks which had received thiouracil. Thyroxine gave a greater increase in O_2 uptake than triiodothyronine or other analogs.

7. Cattle

Bartlett et al. (1954) reported that the daily subcutaneous injection of 5 mg. of L-triiodothyronine was slightly more active than an equal amount of L-thyroxine in stimulating increased milk secretion in dairy cattle. When 2.5 mg. of these substances were injected twice daily, the results were almost identical. However, by the oral route, a dose of 64 mg. of triiodothyronine was much less effective than an equimolar amount of thyroxine (75 mg. daily).

Premachandra et al. (1960a) determined the relative effectiveness of L-thyroxine and L-triiodothyronine in the determination of equivalent thyroxine secretion rates of dairy cattle. Triiodothyronine was 2 to 3 times more effective in blocking thyroidal-I^{131} release and, thus, TSH release.

8. Explanation of the Differences of Fowls and Mammals

In seeking an explanation for the differences in the response of thyroxine and triiodothyronine in birds and mammals, Tata and Shellabarger (1959) suggest the following differences: In mammals L-triiodothyronine disappears ($T_{1/2}$) from the blood 2 to 3 times more rapidly than does thyroxine. In chickens the $T_{1/2}$ of the two compounds is the same, 22.5 ± 1 hours.

In mammals, the serum thyroxine binding protein (between α_1- and α_2-globulin) binds thyroxine about 3 to 4 times more firmly than triiodothyronine. This protein is either present in chicken and duck sera in small amounts or is absent. The hormones are mostly bound to the albumin of the birds. The two hormones in birds are bound with equal intensity.

G. COMPARISON OF L-THYROXINE WITH ITS ANALOGS

Pitt-Rivers and Tata (1959) have presented extensive tables showing the relative biological activity of compounds related to thyroxine.

They point out that the response of amphibia is in general much greater than that of mammals and is also less specific. Compounds which have little or no activity in mammals can stimulate amphibian metamorphosis (see data of Bruice *et al.*, 1954).

Money *et al.* (1958) tested 43 compounds in regard to their metamorphosing effect on *Rana pipiens* tadpoles. Triiodinated compounds with iodines at the 3,3′,5 positions were found more active than tetraiodinated compounds. The 3,3 and 3,5 diiodinated compounds tested also had some activity. None of the monoiodinated compounds showed biological activity. The most active compound studied was 3,3′,5-triiodothyropropionic acid which was 3 times more potent than L-thyroxine.

Stasilli *et al.* (1959) compared the antigoitrogenic and calorigenic activities of thyroxine and 44 analogs. By both methods of assay, 12 of the preparations had activities ranging from 5 to 800% of that of thyroxine. The following generalizations regarding structure and biological activity were presented. (1) Analogs having an intact alanine side chain required iodine at least in the 3 and 5 positions. (2) Thyronines having iodine in the 3, the 3 and 3′, or 3,3′ and 5′ were biologically inactive at relatively high dosage levels. (3) The potency of analogs with deaminated side chains decreased as the chain length increased from 2 to 4 carbons (see Fig. 2).

Money *et al.* (1959) determined the effect of 45 analogs of thyroxine on the suppression of I^{131} uptake by the rat thyroid. Compounds containing iodine were all capable of producing some inhibition provided the dosage was adequate.

Wilkinson (1959) reported that the acetic acid analogs undergo deiodination to a much smaller extent than the iodothyronines.

Mussett and Pitt-Rivers (1957) have studied the biological activity of a number of halogenated analogs of the thyronines in reducing thiouracil-induced goiter in rats. A comprehensive review of the biological activity of compounds structurally related to thyroxine has been presented by Selenkow and Asper (1955a). Readers are referred to a series of papers by Asper (1958) and associates. Bruice *et al.* (1956) have presented a correlation of structure versus thyroxine-like activity for 47 analogs of thyroxine. Barker (1956) used the oxygen consumption of tissues from injected rats to compare the biological activity of a number of thyroxine analogs. Six iodo-L-thyronines were compared by Tomich *et al.* (1960) with triiodothyronine by the mouse anoxia and rat antigoitrogenic methods. Only 3,5-diiodo-L-thyronine showed about 3% activity.

Slater *et al.* (1960) compared the 24-hour thyroidal-I^{131} uptake

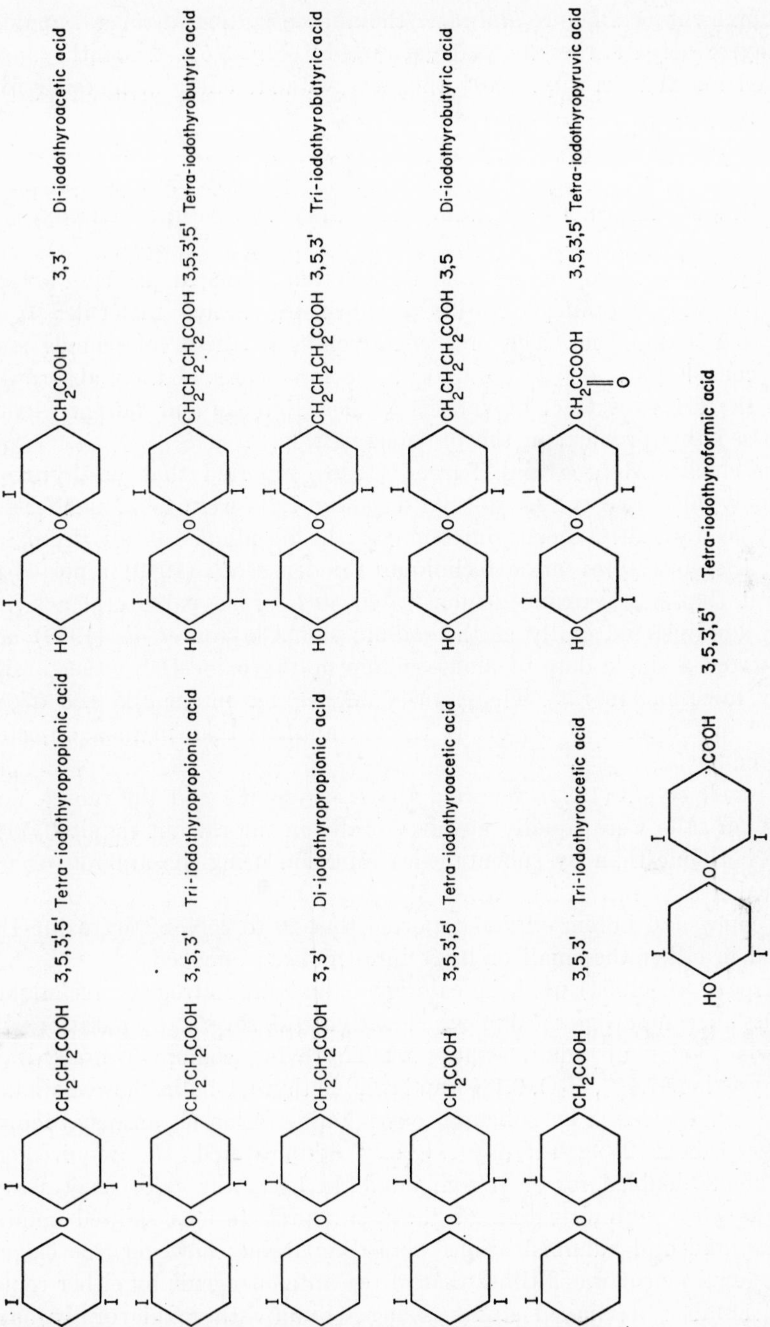

Fig. 2. Some deaminated analogs of thyroxine.

in human subjects before and after the administration of several analogs of thyroxine. Of the compounds tested, only 3,5,3'-triiodothyronine showed marked activity. Even this was without effect in hyperthyroid subjects.

H. COMPARISON OF ORAL AND SUBCUTANEOUS ADMINISTRATION

Thyroxine, thyroglobulin, and thyroactive iodinated proteins are all effective when administered orally since the active molecule is an iodinated amino acid. The oral effectiveness of these compounds may vary considerably, depending upon the completeness of their absorption from the digestive tract of various species. Reineke and Turner (1950) discussed this problem in the previous edition.

In chicks, Monroe and Turner (1949) reported that DL-thyroxine was only 20%, and the mono- and disodium salts were 45%, as effective orally as by subcutaneous injection of the disodium salt of thyroxine using the goiter-prevention technique. Frieden et al. (1949) reported in the rat that DL-thyroxine demonstrated 49% of its parenteral activity when administered orally as the sodium salt. Clayton et al. (1950) administered a single dose of mono-sodium DL-thyroxine-I^{131}, either orally or by injection, to rats. There was a higher percentage (65 and 57%) of I^{131} in the feces of the orally treated animals than in those injected (44 and 39%).

Littrell et al. (1952) reported that L-thyroxine and the mono- and disodium salts were equally effective orally in the rat but required 50% more hormone than by subcutaneous injection using the antigoitrogenic method.

Tenney and Lorenz (1952) reported that 20 to 25% of thyroxine-I^{131} placed in either the small or large intestine was removed.

Kroc et al. (1954) used the calorigenic and antigoitrogenic techniques in rats in comparing the biological activity of several preparations by various modes of administration. L-Thyroxine sodium pentahydrate (L-thyroxine 87.4%, H_2O, 9.1%) and soluble thyroglobulin showed similar antigoitrogen results by subcutaneous administration on an equal iodine dosage (about 2 μg./rat/day). Orally administered, the requirement was about doubled for each compound. In using the calorigenic assay, subcutaneous administration of these two preparations showed similar results, and oral administrations were comparable; however, the calorigenic requirement was 3 times that of the antigoitrogenic by either route.

A number of clinical studies using sodium L-thyroxine orally have shown this compound to be effective in treatment of myxedema in doses of 0.2 to 0.5 mg. daily (Selenkow and Asper, 1955a). Salter and Rosenblum (1952) estimated at least $\frac{2}{3}$ of the thyroxine was absorbed. Each 0.1-mg. tablet appeared equal to 1.5 grains of U.S.P. thyroid.

1. Cattle

Bartlett *et al.* (1954) reported that the feeding of 75 mg. of L-thyroxine stimulated a marked increase in milk yield of dairy cattle, whereas a molar equivalent of L-triiodothyronine had little effect.

In cattle, the oral effectiveness of thyroprotein has been determined in relation to thyroxine by injection (Premachandra *et al.*, 1960b). A sample of thyroprotein containing 1% L-thyroxine required a mean of 1.25 gm./100 lb. body weight to block thyroidal-I^{131} release. In the same group of cattle 1.25 mg. of L-thyroxine by injection was effective. By this comparison, the thyroxine in thyroprotein is absorbed to the extent of 10% from the digestive tract.

Mixner and Lennon (1958a) used, as a criterion of absorption of thyroprotein from the digestive tract, the elevation of protein-bound iodine (PBI) as compared to intravenous injection of L-thyroxine. The mean efficiency from the orally administered thyroprotein was $12.3 \pm 1.33\%$, with a range from 8.3 to 17.4%. In a subsequent study (Mixner and Lennon, 1959) using the same criterion, the mean absorption efficiency of L-thyroxine was 10.85% (range of 4.2 to 17.2%) and of porcine thyroglobulin 10.20% (range of 4.2 to 16.5%). These studies indicate that the oral absorption of L-thyroxine, in the free form, and of thyroprotein and thyroglobulin, are essentially equal.

The low oral effectiveness of thyroxine in ruminant animals (about 10%) as compared to nonruminants (about 50%) raises a question as to the cause. Campbell *et al.* (1950) studied the absorption of thyroprotein-I^{131} from various parts of the digestive tract of sheep by measurement of the radioactivity of the blood at intervals. It was observed that maximum blood-I^{131} was reached after about 10 hours and remained high for about 24 hours. Equal amounts of thyroprotein were administered orally, introduced into the rumen, small intestine, and cecum. The maximum blood-I^{131} levels were the same when fed or introduced into the rumen, about $\frac{2}{3}$ as high when introduced into the small intestine and $\frac{1}{6}$ as high when introduced into the cecum. It is thus seen that maximum uptake of I^{131} occurs when thyroprotein is fed. A study of the blood plasma at time of maximum level indicated that 50% of the I^{131} was extractable with butyl alcohol.

I. DIFFERENT BIOLOGICAL RESPONSES TO THYROXINE

Some of the physiological effects observed following thyroidectomy include alteration in growth rate, mammary gland growth, lactation, metabolic rate, red cell volume, pituitary cytology, ovarian and adrenal structure. Scow and Simpson (1945) reported that incompletely thyroidectomized newborn rats had basal metabolic rates (B.M.R.) similar to those completely thyroidectomized, yet grew at rates nearly ½ that of normal. Griesbach and Purves (1945; and Purves and Griesbach, 1946) reported that normal pituitary acidophil morphology could be maintained in thyroidectomized rats by ⅕ the amount of thyroxine necessary to maintain pituitary basophils.

In a recent study of this problem, Evans et al. (1960) thyroidectomized Long-Evans strain female rats at 28 days (body weight 110 gm.) and then injected L-thyroxine at constant levels of 0.25, 0.50, 1.0, and 5.0 μg. per day for 96 days.

Marked growth was observed at both 0.25 and 0.5 μg. per day. Dosages greater than 1 and less than 5 were required to maintain metabolic rates at normal levels. Red cell volume was normal at 1 and 5 μg. but the lower levels did not prevent anemia. Pituitary acidophils were normal at 1 μg., whereas the basophils required between 1 and 5 μg. for prevention of hyperplasia and hypertrophy. The ovaries were normal in structure and weight at 1 μg. The adrenals were normal only at the higher doses needed for maintenance of calorigenesis.

These data should be considered in the light of the range and mean thyroxine secretion rate of rats. In the Sprague-Dawley-Rolfsmeyer strain, the range in L-thyroxine secretion rate varied from 0.5 to 2.5 μg./100 gm. body weight with a mean of 1.3 μg. (Grosvenor and Turner, 1959). In lactating rats the upper range increased to 3.0 μg. with mean of 2.2 μg. It was subsequently shown that thyroxine at a level of 3.0 μg./100 gm. body weight increased the growth of the mammary gland (Moon and Turner, 1960b) and the intensity of lactation on day 14 (Grosvenor and Turner, 1959b).

Duncan and Best (1958) reported that when L-thyroxine and tetraiodothyroformic acid were administered in amounts having equal goiter-inhibiting activity, the formic acid analog exerted significantly greater effect on cholesterol metabolism than on growth.

Crosley et al. (1960) administered 1.0 mg. per day of D-triiodothyronine to 4-hypercholesteremic patients for 4 weeks. It was reported that this compound was effective in lowering serum cholesterol while at the same time producing negligible effects on the B.M.R., PBI, and the thyroidal-I^{131} uptake.

III. Assays Based on Elevation of the Metabolic Rate

Assays of thyroidal hormones based upon elevation of the metabolic rate were discussed in the previous edition (Reineke and Turner, 1950). While these methods lack the sensitivity of some methods which will be described, they indicate a basic physiological effect of thyroxine. For the interested reader, attention is called to methods described since the previous edition (Lilienthal et al., 1949; Maclagan and Sheahan, 1950; and Holtkamp et al., 1955). Tomich and Woollett (1954) compared the oxygen consumption, anoxia, and antigoitrogen methods. Kroc et al. (1954) described a calorigenic method. This same comparison was made in an extensive study of thyroxine analogs by Stasilli et al. (1959).

In addition to the above techniques on intact animals, methods based upon the metabolic rate of selected tissues are reported.

Barker (1956) method. Sprague-Dawley rats were thyroidectomized at least 4 weeks before the test. Thyroxine and analogs were injected once daily for 4 days. On the fifth day, heart, diaphragm, skeletal muscle, liver, kidney, pancreas, and salivary glands were quickly removed and placed in cold Ringer's solution. The tissues were prepared for study by the method of Barker and Klitgaard (1952). The oxygen consumption measurements were made by the direct Warburg method, in Krebs' Ringer phosphate glucose solution, for 1 hour at 37°C.

Newcomer and Barrett (1960) method. White Leghorn cockerels were given 0.1% thiouracil in drinking water for 7 to 14 days. Twelve hours before sacrifice, L-thyroxine and test compounds were administered intraperitoneally. The ventricular myocardium was removed and placed in an ice-cold phosphate saline solution. The myocardium was cut into uniform slices of 0.5 mm. with a Stadie-Riggs microtome. Two of three slices of tissue from the same heart were placed in a Warburg vessel which contained 3 ml. of cold phosphate saline solution. The vessel was mounted, flushed with pure oxygen for 5 minutes, then allowed to equilibrate in a water bath for 15 minutes at 37°C. Oxygen uptake readings were taken at 10-minute intervals for 1 hour. The slices of myocardium were then removed and dried at 37°C. for 48 hours. Oxygen uptake was calculated as $\mu l.O_2$ per milligram dry tissue per hour. Oxygen uptake from control tissues was 6.0 $\mu l.$ per hour per milligram tissue, whereas in thiouracil-fed chicks the uptake was 4.0 $\mu l.$

Smith, Emmens, and Parkes (1947) method. Male mice weighing 18 to 29 gm. were placed in closed vessels of 870 ml. capacity held at

23°C. Such animals survived about 2 hours. Death occurred when O_2 concentration was down to about 5% and CO_2 up to about 13%. For the assay, 4 groups of 20 were used. Two groups received two levels of the standard, two groups received two levels of the unknown sample. The hormones were injected subcutaneously on alternate days and the test was performed on the second or third day after the last injection. Each mouse was placed in a separate jar and survival time recorded in minutes. This assay should give determinations of relative potency with fiducial limits of error $(P = 0.05)$. Basil *et al.* (1950) described an improved statistical evaluation of thyroid activity by the mouse anoxia method.

Clinical Assays. In clinical practice, based on the original work of Magnus-Levy (1895), the elevation of the metabolic rate in myxedematous patients has been used to determine the calorigenic potency of thyroxine and other analogs. The resultant changes in metabolic rate on administration of thyroidal substances are compared against a standard curve and the potencies established.

Gross *et al.* (1952) reported that triiodothyronine was 3 to 4 times more potent than thyroxine in elevation of the metabolic rate in myxedematous patients to normal, and similar results were also reported by Lerman (1953), Asper *et al.* (1953), and McConahey *et al.* (1953). Apparently, the quantitative differences in potency between thyroxine and triiodothyronine in the elevation of the metabolic rate in myxedema does not seem to be affected whether they are administered intravenously (Lerman, 1953), subcutaneously (Asper *et al.*, 1953), or orally (Selenkow and Asper, 1955b). The last observation would further indicate the high efficiency of absorption of thyroxine when administered orally in humans. Nevertheless, Rawson *et al.* (1953) were not able to find any marked differences between thyroxine and triiodothyronine in evoking the over-all response in basal metabolic rate in myxedema except for the speed of action.

Several acetic acid analogs of thyroxine have been assayed against thyroxine recently by O_2 consumption technique (Selenkow and Asper, 1955a); Wiswell and Asper, 1958). Although some of them are metabolically active, it has not yet been possible to assign any definite role for them at the peripheral level.

IV. Assays Based on Skeletal Changes

Promotion of skeletal maturation is a specific, cumulative, and irreversible effect of thyroxine, which is demonstrated histologically. In normal rats all the ossification centers of the carpus, tarsus, and caudal vertebrae as well as the epiphyseal centers of the extremities are established during the first 3 weeks after birth (Strong, 1925–1926). The time of appearance of each of these centers is so characteristic that skeletal age estimates of normal immature rats may be made with an accuracy of ½ day.

Walker (1957) method. Newborn litters of rats reduced to 6 of each sex were used. L-Thyroxine and its analogs were injected by an intraperitoneal route in divided dosage in volume of 0.05 ml./10 gm. body weight. The animals were examined at 8, 11, 16, or 21 days of age. Age of incisor eruption and eyelid separation was noted. Details of methods of preparing skeleton for examination are presented.

Incisor teeth eruption in rats. Garren and Greep (1955) cited the earlier literature concerning the influence of thyroxine on the rate of eruption of the incisor teeth. It was shown that thyroid hormone accelerated and propylthiouracil depressed the rate. It was suggested that this biological action of thyroxine could be used as an assay procedure.

Embryonic chick limb bones. Fell and Mellanby (1955) reported that the cultivation of chick long bone rudiments *in vivo* to which L-thyroxine was added to the culture medium produced: (a) a stimulatory effect on the maturation of cartilage, and (b) a toxic effect causing retardation of growth and cellular degeneration. Subsequently, it was shown that L-triiodothyronine had the same qualitative histological effect but was about 4 times more effective (Fell and Mellanby, 1956).

V. Assays Based on Goiter Prevention

In normal animals the secretion of TSH by the pituitary gland and of thyroxine by the thyroid gland are in equilibrium. The oral administration of compounds which block thyroxine secretion (goitrogens) reduces the level of circulating thyroidal hormones and thus stimulates increased secretion of TSH. The increased TSH, in turn, stimulates the hyperplasia of the thyroid glands as indicated by an increase in mean thyroid weight. By the injection of thyroxine or other thyroidally active compounds, in amounts equivalent to the animals' thyroxine secretion rate, hyperplasia is prevented (goiter prevention). By the injection of graded amounts of thyroxine, the equivalent thyroxine secretion rate may be determined.

As an assay technique for the estimation of biological activity of analogs of thyroxine, the following procedure is suggested: The assay animals may be mice, rats, chicks, or other experimental animals. The mean thyroid weight of control animals is determined. All groups of experimental animals are given orally a selected goitrogen (thiouracil, methylthiouracil, propylthiouracil, tapazole, or carbimazole) in an amount sufficient to block thyroxine secretion. The groups are then given graded doses of L-thyroxine and of the test substance. After 10 to 20 days, the animals are weighed and the thyroid glands removed and weighed. The mean thyroid weight expressed as a percentage of body weight (or milligram gland weight per 100 gm. body weight) are plotted against the dosage of thyroxine and test compounds.

Mussett and Pitt-Rivers (1957) have calculated the relative potencies of thyroxine analogs by the slope ratio method and the parallel line method and have shown that both calculations lead to similar values.

VI. Assays Based on Use of Tadpoles

The use of tadpoles in the bioassay of thyroidally active compounds was discussed in detail in the previous edition (Reineke and Turner, 1950). In addition, methods of breeding and rearing *Rana pipiens* were presented. Methods to be discussed here will be limited to those which have appeared since 1950 and which have been used in the biological assay of thyroidally active compounds. The reader's attention is called to Lynn and Wachowski's review (1951) on the thyroid gland and its functions in cold-blooded vertebrates.

Rana clamitans larvae, approximately 25 mm. in length, were used by Shellabarger and Godwin (1954) as assay animals. They were reared by a method suggested by Steinmetz (1950). In the assay, the tadpoles were measured individually in a Petri dish placed over graph paper ruled 20 lines per inch. The tadpoles were assigned to 5 bowls so that each bowl contained 16 of the same average length. The bowls were 120-mm. crystallizing dishes containing 500 ml. of filtered tap water (Fulflo-filter BRI03/4) to which was added the hormone. The bowls were aerated continuously, the water plus hormone was changed every other day, and oatmeal baby food (Gerber Co.) was added 24 hours before the water change. Each time the water was changed the tadpoles were measured. The reduction in length during a 10-day period was used as an index of response.

Rana pipiens larvae were reared in spring water at room temperature and fed a diet of boiled spinach. Thyroxine analogs were assayed by the method of Shellabarger and Godwin using length reduction at the end of 10 days as an index of biological activity (Money et al., 1958).

Rana catesbiana larvae of the bullfrog, whose tail widths ranged from 1.2 to 2.0 cm. at the widest point, were fasted for 48 hours and then placed in individual, shallow, transparent, flat-bottomed vessels containing 200 ml. of solution (Bruice *et al.*, 1954). The animals were placed in a large air thermostat at constant temperature (24° or 30°C.) for 48 hours. Solutions of thyroxine and test compounds were prepared, the pH of which was adjusted to 8.0 to 8.5 by addition of potassium carbonate and hydrochloric acid. Changes of tap water were made every 48 hours. The width of the tail-fin at its widest point was measured every 12 to 24 hours by means of a celluloid ruler held vertically at the side of the resting tadpole. Each lot consisted of 8 tadpoles. A rate value (V_c) was obtained by subtracting the rate of decrease of the control from that of the experimental group to provide the V_c dose-response curves.

Typhlotriton spelaeus (Ozark cave salamander) were used by Wells *et al.* (1954) to compare the metamorphosis induced by thyroxine and triiodothyronine.

Lewis and Frieden (1959) Method. A method was developed involving the Warburg apparatus for the study of oxygen consumption of small- and moderate-sized tadpoles. *Rana grylis* (southern bullfrog) tadpoles weighing 1.0 to 1.5 gm. were used. Only animals were included whose respiration rate differed less than 10% from the mean. The animals were maintained in individual stacking dishes and were not fed during respiration experiments. They were measured and weighed prior to each experiment then, placed in large Warburg vessels without center well and enough tap water added to bring the final volume to 5 ml. The side arm was used for the NaOH trap and included an appropriate filter paper accordion. The Warburg vessels were equilibrated for 20 minutes and oxygen consumption determined for the next 60 minutes. The temperature of the bath was 23.0°C.

The hormones were injected intraperitoneally using a 27-gauge needle. Metabolism measurements were taken daily for 2 to 4 days. While a detailed assay procedure was not outlined, the observations indicate the usefulness of these measurements in that both thyroxine and triiodothyronine showed responses up to 70% increase in oxygen consumption. The response to the latter compound was more rapid and quantitatively greater than to the former compound.

VII. Assays Based on Depression of I^{131} Uptake by Thyroid Gland

When animals are administered an amount of thyroxine or other thyroactive compound equal to or slightly in excess of their own thyroxine secretion rate, the further secretion of thyrotropic hormone is blocked. With an absence of TSH, the uptake of iodine is greatly inhibited. In normal animals, the percentage of injected I^{131} which is trapped varies considerably due, not only to variation in TSH secretion rate, but to the iodine content of the ration (Money *et al.*, 1952) and other factors. The degree of depression of I^{131} uptake, under standardized conditions, with varying levels of thyroxine, has been suggested as a technique of biological assay.

Money et al. (*1959*) *Method.* Male Sprague-Dawley rats weighing between 75 and 125 gm. were placed on a low iodine diet and given 0.1% thiouracil in drinking water. After 5 days the thiouracil treatment was stopped. After 24 hours the thyroidal material was injected daily, subcutaneously, for 5 days. Twenty-four hours later a single intraperitoneal injection of 0.1 μc. of I^{131} was given. The thyroids were dissected free of extraneous tissue 24 hours later, weighed, placed in Bouin's solution, and uptake of I^{131} determined in a well-type scintillation counter. L-Thyroxine administered in graded doses and percentage uptake plotted on semilog paper may serve as a standard. It is suggested that controls and 3 levels of unknown be run in each assay.

This method could be modified by the direct determination of I^{131} uptake in the live animal. Selection of animals with a uniform normal uptake of I^{131} should increase the sensitivity of the assay.

VIII. Methods of Determining Thyroxine Secretion Rate

A. The Goiter Prevention Method

Dempsey and Astwood (1943) first showed that the depression of thyroid weight in thiouracil-treated rats bore a quantitative relation to the thyroxine dosage. This technique was used to determine the estimated thyroxine secretion rate at several environmental temperatures. Subsequently, the method was used extensively to determine the estimated thyroxine secretion rate of poultry, rats, mice, and goats. Data were presented by Reineke and Turner (1950) concerning these studies.

By substituting various analogs of thyroxine, the comparative biological activity in respect to goiter prevention, can be determined. This technique has been used extensively.

The chief drawback in the use of this method has been the need of sacrifice of groups of animals to obtain thyroid weight (or thyroidectomy). It is thus limited to experimental animals. Further, the estimated thyroxine secretion rate applies to groups of animals rather than to individuals, so no idea of the range in secretion rate may be obtained.

B. The Thyroidal-I[131] Blockage Method

A technique was proposed by Pipes et al. (1950) to measure the daily output of thyroxine in rats using I[131] as a tracer. It was shown that the release of thyroidal-I[131] by the rat was proportional to the amount of thyroxine daily administered. The daily level of thyroxine which inhibited TSH secretion, and thus inhibited thyroidal-I[131] output, was estimated as the thyroxine secretion rate.

The method does not involve the sacrifice of the animals and individual thyroxine secretion rates may be determined. Domestic as well as experimental animals may be used and successive determinations under varying or constant environmental, physiological, and nutritional conditions may be made.

The details of the method as applied to various types of animals have been presented by Pipes et al. (1957) for cattle; by Henneman et al. (1952) for sheep; by Flamboe and Reineke (1957) for goats; by Biellier and Turner (1957) and Pipes et al. (1958a) for fowls; by Grosvenor and Turner (1960) for pigeons; by Reineke and Singh (1955) and Grosvenor and Turner (1958) for rats; by Amin et al. (1957) and Wada et al. (1959) for mice; by Brown-Grant (1955) for rabbits.

IX. Thyroxine Secretion Rate

The estimation of the L-thyroxine secretion rate in experimental and domestic animals serves many useful purposes. As an assay method, the corresponding biological activity of the analogs of thyroxine can be determined. This technique has been used by Brown-Grant (1955) in the rabbit and by Premachandra et al. (1960a) in cattle in determining the comparative activity of L-triiodothyronine.

The mean thyroxine secretion rate of strains of animals gives thyroid physiologists standards for the use of thyroxine in replacement therapy. In studies of the physiological effects of hyperthyroidism, it is necessary to administer dosages either related to the mean secretion rate or to the higher level indicated by the range. By the administration of thyroxine levels greatly in excess of the normal range, by those unacquainted with these data, it is suggested that the physiological and biochemical effects observed may be due to stress effects rather than to hyperthyroidism.

TABLE I

ESTIMATED L-THYROXINE SECRETION RATE

Animals	L-Thyroxine secretion rate (μg./100 gm./day)	Environment	Reference
Experimental animals			
Rats			
Carworth, male (260–300 gm.)	2.1	74° ± 1° F.	Reineke and Singh (1955)
Carworth, female (200–300 gm.)	2.21–2.56	74° ± 1° F.	Reineke and Singh (1955)
Sprague-Dawley-Rolfsmeyer strain			
Adult female	1.3	78° ± 1° F.	Grosvenor and Turner (1958)
Ovariectomy (190–230 gm.)	0.7	78° ± 1° F.	Moon and Turner (1960a)
Ovariectomy + 1.0 μg. estradiol benzoate	1.1	78° ± 1° F.	Moon and Turner (1960a)
3.6 μg. estrogen/day	1.7	78° ± 1° F.	Grosvenor and Turner (1959c)
Lactating	2.2	78° ± 1° F.	Grosvenor and Turner (1958)
Lactating + growth hormone	2.9	78° ± 1° F.	Grosvenor and Turner (1959a)
Mice			
A/Jax, male (90–140 days)	2.1	74° ± 1° F.	Amin *et al.* (1957)
A/Jax, female (90–140 days)	1.8	74° ± 1° F.	Amin *et al.* (1957)
CAF₁, male (90–140 days)	2.3	74° ± 1° F.	Amin *et al.* (1957)
CAF₁, female (90–140 days)	1.8	74° ± 1° F.	Amin *et al.* (1957)
BALB/c, male (90–140 days)	2.4	74° ± 1° F.	Amin *et al.* (1957)
BALB/c, female (90–140 days)	1.9	74° ± 1° F.	Amin *et al.* (1957)
C57BR/cd, male (90–140 days)	3.3	74° ± 1° F.	Amin *et al.* (1957)
C57BR/cd, female (90–140 days)	2.4	74° ± 1° F.	Amin *et al.* (1957)
BBF₁, male (90–140 days)	3.8	74° ± 1° F.	Amin *et al.* (1957)
BBF₁, female (90–140 days)	2.7	74° ± 1° F.	Amin *et al.* (1957)
C57BL/6, male (90–140 days)	4.2	74° ± 1° F.	Amin *et al.* (1957)
C57BL/6, female (90–140 days)	3.3	74° ± 1° F.	Amin *et al.* (1957)
Swiss-Webster strain			
Males and females (140 days)	1.2	78° ± 1° F.	Wada *et al.* (1959)
Castrate males (140 days)	0.8	78° ± 1° F.	Wada *et al.* (1959)
Castrate females (140 days)	0.9	78° ± 1° F.	Wada *et al.* (1959)
Chickens			
Rhode Island Red, slow feathering (2 weeks)	1.5	February	Boone *et al.* (1950)
Rhode Island Red, fast feathering (2 weeks)	1.6	February	Boone *et al.* (1950)
Delaware × New Hampshire (3 weeks)	1.3	84°–90° F.	Biellier and Turner (1957)
Delaware × New Hampshire (8 weeks)	0.9	60°–82° F.	Biellier and Turner (1957)
Adult New Hampshire (low thyroid enlargement)	2.9	40°–67° F.	Premachandra *et al.* (1958a)
Adult New Hampshire (high thyroid enlargement)	1.0	40°–67° F.	Premachandra *et al.* (1958a)
Adult New Hampshire crossbred (10 weeks)	4.0	40°–67° F.	Mellen and Wentworth (1959)
Turkey			
Beltsville pullets (3 weeks)	0.9	84°–90° F.	Biellier and Turner (1957)
Beltsville pullets (15 weeks)	0.5	69°–76° F.	Biellier and Turner (1957)
B. B. Bronze (3 weeks)	2.7	90°–95° F.	Smyth and Fox (1951)
Jersey Buff (3 weeks)	2.6	90°–95° F.	Smyth and Fox (1951)
Cross (B.B.B. × J.B.) (3 weeks)	2.9	90°–95° F.	Smyth and Fox (1951)

TABLE I *Continued*

Animals	L-Thyroxine secretion rate (μg./100 gm./day)	Environment	Reference
Ducks			
Unsexed white Pekin ducks (3 weeks)	3.8	95° F.	Hoffman (1950)
Pigeons			
Common pigeon (300–400 gm.)	1.9	78° F.	Grosvenor and Turner (1960)
Rabbit	μg./day		
Chinchilla rabbits (adult female)	14.5–19.0	82° F.	Brown-Grant (1955)
Adult rabbits (male)	18.0		Maqsood (1950)
Domestic animals			
Cattle	(mg./100 lb./day)		
Heifer calves	0.71	May	Lodge *et al.* (1957)
Heifer calves	0.55	August– September	Lodge *et al.* (1957)
Bull calves	0.23	Summer	Mixner and Lennon (1958b)
Heifers	0.25	Thermally neutral	Johnston *et al.* (1959)
Lactating and nonlactating cows	0.20	Summer (June–Aug.)	Premachandra *et al.* (1958b)
Lactating and nonlactating cows	0.60	Winter (Sept.–March)	Premachandra *et al.* (1958b)
Lactating cows	0.33	72° F.	Sorensen (1956)
Nonlactating cows	0.08–0.19	Thermally neutral	Hamblin *et al.* (1958)
Dairy Goats			
Mixed breed,			
pregnant	0.26	February	Flamboe and Reineke (1959)
nonpregnant	0.28	February	Flamboe and Reineke (1959)
aged lactating (4–6 years)	0.19	May	Flamboe and Reineke (1959)
aged lactating	0.05	July	Flamboe and Reineke (1959)
young lactating (2 years)	0.26	May	Flamboe and Reineke (1959)
young lactating	0.07	July	Flamboe and Reineke (1959)
Sheep			
Shropshire			
ewes (4–6 months)	0.08	March	Singh *et al.* (1956)
rams (4–6 months)	0.07	March	Singh *et al.* (1956)
wethers (4–6 months)	0.05	March	Singh *et al.* (1956)
Shropshire			
ewes (2 years)	0.20	March	Hennemann *et al.* (1955)
ewes (2 years)	0.04	July	Hennemann *et al.* (1955)
ewes (2 years) open	0.11	September	Hennemann *et al.* (1955)
ewes (2 years) pregnant	0.24	March	Hennemann *et al.* (1955)
ewes (2 years) lactating	0.32	March–April	Hennemann *et al.* (1955)
ewes (4 years) open	0.09	September	Hennemann *et al.* (1955)
ewes (4 years) pregnant	0.15	March	Hennemann *et al.* (1955)
ewes (4 years) lactating	0.21	March	Hennemann *et al.* (1955)
Clun Forest cross (12–14 months)	0.19	March	Freinkel and Lewis (1957)
shorn sheep	0.34	March	Freinkel and Lewis (1957)
Swine			
Young pigs	0.20		Frape *et al.* (1958)

Many factors influencing thyroxine secretion rate may be explored by this technique. It has been shown that seasonal temperature variation markedly influences the thyroxine secretion rate causing a threefold lowering in the summer as contrasted to the winter in cattle (Pipes *et al.*, 1958b). Rats in intense lactation have been shown to have markedly higher secretion rates (Grosvenor and Turner, 1958). It has been shown that 3.6 μg. estradiol benzoate per day increases thyroxine secretion rate 35% in rats (Grosvenor and Turner, 1959), whereas ovariectomy depressed thyroxine secretion 33% (Moon and Turner, 1960a). Injection of 1 μg. per day of estradiol benzoate restored thyroxine secretion to normal.

Data on the estimated mean thyroxine secretion rate of experimental and domestic animals are presented (Table I). Great variability in the thyroxine secretion rate in breeds and strains of experimental and domestic animals has been noted under uniform environmental conditions. Since the secretion rate may be determined in the intact animal it will be possible to relate these normal secretion rate differences to their growth rate, reproductive and lactational performances, etc.

The mode of inheritance of thyroxine secretion rate may be determined by suitable matings of animals differing in secretion rate. If matings of high thyroxine secretion rate animals produce progeny of uniformly high thyroxine secretion rate, such animals would be especially valuable for assay purposes in reducing currently observed variability.

REFERENCES

Amin, A., Chai, C. K., and Reineke, E. P. (1957). *Am. J. Physiol.* **191**, 34.

Anderson, B. G. (1954). *Endocrinology* **54**, 659.

Asper, S. P., Jr. (1958). *Bull. Johns Hopkins Hosp.* **102**, 85, 88, 94, 107, 115.

Asper, S. P., Jr., Selenkow, H. A., and Plamondon, C. A. (1953). *Bull. Johns Hopkins Hosp.* **93**, 164.

Barker, S. B. (1955). *Ann. Rev. Physiol.* **17**, 417.

Barker, S. B. (1956). *Endocrinology* **59**, 548.

Barker, S. B. and Klitgaard, H. M. (1952). *Am. J. Physiol.* **170**, 81.

Bartlett, S., Burt, A. W. A., Folley, S. J., and Rowland, S. J. (1954). *J. Endocrinol.* **10**, 193.

Basil, B., Somers, G. F., and Woollett, E. A. (1950). *Brit. J. Pharmacol.* **5**, 315.

Biellier, H. V., and Turner, C. W. (1957). *Missouri Univ. Agr. Expt. Sta. Research Bull.* **622**.

Blackburn, C. M., McConahey, W. M., Keating, F. R., Jr., and Albert, A. (1953). *J. Clin. Endocrinol. and Metabolism* **13**, 852.

Boone, M. A., Davidson, J. A., and Reineke, E. P. (1950). *Poultry Sci.* **29**, 195.

Brown-Grant, K. (1955). *J. Physiol. (London)* **127**, 352.

Bruice, T. C., Winzler, R. J., and Kharasch, N. (1954). *J. Biol. Chem.* **210**, 1.

Bruice, T. C., Kharasch, N., and Winzler, R. J. (1956). *Arch. Biochem. Biophys.* **62**, 305.

Campbell, D. J., Andrews, F. N., and Christian, J. E. (1950). *Endocrinology* **47**, 242.

Clayton, J. C., Free, H. A., Page, J. E., Somers, G. F., and Woollett, E. A. (1950). *Biochem. J.* **46**, 598.

Crosley, A. P., Jr., Alexander, F. and Strickland, W. H. (1960). *Federation Proc.* **19**, 221.

Deltour, G. H., and Bekaert, J. (1953). *Compt. rend. soc. biol.* **147**, 388.

Dempsey, E. W., and Astwood, E. B. (1943). *Endocrinology* **32**, 509.

Duncan, C. H., and Best, M. M. (1958). *Endocrinology* **63**, 169.

Enneker, C., Kessler, F. J., and Kruskemper, H. L. (1958). *Acta Endocrinol.* **29**, 565.

Evans, E. S., Rosenberg, L. L., and Simpson, M. E. (1960). *Endocrinology* **66**, 433.

Fell, H. B., and Mellanby, E. (1955). *J. Physiol.* (*London*) **127**, 427.

Fell, H. B., and Mellanby, E. (1956). *J. Physiol.* (*London*) **133**, 89.

Flamboe, E. E., and Reineke, E. P. (1957). *J. Animal Sci.* **16**, 1061.

Flamboe, E. E., and Reineke, E. P. (1959). *J. Animal Sci.* **18**, 1135.

Frape, D. L., Gage, J. W., Jr., Hays, V. W., Speer, V. C., and Catron, D. V. (1958). *J. Animal Sci.* **17**, 1275.

Freinkel, N., and Lewis, D. (1957). *J. Physiol.* (*London*) **135**, 288.

Friedberg, W., and Reineke, E. P. (1952). *Federation Proc.* **11**, 50.

Frieden, E., Tuckich, E. B., and Winzler, R. J. (1949). *Endocrinology* **45**, 82.

Garren, L., and Greep, R. O. (1955). *Proc. Soc. Exptl. Biol. Med.* **90**, 652.

Gemmill, C. L. (1953). *Am. J. Physiol.* **172**, 286.

Gilliland, I. C. (1959). *J. Endocrinol.* **18**, xxiv.

Gilliland, I. C., and Strudwick, J. I. (1953). *Mem. Soc. Endocrinol.* **1**, 14.

Griesbach, W. E., and Purves, H. D. (1945). *Brit. J. Exptl. Pathol.* **26**, 13.

Griesbach, W. E., Kennedy, T. H., and Purves, H. D. (1949). *Endocrinology* **44**, 445.

Gross, J., Pitt-Rivers, R., and Trotter, W. R. (1952). *Lancet* i, 1044.

Grosvenor, C. E., and Turner, C. W. (1958). *Proc. Soc. Exptl. Biol. Med.* **99**, 517.

Grosvenor, C. E., and Turner, C. W. (1959a). *Proc. Soc. Exptl. Biol. Med.* **100**, 70.

Grosvenor, C. E., and Turner, C. W. (1959b). *Proc. Soc. Exptl. Biol. Med.* **100**, 162.

Grosvenor, C. E., and Turner, C. W. (1959c). *Proc. Soc. Exptl. Biol. Med.* **101**, 194.

Grosvenor, C. E., and Turner, C. W. (1960). *Am. J. Physiol.* **198**, 1.

Hamblin, F. B., Johnston, J. E., and Schrader, G. (1958). *J. Dairy Sci.* **41**, 728.

Heming, A. E., and Holtkamp, D. E. (1953). *Proc. Soc. Exptl. Biol. Med.* **83**, 875.

Henneman, H. A., Griffin, S. A., and Reineke, E. P. (1952). *J. Animal Sci.* **11**, 794.

Henneman, H. A., Reineke, E. P., and Griffin, S. A. (1955). *J. Animal Sci.* **14**, 419.

Hoffman, E. (1950). *Poultry Sci.* **29**, 109.

Holtkamp, D. E., Ochs, S., Pfeiffer, C. C., and Heming, A. E. (1955). *Endocrinology* **56**, 93.

Johnston, J. E., Hindery, G. A., Burnett, W. T., and Guidry, A. (1959). *J. Dairy Sci.* **42**, 927.

Kroc, R. L., Phillips, G. E., Stasilli, N. R., and Malament, S. (1954). *J. Clin. Endocrinol. and Metabolism* **14**, 56.

La Roche, C., and Rapin, M. (1953). *Ann. endocrinol.* (*Paris*) **14**, 245.

Larson, F. C., and Albright, E. C. (1958). *Endocrinology* **63**, 183.

Larson, F. C., Tomita, K., and Albright, E. C. (1959). *Endocrinology* **65**, 336.

Lerman, J. (1953). *J. Clin. Endocrinol. and Metabolism* **13**, 1341.

Lewis, E. J. C., and Frieden, E. (1959). *Endocrinology* **65**, 273.

Lilienthal, J. L., Jr., Zierler, K. L., and Folk, B. P. (1949). *Bull. Johns Hopkins Hosp.* **84**, 238.

Littrell, J. L., Dolgin, C. K. A., and Fevold, H. L. (1952). *Proc. Soc. Exptl. Biol. Med.* **81**, 670.

Lodge, J. R., Lewis, R. C., and Reineke, E. P. (1957). *J. Dairy Sci.* **40**, 209.

Lynn, W. G., and Wachowski, H. E. (1951). *Quart. Rev. Biol.* **26**, 123.

McConahey, W. M., Blackburn, C. M., Keating, F. R. J., and Albert, A. (1953). *Trans. Am. Goiter Assoc.* p. 3.

Maclagan, N. F., and Sheahan, M. M. (1950). *J. Endocrinol.* **6**, 456.

Magnus-Levy, A. (1895). *Berlin klin. Wochschr.* **32**, 650.

Maqsood, M. (1950). *Nature* **166**, 735.

Mellen, W. J., and Wentworth, B. C. (1959). *Poultry Sci.* **38**, 228.

Mixner, J. P., and Lennon, H. D., Jr. (1958a). *J. Dairy Sci.* **41**, 728.

Mixner, J. P., and Lennon, H. D., Jr. (1958b). *J. Dairy Sci.* **41**, 840.

Mixner, J. P., and Lennon, H. D., Jr. (1959). *J. Dairy Sci.* **42**, 927.

Money, W. L., Rall, J. E., and Rawson, R. W. (1952). *J. Clin. Endocrinol and Metabolism* **12**, 1495.

Money, W. L., Meltzer, R. I., Young, J., and Rawson, R. W. (1958). *Endocrinology* **63**, 20.

Money, W. L., Meltzer, R. I., Feldman, D., and Rawson, R. W. (1959). *Endocrinology* **64**, 123.

Monroe, R. A., and Turner, C. W. (1949). *Missouri Univ. Agr. Expt. Sta. Research Bull.* **446**.

Moon, R. C., and Turner, C. W. (1960a). *Proc. Soc. Exptl. Biol. Med.* **103**, 66.

Moon, R. C., and Turner, C. W. (1960b). *Proc. Soc. Exptl. Biol. Med.* **103**, 149.

Mussett, M. V., and Pitt-Rivers, R. (1957). *Metabolism, Clin. and Exptl.* **6**, 18.

Newcomer, W. S. (1957). *Am. J. Physiol.* **190**, 413.

Newcomer, W. S., and Barrett, P. A. (1960). *Endocrinology* **66**, 409.

Pipes, G. W., Blincoe, C. R., and Hsieh, K. (1950). *J. Dairy Sci.* **33**, 384.

Pipes, G. W., Premachandra, B. N., and Turner, C. W. (1957). *J. Dairy Sci.* **40**, 340.

Pipes, G. W., Premachandra, B. N., and Turner, C. W. (1958a). *Poultry Sci.* **37**, 36.

Pipes, G. W., Premachandra, B. N., and Turner, C. W. (1958b). *Proc. Intern. Conf. Peaceful Uses Atomic Energy, 2nd Conf., Geneva* **27**, 110.

Pitt-Rivers, R. (1953). *Mem. Soc. Endocrinol.* **1**, 11.

Pitt-Rivers, R., and Tata, J. R. (1959). "The Thyroid Hormones." Pergamon Press, New York.

Plamondon, C. A., Selenkow, H. A., Wiswell, J. G., and Asper, S. P., Jr. (1958). *Bull. Johns Hopkins Hosp.* **102**, 88.

Premachandra, B. N., Pipes, G. W., and Turner, C. W. (1958a). *Poultry Sci.* **37**, 399.

Premachandra, B. N., Pipes, G. W., and Turner, C. W. (1958b). *J. Dairy Sci.* **41**, 1609.

Premachandra, B. N., Pipes, G. W., and Turner, C. W. (1960a). *J. Dairy Sci.* **43**, 883.

Premachandra, B. N., Pipes, G. W., and Turner, C. W. (1960b). *Missouri Univ. Agr. Expt. Sta. Research Bull.* **727**.

Purves, H. D., and Griesbach, W. E. (1946). *Brit. J. Exptl. Pathol.* **27**, 170.

Rawson, R. W., Rall, J. E., Pearson, O. H., Robbins, J., Poppell, H. F., and West, C. D. (1953). *Am. J. Med. Sci.* **226**, 405.

Reineke, E. P. (1954). *J. Dairy Sci.* **37**, 1227.

Reineke, E. P., and Singh, O. N. (1955). *Proc. Soc. Exptl. Biol. Med.* **88**, 203.

Reineke, E. P., and Turner, C. W. (1942). *Missouri Univ. Agr. Exp. Sta. Research Bull.* **355.**

Reineke, E. P., and Turner, C. W. (1945). *J. Biol. Chem.* **161,** 613.

Reineke, E. P., and Turner, C. W. (1946). *J. Biol. Chem.* **162,** 369.

Reineke, E. P., and Turner, C. W. (1950). *In* "Hormone Assay" (C. W. Emmens, ed.) Chapter 19, p. 489. Academic Press, New York.

Reineke, E. P., Turner, C. W., Kohler, G. O., Hoover, R. D., and Beezley, M. B. (1945). *J. Biol. Chem.* **161,** 599.

Salter, W. T., and Rosenblum, I. (1952). *Am. J. Med. Sci.* **224,** 628.

Scow, R. O., and Simpson, M. E. (1945). *Anat. Record* **91,** 209

Selenkow, H. A., and Asper, S. P., Jr. (1955a). *Physiol. Revs.* **35,** 426.

Selenkow, H. A., and Asper, S. P., Jr. (1955b). *J Clin. Endocrinol. and Metabolism* **15,** 285.

Shellabarger, C. J. (1955). *Poultry Sci.* **34,** 1437.

Shellabarger, C. J., and Godwin, J. T. (1954). *Endocrinology* **54,** 230.

Singh, O. N., Henneman, H. A., and Reineke, E. P. (1956). *J. Animal Sci.* **15,** 625.

Slater, S., Perlmutter, M., Paz-Carramza, J., and Numeroff, M. A. (1960). *J. Clin. Endocrinol. and Metabolism* **20,** 401.

Smith, A. U., Emmens, C. W., and Parkes, A. S. (1947). *J. Endocrinol.* **5,** 186.

Smyth, J. R., Jr., and Fox, T. W. (1951). *Poultry Sci.* **30,** 607.

Sorensen, P. H. (1956). *Nord. Veterinärmed* **8,** 639.

Stasilli, N. R., Kroc, R. L., and Meltzer, R. I. (1959). *Endocrinology* **64,** 62.

Steinmetz, C. H. (1950). *Proc. Indiana Acad. Sci.* **60,** 324.

Strong, R. M. (1925–26). *Am. J. Anat.* **36,** 313.

Tabachnick, I. I. A., Parker, R. E., Wagner, J., and Anthony, P. Z. (1956). *Endocrinology* **59,** 153.

Tapley, D. F., and Cooper, C. (1956a). *J. Biol. Chem.* **222,** 341.

Tapley, D. F., and Cooper, C. (1956b). *Nature* **178,** 1119.

Tapley, D. F., Davidoff, F. F., Hatfield, W. B., and Ross, J. E. (1959). *Am. J. Physiol.* **197,** 1021.

Tata, J. R., and Shellabarger, C. J. (1959). *Biochem. J.* **72,** 608.

Taurog, A., Wheat, J. D., and Chaikoff, I. L. (1956). *Endocrinology* **58,** 121.

Tenney, A., and Lorenz, N. (1952). *Endocrinology* **50,** 374.

Tomich, E. G., and Woollett, E. A. (1954). *J. Endocrinol.* **11,** 134.

Tomich, E. G., Woollett, E. A., and Pratt, M. A. (1960). *J. Endocrinol.* **20,** 65.

Turner, C. W., Pipes, G. W., and Premachandra, B. N. (1959). *Conf. Isotopes in Agr. Oklahoma,* **TID-7578,** 97.

Wada, H., Berswordt-Wallrabe, R. v., and Turner, C. W. (1959). *Proc. Soc. Exptl. Biol. Med.* **102,** 608.

Walker, D. G. (1957). *Bull. Johns Hopkins Hosp.* **101,** 101.

Wells, P. H., Wallen, T., Eden, J., and Turner, C. W. (1954). *Anat. Record* **120,** 779.

Wilkinson, J. H. (1959). *Biochem. J.* **73,** 334.

Wiswell, J. G., and Asper, S. P., Jr. (1958). *Bull. Johns Hopkins Hosp.* **102,** 115.

Chapter 11

Insulin

K. L. Smith

I. Introduction

Since insulin is unique in that it is a potent drug possessing rapid action and that under or over dosage outside narrow limits is betrayed by unpleasant symptoms, it is unfortunate that a specific chemical test with high inherent accuracy is not available to ensure the uniformity of material issued for clinical use.

However, the qualitative effect of insulin can be demonstrated readily in laboratory animals by the exhibition of falls in blood-sugar level indicated either by actual blood-sugar determinations or by the incidence of convulsions relieved by the ingestion of glucose. Through the years insulin has been reliably assayed by methods employing these reactions.

During recent years physicochemical methods using paper chromatography and biological methods using new systems have been applied to the assay of insulin.

Both groups already have great value, the former as a domestic tool for those interested in problems relating to optimum yield, stability,

413

etc., and the latter for those interested in determining insulin at physiological levels. Neither, however, has yet supplanted the classic methods using animals, which are still the methods officially called for in the examinations of insulin intended for clinical use. It will be appreciated however, that the physicochemical methods have a distinct value in supplementing the biological assay of such insulins.

II. The Standard Preparation

It is essential that when a biological assay is being conducted the assay should be so designed that a simultaneous comparison with a standard preparation may be made.

The first international standard for insulin was established in 1925 and contained by definition 1 unit in 0.125 mg., this unit being intended to approximate the clinical unit defined by Macleod and Orr (1924). The preparation and assay of the second standard set up in 1935 is described in the Quarterly Bulletin of the Health Organisation of the League of Nations (1936). It was accepted as having a potency of 22 U. per milligram, this value being approximately that yielded by the assays on rabbits and somewhat lower than that obtained by the mouse method in 4 out of 5 of the laboratories. It is not surprising that on this occasion the two methods yielded different results when it is considered that the comparisons were made between preparations of widely different purities. Such differences in potency between the two methods should not occur when preparations having the same degree of purity are being compared.

A third international standard for insulin containing 24.5 U. per milligram was established in 1952 and the fourth and present international standard containing 24.0 U. per milligram was established in 1959.

Unlike previous standards for insulin which had been stored under nitrogen and dried over P_2O_5 the fourth standard has been filled over air and contains 5.65% moisture but nevertheless is still hygroscopic.

In this instance the report by Bangham and Mussett (1959) indicates that the potencies by mouse and rabbit methods agreed well (mouse method 24.1 U. per milligram; rabbit twin cross-over tests 23.8; rabbit triplet cross-over tests 23.4).

In use the weighed standard may be dissolved in 0.9% saline acidified with hydrochloric acid to pH 2.5 and containing 0.3% tricresol (or 0.5% phenol) to prevent the growth of microorganisms. If this solution is prepared to contain 20 U. per milliliter and stored at a temperature near to its freezing point it can be considered to be stable for 6 months.

Following their usual custom, the Reference Standards Committee of the United States Pharmacopeial Organization issue their own reference standard for insulin. This is now identical material to that used for the fourth international standard.

The U.S. Pharmacopeia XV instructs that a solution to contain 40 U. per milliliter be effected in water containing 0.1 to 0.25% w/v of phenol or cresol, between 1.4 and 1.8% glycerin, and sufficient hydrochloric acid to produce a pH between 2.5 and 3.5.

III. The Rabbit Method of Assay

A. DESIGN AND INTERPRETATION

1. Early Designs

A report on the preparation of the first international standard for insulin and the definition of the unit of activity (League of Nations, 1926) contained considerations of the principles involved in the assay of this hormone and recorded the test designs which had hitherto been used.

The use of the rabbit for the assay had been suggested (Banting, et al., 1922) since it had been observed that the degree of hypoglycemia produced in rabbits by insulin paralleled its clinical effect in diabetes mellitus.

Since the incidence of hypoglycemic convulsions was usually associated with a blood-sugar level of 45 mg./100ml., the unit of activity had been defined as the smallest amount that would cause this blood-sugar level to be reached within 4 hours of injection.

The earliest designs therefore consisted of attempts to establish this value with regard to the sample under examination without any reference to a standard preparation. When a reference standard had been established the simultaneous comparison with it was made in tests completed in one day.

2. The Cross-over Test

When small numbers of animals are used in comparative assays, completed in one day, the appearance of a particularly sensitive or insensitive animal among those receiving either the standard or the test preparation will bias the result unduly.

To overcome this, Marks (1925) suggested that the animals used on one day should be tested again in the same groupings, and that on this occasion those which had previously received injections of the standard preparation should receive injections of the test preparation and vice versa. He made this suggestion since he had observed that whereas the level of sensitivity of a colony of rabbits might vary from day to day the comparative sensitivities of the individuals remained fairly constant.

He suggested that the response of each rabbit be measured as the per cent blood-sugar reduction and that an indication of relative activity could be obtained by summing the responses yielded by the rabbits receiving the test preparation and expressing it as a ratio of the corresponding responses to the standard preparation. For this purpose he expressed the per cent blood-sugar reduction as

$$\% \text{ (blood-sugar) reduction} = 100 \frac{(\text{I.B.S.} - \text{F.B.S.})}{\text{I.B.S.}}$$

where I.B.S. and F.B.S. are the initial and final blood-sugar levels. Marks (1925) used for F.B.S. the mean blood-sugar level, after injection, in samples of blood taken at hourly intervals for 5 hours.

The cross-over test carried out thus could only show whether, at the potency assumed, the sample was or was not equal in activity to the standard. Many workers (Macleod and Orr, 1926; Culhane *et al.*, 1929; Hershey and Lacey, 1936) considered that reliance could only be placed on tests which indicated equal activity of the standard and test preparations, and apparently only used indications of departures from this identity to enable suitable adjustments to be made so that it could be reached in subsequent tests.

Marks (1926) considered that the cross-over test to be efficient should be capable of demonstrating known differences and showed how by testing known dilutions of standard a curve relating the ratio to true activity could be constructed. In the light of later experience (Marks, 1932), he modified this curve to overcome the correlation exhibited between assumed and estimated potencies and recommended that, to avoid such bias introduced by the use of a curve the slope of which did not strictly apply, an assay should consist of a series of cross-over tests aimed to yield ratios both greater and less than unity.

Marks (1926) had suggested that if the response of a rabbit appeared discordant in view of the previous history of the animal it might be necessary to discard the response of that rabbit altogether, but if this were done a corresponding rabbit should be removed from the other dosage group to compensate for it. The practice of discarding a response because it does not appear satisfactory is gravely suspect. Compensation for the loss of a response through death or convulsions appears to be most satisfactorily provided by working with group averages rather than with sums.

3. The Interpretation of a Series of Cross-over Tests

A review (Fieller *et al.*, 1939a, b) was made of accumulated data from certain laboratories which had followed Marks' suggestion to assay each sample at assumed potencies so as to yield ratios greater than and less than unity. It demonstrated how such data, whether the relative effect was measured by the ratios of the responses to standard and test preparations or by their differences, could be treated to supply an estimate of the log dose-response line (l.d.r.l.) obtaining in the laboratory and to indicate the degree of precision to be expected under those conditions.

Fieller (1940) gave an extensive description of the arithmetical procedures involved in this treatment, using response differences as the criterion of relative efficiency and taking as an example a series of 7 cross-over tests carried out on one sample at assumed potencies ranging from 100 to 160 U./ml.

The series of cross-over tests taken as an example by Fieller had not been carried out with a view to the subsequent calculations which were enumerated. In a planned assay much computational labor may be saved by arranging that the assumed potencies have equal logarithmic intervals, for then the main calculations may be carried out using logs to the base of the dose interval, suitably reduced to yield whole numbers for x, and the necessary correction made later.

4. The Three-Assumption Cross-over Design

Marks (1936) suggested that in the course of a cross-over test the animals receiving the test preparation should be split so that they received it at one of two dose levels, a suggestion which in effect meant the simultaneous conduct of two cross-over tests at two assumed potencies.

Lacey (1941) described a procedure used in the Insulin Committee Laboratory of the University of Toronto which called for a comparison with the standard at three assumed potency levels. Lacey (1946), describing the interpretation of data from such tests, implied that the index of relative activity calculated for each test as

$$\text{Index} = \frac{\text{Mean \% reduction effected by test preparation} \times 100}{\text{Mean \% reduction effected by standard preparation}}$$

should be plotted against log assumed potency and calculated the regression line by the method of least squares.

The data presented by him will be used to show the arithmetical steps needed in the interpretation of a three-assumption cross-over test.

To preserve the similarity with Fieller's treatment of a series of cross-over tests the response will be taken as $y = 100 -$ index, a value suggested by Fieller *et al.* (1939b) and a weight ascribed to each test equal to $2n_1n_2/(n_1 + n_2)$ where n_1 and n_2 are the numbers of rabbits respectively, in each cell of the test.

Lacey (1946) recorded the indexes from three cross-over tests each using 8 rabbits and carried out at assumed potencies of 200, 100, and 50% of the standard (at 40 U./ml.).

As y is to be related to log assumed potencies, then since the assumed potencies are equally spaced on the log scale, whole numbers may be scored for the value $x = $ log assumed potency as given in Table I, suitable correction being made later to convert to common logarithms.

TABLE I

ARITHMETICAL STEPS IN INTERPRETATION OF A THREE-ASSUMPTION CROSS-OVER TEST

Test	Assumed potency (%)	w	$x = \log_2{}^a$ Assumed potency	Index	$y = 100 - $ Index	wx	wx^2	wy	wxy
1	200	4	$+1$	67.8	32.2	4	4	128.8	128.8
2	100	4	0	105.0	-5.0	0	0	-20.0	0
3	50	4	-1	126.8	-26.8	-4	4	-107.2	107.2
		12				0	8	1.6	236.0

^{a} Suitably reduced to yield integers:

$$\bar{x} = Swx \div Sw = 0$$
$$Sw(x - \bar{x})^2 = Swx^2 - \bar{x}Swx = 8 - 0 = 8$$
$$\bar{y} = Swy \div Sw = 1.6 \div 12 = 0.1333$$
$$Swx(y - \bar{y}) = Swxy - \bar{y}Swx = 236.0 - 0 = 236.0$$

Then working in logs to base 2 (2 is the ratio between successive assumed potencies)

$$b = \frac{Swx\,(y - \bar{y})}{Sw\,(x - \bar{x})^2} = \frac{236}{8} = 29.5$$

and the log activity ratio is

$$M = \bar{x} - \frac{\bar{y}}{b} = \frac{-0.1333}{29.5} = -0.0045$$

On converting to common logarithms,

$$M = -0.0045 \times 0.301 = -0.0014 \text{ or } \bar{1}.9986 = \log 0.9968$$

Hence the potency is estimated to be 99.7% of that assumed or 39.9 U./ml.

In this case, of course, a similar result would have been obtained if

w had been taken as unity, but it may often occur that the constituent cross-over tests are not, by reason of lost responses, exactly balanced. The fuller arithmetical procedure has therefore been included.

In contradistinction to the treatment by differences as described by Fieller, there is no value comparable to s^2 (the variance of a single response as described in Chapter 1) and hence the linearity of the l.d.r.l. cannot be checked nor can the significance of the calculated slope and the limits of error to be attached to the estimate be assessed.

5. The Establishment of l.d.r.l. from Multidose Tests

In the designs so far considered the slopes of the l.d.r.l. have been determined wholly from changes in response level effected by changes in the injected dose of the test preparation. Test designs in which consideration is given to the parallelism of the l.d.r.l. for the standard and the test preparations have also been described.

Practical difficulties may make it impossible to consider at the same time the linearity of each l.d.r.l., and it may become necessary to establish the relationship of the response to the dose by means of special experiment. Especially is this so if a new criterion of response is being examined.

Bliss and Marks (1939a) described their investigation into the characteristics of the l.d.r.l. for insulin in rabbits when percentage reductions were used as the response criterion. For this they used the data from 8 rabbits, arranged for treatment by means of 2 randomized 4×4 Latin squares, so that each rabbit received during four testings each of four doses of insulin (equally spaced on a logarithmic scale), each dose being equally represented on each day.

6. The Six-Point Assay

Bliss and Marks (1939b) also illustrated how this design could be applied to the assay of an unknown sample of insulin against a standard. Their treatment has become a pattern for most of the biological assays in which the response is graded. It has not, however, been applied generally to the assay of insulin, solely because of the time needed to collect the data. Under the normal conditions allowing a week to elapse between the separate testings, the time needed to conduct such an assay using two doses of standard and two of test preparations would be 3 weeks. In view of the more recent suggestions that single blood-sugar levels without reference to the initial level provide a satisfactory measure of response to insulin (see Chapter 1 and Young and Romans, 1948), it does become practicable to apply this design even with the use of three doses each of the standard and the test preparations.

To illustrate the interpretation, the data shown in Table II have been taken from such an assay using three doses of standard and three of test preparations, in which the responses were measured as the blood-sugar levels (the sum of duplicate readings) at $1\frac{1}{2}$ hours after the subcutaneous

TABLE II

PROTOCOLS FROM THE ASSAY OF CRYSTALLINE INSULIN 9224B AT 22 UNITS/MG.
Ratio between successive doses $= 1.667$[a]

Rabbit	Standard			Test preparation			Sums
	2 U./ml.	1.2 U./ml.	0.72 U./ml.	2 U./ml.	1.2 U./ml.	0.72 U./ml.	
18	117	116	150	151	158	207	899
23	135	142	146	101	142	191	857
Sums	252 (1)	258 (2)	296 (3)	252 (4)	300 (5)	398 (6)	
64	115	148	163	97	99	160	782
48	134	145	159	137	149	165	889
Sums	249 (6)	293 (1)	322 (2)	234 (3)	248 (4)	325 (5)	
35	159	172	184	155	173	196	1039
8	132	163	147	116	130	157	845
Sums	291 (5)	335 (6)	331 (1)	271 (2)	303 (3)	353 (4)	
46	117	131	135	105	133	157	778
29	169	220	220	138	176	189	1112
Sums	286 (4)	351 (5)	355 (6)	243 (1)	309 (2)	346 (3)	
4	127	144	146	102	123	166	808
21	144	177	240	149	151	178	1039
Sums	271 (3)	321 (4)	386 (5)	251 (6)	274 (1)	344 (2)	
42	133	138	161	139	146	152	869
17	158	188	196	101	142	138	923
Sums	291 (2)	326 (3)	357 (4)	240 (5)	288 (6)	290 (1)	
Total sums	1640	1884	2047	1491	1722	2056	10840

	Days	1	2	3	4	5	6
	Sums	1683	1795	1766	1817	1893	1876

[a] Figures in parentheses indicate day of dosing.

injection of the insulins. The test was completed in 6 consecutive days, injections being made at 9:30 A.M., bleedings made at 11 A.M., and the animals being fed uniformly from 12 noon to 4:30 P.M., at which time the uneaten food was removed. The rabbits were allowed access to water during the whole test.

The data were submitted to an analysis of variance. The results of this analysis are shown in Table III.

TABLE III

ANALYSIS OF VARIANCE FOR DATA IN TABLE II

Source of variation	Sum of Squares	Correction term	Reduced sum of squares	df	Variance
Total	$117^2 + \ldots + 138^2$	$10840^2/72$	61140	71	
Between rabbits	$(899^2 + \ldots + 923^2) \div 6$	$10840^2/72$	21202	11	1927.5
Between days	$(1683^2 + \ldots + 1876^2) \div 12$	$10840^2/72$	2395	5	479
Between doses	$(1640^2 + \ldots + 2056^2) \div 12$	$10840^2/72$	21708	5	4341.6
Residual error			15835	50	$316.7 = s^2$

The significant variance ratio for doses showed that changes in dose were accompanied by real change in response level. A partition of the reduced sum of squares for between doses was made using polynomial coefficients as suggested by Bliss and Marks (1939a).

The results of this examination are shown in Table IV. From it, it

TABLE IV

EXAMINATION OF DOSE-RESPONSE RELATION FOR EXPERIMENTAL DATA IN TABLE II

	St_{100}	St_{60}	St_{36}	T_{100}	T_{60}	T_{36}	$NS(x)^2$	$S(xYp)$	Variance $\dfrac{S^2(xYp)}{NS(x^2)}$	Variance ratio
Difference between samples	−1	−1	−1	+1	+1	+1	72	−302	$1266.7 = D^2$	3.999
Slope of l.d.r.l.	+1	0	−1	+1	0	−1	48	−972	$19683 = B^2$	62.15
Departure from parallelism	+1	0	−1	−1	0	+1	48	158	520.1	1.64
Curvature of combined line	+1	−2	+1	+1	−2	+1	144	22	3.36	0.01
Opposed curvature of separate lines	−1	+2	−1	+1	−2	+1	144	184	235.11	0.75
Total response in 12 rabbits $= Yp$	1640	1884	2047	1491	1722	2056		Sum	21708.27	

Residual variance = 316.7
$s = 17.8$

can be concluded that the individual lines relating response to log dose are linear and parallel and that the mean slope differs significantly from zero. Then the log activity ratio may be calculated as

$$M = \frac{kID}{B}$$

where $I = \log_{10}$ of dose interval $= \log 1.667 = 0.2218$ and in an assay using three doses of each preparation

$$k = \sqrt{8/3} = 1.633$$

i.e., $$M = \frac{(1.633)(0.2218)(35.6)}{(140.3)} = 0.0919 = \log 1.236$$

a. Calculation of Fiducial Limits of Error. When $C_p = B^2/(B^2 - t^2s^2)$ is small, the fiducial limits of M are approximately given by the expressions

$$M + ts_m \quad \text{and} \quad M - ts_m$$

where $s_m = skI \sqrt{B^2 + D^2}/B^2$. In the example given

$$s_m = \frac{(17.8)(1.633)(0.2218) \sqrt{19683 + 1266.7}}{19683}$$

$$= \frac{933.1533}{19683} = 0.0474$$

and $$t(P = 0.05) = 2.01$$

The fiducial limits of M are then $0.0919 \pm 0.0953 = 0.1872$ and $\overline{1}.9966$ or log 1.539 and 0.9922. These formulas are modified by C_p as follows. The true fiducial limits are then

$$C_pM + t_ps_m \quad \text{and} \quad C_pM - t_ps_m$$

where $$_ps_m = \sqrt{C_p} \, skI \sqrt{B^2 + C_pD^2}/B^2$$

They may also be calculated by applying a simplified formula which is the appropriate modification of that given by Smith *et al.* (1944).

$$C_pM \pm \sqrt{(C_p - 1)(8/3 \, I^2 + C_pM^2)}$$

By using the simplified formula in the given example, C_p $(P = 0.05) = 1.0695$ and the true fiducial limits $(P = 0.95)$ of M are $(1.0695)(0.0919) \pm \sqrt{(0.0695)(0.1312 + 0.0090)} = 0.1970$ and $\overline{1}.9996$, or log 1.574 and log 0.9910.

7. The Twin Cross-over Design

The possibility of designing cross-over tests enabling the slopes of the l.d.r.l. for the standard and the test preparations to be compared was referred to by Fieller (1940). He made brief mention of cross-over designs using two or three doses of both standard and test preparations which had been carried out and which used eight and eighteen dosage groups, respectively. Ultimately these were replaced by the twin cross-over test (Smith *et al.*, 1944) which is considered in Chapter 1 and is the design described in the "British Pharmacopeia 1958" (B.P. 1958) and the "United States Pharmacopeia 1955 XV" (U.S.P. XV).

a. The combination of a series of cross-over tests. It was indicated (Smith *et al.*, 1944) that if a series of twin cross-over tests were carried out on one sample of insulin at the same assumed potency and using the same dose ratio, a condition which is most likely to apply if a sample is being assayed in accordance with the requirements of Pharmacopeias, then providing the separate estimates of s^2 are homogeneous (Bartlett, 1937) the mean activity and its fiducial limits could be calculated by the following method.

TABLE V

SUMMARY OF DATA OF A SERIES OF TWIN CROSS-OVER TESTS
(In each test the assumed strength was 22 U./mg. and d 0.3010)

Test No.	n_1; n_2; n_3; n_4	$1/w$	$1/w'$	T	U
1	3; 3; 3; 2	1.5000	−0.1667	+3.30	28.30
2	3; 3; 3; 3	1.3333	0.0	−15.77	26.10
3	3; 3; 3; 3	1.3333	0.0	−1.73	44.67
4	3; 3; 3; 3	1.3333	0.0	+8.60	46.07

For illustration the data from four tests were taken (see Tables V and VI). The mean log activity ratio was calculated as

$$\overline{M} = Yd/X = (-4.48)(0.301)/106.49$$
$$= -0.0127 = \overline{1}.9873 = \log 0.971$$

The mean activity of the sample was calculated as $22 \times 0.971 = 21.4$ U.

TABLE VI

CALCULATIONS ON DATA OF TABLE V AND VALUES OF s^2

Test No.	w	wT	wU	w^2/w'	df	S. of sq.	s^2
1	0.6667	+2.20	18.87	−0.074	7	142.46	20.35
2	0.7500	−11.83	19.57	0.0	8	303.74	37.97
3	0.7500	−1.30	33.50	0.0	8	534.65	66.83
4	0.7500	+6.45	34.55	0.0	8	650.81	80.35
Sums (1–4)	2.9167	−4.48	106.49	−0.074	31	1631.66	52.63
	= W	= Y	= X	= W'			= $\bar{s}^2$

$$t^2(P = 0.05, n = 31) = 4.16$$

per milligram. The fiducial limits of the mean log activity ratio were calculated as the roots of the equation

$$X'^2m^2 - 2\,(XY)'\,dm + Y'^2d^2 = 0$$

where $X'^2 = X^2 - t^2\bar{s}^2W = 10701.5$

$(XY)' = XY - t^2\bar{s}^2W' = -460.88$

$Y'^2 = Y^2 - t^2\bar{s}^2W = -618.51$

whence $(XY)'d = (-460.88)(0.301) = -138.72 = -0.0130\,X'^2$

$Y'^2d^2 = (-618.51)(0.0906) = -56.037 = -0.00524X'^2$

The quadratic reduces to the form

$$m^2 + 2\,(0.0130)\,m - 0.00524 = 0$$

or $(m + 0.0130)^2 = 0.00524 + (0.0130)^2$

$$= 0.005409 = (0.07354)^2$$

The fiducial limits $P = 0.95$ of the mean log activity ratio were calculated to be -0.0130 ± 0.0735, i.e., -0.0865 and 0.0605 or log 0.819 and log 1.150, and the fiducial limits of the activity of the sample to be $22 \times 0.819 = 18.0$ and $22 \times 1.15 = 25.3$ U. per milligram.

A simplified formula was also given which could be applied to those examples in which responses for both days were obtained from all the animals tested or that losses occurred so to render the term $W' = 0$.

This formula necessitates the calculation of the value C_p (Fieller, 1940) which in these instances may be obtained as

$$C_p = X^2/X^2 - t^2\bar{s}^2W$$

The fiducial limits of the log activity ratio are then

$$C_pM \pm \sqrt{(C_p - 1)(d^2 - C_pM^2)}$$

8. The Triplet Cross-over Design

The logical extension of both the twin cross-over test and the three-assumption cross-over test, the triplet cross-over test, was applied in a collaborative assay of a freeze-dried preparation of globin insulin, undertaken by the Department of Biological Standards, National Institute of Medical Research, and the British Insulin Manufacturers Biological Standardisation Committee (1952).

The layout of this design is shown in Table VII. Since it consists of three cross-over tests carried out at different assumed potencies it would be interpreted by the method described by Fieller (1940).

It can also be interpreted by a method comparable to that for a twin cross-over test already described. The data to be extracted may be symbolized as in Table VIII.

Values of S^2 (mean square between rabbits) and s^2 (mean square

TABLE VII

ARRANGEMENT OF THE TRIPLET CROSS-OVER TEST

Dosage group	Treatment in test	
	Day 1	Day 2
1	Standard (high)	Test (low)
2	Standard (middle)	Test (middle)
3	Standard (low)	Test (high)
4	Test (high)	Standard (low)
5	Test (middle)	Standard (middle)
6	Test (low)	Standard (high)

TABLE VIII

DATA TO BE EXTRACTED FROM A TRIPLET CROSS-OVER TEST

Group of rabbits	Mean response to		Observed mean sum	Observed mean difference $T - St$	Number of animals
	Standard	Test			
1	St_3	T_1	Y_1	y_1	n_1
2	St_2	T_2	Y_2	y_2	n_2
3	St_1	T_3	Y_3	y_3	n_3
4	St_1	T_3	Y_4	y_4	n_4
5	St_2	T_2	Y_5	y_5	n_5
6	St_3	T_1	Y_6	y_6	n_6

within rabbits) are calculated by the methods already considered with regard to the twin cross-over test; both will be determined with $(Sn - 6)$ degrees of freedom.

The important aspects of the assay may be checked by computing the quantities and their sampling variances shown in Table IX.

TABLE IX

	Quantity to be calculated	Sampling variance
Agreement between slope.	$(Y_1 + Y_6) - (Y_3 + Y_4)$	$S^2 \left(\frac{1}{n_1} + \frac{1}{n_6} + \frac{1}{n_3} + \frac{1}{n_4} \right)$
Departure from linearity	$(Y_1 + Y_3 + Y_4 + Y_6) - 2(Y_2 + Y_5)$	$S^2 \left(\frac{1}{n_1} + \frac{1}{n_3} + \frac{1}{n_4} + \frac{1}{n_6} + \frac{4}{n_2} + \frac{4}{n_5} \right)$
Common slope (U)	$-y_1 + y_3 + y_4 - y_6$	$s^2 \left(\frac{1}{n_1} + \frac{1}{n_3} + \frac{1}{n_4} + \frac{1}{n_6} \right)$
Differences in responses (T)	$y_1 + y_2 + y_3 + y_4 + y_5 + y_6$	$s^2 \left(\frac{1}{n_1} + \frac{1}{n_2} + \frac{1}{n_3} + \frac{1}{n_4} + \frac{1}{n_5} + \frac{1}{n_6} \right)$

Working in logs to the base of the *extreme* dose ratio, U is an estimate of 4 times the slope of the l.d.r.l. and T is an estimate of 6 times the mean difference between standard and test.

The estimate of $\log_{10}$ activity ratio of the standard and test preparations is $M = 2Td/3U$ where $d = \log_{10}$ of the *extreme* dose ratio.

a. Calculation of fiducial limits. The calculation of fiducial limits may be made in a similar manner to that recorded for the twin cross-over test.

First the values

$$\frac{1}{w_u} = \frac{1}{n_1} + \frac{1}{n_3} + \frac{1}{n_4} + \frac{1}{n_6}$$

$$\frac{1}{w_t} = \frac{1}{n_1} + \frac{1}{n_2} + \frac{1}{n_3} + \frac{1}{n_4} + \frac{1}{n_5} + \frac{1}{n_6}$$

$$\frac{1}{w'} = -\frac{1}{n_1} + \frac{1}{n_3} + \frac{1}{n_4} - \frac{1}{n_6}$$

are calculated.

Then the fiducial limits are the roots of the equation

$$U'^2 m^2 - 2(UT)'dm + T'^2 d^2 = 0$$

where $U'^2 = U^2 - t^2 s^2/w_u$

$(UT)' = 2UT/3 - t^2 s^2/w'$

$T'^2 = 4/9\,(T^2 - t^2 s^2/w_t)$

9. Relative Efficiency of the Designs

The most efficient test design based on a given number of responses, will be that which yields at the proposed probability level the smallest fiducial range to be attached to the potency estimate extracted from the data.

The formula derived by Fieller (1940) measures the square of the half-fiducial range as

$$\frac{t^2 s^2 C_p}{b^2}\left[\frac{1}{n_{St}} + \frac{1}{n_T} + \frac{C_p}{Sw(x - \bar{x})^2}\frac{(\bar{y}_{St} - \bar{y}_T)^2}{b^2}\right]$$

where $C_p = b^2 \bigg/ \left[b^2 - \dfrac{t^2 s^2}{Sw(x - \bar{x})^2}\right]$

and n_{St} and n_T are the number of responses on standard and test preparations.

If $\bar{y}_{St} - \bar{y}_T = 0$, and deviations from this cannot be attributed to animal arrangement this reduces to

$$\frac{t^2 s^2 C_p}{b^2}\left(\frac{1}{n_{St}} + \frac{1}{n_T}\right)$$

The portion

$$\left(\frac{1}{n_{St}} + \frac{1}{n_T}\right)$$

is a minimum when $n_{St} = n_T$ a condition which is imposed by those designs using a cross-over technique or modifications of it. In such cases the expression is reduced to $t^2 s^2 C_p / b^2 N$ where $N = \frac{1}{4}$ the total number of responses.

A measure of the efficiency is given by the value $Wf = Nb^2 / t^2 s^2 C_p$ which may be written

$$\frac{Nb^2}{t^2 s^2} - \frac{N}{Sw(x - \bar{x})^2}$$

since $1/C_p$ may be written

$$\left(\frac{b^2}{s^2} - \frac{t^2}{Sw(x - \bar{x})^2}\right) \bigg/ \frac{b^2}{s^2}$$

The values in Table X have been extracted by examining the varying designs which have been discussed, keeping the number of responses constant $(= 4N)$ and considering the extreme log-dose interval $(= d)$ (and equal for both standard and unknown if both are split).

TABLE X

VALUES OF $Sw(x - \bar{x})^2$ AND Wf IN VARIOUS CROSS-OVER DESIGNS USING $4N$ RESPONSES

Design	Doses of standard	Doses of unknown	$Sw(x - \bar{x})^2$	Wf	df for s^2
Bliss and Marks	2	2	Nd^2	$(Nb^2/t^2s^2) - (1/d^2)$	$3N - 6$
Bliss and Marks	3	3	$2Nd^2/3$	$(Nb^2/t^2s^2) - (3/2d^2)$	$3N - 10$
Twin cross-over	2	2	Nd^2	$(Nb^2/t^2s^2) - (1/d^2)$	$2N - 4$
Triplet cross-over	3	3	$2Nd^2/3$	$(Nb^2/t^2s^2) - (3/2d^2)$	$2N - 6$
Three-assumption cross-over	1	3	$Nd^2/6$	$(Nb^2/t^2s^2) - (6/d^2)$	$2N - 6$

From this it would be concluded that with a given number of responses the smallest fiducial range is yielded by those designs in which both standard and test preparations are injected at two dose levels, and that the inclusion of an intermediate dose while allowing for a check on linearity to be made widens this range.

The apparent difference in efficiency of the designs, however, will be small if $1/d^2$ itself is small compared with Nb^2/t^2s^2.

If the average value of b^2/s^2, encountered in insulin assay on rabbits, is taken to be of the order 40, tables may be constructed to show the approximate number of responses necessary to yield fiducial limits of given order at the probability levels $P = 0.95$ and $P = 0.99$, when the various designs are used and the extreme dose ratio is that described in the official tests of the B.P. 1958 and the U.S.P. XV (see Table XI).

TABLE XI

THE APPROXIMATE NUMBER OF RABBIT RESPONSES NEEDED TO YIELD FIDUCIAL LIMITS OF GIVEN ORDER WHEN $b^2/s^2 = 40$

Design	Doses of standard unknown		Error Wf	10% 583.22		15% 271.26		25% 106.50		50% 32.25	
				$P = 0.99$	$P = 0.95$	$P = 0.99$	$P = 0.95$	$P = 0.99$	$P = 0.95$	$P = 0.99$	$P = 0.95$
Bliss and Marks	2	2		404	233	196	112	84	49	34	22
Bliss and Marks	3	3		407	235	200	115	88	51	38	25
Twin cross-over	2	2	$d = 0.3010$	404	233	197	114	85	51	35	23
Triplet cross-over	3	3		407	235	201	116	89	53	40	26
Three-assumption cross-over	1	3		441	255	233	135	123	72	73	44

The conclusions to be drawn from Table XI are that when $b^2/s^2 = 40$, all designs are roughly of equal efficiency when high orders of precision are aimed at and the dose ratio is 2 to 1. The three-assumption cross-over design is the least efficient and would become more so if the dose ratio is narrowed.

Figure 1 illustrates the number of responses needed for varying values of b^2/s^2 for certain conditions.

10. Test for Delayed Activity

Although the clinical action of the insulin preparations which possess delayed activity may not be reflected identically in the response of the normal unfed rabbit, a test for delayed action may be performed on rabbits which gives some indications of the relative efficiency of such preparations and may be used to examine them for uniformity either by making comparison with soluble insulin or preferably with a standard preparation of like composition.

In such tests the cross-over principle may also be employed. The data recorded are the mean blood-sugar levels of the groups of rabbits at fixed intervals after injection, and may or may not be expressed as a percentage of the initial level. There seems some advantage in expressing the level in this way since if it is then plotted against time, the resulting curves will have a common origin.

It is customary to carry out the comparison at one assumed level only

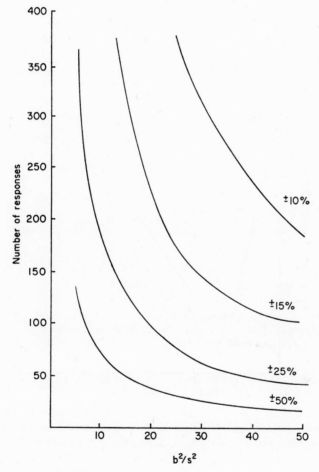

FIG. 1. Graphs showing the number of responses needed to achieve certain degrees of precision $(P = 0.95)$ for different values of b^2/s^2, using optimal conditions in design and a dose interval of 2 $(d = 0.301)$.

and since the character of the delayed-action insulins may be otherwise impaired the injection is made without dilution and at equal levels of concentrations for both standard and test preparations. For this reason the volumes to be injected will be very small and of the order 0.01 or

0.02 ml. for preparations containing 80 or 40 U. per milliliter. Injections of such volumes may be readily made by means of the micrometer syringe designed by Trevan (1925). Lacey (1946) has also referred to the use of 0.25-ml. syringes graduated m 0.01 ml. for this purpose.

The precision of the U.S.P. XIII test for delayed activity was examined by Bliss (1949); he considered that the test could distinguish finer differences than it was called to make in practice.

Thorp (1944a) has shown that the handling of the rabbits during the course of the assay affects considerably the speed with which their blood sugars return to normal. His results, shown in Fig. 2, indicate that this

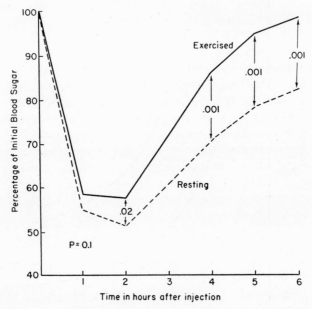

Fig. 2. Graph to show the reliability of the differences between the responses of "exercised" and "resting" rabbits after injection of soluble insulin. The significance of the differences at each hour is shown by the arrows. From Thorp (1944a).

is more marked in the case of soluble insulin than in the case of delayed-action preparations.

Stewart and Smart (1953) described the use of guinea pigs in tests for delayed activity. Guinea pigs of one sex weighing from 200 to 500 gm. are considered suitable but in any one test the weight range is restricted to 160 gm. The blood samples are removed by heart puncture and no cross-over technique is adopted, the test being completed in one day.

B. Manipulative Procedures

1. Rabbit Colony

If it were possible to set aside sufficient space for breeding or to purchase such animals, the use of one breed of rabbits for the purpose of insulin assay might be preferable.

Bliss and Marks (1939b) considered the ways in which the reactions of individual rabbits could affect the precision of the assay. They concluded in their experiment that those of the Sandy Lop breed were less sensitive to insulin than the 12 Himalayans which were retained and on which their subsequent calculations were made. A valid treatment in which individual sensitivities are allowed for will be referred to later (dosage of animals); its use here might have made all animals in this group equally suitable.

Among the Himalayans retained by Bliss and Marks however, there was no evidence that the rabbits varied in their reactions either to dose changes or to differences in days although there was still evidence of a wide variation in their over-all susceptibility. Certain rabbits showed more erratic responses than others and it was suggested that it might be profitable to replace such animals in future tests. Retaining the Himalayans the estimate of variance was $s^2 = 41.4$ $(77df)$, but if the erratic rabbits were removed this was reduced to 28.7 $(49df)$.

In the conduct of cross-over tests variations in the slopes of the l.d.r.l. of individual rabbits would produce larger effects on the value of s^2 when the doses administered to the rabbit were more widely spaced. Fieller (1940) noted that in the simple cross-over tests he had examined and which had been carried out on mixed breeds there was no evidence of this. From similar tests carried out from 1933 to 1938 a mean estimate of $s^2 = 35.18$ $(5825df)$ was recorded (Fieller et al., 1939b). Data from the same laboratory, for the period 1941 to 1945 when larger differences in the doses were effected by the use of the twin cross-over design, gave an estimate of variance of 48.16 $(3749df)$.

This higher variance could indicate that variations in the slopes of l.d.r.l. for individual rabbits did occur but such an assumption could not be substantiated, nor could it be assumed that the use of rabbits of one breed would have obviated this.

In all the assay laboratories with which we are acquainted the colonies used for insulin assay are composed of mixed breeds purchased from reputable dealers and weigh from 2 to 3 kg.

Often it is found that on arrival the rabbits' ears are infested with mites, a condition which may be successfully treated with phenolized oil, the use of which as a prophylactic for this purpose is also to be recommended.

2. Selection for Test

When animals are being selected for test the record cards of those considered suitable may be shuffled and dealt into heaps, corresponding in number to the number of dosage groups, until the number decided as convenient for use has been selected.

The doses to be assigned to these groups are decided by further randomization. In cross-over tests the dose on the second day is determined by that administered on the first.

In 4- or 6-day tests a more elaborate randomization may be employed such as is described by Bliss and Marks (1939a) using the basic patterns tabulated by Fisher and Yates (1938).

The pattern must be further randomized by interchanging rows and columns by use of shuffled numbered tags or by use of random numbers. The doses are assigned to the letters and finally the groups of rabbits or individual rabbits assigned to the rows.

Since this procedure is laborious, it has been worth while to record all the 4×4 combinations possible, paying due regard to the relative frequency to be applied to the basic patterns, and to assign a consecutive number by randomization to each combination, and to make the final selection by a method similar to that used above to select the basic pattern.

Although theoretically similar frequencies in the 6×6 design should be considered, in practice it is adequate to randomize the interchange of rows and columns from one block.

It is a normal practice on the completion of a test, to split up the groups of animals used so that random selections for a new test may be made. In the conduct of cross-over tests this may be modified so that, on the day a test is completed, further groups of animals are injected with dilutions of a new test preparation and these groups, together with the original groups receiving standard, form the beginning of a new test. The economy in animals is considerable and the procedure has only the objection that the groups retain their identity for three consecutive appearances, losing it when they have received the test preparation on the day the second test is completed.

3. Colony Diet

It does not seem that the nature of the colony diet, providing it is adequate, has a marked effect on the precision of insulin assay. In practice it was found that feeding a mixture of bran and oats supplemented with fresh green food and allowing access to water continuously gave results roughly parallel to those obtaining in other laboratories. In another laboratory, the use of cubed diet without supplements of fresh green food (Bruce and Parkes, 1946) proved equally satisfactory.

4. Dosage of Animals

In single-day tests it is imperative that the doses be administered on a strictly defined basis (e.g., units per kilogram), and as has been previously noted the presence of an unduly sensitive or insensitive rabbit would materially affect the result obtained.

Use of the cross-over technique, or modifications of it, allows for animals of widely differing sensitivities to be used without bias, but even so it is wise to avoid using those animals which respond only slightly to the defined dose or to an extent approaching convulsive levels. This could be achieved by submitting all animals to a prior standardization and discarding those which respond outside certain predetermined levels.

Marks (1925) considered that although doses could be related to the weight of the animal the dose received by an animal throughout a test should be constant and not fluctuate with its weight changes, which would of course be small if they occurred at all. This principle is also implied in the conditions specified in the U.S.P. XV.

Constancy of dose in a test is also maintained in a practice followed to render a greater proportion of the colony available for test. In this method that dose which will produce a satisfactory response is determined for each animal and is expressed in millimeters of a standard solution containing 2 U. per milliliter. This volume is called the "standard volume" and may vary from 0.3 to 0.8 ml. Whenever an animal appears on test it receives its "standard volume" of the preparation suitably diluted to allow for different levels of dosage to be employed.

This procedure has been examined critically (Fieller *et al.,* 1939b) and shown to be valid.

It has been customary to make the injection of insulin in concentrations of the order 2 U. per milliliter using 1-ml. tuberculin syringes. These are usually of high order of accuracy, but it will be appreciated that if the method of dosage employing use of "standard volumes" is followed inaccuracy in graduations of the syringe, providing it is used without change for the whole test, will be of no importance.

Lacey (1946) has reported that satisfactory results may be achieved by making injections without dilution by means of a micrometer syringe or by using a 0.25-ml. syringe graduated to 0.01 ml. This, it is claimed, does not mask the difference in action between insulins of differing purities which has greater importance in experimental work than in the routine assay of insulin solutions for clinical use.

It has also been customary to make the injections subcutaneously. Young and Romans (1948) have reported experiments which show that intravenous injections, with blood-sugar levels determined at 50 minutes after injection, are perfectly satisfactory. Experience shows that the levels of dosage required for intravenous or subcutaneous injections are the same and that one route has little advantage over the other from the point of view of precision, although the subcutaneous injection has the advantage of manipulative simplicity.

5. Blood Samples

The method adopted for the taking of blood samples will depend on individual preferences. The following procedure which has been used quite satisfactorily over a long period is recorded in some detail.

The blood is removed via the ear by venipuncture. The ear of the rabbit is first shaved, a small paper clip fastened to the base, and the veins are further dilated by means of a 32-candle power carbon filament lamp which serves also to illuminate the venous pattern of the ear (Fig. 3). The vein is punctured by means of a No. 13 triangular surgical needle, the incision being made in the external vein and in the first instances as near to the base of the ear as is convenient. The external vein should preferably be used, since incision of the larger mid-veins soon renders the ear unsuitable for the taking of further samples. The blood is encouraged to flow by a minimum of massage and is collected into a small pot containing a few crystals of potassium oxalate, from which it is pipetted into suitable deproteinizing solutions. Subsequent bleedings are induced at this puncture by the same operations and usually, but not always, necessitate reopening of the puncture by means of the needle. There are other means by which the necessary dilation of the veins may be induced. It can be accomplished by the use of xylol which does, however, tend to harden the ear.

Although the use of heparin or special resins will suggest themselves for the purpose of rendering shed blood noncoagulable the use of potassium oxalate as described has been found quite satisfactory. If more accurate oxalation is desired it may be obtained by pipetting exact volumes of potassium oxalate solution into clean tubes and then drying off the liquid in an oven.

It is to be expected that excitement, with the consequent liberation of adrenaline, will cause a considerable rise in blood-sugar level and it is therefore desirable that a minimum amount of disturbance to the animals should be allowed.

Fig. 3. The restraining box for bleeding rabbits.

It has been found satisfactory to allow the animals freedom of movement between bleedings by housing them in suitable cages whence they are removed in turn to a restraining box so that the bleeding may be more easily accomplished (Fig. 2). The front of this box is in the form of stocks secured by means of a sliding lid. The box is also fitted with a movable partition so that rabbits of varying sizes may be accommodated.

This removal from the cage to the box cannot be done without some disturbance, and the effect of the treatment on the blood-sugar level of untreated fasting animals has been studied.

It was concluded that removing the animals for the taking of blood

samples at hourly intervals would not affect the response unduly, especially when it was considered that each animal would receive equivalent
treatment.

Another procedure consists of restraining the animals for the duration
of the test either by tying the animals in a bundle by means of a cloth
square so that only the head is visible, a condition which is endured
without struggle, or by confining them to the restraining box. For this
purpose Thorp (1944b) found a specially designed metal box, reproduced
diagrammatically in Fig. 4, to be most convenient. It had the advantage

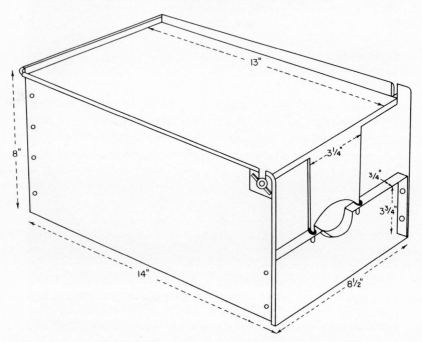

Fig. 4. Details of the rabbit box. From Thorp (1944b).

that it was readily cleaned and so designed that damage to the spine was
practically impossible. Thorp found that the animals soon accustomed
themselves to remaining in such boxes for long periods without struggling.
It is our experience that struggling does occasionally occur; the disturbance then is more severe than that caused by removal to a separate
bleeding box and is, of course, less uniform for the group of animals.

Thorp (1944a) compared the effect of this procedure with that in
which a uniform amount of exercise was applied to each rabbit before
each bleeding and showed that the curves relating blood sugar to time
differed markedly between the exercised and nonexercised rabbits when

treated with soluble insulin. The graph prepared by him is reproduced in Fig. 2.

6. Blood-Sugar Determinations

The method of Hagedorn and Jensen (1923) using Somogyi's (1930) method of protein precipitation lends itself most readily to multi-blood-sugar analyses, and relatively unskilled workers soon attain a high degree of accuracy in its use.

Whether to contribute to greater accuracy or to avoid lost readings through accident it is customary to determine blood sugars in duplicate. Actually our practice has been to make the bleedings in duplicate and make one determination on each filtrate. From data available to him and which had been obtained in this manner but using the Shaffer and Hartman (1921) method of blood-sugar determination, Fieller (1940) considered that the standard error of a single determination to be of the order 3.7 mg. and calculated that with an I.B.S. of 120 mg./100 ml. and a F.B.S. ranging from 70 to 100, values ranging from 6.4 to 8.1 would be contributed to the residual variance of a percentage reduction. If only single determinations were made we would expect the residual variance to be increased by a further amount ranging from 6.4 to 8.1 under similar conditions.

Since the efficiency of an assay is inversely proportional to the residual variance of a single response but proportional to the number of response obtained, any loss of efficiency resulting from the use of single in place of duplicate determinations could be allowed for, in the extreme of the case quoted above, by multiplying the number of responses by $(s^2 + 8.1)/s^2$.

If a value of s^2 of the order 36 (Fieller, 1940) is to be expected this factor would then be 1.225.

7. Criterion of Response

The B.P. 1958 preserves the early conception that the most informative response is the blood-sugar level measured over 5 hours after injection and related to the I.B.S., but does not specify the nature of the relationship.

It has also been shown (Bliss and Marks, 1939a; Fieller 1940) that a linear relationship exists between the per cent reduction and the log dose. Many workers (Hemmingsen and Marks, 1932; Fieller, 1940; Bliss and Marks, 1939a) however, have shown that if the F.B.S. is related to the I.B.S. in this manner a correlation still exists between the resulting per cent reduction and the I.B.S., and methods have been described by which this degree of correlation may be assessed and corrected.

Since it was found in one laboratory that the correlation factor had remained stable over a number of years it was suggested that adjusted responses should replace the per cent reductions and for this purpose per cent reductions—0.3 I.B.S. (in mg./100 ml.) were used.

It has been suggested (Emmens, 1948; Young and Romans, 1948) that an efficient response is the bloodsugar level determined at that time at which experience suggests the lowest level is reached. Thus with intravenous injections Young and Romans were content to take single blood samples after 50 minutes had elapsed. Pugsley and Rampton (1948) have confirmed that the use of the single reading following intravenous injections, as a measure of response compares very favorably with that of the mean blood-sugar level, over 5 hours, related to I.B.S. following subcutaneous injections. Data presented in this chapter to illustrate the interpretation of Bliss and Marks show that with subcutaneous injection blood sugars at $1\frac{1}{2}$ hours yield a satisfactory response. The U.S.P. XV uses as the measure of response the summed blood-sugar levels at 1 and $2\frac{1}{2}$ hours after injection without reference to the I.B.S.

8. Fasting Period and Frequency with Which Animals May Be Used

The frequency with which animals may be used will depend to a large extent on the fasting period imposed and the bleeding schedule. A 6-day interval between usage will allow for almost any accepted fasting period and for any bleeding schedule to be applied.

With this interval it has been found convenient to arrange that the animals are not fed on the day before the test or on the day of the test until the last bleeding, 5 hours after injection, has been made. On occasions, to accommodate the usage of animals twice in one week, the animals have been fed in the morning of the day before the test and the remaining food removed at 4:30 P.M. A similar pretesting treatment has been imposed for the completion of the test with a 2-day interval between the two halves of the test.

No great differences in reaction were noted on these occasions except that it was found necessary to increase the dose of insulin injected, by approximately 30%.

If the bleeding schedule is such that only one blood sample is taken (Young and Romans, 1948), the frequency of use may be greatly increased. The data quoted in Table III, were obtained on 6 successive days by taking blood samples $1\frac{1}{2}$ hours after the subcutaneous injection of insulin and arranging that the animals were fed uniformly from noon to 4:30 P.M.

It is not considered that this treatment is too severe: in fact animals used in this way are fed more uniformly, and the number of bleedings per rabbit in one week is less than the number carried out in one day if the method followed is that which has hitherto been considered normal. Young and Romans (1948) reported that with a week's rest between successive tests it was possible to use each animal in this manner for 4 to 5 tests.

IV. The Mouse Method of Assay

A. DESIGN AND INTERPRETATION

1. Early Designs

The fact that mice, though able to withstand the effects of large doses of insulin at normal environmental temperatures, showed characteristic convulsive symptoms at elevated temperatures led to their extensive use.

The dose needed to cause 50% convulsions, the mouse dose of insulin, was estimated by Hemmingsen and Krogh (1926) under their conditions to have 1/600 of the value of the original Toronto rabbit unit. It was reported purely for the sake of interest since the inadequacy of this measure of response was appreciated.

Construction of dose-response curves resulted sooner with this response than had been the case with the rabbit response although as first described some differences in the nature of the relationship of per cent convulsions to dose were recorded.

Hemmingsen and Krogh (1926) presented graphs in which the per cent convulsions were linearly related to log dose. Trevan and Boock (1926) plotted per cent convulsions against dose, but this was done for expediency in calculation since they considered the ratio of the doses necessary to induce identical changes in response level on different days to be equal.

A uniform treatment of data supplied by animals yielding "all-or-none responses" was suggested by Gaddum (1933) which indicated that a mathematical function of the response, its normal equivalent deviation (N.E.D.) was linearly related to log dose. To avoid negative values, Bliss (1934) suggested that the N.E.D. values should be increased by 5 and called probits.

Hemmingsen (1933) applied this treatment specifically to insulin assays using data from his own laboratory and that published by others (Trevan and Boock, 1926; Trevan, 1927). He showed that not only was the probit of the response of mice to insulin linear to log dose but that the variation in the slopes of the l.d.r.l. so calculated exceeded that expected by the random sampling of mice.

2. The 2 + 2 Test

Tests using two doses of the standard and two of the test preparations at the same time enable checks to be made on the parallelism of the slopes of the l.d.r.l. for standard and test preparations.

Table XII shows the responses which were obtained in the course of

TABLE XII

RESPONSES FROM THE 2 + 2 TEST

Dose	Standard high	Standard low	Test high	Test low
Response	18/24	1/24	15/24	4/24
Probit	5.674	3.269	5.319	4.033
B	0.54	0.20	0.61	0.45
n	24	24	24	24
nB	12.96	4.80	14.64	10.80

such an assay and records the probits, the weighting factors appropriate to them $(= B)$ and the over-all weighting factor to be attached to the points $(= nB)$.

The calculations to be applied to the responses to the standard preparation are shown in Table XIII, and similar treatment of the responses

TABLE XIII

CALCULATIONS APPLIED TO 2 + 2 TEST RESPONSES

Dose	Response	Probit $= y$	$nB = N$	x	Nx	Nx^2	Ny	Nxy
60	1/24	3.269	4.8	0	0	0	15.6912	0
100	18/24	5.674	12.96	1	12.96	12.96	73.5350	73.5350
Sum			17.76		12.96	12.96	89.2262	73.5350

$$\bar{x} = SNx \div SN \qquad 12.96 \div 17.76 = 0.7294$$
$$\bar{y} = SNy \div SN \qquad 89.2262 \div 17.76 = 5.0240$$
$$SN(x - \bar{x})^2 = SNx^2 - \bar{x}SNx \qquad 12.96 - 9.4569 = 3.5031 = p$$
$$SNx(y - \bar{y}) = SNxy - \bar{x}SNy \qquad 73.5350 - 65.1084 = 8.4266 = q$$
$$[SNx(y - \bar{y})]^2 \div SN(x - \bar{x})^2 \qquad (8.4266)^2 \div 3.5031 = 20.2699$$
$$1/SN \qquad 1 \div 17.76 \qquad = \qquad 0.0563$$

to the test preparation will also be necessary. Since the dose ratios for the standard and the test preparations are equal the calculations may again be simplified by using integers for $x = $ log dose, writing 1 for log high dose and 0 for log low dose and making suitable correction later to convert to terms of common logarithms.

These values together with those obtained by similar treatment of the data for the test preparation are collected together in Table XIV

TABLE XIV

COMBINATION OF VALUES ARISING FROM CALCULATIONS ON DATA FROM 2 + 2 TEST

	$1/SN$	q	p	q^2/p	$\bar{y}$	$\bar{x}$
Standard	0.0563	8.4266	3.5031	20.2699	5.0240	0.7297
Test	0.0393	7.9892	6.2147	10.2704	4.7731	0.5755
Sum	0.0941	$16.3577 = Q$	$9.7178 = P$	30.5403	—	—
Difference	—	—	—	—	0.2509	0.1542

$$\bar{b} = Q/P = 1.683 \qquad Q^2/P \qquad 27.5345$$
$$Sq^2/p - Q^2/P \ (\chi^2 \text{ Slopes}) \qquad 3.0058$$

where the additions and subtractions subsequently called for may be conveniently made.

On working in common logarithms, the log activity ratio of unknown to standard is

$$M = d[(\bar{x}_{St} - \bar{x}_T) - (\bar{y}_{St} - \bar{y}_T)/\bar{b}]$$

where d = log dose ratio which in the example = log 1.667 = 0.2218.

Thus $M = 0.2218\,[0.1542 - (0.2509/1.683)] = 0.0016 = \log 1.003$

We therefore estimate the potency of the unknown to be 100.3% of that assumed. The rest of the calculations follow as indicated in Chapter 1.

a. Treatment of zero or total convulsions. It may happen that zero or total convulsions are encountered in a test. When using groups of 24 mice the convention of treating such responses as $\frac{1}{2}$ or $23\frac{1}{2}$ out of 24 has been adopted by the author. If in any test two total or two zero responses have been recorded, these responses have only been used to estimate the slope of the l.d.r.l. and the estimate of relative potency has been based on the remaining two responses.

Such treatment may not be perfectly valid but it seems preferable to the discarding of any data which indicate the relative potency of the standard and test preparations.

Although simplified calculations have been suggested for the interpretation of 2 + 2 assays, the more extensive method described is preferable. If certain conditions are standardized, much computational labor may be saved by the preparation of suitable tables.

3. Cross-over Tests with Mice

Hemmingsen (1939) has described the application of the cross-over technique to the mouse method of assay.

A unit cross-over test using a single dose each of standard and test preparations was conducted so that on the second day those mice which had previously received the standard preparation now received the test preparation and vice versa.

Hemmingsen imposed a further restriction in that the group was preserved intact and used for a series of cross-over tests at varying assumed potencies.

He interpreted the data simply by recording the difference in the proportion of mice convulsing on standard and test preparations in each test and relating this difference to the l.d.r.l. calculated by dividing the range of the differences effected by extreme change in assumed potency by the log of the ratio of these assumed potencies.

He pointed out that if the convulsion rates were between 10 and 90% this result would be practically the same as would have been obtained if probits had been used.

He assessed precision by recording the standard deviation of the estimated potencies and concluded that by making the comparison between standard and test preparations in a series of cross-over tests on the same mice the standard deviation of a test comprising 160 mice was reduced from 12–25 to 7–10%.

B. MANIPULATIVE PROCEDURES

The assay of insulin in mice has been successfully applied using animals purchased from dealers and those bred within the laboratory.

1. Mouse Colony

It could be expected that the laboratory-bred mice would have the advantage for the animals are likely to be more uniform, but we have no evidence to suggest that this is so. Certainly they are not subjected to the disturbances associated with the delivery journey and with the change in colony diet but it appears that the effects of such disturbances, if they exist, are nullified by allowing an interval of 7 days to elapse between the receipt of the animals and their use for test purposes.

It is a satisfactory practice to house the animals on sawdust in sheet metal boxes with a mesh lid, in a room having a temperature range of 65° to 70°F. Boxes with dimensions $12 \times 12 \times 6$ in. are considered adequate to hold 35 mice weighing up to 30 gm.

2. Colony Diet

Rowlinson and Lesford (1948) suggested that a change in colony diet can cause a real change in the slope of the l.d.r.l. and hence, of course, affect the over-all efficiency of the test. The data indicated that with a diet consisting of bread the mean slope of the l.d.r.l. was 4.68 whereas with a mixed diet, fed in the form of cubes and containing more protein and fat but less carbohydrate, the slope of the l.d.r.l. was 3.96. The difference between these two values was stated to be significant at $P = 0.95$ level. With both diets the animals received water *ad libitum*.

The slope of the l.d.r.l. was examined by us over two periods while the animals were being maintained on a typical mixed diet supplemented by crushed oats which were fed in a very moist state with no extra water. In the period November 1944 to July 1945, covering 269 tests the mean slope was estimated to be 5.44, significant heterogeneity being indicated ($\chi^2 = 407$). During the first half of 1948 the mean slope from 231 tests was estimated to be 5.32 ($\chi^2 = 284$).

3. Fasting Periods

It is possible that the use of some precise fasting period would provide more uniform animals for test purposes.

A more convenient procedure however, has been satisfactorily followed for several years. In using a powdered diet, mixed to a crumble with water and supplemented with soaked bread and crushed oats, the animals set aside for insulin assay are fed each day at noon and supplied with water *ad libitum*.

On the next morning all are considered equally fasted and suitable for test. Those required are removed to clean boxes and subjected to test from 1 to 6 hours later.

The influence of this difference in the fasting period on the CD_{50}

TABLE XV

THE INFLUENCE OF EXTENDED PERIOD OF FASTING ON CD_{50} AND SLOPE OF l.d.r.l.

Time tested	No. of tests	Log CD_{50} in mU./gm. and S.E.	χ^2 between tests	Slope of l.d.r.l. and S.E.	χ^2 between tests
Morning	97	$\bar{1}.7409$ (0.011)	769.9	5.470 (0.143)	6.43
Afternoon	134	$\bar{1}.7407$ (0.009)	870.7	5.193 (0.116)	155.95

	χ^2 between times 0.00			χ^2 between times 2.27	
	Critical $\chi^2 P = 0.05$	$n = 133$	$n = 96$	$n = 1$	
		166.35	124.50	3.84	

(the dose causing 50% convulsions) and on the slope of the l.d.r.l. during 231 tests has been examined by comparing those tests carried out during the morning with those carried out during the afternoon. The summarized results of this examination are shown in Table XV. They indicate that the extended fasting period imposed by delaying the tests until the afternoon has no effect on the sensitivity level of the mice and no significant effect on the slope of the l.d.r.l.

4. Selection of Animals for Test

a. Selection on basis of weight. The fasted mice are weighed and sorted into groups with restricted weight ranges.

Hemmingsen (1939) has reported the use of mice weighing 12 gm., but we limit our use to those weighing 17 to 30 gm., segregating them into groups weighing 17/20, 20/25, and 25/30 gm.

The mice for any one test are taken from one only of these weight groups, and for the purpose of this test are considered to be of equal weight.

The influence of different weight groupings on the CD_{50} and on the slope of the l.d.r.l. during 231 tests has been examined.

The summarized results of this examination are shown in Table XVI.

TABLE XVI

INFLUENCE OF WEIGHT GROUPS ON THE CD_{50} AND ON THE SLOPE OF THE l.d.r.l.

Weight group (gm.)	No. of tests	Log CD_{50} in mU./gm. and S.E.	χ^2 between tests	Slope of l.d.r.l. and S.E.	χ^2 between tests
17/20	80	$\bar{1}.7040$ (0.012)	535.8	5.156 (0.151)	101.88
20/25	123	$\bar{1}.7604$ (0.009)	868.3	5.385 (0.125)	125.46
25/30	28	$\bar{1}.7518$ (0.016)	129.9	5.396 (0.259)	35.79

		χ^2 between groups 14.7		χ^2 between groups 1.51	
Critical $\chi^2 P = 0.05$		$n = 122$ $n = 79$	$n = 27$	$n = 2$	
		154.0 104.98	40.113	5.99	

They indicate that while in the case of the 20/25 and 25/30 gm. groups dosing may be based on the mean of the weight range, in the case of the 17/20 gm. some extra compensation is called for to allow for their greater sensitivity. The different weight groupings have no effect on the slope of the l.d.r.l.

b. Selection on basis of previous usage. Mice surviving the test may be used again, but those chosen for test should be segregated according to whether they are new mice, mice which have been used once, used twice, etc.

The effect of previous usage of mice on their reactions to insulin during 231 tests has been examined. The summarized results of this examination are shown in Table XVII. They show that the prior usage

TABLE XVII

INFLUENCE OF PREVIOUS USAGE ON THE CD_{50} AND ON THE SLOPE OF THE l.d.r.l.

Times used previously	No. of tests	Log CD_{50} in mU./gm. and S.E.	χ^2 between tests	Slope of l.d.r.l. and S.E.	χ^2 between tests
0	85	$\bar{1}.6842$ (0.012)	634.5	5.154 (0.148)	109.68
1	58	$\bar{1}.7316$ (0.012)	356.9	5.639 (0.181)	52.33
2	45	$\bar{1}.8023$ (0.010)	136.6	5.323 (0.206)	52.02
3	27	$\bar{1}.8038$ (0.014)	90.04	5.394 (0.266)	35.85
4	13	$\bar{1}.7867$ (0.025)	50.	4.782 (0.115)	4.73
5	3	$\bar{1}.7983$ (0.049)	11.38	4.549 (0.257)	2.53

χ^2 between usage   43.5 $\qquad\qquad$ χ^2 between usage   7.49

Critical $\chi^2 P = 0.05$ $n = 84$ $n = 67$ $n = 44$ $n = 26$ $n = 12$ $n = 2$ $n = 5$

$\qquad\qquad\qquad$ 110.71   79.25   63.70   38.88   21.03   5.99   11.07

of mice has a significant effect on the CD_{50} which is lower for new mice and those used once.

A possible explanation of this is that the mice lost through deaths during the early tests are the more sensitive ones. It would also appear permissible to telescope the groups of mice after they have been used twice previously. The prior usage of mice has no significant effect on the slope of the l.d.r.l.

c. *Selection on basis of sex.* For practical reasons the use of one sex is to be preferred.

TABLE XVIII

INFLUENCE OF SEX ON THE CD_{50} AND ON THE SLOPE OF THE l.d.r.l.

Sex	No. of tests	Log CD_{50} in mU./gm. and S.E.	χ^2 between tests	Slope of the l.d.r.l. and S.E.	χ^2 between tests
Male	182	$\bar{1}.7482$ (0.008)	1389.2	5.3093 (0.102)	198.88
Female	49	$\bar{1}.7106$ (0.013)	232.9	5.2863 (0.193)	65.75

χ^2 between sexes   6.3 $\qquad\qquad$ χ^2 between sexes   0.0108

$\qquad$ Critical $\chi^2 P = 0.05$ $n = 181$ $n = 48$ $n = 1$

$\qquad\qquad\qquad\qquad$ 219.66   68.527   3.841

The influence of sex on the reactions of mice to insulin during 231 tests has been examined. The summarized results are shown in Table XVIII. They indicate that sex has some effect on the CD_{50} but not on the slope of the l.d.r.l.

5. Preparation of Solutions for Test and Their Injection

It has been considered preferable to effect change in the doses of insulin by changing the concentration and to administer all doses in the same volume. It is felt that it should not exceed 0.5 mls., and in practice a volume of 0.25 ml. per mouse has been found quite convenient.

It is customary to make the injections subcutaneously. Trevan and Boock (1926) reported that they found intravenous and subcutaneous injections equally efficient.

6. Treatment of Mice During the Test

After injection and for the duration of the test the animals are normally maintained at an elevated temperature. Trevan and Boock (1926) used for this purpose a thermostatically controlled water bath in which heavy containers were placed to hold the mice. Hemmingsen and Krogh (1926) described the use of an air incubator with a glass front, and it is with such an apparatus that we have been accustomed to work. It has the advantage that the mice may be observed during the test; those which convulse can be removed quickly and given a therapeutic injection of glucose.

Our testing cabinet (Fig. 5) is a shallow cupboard in which access to 6 shelves is provided separately by means of glass slides. It is warmed by electric heater wires fitted below each shelf, the temperature is thermostatically controlled, and the air within the cabinet is mixed by means of a fan placed in the space at the rear of the shelves.

The cabinet holds 48 glass jars to house 96 treated mice; those jars which are to hold mice having the same dose are similarly colored and distributed throughout the cabinet so that the small temperature gradient which exists is applied equally to all doses.

The positions of these colored jars in the cabinet are constant and in each test the doses are assigned to the various colors at random.

Thorp (1948) has referred to the construction of a glass fronted cabinet of cubic form. Air warmed by passage over suitable heating pads is supplied through the roof of the cabinet by means of a fan and the temperature is thermostatically controlled. The jars to hold the mice are placed on small movable racks and the apparatus has the distinct advantage in that it is readily cleaned.

Thompson (1946) has described the use of an inclined wire for the

Fig. 5. An insulin testing cabinet for mice.

observation of mice showing the hypoglycemic reactions. This mesh screen, 24 × 36 in., which will hold 100 or more mice is fitted at an angle of 60° and so arranged that the injected mice placed on it can only leave the screen over an edge which is 8 inches or more from any other surface. Mice with advanced symptoms fall from the screen into a tray from which they may be removed to be injected with glucose.

A modification has been described by Young and Lewis (1947): the screen is replaced by a wire mesh drum of 8 inches diameter which is caused to revolve continuously, rotating once every 40 seconds. Under these conditions the mice apparently lose their hold before severe hypoglycemia has developed and feed on a suitable diet in the receiving tray so rendering the injection of glucose unnecessary.

7. Temperature for the Conduct of the Test

Elevated temperatures are necessary if mice are to exhibit the characteristic convulsions associated with hypoglycemia. The use of varying temperatures for the assay of insulin in mice has been described.

Trevan reported results using a temperature of 37°C. while Hemmingsen preferred a temperature of 29°C., for at this temperature he found that his losses of animals were less. For many years we have used a temperature of 32°C., at which temperature the mice did not display the signs of discomfort shown at 37°C. and appeared to respond more consistently than when a temperature of 29°C. was applied.

Differences in the slopes of the l.d.r.l. obtained in the various laboratories may have been attributed to the temperature used but it is certain that other factors have also contributed to these differences.

Data supplied by Trevan and Boock (1926) working at 37°C. indicated a slope (probit v log dose) of the order 5, but a review (Irwin, 1943) of data accumulated later in the same laboratory while this temperature was still maintained indicated a slope of 3.0. Hemmingsen (1933) working at 29°C. has recorded a slope of 4.9. In our own laboratory the mean slopes recorded for 269 tests during the period 1944 to 1945 was 5.43, and during 1948 the mean slope in 231 tests was 5.32. These tests were carried out at 32°C., but the slope value is higher than that reported by Rowlinson and Lesford (1948) working at 34°C.

The use of wire meshes, either fixed or revolving, since it determines the onset of less severe hypoglycemic symptoms has particular application in the conduct of insulin assays at temperatures lower than those normally applied.

Even though temperature may not have marked effect on the slope of the l.d.r.l., and therefore on the precision of the assay, it is certain that it has marked effect on the level of sensitivity, and for this reason it is important that whatever temperature is applied it should be controlled as closely as possible.

8. Convulsive Symptoms

The reacting mice mostly convulse violently; often, however, a mouse may pass into a state of collapse determined by the failure of the animal to right itself when placed on its back.

Both symptoms are considered equally positive. The animals are removed from the cabinet, and injected with 0.5 ml. of a 15% glucose solution. They are not separated on removal, for the final score may be easily made by counting the empty spaces in the cabinet.

9. Duration of the Test

At 32°C. convulsions may commence within 20 minutes of injection, reach their peak incidence in $\frac{3}{4}$ to 1 hour but rarely occur after $1\frac{1}{2}$ hours. For this reason it is adequate to observe the mice for $1\frac{1}{2}$ hours after injection. When the injection of one dose is completed the time is noted and readings taken from that point. Since the injection of 96 mice may be completed in 15 minutes the over-all time taken for a test is $1\frac{3}{4}$ hours.

10. Frequency of Use of Mice

Animals on test on any day are fed at the completion of the test. They are suitable for test after a further 2 days of normal feeding. Thus, mice which have been used for test on Monday can be used again on Thursday.

11. Number of Times to Be Used

Mice can be satisfactorily used up to 6 times: their use on more occasions than this is seldom possible since at that time it is difficult to obtain sufficient mice of the correct weight range and "times used" to give full groups. The information in Table XVII, however, suggests that segregation on the basis of usage may be abandoned after the mice have been used twice previously.

Table XVII also indicates that during these tests 85 groups of new mice were taken and 231 tests conducted. This means that on the average, under these conditions, each mouse was used 2.70 times, although the value would in fact be higher than this since some of the mice would have been used for other approximate assays. The magnitude of this value will naturally depend on the amount of testing to be done since a larger float of animals and pressure of testing allows them to be used more efficiently. Estimates made on two other occasions indicated that on the average the mice are used 3.7 and 4.1 times. These two estimates were from periods in which the mice used were of one sex.

V. Comparison of Rabbit and Mouse Methods of Assay

A. AGREEMENT BETWEEN THE METHODS

The results obtained in 4 out of 5 laboratories during the standardization of the second international standard against the first suggested that the mouse method yielded results different from those obtained by the rabbit method. This has been explained by the fact that in this case comparison was being made between preparations of widely differing purities, and it has been considered that such differences should not occur when samples of similar purities were being examined.

A comparison of results obtained in one laboratory under these conditions using both rabbit and mouse methods of assay is shown in Table XIX. The rabbit tests used were the twin cross-over tests and

TABLE XIX

AGREEMENT BETWEEN RABBIT AND MOUSE METHODS OF ASSAY

	Rabbit method					Mouse method					
Sample	Estimated potency	No. of rabbit responses	No. of tests	Sw	χ^2 between tests	Estimated potency	No. of mice	No. of tests	Sw	χ^2 between tests	χ^2 between methods
H487	63.96	96	3	536.6	1.26	66.22	524	5	860.8	2.89	0.07
H488	168.5	160	5	2204.3	1.03	147.2	452	4	1259.0	1.88	2.76
H489	217.0	128	4	624.8	0.82	203.2	560	4	1182.1	1.49	0.33
H490	190.8	160	5	1845.1	8.41	195.4	1120	7	2199.7	8.08	0.11
H491	220.1	160	5	688.9	1.69	248.5	384	2	870.8	0.10	1.09
Sum		704		5899.7			3040		6372.4		

each was weighted inversely as the variance of the estimated potency and this weight used to calculate a weighted mean potency. The individual mouse tests were weighted similarly.

For each sample the agreement of the individual results obtained by each method was checked by means of the χ^2 test, and a further χ^2 test was made to check the agreement between the two methods.

Only with sample **488** was there a somewhat wide difference between the mean potencies estimated by the two methods but this was not significant at $P = 0.95$ level.

B. RELATIVE EFFICIENCY OF THE TWO METHODS

On ignoring all other factors which must be considered in assessing the relative efficiency of the two methods, the data summarized in Table XIX indicate that the average contribution to Sw made by one rabbit = 5899.7/704 = 8.38 and that the corresponding contribution made by one mouse = 6372.4/3040 = 2.10. It would, therefore, be concluded in this instance that 4 mice had an efficiency equivalent to 1 rabbit.

From the point of view of the labor and space required for the housing and the feeding of the animals and for the conduct of the assay, reliance on the mouse method has distinct advantages; but perhaps its greatest value lies in the speed with which a result may be obtained.

Since, however, it is most probable that a colony of rabbits will be maintained in any case, the possibility of using this to the full to supplement the mouse method of assay must be considered.

This possibility will be approached with hesitancy if the method proposed involves blood-sugar readings over 5 hours and the use of a

7-day interval between the separate stages of the test. It becomes more attractive, however, when it is considered that each member of the colony could supply a response to insulin on each day if the response were measured by means of a single blood-sugar reading taken 1 to $1\frac{1}{2}$ hours after injection.

VI. Assay of Insulin at Physiological Levels

A specific and sufficiently sensitive chemical or immunological method is not yet available for the assay of the small amounts of insulin to be found in blood, and the methods so far developed are biological ones based on the effect of insulin both *in vivo* and *in vitro*.

A. *In Vivo* METHODS

Anderson *et al.* (1947) and Anderson and Long (1947a, b, 1948) described the use of the glucose-fed, alloxan diabetic, hypophysectomized, adrenodemedullated rat (A.D.H.A. rat) and used it for detecting the presence of insulin in perfusates from the isolated rat pancreas (Anderson and Long, 1948).

A.D.H.A. rats were given 5 ml. of 20% glucose by stomach tube, submitted to pentobarbitone anesthesia, and, after 29 minutes at 38.3°C., were injected with the sample under test *via* the exposed jugular vein. Blood samples were taken 1, 15, and 30 minutes after injection, i.e., 30, 45, and 60 minutes after the glucose was given and falls of blood sugar of about 50% were produced by the injection of 1 mU. of insulin.

A method employing A.D.H.A. rats has also been described by Bornstein (1950) and has been widely used. A.D.H.A. rats are placed in individual cages in an incubator at 37°C. with access to water but not to food. After one hour a blood sample is taken from the tail vein and the sugar determined. Injections of test solutions are made subcutaneously and a further blood-sugar determination made after one hour. Bornstein showed that over the range 0.5–0.05 mU. the blood-sugar concentration was linearly related to the log insulin concentration by the equation $D = 75 + 49.1\ L$ where $L = $ log insulin in milliunits. His results indicated that b^2/s^2 had a value of the order 25 (see Fig. 1).

Biegelman *et al.* (1956) refer to the use of hypophysectomized alloxanized mice (H.A. mice) and in experiments using H.A. rats obtained a value for b^2/s^2 of 10.7 with insulin in an albumin solution but indicate that it is too imprecise for use with aqueous solutions of insulin.

B. *In Vitro* METHODS

Gemmill (1941) reported that insulin acting on the isolated rat diaphragm caused increased synthesis of glycogen from glucose. Assays measuring glucose uptake of the hemidiaphragm under the influence of insulin have been described (Groen *et al.*, 1952; Vallance Owen and Hurlock, 1954; Randle, 1954). Randle examined the precision of the method under the following conditions. Normal male rats weighing 100 to 150 gm., deprived of food for 18 to 24 hours before use, are killed by a blow and exsanguinated. The diaphragms are removed, divided, and washed for exactly 5 minutes in ice-cold buffer glucose. [Buffer (Gey and Gey, 1936) containing 2.5 mg. glucose per milliliter previously saturated with 93% O_2 and 7% CO_2.] The hemidiaphragms are removed, blotted dry, and transferred to the main compartments of Warburg manometer flasks containing the appropriate quantity of insulin in 1 ml. of glucose buffer. Incubation is allowed to proceed for 3 hours at 37°C. at a shake rate of 100 cycles per minute, the gas phase during incubation being 93% O_2 and 7% CO_2.

After incubation the flasks are cooled and the glucose estimated on 0.2 ml. by the method of Somogyi (1945). The hemidiaphragms are blotted dry, weighed on a torsion balance, and the glucose uptake expressed as milligram per glucose per gram of wet weight diaphragm per hour. The cube root of this uptake is linearly related to the log insulin concentration. The value for b^2/s^2 in Randle's examination was 7.7 (see Fig. 1).

Martin *et al.* (1958) described the use of rat epididymal adipose tissue for the *in vitro* assay of insulin.

Rats fed *ad libitum* are killed by a blow and rapidly exsanguinated. The epididymal adipose tissue is lifted gently at the base and removed with a single cut. Without further manipulation or chilling it is divided into 3 parts and each piece, weighing from 80 to 200 mg., is transferred separately to 10-ml. preweighed rubber-stoppered flasks, containing 2 ml. of plasma or Kreb's bicarbonate buffer containing 2 mg. gelatin per milliliter and with the glucose adjusted to be 3 mg. per milliliter containing 0.2 μc. of glucose-1-C^{14} (1.9 ml. buffer or plasma + 0.1 ml. glucose-1-C^{14}). After reweighing to obtain the tissue weight the flasks are gassed with 5% CO_2 95% O_2 through hypodermic needles inserted through rubber sealed ports in the rubber stopper. Below one port a small plastic cup is suspended. The needles are withdrawn, leaving the system airtight, and the flasks are incubated for 2 hours at 72°C. at a shake rate of 72 cycles per minute.

After incubation, 0.2 ml. of NaOH (freshly diluted 1:10 from saturated NaOH with CO_2-free water) is injected into the cup and 0.2 ml. 10 N H_2SO_4 into the medium. After at least 2 hours the contents of the cup are quantitatively transferred to a weighed centrifuge tube containing $BaCl_2$ and the precipitated $BaCO_3$ is washed 3 times with CO_2-free water, dried, and reweighed to give the total $BaCO_3$ present.

An aliquot is transferred to a weighed planchette and the specific activity is determined in a proportional flow counter. The results are expressed in counts per minute per total CO_2 as $BaCO_3$ per 100 mg. of adipose tissue, the square root of which has been found to be linearly related to the log concentration of insulin.

Martin *et al.* (1958) also indicated that the method may be used by making measurements of the glucose uptake. Then, only 0.8 ml. of buffer or plasma is used, the glucose concentration is 2 mg./ml., incubation is for 4 hours, and a sample solution of buffer or plasma is run concurrently without tissue.

The glucose concentration is determined in duplicate on 0.5-ml. aliquots using the method of Nelson (1944).

The results are expressed as micromoles of glucose uptake per gram adipose tissue. The value of b^2/s^2 in Martin's experiments was 10.4 (see Fig. 1).

Using I^{131}-insulin, Piazza *et al.* (1959) have assessed the degradation of insulin during the *in vitro* assays using the rat diaphragm methods of Randle (1954), Willebrands and Groen (1956), and Vallance Owen and Hurlock (1954) and the rat adipose tissue method of Martin *et al.* (1958). Degradation was appreciable in all systems but greatest in the rat muscle preparations, and proteolytic enzymes were leached into the medium. Insulin degradation was least in the adipose tissue preparation and the leaching phenomena minimal. In all cases the degradation was proportional to the mass of incubated tissue and to the extracellular concentration of insulin and was significantly inhibited by factors present in normal plasma.

VII. Method Using Insulin Antiserum

Sera containing insulin antibodies have been produced in the guinea pig, the horse, the rabbit, and the sheep (Moloney and Coval, 1955; Moloney and Goldsmith, 1957). Moloney and Coval produced it in guinea pigs by making successive subcutaneous injections of 1 mg. crystalline insulin spread over two sites contained in a stable water-in-oil emulsion with Freund's adjuvant (Freund and McDermott, 1942).

Arquilla and Stavitsky (1956) produced insulin antiserum in rabbits by injecting them intravenously on successive occasions with 2.5 mg. of alum-precipitated insulin and described how it could be used to assay microgram quantities of insulin in pure solutions. In principle, their method measured the release of hemoglobin produced by the residual amounts of antiserum after incubation with graded quantities of insulin acting in the presence of guinea pig complement on insulin-sensitized erythrocytes, prepared by coupling insulin to washed rabbit erythrocytes by means of bis-diazobenzidine. The method required optimally that the antiserum dilution should be that which shows the greatest inhibition of lysis when it is incubated with 10 μg. of insulin, and under these conditions the hemoglobin released is inversely and linearly related to the log of the insulin concentration.

VIII. Chromatographic Methods

Chromatographic methods using columns have been described for the separation of insulin from its associated impurities (Porter, 1953; Porath and Li, 1954; Dickinson, 1956). Robinson and Fehr (1952) used a paper chromatographic method to estimate the insulin present in protamine-zinc-insulin preparations. Paper chromatographic methods have also been described by Grodsky and Tarver (1956) and Light and Simpson (1956).

Bouman and Homan (1958) and Fenton (1959) have described the systemized application of paper chromatographic methods applicable to the routine comparison of insulins with a standard preparation.

Fenton (1959), using a micrometer syringe, applies quantities of the order 50 μg. of insulin as standard and test preparations as spots at distances of 2.5 cm. along a line drawn 4 cm. from the bottom edge of a sheet of Whatman No. 1 paper 28 $\times$ 13 cm. wide in the order A.B.B.A. The paper is allowed to dry at room temperature for 2 to 24 hours. A fold is made 2.5 cm. from the top and punched centrally to allow the paper to be suspended in chromatographic tanks (dimensions:height 42 cm., base 27 $\times$ 9 cm.) above the development solvent described by Light and Simpson (1956-. [Butane-2-ol, 1% acetic acid (1:1 v/v) is shaken vigorously for several minutes in a large separating funnel and placed in the chromatography room for 24 hours. The lower phase is discarded and the upper phase run into the tank to a depth of 1 to 1.5 cm.] The tanks are covered with a glass lid, the joint being sealed with silicone grease. The lid is drilled centrally so that the glass frame carrying the papers may be raised or lowered without breaking the seal. After equilibration for 4 to 6 hours the papers are lowered so that the 2 to 4 mm. of the bottom edge are immersed in the solvent. Development is allowed to continue until the solvent front has moved 20 cm. up the paper. The papers are removed, blotted, and dried in an air oven at 80°C. for 10 minutes. They are then immersed in a protein-staining solution (0.02% bromocresol green in a mixture prepared by diluting 12 ml. acetic acid to 2 liters and adding 125 ml. of 0.1 N sodium hydroxide). After staining for 15 hours, the papers are removed, blotted dry, and washed by immersion for 3 minutes with occasional agitation in 4 successive quantities of 1% (v/v) acetic acid solution. The papers are pressed between clean blotting paper and returned to the drying oven for 10 minutes.

The staining of the specific insulin spots is intensified by holding them above 5 N ammonia, while their location is circumscribed by means of a pencil. These areas, together with an area of similar size to serve as a blank which is taken at a point removed from the spots, are cut out and placed in a series of test tubes 12 × 1.5 cm. To each tube is added 5 ml. of eluant [0.1 N sodium hydroxide and ethanol (1:1 v/v)], the tube agitated at intervals during 30 minutes, and the extinctions compared with that of the blank at 625 mμ in 10-cm. cells.

Fenton (1959) showed that the lines relating extinction to concentration passed through the origin so that the relative activity using single levels of test and standard was proportional to the extinction values.

Since this condition may not always apply, there would be some advantage in using two or more levels of each preparation to establish this point in each assay. The data so obtained would be amenable to the treatment applied for slope ratio assays.

Garratt (1957) has noted that paper chromatography does not separate insulin from its gelled form and hence the usefulness of this method is limited when applied to stored insulin solutions. When the purity of the component insulin is known, its concentration in solutions could be determined by applying measured quantities to filter paper and carrying out the drying, staining, and elution procedures but omitting the development. Such a method could certainly be applied to limit the concentration of insulin in the supernatant fluids of precipitated insulins.

REFERENCES

Anderson, E., and Long, J. A. (1947a). *Endocrinology* **40**, 92.
Anderson, E., and Long, J. A. (1947b). *Endocrinology* **40**, 98.
Anderson, E., and Long, J. A. (1948). *Recent Progr. in Hormone Research* **2**, 209.
Anderson, E., Lindner, E., and Sutton, V. (1947). *Am. J. Physiol.* **149**, 350.
Arquilla, E. R., and Stavitsky, A. B. (1956). *J. Clin. Invest.* **35**, 458.

Bangham, D. R., and Mussett, M. V. (1959). *Bull. World Health Organization* **20**, 1209.

Banting, F. G., Best, C. H., Collip, J. B., Macleod, J. J. R., and Noble, E. C. (1922). *Am. J. Physiol.* **62**, 162.

Bartlett, M. S. (1937). *Proc. Roy. Soc.* **A160**, 268.

Biegelman, P. M., Goetz, F. C., Antoniades, H. N., and Thorn, G. W. (1956). *Metabolism, Clin, and Exptl.* **5**, 35.

Bliss, C. I. (1934). *Science* **79**, 38.

Bliss, C. I. (1949). *J. Am. Pharm. Assoc., Sci. Ed.* **38**, 560.

Bliss, C. I., and Marks, H. P. (1939a). *Quart. J. Pharm. and Pharmacol.* **12**, 82.

Bliss, C. I., and Marks, H. P. (1939b). *Quart. J. Pharm. and Pharmacol.* **12**, 182.

Bornstein, J. (1950). *Australian J. Exptl. Biol. Med. Sci.* **28**, 87.

Bouman, J., and Homan, J. D. H. (1958). *Biochim. et Biophys. Acta* **29**, 417.

"British Pharmacopeia 1958." General Medical Council, London.

Bruce, H. M., and Parkes, A. S. (1946). *J. Hyg.* **44**, 501.

Culhane, K., Marks, H. P., Scott, D. A., and Trevan, J. W. (1929). *Biochem. J.* **33**, 397.

Department of Biological Standards. N.I.M.R. and British Insulin Manufacturers Biological Standardisation Committee (1952). *J. Pharm. and Pharmacol.* **4**, 382.

Dickinson, W. (1956). *Nature* **178**, 994.

Emmens, C. W. (1948). "Principles of Biological Assay," p. 191. Chapman & Hall, London.

Fenton, E. L. (1959). *Biochem. J.* **71**, 507.

Fieller, E. C. (1940). *Suppl. J. Roy. Statist. Soc.* **7**, 63.

Fieller, E. C., Irwin, J. O., Marks, H. P., and Shrimpton, E. A. G. (1939a). *Quart. J. Pharm. and Pharmacol.* **12**, 206.

Fieller, E. C., Irwin, J. O., Marks, H. P., and Shrimpton, E. A. G. (1939b). *Quart. J. Pharm. and Pharmacol.* **12**, 724.

Fisher, R. A., and Yates, F. (1938). "Statistical Tables for Biological Agricultural and Medical Research," pp. 44–45. Oliver & Boyd, Edinburgh.

Freund, J., and McDermott, K. (1942). *Proc. Soc. Exptl. Biol. Med.* **49**, 548.

Gaddum, J. H. (1933). *Med. Research Council (Brit.) Spec. Rept. Ser.* **183**.

Garratt, D. C. (1957). *Proc. Congr. Modern Anal. Chem. Ind. Univ. St. Andrews*, p. 77.

Gemmill, C. L. (1941). *Bull. Johns Hopkins Hosp.* **68**, 50.

Gey, G. O., and Gey, M. K. (1936). *Am. J. Cancer* **27**, 45.

Grodsky, G., and Tarver, H. (1956). *Nature* **177**, 223.

Groen, J., Kamminga, O. E., Willebrands, A. F., and Blickman, J. R. (1952). *J. Clin. Invest.* **31**, 97.

Hagedorn, H. C., and Jensen, B. N. (1923). *Biochem. Z.* **135**, 46.

Hemmingsen, A. M. (1933). *Quart. J. Pharm. and Pharmacol.* **6**, 39.

Hemmingsen, A. M. (1939). *Skand. Arch. Physiol.* **82**, 105.

Hemmingsen, A. M., and Krogh, A. (1926). Pubs. *League Nations,* III Health, III, C. H. 398.

Hemmingsen, A. M., and Marks, H. P. (1932). *Quart. J. Pharm. and Pharmacol.* **5**, 245.

Hershey, J. M., and Lacey, A. H. (1936). *Quart. Bull. Health Organization League Nations* (Nov.), p. 584.

Irwin, J. O. (1943). *Quart. J. Pharm. and Pharmacol.* **14**, 352.

Lacey, A. H. (1941). *Endocrinology* **29**, 866.

Lacey, A. H. (1946). *Endocrinology* **39**, 344.

League of Nations. (1926). III, Health III, C. H. 398.

Light, A., and Simpson, M. V. (1956). *Nature* **177**, 223.

Macleod, J. J. R., and Orr, M. D. (1924). *J. Lab. Clin. Med.* **9**, 591.

Macleod, J. J. R., and Orr, M. D. (1926). Pubs. *League Nations,* III, Health III, C. H. 398.

Marks, H. P. (1925). *Brit. Med. J.* **ii**, 1102.

Marks, H. P. (1926). Pubs. *League Nations* III, Health, III, C. H. 398.

Marks, H. P. (1932). *Quart. J. Pharm. and Pharmacol.* **5**, 255.

Marks, H. P. (1936). *Quart. Bull. Health Organisation League Nations* Special number, November.

Martin, D. B., Renold, A. E., and Dagenesis, Y. M. (1958). *Lancet* **ii**, 76.

Moloney, P. J., and Coval, M. (1955). *Biochem. J.* **59**, 179.

Moloney, P. J., and Goldsmith, L. (1957). *Can. J. Biochem. and Physiol.* **35**, 79.

Nelson, N. (1944). *J. Biol. Chem.* **152**, 375.

Piazza, E. A., Goodner, C. J., and Frienkel, N. (1959). *Diabetes* **8**, 459.

Porath, J., and Li, C. H. (1954). *Biochim. et Biophys. Acta* **13**, 268.

Porter, R. R. (1953). *Biochem. J.* **53**, 320.

Pugsley, L. I., and Rampton, S. (1948). *Endocrinology* **42**, 31.

Quart. Bull. Health Organisation League Nations (Nov. 1936).

Randle, P. J. (1954). *Brit. Med. J.* **i**, 1237.

Robinson, F. A., and Fehr, K. L. A. (1952). *Biochem. J.* **51**, 298.

Rowlinson, H. R., and Lesford, J. M. (1948). *Quart. J. Pharm. and Pharmacol.* **21**, 259.

Shaffer, P. A., and Hartman, A. F. (1921). *J. Biol. Chem.* **45**, 365.

Smith, K. W., Marks, H. P., Fieller, E. C., and Broom, W. A. (1944). *Quart. J. Pharm. and Pharmacol.* **17**, 108.

Somogyi, M. (1930). *J. Biol. Chem.* **86**, 655.

Somogyi, M. (1945). *J. Biol. Chem.* **160**, 61.

Stewart, G. A., and Smart, J. V. (1953). *J. Pharm. and Pharmacol.* **5**, 939.

Thompson, R. E. (1946). *Endocrinology* **39**, 62.

Thorp, R. H. (1944a). *Quart. J. Pharm. and Pharmacol.* **17**, 75.

Thorp, R. H. (1944b). *J. Pathol. Bacterial.* **54**, 270.

Thorp, R. H. (1948). Ph.D. Thesis. University of London.

Trevan, J. W. (1925). *Biochem. J.* **19**, 1111.

Trevan, J. W. (1927). *Proc. Roy. Soc.* **B101**, 483.

Trevan, J. W., and Boock, E. (1926). Pubs. *League Nations* III, Health, III C. H. 398.

"United States Pharmacopeia." (1955) Fifteenth Revision. Mack Publ., Easton, Pennsylvania.

Vallance-Owen, J., and Hurlock, B. (1954). *Lancet* **i**, 68.

Willebrands, A. F., and Groen, J. (1956). *Diabetes* **5**, 378.

Young, D. M., and Lewis, A. H. (1947). *Science* **105**, 368.

Young, D. M., and Romans, R. G. (1948). *Biometrics* **4**, 122.

Chapter 12

Glucagon

WILLIAM W. BROMER AND OTTO K. BEHRENS

I. Introduction

Although the existence of glucagon was suggested in 1924, shortly after the discovery of insulin, only in the past few years has glucagon gained general recognition as a second hormone of the pancreas. Undoubtedly, much of the early apathy toward glucagon may be attributed to the overshadowing interest in insulin because of its role in the control of diabetes; nevertheless faster progress on glucagon might have been expected if a convenient and precise assay method had been available. Within the past decade refinements of existing methods have facilitated advances in the chemistry and physiology of glucagon: the hormone has been prepared in crystalline form, and its structure has been determined; the mechanism of the hyperglycemic-glycogenolytic effect of glucagon has been well characterized. In addition, with the availability of crystalline glucagon, many and diverse biological effects of the hormone have been established. Despite such great strides, a comprehensive understanding of the biological function of glucagon is clearly lacking today. An important factor in the attainment of this knowledge may be the development of improved methods of assay for glucagon in blood and in tissues.

A. CHEMICAL ASPECTS OF GLUCAGON

The discussion of the chemistry of glucagon is intended to serve as a background for the assay methods. A more detailed review may be found elsewhere (Behrens and Bromer, 1958).

1. Homogeneity of Glucagon

The isolation of a virtually homogeneous glucagon preparation is a prerequisite for the application of analytical methods based on physical or chemical properties of the hormone. Staub *et al.* (1955) demonstrated the high purity of crystalline glucagon preparations by means of chemical end-group analysis and zone electrophoresis. Repeated crystallizations afforded no increase in biological activity, and the protein in the mother liquor was as active as the isolated crystals. A high degree of homogeneity was also indicated from preliminary counter-current distribution studies (Bromer, 1959) using *n*-butanol: 0.5% trichloroacetic acid in 0.025 N HCl (1:1).

2. Properties of Glucagon

Glucagon contains many functional groupings capable of binding small ions; however, the active hormone can be isolated in crystalline form without significant contamination from metals or other charged substances (Staub *et al.*, 1955). On the basis of zone electrophoretic data the isoelectric region of glucagon lies between pH 7.5 and 8.5. Evidence exists (Bromer, 1959) that fibrils, freshly prepared from a 1% glucagon solution at pH 1.5, retain full biological potency. However, fibrils formed over a period of months from a 0.1% solution, pH 2.5, at 37° to 50°C. appear to be inactive and cannot be regenerated by alkaline treatment. Additional work will be required to elucidate the differences between fibril types and to evaluate the effect of fibril formation on biological activity.

3. Structure of Glucagon

Glucagon is composed of a single chain of 29 amino acids (Bromer *et al.*, 1957) containing N-terminal histidine and C-terminal threonine. The hormone has a molecular weight of 3485 on the basis of structural studies. The structure was elucidated through (1) digestion with enzymes into small fragments, (2) isolation of the fragments by means of Dowex 50 columns, (3) characterization of the peptide fragments, and (4) correlation of the data in an unequivocal manner. The following amino acid sequence was established: his.ser.glu(−NH₂).gly.thr.-phe.thr.ser.asp.tyr.ser.lys.tyr.leu.asp.ser.arg.arg.ala.glu (−NH₂) .asp.phe.-val.glu(−NH₂).try.leu.met.asp(−NH₂).thr.

The high concentration of functional groupings in glucagon is noteworthy. For example, the two tyrosine and single tryptophan residues in the chain absorb strongly in the ultraviolet at 276 mμ, providing a convenient assay for crystalline glucagon in solution. Other amino acids present in glucagon, such as the single residues of methionine and of histidine also provide a basis for analysis of purified samples. Clearly, such chemical methods can only be employed in conjunction with a physiological assay.

B. PHYSIOLOGICAL ASPECTS OF GLUCAGON

Early in the history of insulin, investigators noted that the injection of some pancreatic extracts into animals produced a rapid transitory hyperglycemia. The liver was implicated as the site of this hyperglycemic action by several lines of evidence. In 1945 Shipley and Humel noted that insulin preparations stimulated glycogenolysis in liver slices. Sutherland and Cori (1948) showed that the glycogenolysis was attributable to a "glycogenolytic factor" in the insulin preparations and thus prepared the way for intensive study of the mechanism of this effect. Since the advent of crystalline glucagon (Staub *et al.*, 1955) the hormone has been shown to affect a wide variety of systems in addition to glycogenolysis in the liver.

1. Effects in Liver

After Sutherland and Cori (1948, 1951) showed that glucagon affected the rate-limiting phosphorylase step of liver glycolysis, much attention was focused on the phosphorylase system. Largely through the efforts of Sutherland and his collaborators (Wosilait, Rall, and Berthet), many of the details of the glycogenolytic action of glucagon in liver have been elucidated. Liver phosphorylase (LP) concentration depends on a balance between a phosphorylase-activating enzyme (dephosphophosphorylase kinase) and a LP-inactivating enzyme (phosphorylase phosphatase). Rall *et al.* (1957) and Sutherland and Rall (1957, 1958) further demonstrated in a cell-free system that either glucagon or epinephrine acts on a particulate liver fraction to form adenosine-3′,5′-phosphoric acid which in turn stimulates phosphorylase activation. As a consequence, an accumulation of active phosphorylase occurs, and glycogenolysis is promoted. The glycogenolytic system, in either a direct or indirect fashion, provides the basis for nearly all of the methods of glucagon bioassay presently in use.

2. Effects in Other Systems

A few of the striking effects of glucagon in other systems are cited since these actions could be used as a basis for glucagon assay. The now well-documented actions of glucagon probably not mediated by hyperglycemia include: (1) marked reduction in intestinal motility and gastric secretion, (2) enhanced excretion of electrolytes by the kidney, and (3) increased urinary nitrogen and decreased blood amino nitrogen levels.

II. Methods of Assay

Various methods for the assay of glucagon have been outlined that may be applicable to the crystalline hormone or to crude mixtures containing very small concentrations. The methods are considered critically, and the limits of applicability and sensitivity are discussed. Many of the methods of assay will be cited, but only a few have been given detailed consideration.

A. PHYSICAL METHODS

Methods dependent on the physical properties of glucagon are useful with highly purified preparations, but require confirmation and correlation with a bioassay. Such procedures are applicable principally to the determination of the concentration of crystalline glucagon in solution, to the analysis of purity, and in some instances to the separation of glucagon from complex mixtures. Most of the methods have not been developed as quantitative assay procedures although all are suitable for such development.

1. Ultraviolet Absorption

The concentration of crystalline glucagon in aqueous solution (pH 1–9) may readily be obtained by measurement of the ultraviolet absorption at 276 mμ, followed by comparison with the $E_{1\,cm}^{1\%}$ value of glucagon: 21.15, with a standard deviation of 0.54 (Kuzel and Holzer, 1959). This value was obtained from measurements on 12 different lots of crystalline glucagon.

2. Electrophoretic Methods

Light and Simpson (1956) have suggested that the paper electrophoretic separation of insulin and glucagon may be useful in determining small amounts of glucagon in insulin. Glucagon remained immobile after electrophoresis for 24 hours at about 6.7 volts per centimeter, 2°C., on Whatman No. 1 paper in 0.03 M pH 7.5 sodium phosphate buffer; insulin moved toward the anode. No indication of the sensitivity of the method was offered.

Starch electrophoresis has been employed to provide data on purity of glucagon by Staub *et al.* (1955). Five milligrams of crystalline glucagon were applied to starch troughs using 0.075 *M* glycine buffer, pH 9.9. The electrophoresis was conducted for 40 hours at 4°C., 160–170 volts, and 13–15 milliamperes.

B. BIOASSAY METHODS

1. Measurement of the Hyperglycemic Effect of Glucagon

The rise in blood sugar in an experimental animal is measured following the injection of glucagon. The methods differ primarily in the species of animal employed, in the experimental design, and in the procedure for handling the data. For example, the hyperglycemic response of rats (von Holt *et al.*, 1956), rabbits (Rowlinson and Lesford, 1951; Lazarus *et al.*, 1957), chicks (Beekman, 1958), and cats (Staub and Behrens, 1954) has been used as a quantitative measure of glucagon. The chief virtues of the *in vivo* methods lie in the simplicity and the reproducibility of the procedures. The difficulties encountered with such methods include individual variation, lack of specificity, slowness, and the need for large numbers of animals. Several of the above methods have been tried in the Lilly Laboratories (Diller, 1959). The one selected for detailed consideration is a recent modification (Smith and Robbins, 1959) of the cat method of Staub and Behrens (1954).

Sixteen hours prior to assay, cats weighing 2.5–3 kg. are injected intraperitoneally with 25 gm. of glucose and are deprived of food but not water. Just prior to assay the animals are placed under surgical anesthesia with an intraperitoneal injection of 170 mg. per kilogram of phenobarbital. Both femoral veins are exposed; one is used for injection of the test solutions and the other for removal of blood samples. A normal blood sample (0.9 ml.) is taken and added immediately to 0.1 ml. of a solution containing 2 mg. sodium fluoride and 10 units of heparin; all subsequent blood samples are handled in similar fashion. Recrystallized glucagon is employed as a standard, at both 0.1 and 0.2 μg. per kilogram. Immediately after removal of the normal blood a glucagon solution is injected by vein, and 4 blood samples are taken at 8-minute intervals. After an additional 45 minutes (about 1 hour, 17 minutes between injections) another normal blood sample is taken and another glucagon solution is injected. The procedure is continued until 4 samples have been injected. The assay is based on the Latin square technique using 4 animals per group with a series of 4 injections per animal, e.g., high and low standard (SH, SL), high and low unknown (UH, UL). The following schedule is customarily employed for each series of 4 cats:

Cat	Sample injection			
	1	2	3	4
1	SH	UL	SL	UH
2	UL	SL	UH	SH
3	SL	UH	SH	UL
4	UH	SH	UL	SL

The blood-sugar analyses are performed routinely using a Technicon Autoanalyzer. The analytical method of Hoffman (1937) has been adapted by Technicon for the apparatus. All values are compared to a standard glucose curve determined for each experiment using standard solutions of 0.25 to 2.0 mg. per milliliter (in 0.25 mg. per milliliter increments). The net rise in blood sugar is found for each sample by subtraction of the appropriate control value. The mean of the 4 net sugar analyses for each glucagon sample is calculated, providing the basic unit of measurement for subsequent calculations.

By applying the method of least squares and the usual calculations for a parallel line assay (e.g., see "Pharmacopeia of the United States, 14th Revision," Mack Printing Company, Easton, Pennsylvania, p. 610), a direct comparison is obtained between the unknown and the standard. The standard preparation (Lot 258-234B-167-1), when assayed in 31 cats as above at 0.1 and 0.2 μg. per kilogram, provided a blood-sugar rise of $31 \pm S.D.8.3.$ and $50 \pm S.D.17.7$ mg.%, respectively. When 16 animals are employed, a standard error of approximately $\pm20\%$ is obtained. With 8 animals the error is about $\pm30\%$ and with 4 the error is nearly $\pm40\%$. If a 1 ml. per kilogram sample injection is employed, as little as 0.035 μg. of glucagon per milliliter (1×10^{-5} μmoles per milliliter) can be measured. Since Makman et al. (1958) found a level of about 0.06 μg. per milliliter of glucagon-like activity in human blood plasma, the cat method is probably sensitive enough to be used in blood measurements.

One of the major disadvantages of the method stems from the requirement that any substance which affects blood-sugar levels, such as insulin, must first be removed from the glucagon sample. In the analysis of glucagon in insulin preparations selective destruction of most of the insulin activity can readily be accomplished by incubation with cysteine (Staub and Behrens, 1954). In addition, the exclusion of nonspecific effects is inherently more difficult in the intact animal than in an in vitro system. The possibility that changes in blood sugar may be mediated by obscure secondary effects cannot be completely eliminated. Despite these objections, the usefulness of the hyperglycemic assay cannot be denied. Since hyperglycemia per se is often the response desired from glucagon when injected into humans or animals, an assay based on measurements of increased levels of blood sugar has special merit. The value of the method was demonstrated in facilitating the isolation of glucagon in crystalline form (Staub *et al.*, 1955) from crude pancreas fractions.

2. Measurement of the Glycogenolytic Effect of Glucagon

As previously discussed, glucagon promotes the activation of liver phosphorylase which, in turn, is responsible for glycogenolysis; thus, measurement either of the enzyme or of glucose provides a basis of assay for the pancreatic hormone.

a. Liver slice method. Sutherland and Cori (1948) first utilized the glycogenolytic reaction in liver slices as a means of assay for the "glycogenolytic factor" (glucagon) in insulin preparations. Since that time the method has been modified by Audy and Kerly (1952a, b), Please (1952), Vuylsteke *et al.* (1952), de Duve and Vuylsteke (1953), and Tyberghein and Williams (1958). Perhaps the most extensive treatment of the liver slice method was published by Vuylsteke and de Duve (1957). Their method will be considered in some detail, although a full appreciation of the technique can best be obtained from the original publication.

In essence the procedure involves measurement of the glucose liberated into the medium by the action of glucagon on liver slices. In view of the large degree of variability observed, the assay has been designed to include an internal standard and to utilize the 2- × 3-point method (Bliss and Marks, 1939) so that statistical analysis may be employed. Each unit cell is composed of 6 matched liver slices added randomly to 6 flasks each containing a different amount of standard or unknown. In other unit cells it is advisable to provide for control slices without glucagon and for slices with an excess of the hormone so that the maximal response can be ascertained.

Healthy adult rabbits are sacrificed by bleeding under pento-barbital anesthesia and a portion of the liver, preferably the middle lobe, is quickly removed. Only apparently normal livers that contain qualitatively a reasonable amount of glycogen are used. (The amount of glycogen precipitate is estimated from the addition of 1.1 volumes of 95% ethanol to a hot 20% NaOH digest of a small amount of liver.)

The liver is placed in ice-cold saline and the suspension is stirred for 5 minutes. The chilled liver is cut free-hand parallel to the capsule by the method of Deutsch (1936) into slices about 2×3 cm. The large slices are further cut into 6 smaller slices, as nearly alike as possible, of about 40 to 60 mg. each, which are used together as a unit cell. Precautions should be taken to keep the tissue cold before and after slicing. The slices are weighed and are added at random, each to 1 of the 6 flasks of a unit cell previously prepared with medium and sample. A minimum of 3 unit cells is suggested per sample.

Each unit cell of 6 flasks contains 3 logarithmically spaced concentrations of sample and of standard, e.g., suitable concentrations for crystalline glucagon are 4×10^{-3}, 8×10^{-3}, and 1.6×10^{-2} μg. per milliliter.

The procedure employing 20-ml. beakers shaken in air in a Dubnoff metabolic incubator is described; equally satisfactory results may be obtained with 2.5- $\times$ 15-cm. test tubes in a Warburg bath. The 2.4 ml. of medium per beaker is 0.02 M pH 7.4 potassium phosphate buffer (Sutherland and de Duve, 1948) containing 0.12 M sodium chloride and 100 μg. of glucagon-free insulin. The slices of a unit cell are incubated simultaneously for 40 or 45 minutes at 37°C.; the incubation is stopped by adding 5 ml. of 0.15 M barium hydroxide followed by 5 ml. of 0.15 M zinc sulfate. The mixture is filtered, and glucose is determined on the filtrate according to Nelson (1944). Alternatively, glycogen or phosphate may be determined if appropriate adjustments are made in the procedure. The amount of inorganic phosphate liberated is used as a measure of phosphorylase activity. The results are generally reported as milligram of glucose formed per gram of liver per 40 minutes. The data are treated by the method of factorial coefficients as described by Emmens (1948).

Advantages of the method include sensitivity and economy of time, animals, and labor. The variability observed in 10 unit cells compares well with that observed for 16 animals in the cat assay (Staub and Behrens, 1954), and the livers from only 2 or 3 rabbits are needed. A probable saving of nearly 50% in time and labor is effected. Like the *in vivo* assays, the slice method is also beset with difficulties from nonspecific glycogenolytic effects and from occasional extreme variability in response. That the glycogenolytic response is due to glucagon may be partially verified by determining whether or not the response is potentiated by insulin and is insensitive to ergotamine. Vulysteke and de Duve (1957) pointed out that the standard deviation is not independent of the response, a finding in conflict with one of the criteria set forth by Gaddum (1931) for a reliable bioassay. However, the standard deviation varies over a limited range, making possible a variance analysis if the assay is well balanced. Another difficulty is the lack of parallel response when crystalline glucagon as a standard is compared with crude glucagon-containing materials. The authors suggest the use of an arbitrary standard comparable in purity to the unknowns.

b. *Liver homogenate method.* While elucidating the interesting series of reactions leading to the formation of liver phosphorylase (LP), Rall *et al.* (1957) discovered that certain liver homogenates were capable of supporting the same series of reactions that occur in slices. Shortly thereafter Berthet *et al.* (1957) published a method of assay for glucagon and epinephrine based on the use of liver homogenates. Cat or dog liver homogenates were found to be satisfactory, while rabbit and rat liver homogenates gave relatively poor responses.

Dog livers are generally employed in the present method. Mature animals are sacrificed by bleeding from the neck under deep secobarbital anesthesia. The livers are perfused *in situ* via a portal vein cannula with cold 0.9% sodium chloride, are then removed and are cooled in saline for 10 minutes. Slices of about $25 \times 20 \times 2$ mm. are prepared in the cold room and are washed in 15-gm portions by swirling for 1 minute with 5 to 6 volumes of cold 0.9% sodium chloride. The supernatant fluid is decanted and the slices are incubated with 3 volumes of medium for 15 minutes at 37°C. to wash out glucagon and epinephrine and to reduce the LP level. The supernatant fluid is again discarded and the slices are chilled, washed with cold 0.33 M sucrose, and are homogenized in 2 volumes of 0.33 M sucrose in a loosely fitting glass homogenizer. The homogenates are centrifuged for 45 seconds at 900 g and the pellet is discarded. The supernatant fluid is either used immediately or is quick-frozen and stored in dry ice.

Into cold 15- $\times$ 125-mm. tubes are placed 0.1 ml. of a medium containing the glucagon dilution, followed by an 0.15-ml. aliquot of about a 1:3 dilution of the liver homogenate. For purposes of measuring small amounts of glucagon in biological material, the tubes contained according to Berthet *et al.* (1957), "at final concentration, 75 mg.[1] per ml. of homogenate of dog or cat liver, 0.05 M buffer[2] (tris or imidazole), 0.0004 M adenosine triphosphate, 0.0005 M MgSO$_4$, either 0.1 mg. per ml. of casein[3] or 0.01 mg. per ml. of insulin[3] (glucagon-free), 0.0005 M caffeine,[4] 0.04 mg. per ml. of ergotamine tartrate,[5] 0.18 M sucrose, and 1.2 to 1.5 units

[1] When highest sensitivity and accuracy are not required, acceptable results can probably be obtained by incubations containing approximately 150 mg.

[2] The optimal pH range 7.0–7.4 was obtained by dilution of 1 M stock solution of either tris (pH 7.4–7.8) or imidazole buffer (pH 7.2–7.7).

[3] Inhibits destruction of glucagon.

[4] Protects the adenosine,-3',5'-phosphoric acid intermediate.

[5] Reduces interference of sympathomimetic amines.

per ml. of dephospho-LP.[6]" The tubes are incubated at 30°C. for 10 minutes. Phosphorylase activity is estimated by addition of 2.8 ml. of phosphorylase assay reagent[7] to each tube, followed by a 10-minute incubation at 37°C. One milliliter of 15% trichloracetic acid is added to stop the reaction and inorganic phosphate is determined on a 0.15-ml. aliquot of the reaction mixture according to the method of Fiske and SubbaRow (1925).

Makman *et al.* (1960) reported that as little as 0.001 μg. of glucagon per 0.25 ml. reaction mixture is readily detectable in the system. In addition, Berthet *et al.* claimed that the liver homogenate method is 2 to 7 times more precise than the liver slice method (Vuylsteke and de Duve, 1957). The homogenate method in the hands of Sutherland and his collaborators is clearly the most sensitive and most accurate method for glucagon assay.

For a variety of reasons, however, the method has not gained wide acceptance. The procedure is unquestionably a laborious and difficult one. The preparation of dephospho-LP is time consuming and tedious, and without the supplementation of dephospho-LP the method probably loses most of its advantage in sensitivity and accuracy over the slice technique. In addition, repeated efforts (Manthey and Kuether, 1958) to prepare homogenates that did not require dephospho-LP were unsuccessful.

c. Slice-homogenate method. Prior to the development of the homogenate assay, Fodden and Read (1955) and Ui *et al.* (1956) made the very interesting observation that glucagon could be assayed in a two-step procedure: (1) phosphorylase was activated by glucagon in liver slices, and (2) following homogenization of the slices, added glycogen was degraded by the activated phosphorylase. Details of the method have been published by Ui and colleagues (1956).

Rabbits about 1 month old are sacrificed under pentobarbital anesthesia by severing the carotid artery. The liver is removed rapidly and is placed in a cold solution of 0.72% sodium chloride in 0.02 M phosphate buffer pH 7.4. Rectangular blocks of tissue with an end area of about 1 cm.² are prepared from which are cut slices of about 150 mg. each. Two or three slices are shaken aerobically for 10 minutes (Ui, 1959) at 37°C. (110 oscillations per minute) in 3 ml. of the above medium containing the glucagon sample. The contents of the flask are homogenized in a Potter-Elvehjem homogenizer and 2 mg. of glycogen are added per 100 mg. of tissue. Medium is added to a final concentration of 25 mg. of tissue

---

[6] Necessary for highest sensitivity and accuracy. Prepared according to Rall *et al.* (1956).

[7] 0.36 M glucose-1-phosphate, 0.1 M sodium fluoride, 0.0014 M adenosine monophosphate and 4 mg. glycogen per milliliter.

per milliliter. The homogenate is centrifuged at low speed, and the supernatant fluid is divided into five 2-ml. aliquots which are incubated for 3 hours (Ui, 1959) under conditions described above. A 0.6-ml. aliquot is removed, is diluted with 2.9 ml. water, and is deproteinized by 0.2 ml. each of 5% zinc sulfate and 0.3 N barium hydroxide. Glucose is determined on 2 ml. of the supernatant fluid by the Nelson (1944) method.

When the above procedure was performed with 5 different levels of cysteine-inactivated insulin, 2 assumed to be the "standard," the other 3 the "unknown," the relative potency was reported as 1.03, with 95% fiducial limits of 0.962–1.105. Ui (1959) has indicated that the addition of crystalline glucagon in quantities of 0.2, 0.3, and 2.0 μg. per flask caused an increase in glucose output of 10, 16, and 64%, respectively; thus, as little as 0.2–0.5 μg. of glucagon can be detected.

This blending of techniques appeared to eliminate many of the variables associated with the slice method, and the design of the slice-homogenate method provided excellent reproducibility within a single liver preparation. A high blank value possibly may be minimized by pre-incubation of the slices according to Sutherland and colleagues. Apparently the gain in precision is accompanied by about a tenfold loss in sensitivity. The fact that insulin provided a better response (two- to fivefold) but gave a lower slope of the dose-response curve than cysteine-inactivated insulin has been interpreted by the authors on the basis of (a) a partial destruction of glucagon by cysteine and/or HCl and (b) an inhibition of insulin on glucagon activity. These data may be compared to the findings of Vuylsteke and de Duve (1957) that a 100-fold increase in the activity of crystalline glucagon was found when 100 μg. of insulin was added per flask. In addition, in the latter study, the log-dose-response lines were reasonably parallel. Vuylsteke and de Duve (1957) have further shown that the potentiation effect of insulin may be most likely ascribed to the protection of glucagon from proteolysis. Thus, although the slice-homogenate assay appears to be a relatively simple and precise method, additional evaluation work is needed.

C. IMMUNOCHEMICAL METHOD

Unger and co-workers (1959, 1960) recently described the production of antibodies to glucagon and their use as a basis for an immunoassay for glucagon. Crystalline glucagon of mixed pork and beef origin is suspended in Freund's adjuvant and is administered subcutaneously once a month to female rabbits. A monthly dosage of 1 mg. of glucagon per rabbit is used (Unger, 1960). The presence of nonprecipitating glucagon antibodies is detected in the rabbit serum after 3 months by a method similar to that used by Berson *et al.* (1956) for insulin antibodies; 0.01 μg. of glucagon-I[131] and 1 ml. of rabbit serum are incubated at 37°C. for 2 hours. Ten to fifty microliters of the incubate are applied to strips of Whatman No. 3 MM paper and horizontal (Unger, 1960) chromatography is applied for 1 to 2 hours using pH 8.6 barbital buffer, μ = 0.025 to 0.1. Sometimes this procedure is followed by 16 hours of electrophoresis at 150–250 volts and 1–3 milliamperes. The paper is dried for 1 hour at 120°C., is stained with naphthalene blue-black, is washed for 10 minutes in a 10% acetic acid solution in methanol, and is cut into appropriate segments. Glucagon-I[131] is located in the paper strips using either a well-type scintillation counter or a Geiger-Müller tube with an automatic recording attachment.

When normal rabbit serum is incubated with glucagon-I[131], 91.2–95.2% of the radioactivity is tightly adsorbed to the point of application. However, when sera from glucagon-treated animals is incubated and subjected to electrophoresis, only 12.7–54.1% of the radioactivity is found at the origin, 45.9–87.3% migrating with the γ-globulin fraction. These data are consistent with the interpretation (Berson *et al.* 1957) that free glucagon is strongly bound on paper and does not move unless it is pre-bound to a glucagon antibody.

The presence of glucagon antibodies is also detectable by the method of Skom and Talmage (1958) wherein antiglobulin is used to precipitate the glucagon-I[131]-globulin complex. The precipitate is washed by centrifugation and is counted as above. Results nearly identical to the electrophoresis method were obtained when sera from normal and from glucagon-challenged rabbits were compared as above.

These findings were used as the basis for an assay in the following manner. Various amounts of crystalline glucagon were incubated with the antisera followed by incubation with glucagon-I[131]. The amount of glucagon-I[131] that was bound by the antibodies decreased in inverse ratio to the quantity of unlabeled glucagon that had been added.

Thus, samples of 100 to 1000 μμg. per milliliter (Unger, 1960) of crystalline glucagon are preincubated with 1:100 antisera, followed by incubation with 100 μμg. of glucagon-I[131] and by electrophoresis or by precipitation. Increasing amounts of nonradioactive glucagon replaced proportionately greater amounts of glucagon-I[131] from the antigen-antibody complex. As little as 50 to 100 μμg. of glucagon has been detected by this technique (Unger, 1960). Although only preliminary data are available for the immunoassay, the method promises a high degree of sensitivity and specificity. Another advantage appears to be relative simplicity. However, the question of precision cannot be adequately judged on the basis of present information; obviously additional data are required before the assay can be considered in a critical manner.[8]

III. Measurement of Glucagon in Blood

Despite a growing knowledge of the effects of glucagon, a real understanding of the physiological role of this hormone remains to be achieved. Perhaps the key to this problem lies in the application of newer, more sensitive assay methods to the determination of glucagon in blood and in tissues. Some of the assay methods described in the preceding pages probably are of sufficient sensitivity, but lack the absolute specificity required for a straightforward application to serum and crude tissue extracts. Therefore, the problems of assay in blood and tissue extracts become largely those of purifying glucagon and of establishing whether or not the measured response is attributable to glucagon alone.

The importance of these aspects is apparent after consideration of some of the reports in the last decade on the detection of glucagon-like effects in blood and pancreas tissue (Sutherland and de Duve, 1948; Foa et al., 1949; Bornstein et al., 1951; Audy and Kerly, 1952a; Foa et al., 1953; Fodden and Read, 1955; Berthet et al., 1957; Sirek, 1957; Ito et al., 1958). The recent critical work of Tyberghein and Williams (1958) and Makman et al. (1958, 1960) on the assay of glucagon in blood may be cited particularly to emphasize some of the problems relevant to glucagon extraction and identification.

Despite the apparent specificity of any assay method, the assignment of the measured response to glucagon should be verified by other means. Utilization of a second assay procedure based on a different principle offers one approach. Another approach is available through preparation of partially purified extracts as devoid as possible of nonspecific substances that inhibit or potentiate the particular assay response for glucagon. The method developed by Makman et al. (1958) for extraction of glucagon-like activity from blood may be cited as an illustration. Unfractionated plasma was found to contain unspecified factors that were strongly inhibiting to the liver homogenate assay system. Tyberghein and Williams (1958) also reported that plasma could not be assayed using the liver slice method because of the presence of interfering materials. They suggested that the most important interference came from amylase, which has a strong glycogenolytic effect in liver slices. Since Makman et al. measured phosphorylase, and Tyberghein and Williams measured glucose, it is apparent that the former expression of glucagon

[8] *Note added in proof:* Since the preparation of this manuscript another immunoassay technique has been described by Grodsky et al. [*Proc. Soc. Exptl. Biol. Med.* **107**, 491 (1961)]; furthermore, Unger and associates [*J. Clin. Invest.* **40**, 1280 (1961)], have extended their immunoassay, providing a basis for the measurement of circulating glucagon.

activity is more specific than is the latter. Nevertheless, considerable fractionation was required to remove or destroy the substances inhibitory to the homogenate system.

The plasma or serum is extracted with acid-alcohol, the suspension is centrifuged, and the supernatant fluid is adjusted to pH 7.7 with ammonium hydroxide. Alcohol and ether are added to precipitate the proteins. The precipitate is suspended in dilute HCl for 2 hours to complete the destruction of inhibitors, and ammonium sulfate is added to precipitate the glucagon-like activity. Salt is removed by dialyzing for 1 or 2 days; 70% of crystalline glucagon added to blood is recovered in the impermeate fraction.

About 0.05 ml. of the final fraction (equivalent to about 0.25 ml. of plasma) was sufficient to provide a response greater than half-maximal stimulation in the homogenate assay. Log-dose-response curves for the plasma fraction and for crystalline glucagon were reasonably parallel. In utilizing such procedures, dog plasma was found to contain 0.9 to 15.7 μg. of glucagon-like material per 100 ml., while human plasma assayed 3.8 to 8.8 μg. per 100 ml.

Although a relatively low order of purification (five to sevenfold) of glucagon was obtained by Makman *et al.*, these data nevertheless provide evidence for the identity of the blood factor with glucagon. Further evidence was obtained by the parallelism of the log-dose-response curves and by the similarity of action on liver phosphorylase. In addition, the assay system was designed to eliminate interference from amylase and from epinephrine, the latter through use of ergotamine. The blood factor also behaved similarly to glucagon as regards lability to alkali, trypsin, and insulinase. When 100 μg. per kilogram of crystalline glucagon was injected into the portal vein of a dog, high glucagon activity levels were detected within a few minutes in peripheral blood. Within about 20 minutes the glucagon level had fallen to near normal values.

Despite these convincing data that pointed to the identity of the blood factor with glucagon, Makman *et al.* (1960) later showed unequivocally that the two were not identical: the blood factor, but not glucagon, was found to increase the rate of phosphorylase activation in supernatant fractions of liver homogenates. Additionally, glucagon, but not the blood substance, promoted the accumulation of adenosine-3',5'-phosphoric acid in the presence of particulate liver fractions. Whether or not the glucagon-like substance has physiological significance remains to be determined.

The careful work of Sutherland and his collaborators emphasizes the requirement for thorough verification that the activity measured is, in fact, attributable to glucagon. Despite the somewhat discouraging aspect of the present status of the measurement of glucagon in blood, the problem is under active investigation and the procedures described in this chapter most likely will form a basis for an early development of an unequivocal assay.

IV. Summary

Nearly all the current methods for glucagon assay have as a basis the reactions involving the liberation of glucose from liver glycogen. Glucagon exhibits many other physiological effects, probably unrelated to liver glycolysis, that might be used as sensitive means of analysis. Analyses based on the physical and chemical properties of glucagon have not been extensively explored. Investigation in these areas may result in new assay techniques and in addition may render existing methods more reliable. For example, a method using paper electrophoretic separation of glucagon from blood may provide samples of sufficient purity to permit unequivocal analyses with liver slices, homogenates, or intact animals.

The cat method of glucagon assay has been described since the technique is relatively simple and sensitive and since hyperglycemia per se is usually the physiological effect desired of glucagon. The *in vivo* methods in general suffer from variability, large expenditures of time and animals, and lack of specificity.

The liver slice technique has been thoroughly tested by several investigators and found to be reliable, sensitive, reasonably specific, and not overly demanding in terms of time or number of animals. With careful experimental design the effects of variability can be minimized.

The liver homogenate method has been extensively exploited in one laboratory and, on the basis of these data, stands out as perhaps the most specific and sensitive, and the least variable assay available. The method is, however, rather demanding and laborious for a routine assay procedure.

The slice-homogenate and the immunochemical methods have not been thoroughly explored and thus cannot be critically evaluated. Both hold considerable promise; the former method may give increased precision, and the latter may provide great sensitivity and specificity.

Measurement of glucagon in blood or tissue extracts requires that the assay procedure possess high specificity. As exemplified by the findings of Makman et al. (1960), other criteria must also be applied to verify that glucagon alone is being measured. Such an unequivocal demonstration of glucagon in blood, presumably en route from the pancreas to the liver and other tissues, has not been reported. However, newer methods, possibly utilizing physical or immunochemical techniques, provide an encouraging outlook for the future.

REFERENCES

Audy, G., and Kerly, M. (1952a). *Biochem. J.* **52**, 70.
Audy, G., and Kerly, M. (1952b). *Biochem. J.* **52**, 77.
Beekman, B. E. (1958). *Poultry Sci.* **37**, 595.
Behrens, O. K., and Bromer, W. W. (1958). *Vitamins and Hormones* **16**, 263.
Berson, S. A., Yalow, R. S., Bauman, A., Rothschild, M. A., and Newerly, K. (1956). *J. Clin. Invest.* **35**, 170.
Berson, S. A., Yalow, R. S., Volk, B. W. (1957). *J. Lab. Clin. Med.* **49**, 331.
Berthet, J., Sutherland, E. W., and Rall, T. W. (1957). *J. Biol. Chem.* **229**, 351.
Bliss, C. I., and Marks, H. P. (1939). *Quart. J. Pharm. and Pharmacol.* **12**, 182.
Bornstein, J., Reid, E., and Young, F. G. (1951). *Nature* **168**, 903.
Bromer, W. W. (1959). Unpublished data.
Bromer, W. W., Sinn, L. G., Staub, A., and Behrens, O. K. (1957). *J. Am. Chem. Soc.* **79**, 2807.
de Duve, C., and Vuylsteke, C. A. (1953). *Arch. intern. physiol.* **61**, 252.
Deutsch, W. (1936). *J. Physiol. (London)* **87**, 56P.
Diller, E. R. (1959). Unpublished data.
Emmens, C. W. (1948). "Principles of Biological Assay." Chapman & Hall, London.
Fiske, C. H., and SubbaRow, Y. (1925). *J. Biol. Chem.* **66**, 375.
Foa, P. P., Weinstein, H. R., and Smith, J. A. (1949). *Am. J. Physiol.* **157**, 197.
Foa, P. P., Berger, S., Santamaria, L., Smith, J. A., and Weinstein, H. R. (1953). *Science* **117**, 82.
Fodden, J. H., and Read, W. O. (1955). *Am. J. Physiol.* **182**, 513.
Gaddum, J. H. (1931). *Biochem. J.* **25**, 1113.
Hoffman, W. S. (1937). *J. Biol. Chem.* **120**, 51.
Ito, Y., Kobayashi, B., Kim, Y. E., Ui, M., and Moriwaki, C. (1958). *Endocrinol. Japon.* **5**, 1.
Kuzel, N. R., and Holzer, F. H. (1959). Unpublished data.
Lazarus, S. S., Volk, B. W., and Lew, H. (1957). *J. Clin. Endocrinol. and Metabolism* **17**, 542.
Light, A., and Simpson, M. V. (1956). *Biochem. et Biophys. Acta* **20**, 251.
Makman, M. H., Makman, R. S., and Sutherland, E. W. (1958). *J. Biol. Chem.* **233**, 894.
Makman, M. H., Makman, R. S., and Sutherland, E. W. (1960). *In* "Hormones in Human Plasma" (H. N. Antoniades, ed.), p. 119. Little, Brown, Boston, Massachusetts.
Manthey, J. A., and Kuether, C. A. (1958). Unpublished data.
Nelson, N. (1944). *J. Biol. Chem.* **153**, 375.
Please, N. W. (1952). *Biochem. J.* **52**, 75.
Rall, T. W., Sutherland, E. W., and Wosilait, W. D. (1956). *J. Biol. Chem.* **218**, 483.
Rall, T. W., Sutherland, E. W., and Berthet, J. (1957). *J. Biol. Chem.* **224**, 463.
Rowlinson, H. R., and Lesford, J. M. (1951). *J. Pharm. and Pharmacol.* **3**, 887.
Shipley, R. A., and Humel, E. J., Jr. (1945). *Am. J. Physiol.* **144**, 51.
Sirek, A. (1957). *Nature* **179**, 376.

Skom, J. H., and Talmage, D. W. (1958). *J. Clin. Invest.* **37,** 783.

Smith, F. A., and Robbins, E. B. (1959). Unpublished data.

Staub, A., and Behrens, O. K. (1954). *J. Clin. Invest.* **33,** 1629.

Staub, A., Sinn, L., and Behrens, O. K. (1955). *J. Biol. Chem.* **214,** 619.

Sutherland, E. W., and Cori, C. F. (1948). *J. Biol. Chem.* **172,** 737.

Sutherland, E. W., and Cori, C. F. (1951). *J. Biol. Chem.* **188,** 531.

Sutherland, E. W., and de Duve, C. (1948). *J. Biol. Chem.* **175,** 663.

Sutherland, E. W., and Rall, T. W. (1957). *J. Am. Chem. Soc.* **79,** 3608.

Sutherland, E. W., and Rall, T. W. (1958). *J. Biol. Chem.* **232,** 1077.

Tyberghein, J. M., and Williams, R. H. (1958). *Metabolism, Clin. and Exptl.* **7,** 635.

Ui, M. (1959). Personal communication.

Ui, M., Kobayashi, B., and Ito, Y. (1956). *Endocrinol. Japon.* **3,** 191.

Unger, R. H. (1960). Personal communication.

Unger, R. H., Eisentraut, A. M., McCall, M. S., Keller, S., and Madison, L. L. (1959). *J. Lab. Clin. Med.* **54,** 952.

Unger, R. H., Eisentraut, A. M., McCall, M. S., Keller, S., Lanz, H. C., and Madison, L. L. (1960). *Proc. Soc. Exptl. Biol. Med.* **102,** 621.

von Holt, C., von Holt, L., Kroner, B., and Kuhnau, J. (1956). *In* "Ciba Foundation Colloquia on Endocrinology" (C. B. W. Wolstenholme, and C. M. O'Connor, eds.), Vol. 9, p. 14. Little, Brown, Boston, Massachusetts.

Vuylsteke, C. A., and de Duve, C. (1957). *Arch. intern. pharmacodynamie* **111,** 437.

Vuylsteke, C. A., Cornelis, G., and de Duve, C. (1952). *Arch. intern. physiol.* **60,** 105.

Chapter 13

Parathyroid Hormone

R. H. Thorp

I. Introduction

The hormone from the parathyroid gland has not been isolated in a pure form, although extracts containing the hormone were first prepared in 1924. Little is known of the chemistry of this hormone although it is almost certainly a protein, since extracts give the characteristic protein reactions and the activity is destroyed after digestion with proteolytic enzymes.

The parathyroid hormone plays a major part in calcium and phosphorus metabolism, and in deficiency states an abnormally low concentration of calcium is present in the blood serum together with elevation of the renal threshold to phosphate excretion; there is also reduction in the amount of phosphate lost from the body in the urine. The most predominant effect of parathyroid hormone deficiency is an increase in the ratio of phosphate to calcium in the serum and, conversely, the administration of extracts of the hormone causes an increase in serum calcium together with a slight reduction in the phosphate ion concentration. Many methods used for the assay of parathyroid hormone have been based upon the rise in blood calcium, and various devices using this criterion have been employed, ranging from direct measurement of the blood calcium concentration to the antagonism of magnesium anesthesia, which had previously been observed after injection of ionizable calcium preparations.

Studies of the excretion of calcium in the rat or phosphate in rats and mice have also been used as bases for assays, and Gellhorn (1935) has suggested the possibility of using the sensitivity to calcium of hypodynamic skeletal muscle in an isolated preparation as an indicator of parathyroid extract potency.

II. Possibilities of a Standard Preparation

There is no international standard for the parathyroid hormone, and the assays which have been described either define the potency of the preparation in terms of a response or by comparison with a private standard, adopted by that particular laboratory, which has itself been standardized in terms of a biological response.

It is now universally appreciated that a standard preparation of similar constitution to that of the material under examination is essential for any biological assay and the work of Dyer (1936) or L'Heureux et al. (1947) may lead to the production of suitable material for this purpose.

Dyer described a stable powder which he suggested could be used as a standard preparation and which he prepared in the following manner. Fresh ox parathyroid glands were frozen and minced and then mixed with picric acid. The mush was then covered with 10% acetone and left in a refrigerator for 24 hours. After filtration the residue was pressed and shaken with 70% acetone at 0°C. for a further period of 24 hours and then filtered again. The filtrates were bulked and the acetone recovered in vacuo. The residue was dissolved in acid alcohol at pH 4.6–5.0, the alcohol distilled off, and the residue air-dried and purified by solution in hot phenol and reprecipitation from the cold solution with ether. The solid material was washed with ether and stored at a low temperature over phosphorus pentoxide. Dyer prepared four such batches and found an activity of 80 Collip units per gram in each case.

L'Heureux and his colleagues, following the work of Ross and Wood (1942), who prepared extracts 2 to 3 times as potent as those of Collip and Clark (1925), described a method for preparing a powder which is soluble in water below pH 4.5 and has a potency of 200–300 U.S.P. units per milligram of nitrogen. This material is similar in activity to that obtained by Ross and Wood but is obtained in greater yields, a total of 10,000 U.S.P. units, having been derived from 100 gm. of fresh ox parathyroid gland. Electrophoresis examination of L'Heureux's material showed it to be heterogeneous and to consist of two main components, but the separation of these and measurements of their relative activities has not yet been described.

For their assays L'Heureux *et al.* used a method (described later in this chapter) in which comparison was made with a commercial sample of parathyroid extract retained as a standard throughout their work, thus ensuring that the results they obtained were internally comparable.

III. The Unit of Parathyroid Activity

In the absence of a standard preparation the activity of parathyroid preparations has been stated in terms of the biological response and two units were described in this way.

Collip and Clark (1925) originally defined that unit as 1/100 part of the amount of an extract required to raise the serum calcium of a dog weighing 20 kg. by 5 mg./100 ml., but Hanson (1928) proposed a smaller unit consisting of 1/100 of the amount causing a rise of 1 mg./100 ml. in the serum calcium of parathyroidectomized dogs.

The unit described in the U. S. Pharmacopeia (XVI revision) is similar to that of Hanson (1928) except that the rise in the serum calcium is that produced in normal dogs within 16–18 hours after administration of the hormone preparation.

IV. Methods of Assay

A. METHODS BASED ON THE ELEVATION OF SERUM CALCIUM

1. *Methods Using Dogs*

The method originally used by Collip and Clark (1925) involved the measurement of the rise in serum calcium after dosage with parathyroid extracts in groups of 10 dogs.

Blood samples were taken from the ear veins of 10 normal dogs of approximately 20 kg. weight, and the calcium content of the serum was determined. In the late afternoon of the same day (6.00 P.M.) the dogs were given a subcutaneous injection of the parathyroid extract under examination and the serum calcium was again determined at 9.00 A.M. the following day. The calculation of potency in this case was a simple arithmetic proportion based on a rise of 5 mg./100 ml. being produced by 100 units of parathyroid activity.

The method originally described by Collip and Clark has been the

subject of many modifications and improvements of which probably the
most significant are the investigations of this method by Miller (1938)
and Bliss and Rose (1940).

Miller first examined the dose-response relationship for the parathyroid elevation of serum calcium and showed, as one would expect,
that the linear part of this relationship was small and corresponded
only to a threefold change in dose. He found that when no account
was taken of this relationship very variable results were obtained, and
one of the samples examined gave results varying from 75–222 U.S.P.
per milliliter when the dose given was varied from 2 to 6 ml. per dog.
Efforts to extend the dose range, over which a steep response relationship
would be obtained by modifications of the diet of the dogs, were without success. Miller concluded that the dose given must be one producing
a significant response, which is submaximal, using a group of at least 5
dogs. In his experiments a rise of serum calcium of approximately 5
mg./100 ml. was a maximal response.

The examination of the method by Bliss and Rose (1940) followed
upon the work of Miller and was directed principally toward determining the accuracy and reproducibility of the results obtained in such
assays. These authors pointed out the great variation in sensitivity
from dog to dog and the necessity for the use of a standard preparation.
They examined data supplied by Miller as well as those derived from
their own experiments.

Two experimental designs were used in the experiments which Bliss
and Rose made, either 5 groups of 4 dogs each being tested 4 times
in a Latin square arrangement, or 3 groups of 12 dogs each being tested
twice in an arrangement of symmetrical pairs. In order to achieve
comparable results the standard employed was that used in the Lilly
Research Laboratories. Their investigations can best be discussed under
several headings.

a. The dose-response curve for parathyroid extract. By using Miller's
data obtained on 12 dogs each treated with 7 doses of the extract ranging from 0.5 to 6.0 ml., and with determinations of serum calcium 7
hours before and 17 hours after injection, separate dose-response curves
were plotted for each of 10 dogs which had contributed results all
through the experiments.

The data used were both the absolute values of serum calcium after
the hormone and the rise in serum calcium above the initial value for
each dog. Using the latter data, Bliss and Rose showed that the
slope of the dose-response curves varied from $b = 4.30$ to 9.49 with a
combined value of 6.846. They calculated an analysis of the variance
of the results and they showed that computations from responses within

dogs were more consistent than between different dogs. The slope of the dose-response curve for individual dogs agreed within normal experimental limits.

When these results were plotted as the rise in serum calcium against log dose and constant terms were added to reduce individual curves to a common basis, it was shown that the relationship was linear and maximal, for the extract employed, with doses of 6 ml. per dog. The relationship obtained in this way could not be reconciled with the implied relationship of the U.S.P. (XI revision).

When only the final serum calcium data were used the combined slope was $b_c = 7.330$ and ranged from $b = 4.27$ to 10.22. In this case the variation between animals was more marked but the authors concluded that no criterion involving the initial serum calcium gave better results than using the final serum calcium value alone.

These findings were confirmed by the experiments conducted by Bliss and Rose themselves, and again, the final serum calcium level was a satisfactory criterion. Separate estimates of slope did not vary to significantly lower values than those from Miller's data. The combined slopes in Bliss's experiment being $b_c = 4.133$ for the increase in serum calcium and $b_c = 4.082$ for final serum calcium alone, emphasized the importance of an integral determination of slope in such an assay.

b. *Suggested assay design.* Bliss and Rose proposed that a satisfactory assay should be a comparative test with a standard preparation, should have an internal determination of slope and error, and the difference in over-all sensitivity should be separated from the estimates of potency and error. They proposed the use of a Latin square design to encompass these requirements (Bliss and Marks, 1939a, b) and consequently investigated an arrangement of five 4×4 squares in parallel, with all 5 squares conducted on each day.

Analysis of variance showed that the difference between days was small, between dogs large, and once again, the final serum calcium value was an adequate criterion. The sums of squares for treatments were subdivided by factorial analysis, and it was shown that differences in dosage contributed mostly to the value, while the divergence from parallelism of the curves for the standard and test materials, was of no significance.

With 40 observations on both standard and test preparations the standard error exceeded ±10% partly because of the smaller slope in Bliss and Rose's experiments and partly because the strength of the sample used as the test material in these experiments was 30% more potent than postulated.

Using the design of symmetrical pairs described by Yates (1936), these workers obtained a result with a standard error of ±13% (when the determined potency was 113% of that of the standard material) using 36 dogs with two tests on each. They described the application of this design quite fully and also pointed out that unless the body weight of the animals is uniform throughout the group, it is essential to make a correction for the different values.

On using Miller's data, accuracy of a similar order was obtained with 11 dogs for both standard and test preparations, due to the steeper slope obtained in his laboratory.

The actual technique of the dog serum calcium method has been examined by Allardyce (1931) who stated that a meat diet with cod liver oil gave better results but that the addition of calcium as calcium lactate did not result in an increased response to parathyroid hormone. Since the more recent statistical designs were not current at this time, further work on these lines might reduce slope variation between dogs and reduce the number of observations required for a given degree of accuracy in this assay. Allardyce found incidentally that cats did not show appreciable hypercalcemia after parathyroid injection and hence could not be used as test objects for this purpose.

c. Method of United States Pharmacopeia. The method which follows is that described in the U. S. Pharmacopeia (XVI revision) and embodies the considerations which Miller showed to be important.

Select male dogs free from gross evidence of disease and accustomed to venipuncture, but which have not been used during the previous four weeks for the purposes of this assay. The dogs selected are mature, as indicated by the presence of their second teeth, and weigh between 8 and 16 kg. but do not differ in weight by more than 5 kg. Employ not less than 10 dogs in each test. During the assay, maintain the dogs under similar conditions with respect to diet and environmental influences.

Select, by preliminary trial, a dose of the preparation to be assayed such that its injection will be expected to produce increases in the serum calcium content of the dogs selected of between 2 and 5 mg./100 ml.

Withdraw 10 ml. of blood from each dog, using a clean, dry syringe containing no anticoagulant. Transfer the blood immediately to a centrifuge tube, and allow it to clot. Free the clot with a glass rod, and centrifuge sufficiently to yield the serum as a clear supernatant layer. Siphon off the serum by suitable means, and if necessary centrifuge the serum again after its separation from the clot to ensure the removal of cellular material. Determine the serum calcium.

Inject subcutaneously into each dog the selected dose of parathyroid sample. Between 16 and 18 hours after the injection again determine the serum calcium.

Determine for each dog the increase in serum calcium (milligrams per 100 ml. of serum) and determine the average of these values for all the animals injected. The potency of a sample of parathyroid injection is required to be such that the average increase is not less than 1 mg./100 ml. of serum per milliliter of parathyroid injection.

The method for the determination of serum calcium requires little comment and a suitable one is described in the U. S. Pharmacopeia (XVI revision) in the description of the assay.

2. The Use of Rabbits

Hamilton and Schwartz (1932) described a method using rabbits in which parathyroid hormone caused a delay in the rise of serum calcium after administration of calcium chloride by mouth.

Full-grown rabbits were used and the serum calcium was determined before and 15 minutes after doses of calcium chloride (100 mg. Ca) given by stomach tube at intervals of 0, 1, 3, and 5 hours. Doses of 0.3 to 4.0 U.S.P. units of parathyroid hormone delayed the peak serum calcium rise until 3 hours in the case of 1.0 unit, whereas in normal rabbits the maximum serum calcium value was observed after 1 hour from the administration of calcium chloride and showed a gradual fall although subsequent doses of calcium were given.

These authors used the method merely as an approximate test for parathyroid hormone in biological substances and used as their criterion a serum calcium value greater than 4.00 mM. per liter to indicate that the injected sample contained more than 1.5 units per dose.

Hamilton and Highman (1936) used this test to detect abnormally large amounts of parathyroid hormone in blood. Bauman and Sprinson (1940) also used this method but found that there was a marked species difference and that Dutch and Belgian rabbits were more sensitive than New Zealand white or Chinchilla rabbits which required approximately three times as great a dose to produce the effect defined as positive by Hamilton and Schwartz.

Dyer (1935a) examined the method of Hamilton and Schwartz in a detailed manner and found that the variations in normal serum calcium values in rabbits and the values after parathyroid injections were very great so that it was not possible to give an average figure for the response to a given dose of parathyroid hormone or to compare the potency of two extracts by measuring the increase in serum calcium.

In two experiments in which 12 rabbits were used, graded doses of the same parathyroid extract did not produce a graded rise in serum calcium, and Dyer concludes that the method of Hamilton and Schwartz is of value as a means of detection of parathyroid hormone, but is not satisfactorily quantitative for assay purposes.

The methods based on elevation of serum calcium are therefore satisfactory when used as described by Bliss and Rose (1940) but can have little meaning without the use of a standard preparation and an adequate statistical design.

3. The Use of Parathyroidectomized Rats

The normal rat has been shown to be very insensitive to injected parathyroid hormone and Biering (1950) found that large doses of parathyroid extract up to approximately 1000 U.S.P. units were necessary to produce a rise in serum calcium of 3 mg./100 ml. of serum. Tweedy and Chandler (1929) showed that parathyroidectomy produced an increase in sensitivity and Davies and her colleagues (1954) studied the use of such animals for an assay. These workers used hooded rats weighing 200–250 gm. and performed parathyroidectomy by cauterization (Davies and Gordon, 1953), using the animals 3–21 days later. They used a method for plasma calcium determination which makes use of chelation of calcium by sodium versenate, the end point being the loss of the pink color of the indicator Eriochrome T. The method is described in full in their paper. These workers showed that the response of the rat is best found at 21 hours after injection and they used this interval in subsequent experiments. It was also shown that 50 units of Parathormone produced approximately the same rise in operated rats as 200 units in normal animals so that there was approximately a fourfold increase as a result of the operation. Since the rise of plasma calcium is dependent upon the initial plasma calcium + magnesium level which is very variable from rat to rat, these workers used a corrected response which measured the effect of the hormone free from this dependence. The use of this corrected response resulted in a reduction of the spread of the experimental values and an increase in accuracy of the assay together with a simplification of the method of calculation.

These authors concluded that the parathyroidectomized rat has advantages over the dog in that it is a cheaper and more convenient experimental animal, the level of accuracy using the same number of animals is about the same as that for the dog, and less hormone is required.

Rasmussen and Westall (1956) showed that if crude parathyroid extracts were fractionated the time duration of the rise of plasma calcium in the rat differed according to the fraction and the method of Davies et al. (1954) showed apparent inactivity in some of their samples but if plasma samples were taken earlier after injection the plasma calcium value reached a peak at 5–7 hours in these cases and had returned to normal after 12–14 hours. They concluded therefore that assay methods in which the plasma calcium determinations are made after 16–18 hours can easily give an incorrect result when studying fractionated preparations.

B. The Antagonism of Magnesium Anesthesia by the Rise in Serum Calcium Produced by Parathyroid Hormone

The reversal of magnesium depression by calcium ions has been known since 1905 (Meltzer and Auer, 1905, 1908, 1913) and Simon (1935) showed that in normal mice subcutaneous injections of parathyroid hormone had the same effect upon magnesium narcosis as injections of calcium chloride due to the rise in serum calcium produced by the hormone. He also found that there was an optimal dose of parathyroid hormone which prevented magnesium narcosis in the greatest number of mice. Simon suggested the assay of parathyroid hormone by comparison of this optimal dose for different preparations in comparison with that obtained with a standard preparation.

Dyer (1935b) examined this method in detail, making use of the observations of Wokes (1931) who constructed a curve relating the percentages of mice affected by different doses of magnesium sulfate. When magnesium sulfate is injected subcutaneously into mice they become drowsy and unconscious, and unless a fatal dose has been given, respiration continues in a regular manner. Dyer used as his criterion of narcosis the inability of a mouse to right itself when turned on its back.

Dyer first investigated the effect of single and repeated doses of parathyroid hormone prior to magnesium narcosis and showed that a given dose of parathyroid extract was much more effective in antagonizing magnesium narcosis when injected in three increments at intervals of 3 hours, the dose totaling 0.09 ml. of parathyroid extract, than when given as a single dose. In fact a single dose had practically no effect on magnesium narcosis $2\frac{1}{2}$ hours later, in both cases over 80% of the mice remaining narcotized an hour later. The same dose given in three injections reduced the percentages narcotized at this time to below 10%. In this experiment also, Dyer showed that the effect of a total dose of 0.09 ml. of parathyroid extract given in two or three doses was greater than that produced by 0.18 ml. given as a single dose, although this produced a more marked antagonism than a single dose of 0.09 ml. By using doses ranging from 0.3 to 0.9 ml. of an extract given in three divided doses to groups of mice at 2-hour intervals, Dyer showed that the percentage of mice narcotized was related to the dose of parathyroid extract and a smooth curve could be drawn relating the two. Dyer's curve is reproduced in Fig. 1. For this experiment he used the percentage of mice narcotized 1 hour after the injection of magnesium sulfate when this was given in a dose of 1.5 mg. per gram of body weight, 1½ hours after the last injection of parathyroid hormone.

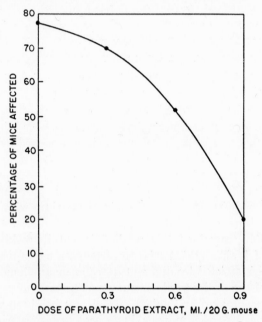

Fig. 1. The effect of parathyroid extract in preventing narcosis in mice produced by injections of magnesium sulfate (Dyer, 1935b).

Dyer compared the potency of two extracts, assayed by another method, by the use of this technique and although it happened that the percentage of mice narcotized was the same in each case, and thus the potency was in inverse ratio of the doses given, the results agreed very well with that previously obtained. A statistical evaluation of this method has not been described, but it has the advantage of simplicity and rapidity and would appear worthy of extension.

C. Assay Methods Using the Fall of Serum Phosphate

Tepperman et al. (1947) were interested in assaying large numbers of samples of parathyroid hormone and fractions derived from it and found the serum calcium method in dogs too costly and time consuming for this purpose. These workers developed a method using the fall in serum inorganic phosphorus in the rat after parathyroid hormone and obtained a linear relationship between response and log dose over the range 12.5–

100 U.S.P. units and a similar degree of accuracy to that obtained by the dog serum calcium method.

Tepperman and her colleagues describe two designs for the assay of parathyroid hormone by this method, one in which a previously established standard dose-response curve is used and a more complete design in which an integral determination of the slope of the dose-response curve is made by using two doses of each preparation.

The general technique, applicable in each case, consists of using groups of male albino rats fed on Purina dog chow for at least 2 weeks before use, but not fasted prior to the experiment, although during the experiment only water is allowed. Blood samples are taken from the cut tip of the tail and 0.6 ml. is collected from each rat into centrifuge tubes, centrifuged for 10 minutes and 0.2-ml. samples of the serum are pipetted into 6 ml. of 10% trichloroacetic acid; this is centrifuged and 5-ml. aliquots from the supernatant protein-free solution are used for the estimation of inorganic phosphorus by the method of Fiske and Subbarow. Tepperman *et al.* used an Evelyn photoelectric colorimeter for the final reading of the color.

In their experiments these authors have used parathyroid extract (Lilly) as a standard in the absence of any official preparation and they measured the serum phosphorus initially and 3 hours after subcutaneous injection of parathyroid hormone.

Figure 2 shows the dose-response curve obtained by this method and it will be seen that the relationship between log dose and response is substantially linear. The number of observations at each point varied from 121 at a dose of 50 U.S.P. units per rat to 22 in the case of the 100-unit dose.

For assay of relative potency by the shorter technique these workers describe a design in which two doses of the test preparation are used with group of 3 rats for each dose. The fall in serum phosphorus is determined 3 hours after injection and an adjustment made for differences in the initial serum phosphorus level since it had been shown earlier that this factor influenced the fall to a considerable extent and that regressions of the fall in serum phosphorus on initial level had similar slope values for different dose levels of the hormone. This adjustment corrects all responses for an initial value of 9.15 mg. %, the mean value obtained by these authors. The log ratio of the potencies of the unknown and standard preparation is then calculated by the standard procedure using a modification which incorporates the use of a predetermined standard curve. This modification involves a test of parallelism of the regression lines for each preparation and correction for any difference which may be found before calculating the variances of the mean response to the test sample.

The potency of the unknown sample and its standard error can then be calculated. A sample assayed in this way gave a value of 173 U.S.P. units per milligram of nitrogen with a standard error of ±33 U.S.P. units.

In view of the crudity of many of the preparations these workers were testing, such a method was adequate, but they also describe in detail the complete assay mentioned earlier in which Yates's design of "symmetrical pairs" is used. This design enables the rat serum phosphorus method to give results comparable with the results obtained by Bliss and Rose

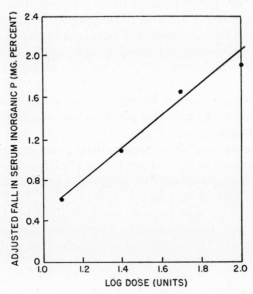

FIG. 2. Dose-response curve obtained on rats using parathyroid hormone to produce a fall in serum inorganic phosphorus (Tepperman *et al.,* 1947).

(1940) by the dog method, but with much less technical effort and expense. In an experiment using 12 rats in the symmetrical pairs design calculation of confidence limits ($P = 0.95$) indicated that upon repetition, only 1 assay in 20 would be expected to give an estimate outside the limits 60–142%, the potency being 93% of that of the standard in this case. In Bliss and Rose's experiments 36 dogs gave confidence limits of 87–140% at $P = 0.95$ when the standard and unknown were of identical potency. The use of the same number of rats, therefore, should produce results of accuracy comparable to those of the dog method.

The methods were found to be successful only with fed rats, the fall in serum inorganic phosphate being erratic and ill defined in fasted animals. This has not been further reported upon but may mean that increased sensitivity could be produced by dietary modifications.

D. METHODS BASED ON THE URINARY EXCRETION OF PHOSPHATE

Since it had been claimed (Stewart and Bowen, 1952) that the two actions of parathyroid preparations in causing an elevation of plasma calcium and inhibiting the renal reabsorption of phosphate are chemically separable, Davies and her colleagues (1955) examined assay methods based on phosphate excretion in the urine. They studied the increase of urinary phosphate excretion which occurs during a period of $3\frac{1}{2}$ hours following the injection of parathyroid hormone.

Using albino mice weighing 20–25 gm. and hydrated by giving 1 ml. of 0.9% saline intraperitoneally per 5 gm. of body weight at the commencement of the experiment, these workers collected urine from 15 minutes to $3\frac{1}{4}$ hours after giving parathyroid extracts subcutaneously. They showed that the output of phosphate was high when the urine volume was high and therefore they devised a correction for the milligrams of phosphorus excreted per hour, to remove the dependence of this upon urine volume. The use of this correction gave higher slope values, smaller error variance, and smaller limits of error to the estimate of potency. It was shown that this assay was better than that of Tepperman *et al.* (1947) on the fall in serum phosphate in the rat and comparable in accuracy with the dog plasma calcium assay or the parathyroidectomized rat plasma calcium assay. Davies *et al.* (1955) used this method to study the ratio of renal phosphate activity/calcium mobilizing activity for various different parathyroid extracts. They found that this ratio differed in these cases from that given by Parathormone and they suggest that standardization in terms of both activities is desirable.

The use of radiophosphorus (P^{32}) excretion as a basis for an assay technique was suggested by Tweedy *et al.* (1947) and this method was examined by Rubin and Dorfman (1953) who showed that the use of thyroparathyroidectomized rats given P^{32} enabled doses of 0.5 U.S.P. unit or more of parathyroid hormone to be detected.

These authors collected the urine for 3 hours and pointed out that the elimination of tedious chemical work and the increased sensitivity over the plasma calcium dog method, together with the rapidity of this method were features which render it an improvement over those previously described.

It would seem that the mouse phosphate excretion method of Davies *et al.* (1955) could be simplified by using radioactive phosphate in this way in preference to chemical estimation.

E. Methods Based on the Urinary Excretion of Calcium

In some preliminary experiments with parathyroid hormone Dyer (1932) found an increase in calcium excretion in the urine of the rat and tentatively suggested that this might form the basis for a method of assay. Later, however, Dyer performed a number of experiments in which no rise in calcium excretion was observed, and this observation was also made by Pugsley (1932) who found that daily injections of the hormone were necessary to ensure a rise in urinary calcium.

In a later paper Dyer (1933) described further experiments in which he used rats weighing from 120 to 160 gm. in groups of 10 animals and fed upon a diet containing 1% calcium carbonate. The effect of para-thyroid extract was much greater with the high calcium diet. The rats were housed in groups of 5 in metabolism cages with a mesh floor and a device to separate the urine from the feces. After an initial period of 4 days, during which daily estimations were made of the calcium excreted in the urine, injections of parathyroid extract were made once daily for 3 successive days and the urinary calcium excretion was again determined each day and for the fourth day. The normal excretion for such a group of rats Dyer found to be approximately 1.3 mg. per day, and this rose to 7.8 mg. per day when the parathyroid hormone was injected.

The test as Dyer used it comprised two groups of at least 5 rats, and he used one group for each of the materials under comparison. The doses used were 0.4 ml. of an extract equivalent to Parathormone (Lilly), and by retaining the rats for a further period of 4 days after the last injection it was possible to perform a cross-over test by giving the two samples to opposite groups for another period of 3 days.

The relationship between the dose of parathyroid hormone and the rise in calcium excretion had not been fully established but available evidence indicated it to be a linear one.

Truszkowski et al. (1939) reinvestigated methods for the assay of parathyroid hormone and considered that Dyer's method could be useful. They used larger rats weighing 150–200 gm. and housed them in groups of 5 in glass metabolism cages. The diet used in this case contained ap-proximately 0.3% of calcium carbonate and was fed to the rats in different cages once daily.

These workers found the normal calcium excretion to be 0.404 mg./ 100 gm. per day and they showed that the standard deviation of the dif-ference between two groups treated at the same time was less than half that for the same animals at different times; so, they suggested that the rise in the difference in calcium excretion between two similar groups of rats at the same time is more significant than for the same group of rats at different times.

The method favored by Truszkowski and his colleagues, therefore, was to record the daily excretion of calcium for about 7 days and then to give an injection of parathyroid hormone to one of two groups. This produced a steep rise in calcium output followed by a rapid fall, and the extra excretion was complete in 72 hours. The control group was then used to provide a base line for the treated group, and the area of the curve due to the injection of parathyroid hormone was plotted against the dose given.

It was shown that there was a linear dose-response relationship for a 6X change in dose, although the exact doses given cannot be stated since the extract used was not described in terms of a unit but given by weight.

Divided doses were tried, but although the response obtained was greater Truszkowski *et al.* did not consider the increase outweighed the extra work involved.

F. Gellhorn's Work with Parathyroid Hormone on Hypodynamic Muscle

A survey of methods for the assay of parathyroid hormone could hardly fail to include the interesting observations made by Gellhorn (1935) which might be adapted for assay purposes.

Skeletal muscle is highly sensitive to calcium ions when in a hypodynamic state, and Gellhorn set up hind-limb preparations of *Rana esculenta* arranged for perfusion through the abdominal aorta, and in some experiments each limb separately via the iliac arteries. The tendons of the gastrocnemius muscles were attached to isotonic levers magnifying the contraction 7 times. Nerve stimulation was by condensor discharges at a rate of 40 per minute until the height of contraction was reduced by 50%. After 15–30 minutes rest, stimulation was resumed at 15 per minute and the preparation was used for experiments as soon as it had settled to a steady response.

Gellhorn used dilutions of 1 in 100 to 1 in 1000 of Parathormone (Lilly; 20 Collip units per milliliter) in phosphate-buffered Ringer's solution of pH 7.2 and found that there was always an increase in the height of contraction and this increase was graded according to the concentration of the hormone.

The effect took about 2–5 minutes to commence, and periods of 5–10 minutes stimulation were used alternately with the same periods of rest. Gellhorn did not find this effect when the hormone was inactivated and, although it had been shown earlier that similar effects could be produced by calcium ions this was not the mechanism in Gellhorn's experiments. He therefore concluded that the hormone aided recovery from fatigue and augmented the height of contraction by its action in raising the calcium level.

The method has not been developed for assay purposes but might well be worthy of further consideration as it would have the advantage of being a much quicker method than any of the others described in this chapter.

In conclusion it would seem that the methods used by Davies *et al.* (1954, 1955) based upon the rise of plasma calcium in the parathyroidectomized rat and the excretion of phosphate in the mouse, provide the simplest and least expensive methods presently available.

References

Allardyce, W. J. (1931). *Am. J. Physiol.* **98**, 417.

Bauman, E. J., and Sprinson, D. B. (1940). *Proc. Soc. Exptl. Biol. Med.* **44**, 407.

Biering, A. (1950). *Acta Pharmacol. Toxicol.* **6**, 59.

Bliss, C. I., and Marks, H. P. (1939a). *Quart. J. Pharm. and Pharmacol.* **12**, 82.

Bliss, C. I., and Marks, H. P. (1939b). *Quart. J. Pharm. and Pharmacol.* **12**, 182.

Bliss, C. I., and Rose, C. L. (1940). *Am. J. Hyg.* **31**, 79.

Collip, J. B., and Clark, E. P. (1925). *J. Biol. Chem.* **64**, 485.

Davies, B. M. A., and Gordon, A. H. (1953). *J. Endocrinol.* **9**, 292.

Davies, B. M. A., Gordon, A. H., and Mussett, M. V. (1954). *J. Physiol.* (*London*) **125**, 383.

Davies, B. M. A., Gordon, A. H., and Mussett, M. V. (1955). *J. Physiol* (*London*) **130**, 79.

Dyer, F. J. (1932). *J. Physiol.* (*London*) **75**, 13P.

Dyer, F. J. (1933). *Quart. J. Pharm. and Pharmacol.* **6**, 426.

Dyer, F. J. (1935a). *Quart. J. Pharm. and Pharmacol.* **8**, 197.

Dyer, F. J. (1935b). *Quart. J. Pharm. and Pharmacol.* **8**, 513.

Dyer, F. J. (1936). *J. Physiol.* (*London*) **86**, 3P.

Gellhorn, E. (1935). *Am. J. Physiol.* **111**, 466.

Hamilton, B., and Highman, W. J., Jr. (1936). *J. Clin. Invest.* **15**, 99.

Hamilton, B., and Schwartz, C. (1932). *J. Pharmacol. Exptl. Therap.* **46**, 285.

Hanson, A. M. (1928). *J. Am. Med. Assoc.* **90**, 747.

L'Heureux, M. V., Tepperman, H. M., and Wilhelmi, A. E. (1947). *J. Biol. Chem.* **168**, 167.

Meltzer, S. J., and Auer, J. (1905). *Am. J. Physiol.* **14**, 361.

Meltzer, S. J., and Auer, J. (1908). *Zentr. Physiol.* **21**, 788.

Meltzer, S. J., and Auer, J. (1913). *Zentr. Physiol.* **27**, 632.

Miller, L. C. (1938). *J. Am. Pharm. Assoc., Sci. Ed.* **27**, 90.

Pugsley, L. I. (1932). *J. Physiol.* (*London*) **76**, 315.

Rasmussen, H., and Westall, R. G. (1956). *Nature* **178**, 1173.

Ross, W. F., and Wood, T. R. (1942). *J. Biol. Chem.* **146**, 49.

Rubin, B. L., and Dorfman, R. I. (1953). *Proc. Soc. Exptl. Biol. Med.* **83**, 223.

Simon, A. (1935). *Arch. exptl. Pathol. Pharmakol., Naunyn-Schmiedeberg's* **178**, 57.

Stewart, G. S., and Bowen, H. F. (1952). *Endocrinology* **51,** 80.

Tepperman, H. M., L'Heureux, M. V., and Wilhelmi, A. E. (1947). *J. Biol. Chem.* **168,** 151.

Truszkowski, R., Blauth-Opieńska, J., and Iwanowska, J. (1939). *Biochem. J.* **33,** 1, 1005.

Tweedy, W. R., and Chandler, S. B. (1929). *Am. J. Physiol.* **88,** 754.

Tweedy, W. R., Chilcote, M. E., and Patras, M. C. (1947). *J. Biol. Chem.* **168,** 597.

U. S. Pharmacopoeia. Eleventh and Sixteenth Revisions. Mack Publ. Co., Easton, Pennsylvania.

Wokes, F. (1931). *J. Pharmacol. Exptl. Therap.* **43,** 531.

Yates, F. (1936). *Ann. Eugenics.* **7,** 121.

Chapter 14

Posterior Pituitary Hormones

R. H. Thorp

I. Introduction

In 1928 Kamm and his colleagues prepared fractions of posterior pituitary extract with nearly complete separation of the oxytocic and pressor components and Livermore and du Vigneaud (1949) isolated pure oxytocin from the pituitary gland some 20 years later. This substance was later synthesized by du Vigneaud and his colleagues (1953) and a method was developed for the synthesis of oxytocin on a commercial scale by Boissonnas *et al.* (1955) so that it is now available for therapeutic use in this form.

Vasopressin was also studied by du Vigneaud *et al.* (1953) who showed that both of these substances were octapeptide amides differing only in the nature of two of the amino acids present.

The chemical structures of vasopressin and oxytocin are discussed in a monograph by Berde (1959) who also reviews the work on the relation between chemical structure and pharmacological activity in these compounds and their synthetic analogs.

Since the two compounds oxytocin and vasopressin are so closely related chemically it is not surprising that pure vasopressin possesses some oxytocic activity and vice versa (van Dyke *et al.*, 1955).

Correlated with the chemical studies on these hormones from the posterior pituitary gland, improved assay methods have been developed and more extensive pharmacological studies have been made.

Both the U. S. Pharmacopeia (1960) and the British Pharmacopeia (1958) now recommend for the assay of oxytocin a procedure based upon the method described by Coon (1939) using the depressor response in the anesthetized chicken as a commercial assay method although the British Pharmacopeia also suggests the isolated rat uterus preparation of Holton (1948) as an alternative method.

Earlier methods involving the use of the isolated uterus of the guinea pig are now superseded since this preparation often proved erratic and unreliable and was incapable of giving a sufficient number of responses to permit of adequate statistical analysis being applied to the results.

These two official methods can be regarded as the basic assay technique for the control of oxytocin preparations industrially, and methods based on the elevation of the rat blood pressure or the antidiuretic response in rats serve a similar purpose in the case of vasopressin.

None of these official methods is very sensitive and they are unsuitable for the estimation of very small quantities of these hormones in blood or biological fluids, but methods have been developed for studies of this kind and these are considered separately. The use of paper chromatography as a preliminary means of purifying the preparations has recently been introduced and has enabled further increases in sensitivity to be made.

II. Standard Preparations

A. International Standard

In order to achieve uniformity, an international standard was set up for posterior pituitary lobe extracts in 1925 from a powder prepared by Smith and McClosky (1924), but at this time any worker was permitted to prepare a similar powder using the methods described by these workers and to regard such a preparation as equivalent to the international standard.

In 1935 it was decided by the Commission on Biological Standardisation of the Health Organisation of the League of Nations to have only one international standard and the material is now held at national centers in the various countries concerned. The international standard has an activity of 2000 units per gram and the unit is defined as the activity of 0.5 mg. of this material both for oxytocic and pressor assays.

B. Preparation of Subsidiary Standard

It is sometimes convenient to prepare material for use as a subsidiary standard, particularly in a laboratory concerned with the large-scale preparation of extracts of posterior pituitary lobe for clinical use. The following method can conveniently be employed.

The pituitary glands should be collected as fresh as possible at a slaughter house and frozen in a jar surrounded by solid carbon dioxide. Upon arrival in the laboratory the posterior lobes are dissected from the remainder of the gland. This is not very easily done unless the glands are allowed to thaw a little as there is an optimum hardness at which the removal is most readily accomplished. The posterior lobes are then placed in cold acetone using about 4 ml. for each lobe and keeping the container surrounded by refrigerant. After about 3 hours the lobes can be cut up and transferred to a similar volume of fresh acetone and left overnight. The acetone is then poured off and the glandular material dried in a desiccator over phosphorus pentoxide. The dried material is next powdered to the size of a No. 40 mesh sieve and further dried in the desiccator. Fat removal is next completed by extraction with pure acetone in a Soxhlet extractor for 3 hours and, after drying, the powder may be stored in a desiccator or in sealed tubes at a low temperature. After adequate assays in comparison with the international standard preparation, such material may be adopted as a working standard for the particular laboratory. It is unlikely to be as potent as the international standard but the activity of 1200 to 1600 units per gram is typical of powders prepared in this way.

C. Preparation of Standard Extracts

In order to use the standard preparations an extract must be prepared by weighing out a portion of the solid of approximately 10 mg. in a stoppered weighing bottle and taking great care to avoid undue exposure of the powder to air in view of its hygroscopic nature (Gaddum, 1927). The weighed sample of the powder is then transferred quantitatively to a hard-glass boiling tube with the aid of 0.25% acetic acid and the volume adjusted to 1 ml. for each milligram of the powder. The tube is plugged with cotton wool and placed in a boiling water bath for 2 minutes, cooled, and the contents filtered through a small filter paper. The filtrate contains an activity of 2 units per milliliter. It is essential to prepare the standard extract in exactly this way since slight variations produce differences which can be detected in differential assays of the component activities.

D. Potency of the Synthetic Substances

The potency of synthetic oxytocin is such that 1 mg. corresponds to 500 international units (I.U.) and for vasopressin 1 mg. is equivalent to 600 I.U.

III. Methods of Assay

The potency of the crude extract of posterior pituitary lobe can be assayed by means of any of the three characteristic properties described previously, although it is usual to assay simple extracts by means of the oxytocic action alone, especially as this is the action most frequently employed in therapeutics.

The methods of assay most commonly employed are the rat uterus assay and the chicken blood pressure method for oxytocic activity, the anesthetized rat method for pressor activity, and the delay in water diuresis in the rat for the antidiuretic activity. There are various more recent methods and modifications of the standard ones which are described in proximity to the description of the relevant usual methods.

A. The Isolated Rat Uterus Method

This method comprises a comparison of the action of the test and standard preparations upon rat uterine muscle suspended in a modified Ringer's solution and arranged to record quantitatively changes in length upon a kymograph.

A convenient arrangement of the apparatus is shown in Fig. 1 and consists of a water bath surrounding 2 glass inner vessels in which the muscle strips are suspended. The apparatus illustrated uses a 250-watt immersion heater controlled by a bimetal thermoregulator, and the bath capacity is about 10 liters. The temperature in the outer bath is thus regulated to 32°C. with a differential of approximately ±0.5°C., and the mixing of the water is achieved by aeration through a metal tube perforated with a number of small holes and extending the full width of the bath.

The inner vessels may be of any convenient size but those depicted hold approximately 20 ml. Filling and emptying is controlled by glass stopcocks and there is a glass spiral of large capacity in the outer bath to ensure that the Ringer's solution enters the inner chambers already warmed.

The lower end of the uterine segment is held at the bottom of the bath by hooking it over a sharp prong on a bent glass tube which is also

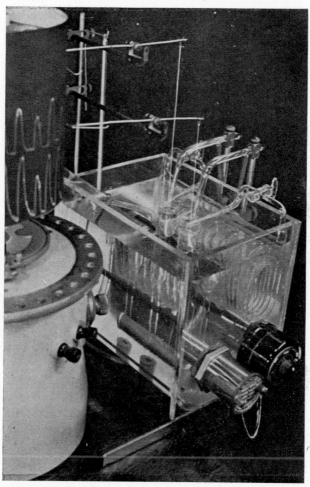

FIG. 1. General arrangement of isolated organ bath for use in rat uterus assay of oxytocic activity.

used to oxygenate the saline solution. The upper end of the uterus is attached by cotton to an isotonic frontal-writing level recording on a kymograph. The lever should have a magnification of about $4\times$ and should load the uterus to about 1.2 gm.

The composition of the Ringer's solution used in this assay is as follows:

Sodium chloride (NaCl)	9.00	gm.
Potassium chloride (KCl)	0.42	gm.
Calcium chloride (CaCl$_2$)	0.12	gm.
Sodium bicarbonate (NaHCO$_3$)	0.5	gm.
Dextrose	0.25	gm.
Magnesium chloride (MgCl$_2$)	0.0025	gm.
Water to	1.0	liter

The distilled water used should preferably be obtained by condensation in glass although a stainless steel condenser tube gives satisfactory results also. It is essential to avoid contamination with copper and alloys containing copper since this element is quite toxic to preparations of this kind.

The solution is oxygenated with a mixture of 95% oxygen and 5% carbon dioxide (carbogen). To set up the preparation a female rat in diestrus, weighing between 120 and 200 gm. is killed and one horn of the uterus is suspended in each of the baths thus allowing a duplicate assay to be performed. Two dilutions of the standard preparation are then found which produce clearly discriminated submaximal contractions and when these are complete the solution in the bath is replaced by fresh solution and the muscle allowed to relax. The unknown solution is then diluted suitably to give 2 responses similar to those obtained with the standard when similar volumes are added to the bath.

The ratio between the high and low doses of both the test preparation and the standard should be the same and must be kept constant throughout the assay.

The two doses of the standard preparation and the two doses of that under test are then given in random order and at least 4 responses to each dose are recorded. It is usually found that these may be given at intervals of 3 to 5 minutes depending on the rate of relaxation of the muscle. The responses are then measured on the kymograph record and the result of the assay is calculated by the standard statistical methods applicable to a (2 + 2) dose assay.

This method was originally described by Holton (1948) who found that, out of 9 rats, 6 gave good responses. The doses of pituitary extract were given at intervals of 3 or 4 minutes and 2 doses were found, such that the contraction for the higher dose was at least twice as great as that of the lower. The ratio usually employed for these 2 doses was 4:3, but only contractions below 80% of the maximal could be employed in order to ensure a linear relationship between response and log dose. Little trouble was experienced due to spontaneous contractions, but when these did occur they were often overcome by reducing the temperature of the bath, or the interval between successive doses.

One of Holton's tracings is reproduced in Fig. 2 and shows the results obtained in one assay. This method enables an estimate of potency to

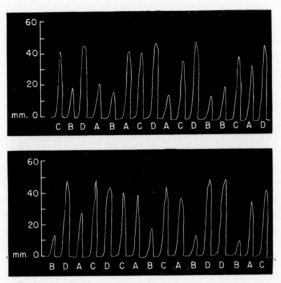

FIG. 2. An assay of posterior pituitary extract on the isolated rat uterus. The record shows 32 recordings of the contraction of the uterus in response to 4 different doses of posterior pituitary extract A, B, C, and D, each of which is given once in each group of 4 contractions. A = 0.05 units, B = 0.04 units, C = 0.064 units, and D = 0.08 units. B and C were regarded as "standard" and A and D as "unknown." A/D = B/C = ⅘. Estimate of unknown/standard = 1.25. True value unknown/standard = 1.25. A dose was put into the bath every 4 minutes and washed out after 45 seconds. The temperature of the bath was 34–36°C. and the load on the uterus (from a 140-gm. rat) was 1.3 gm. (Holton, 1948).

be obtained with an integral determination of the slope of the dose-response curve. The error of the assay is calculated by variance analysis, and the slopes of the dose-response curves for the standard and test preparations are tested for concordance. The calculated standard error for a series of 8 assays, using this method, was 2.84%, approximately half the value found by Gaddum (1938) for the older guinea pig uterine assay.

B. The Chicken Depressor Method

Of the methods for oxytocic activity other than by uterine contraction the principal research has been upon the utilization of the transient fall of blood pressure which oxytocin produces upon injection into birds. This phenomenon was first observed by Paton and Watson (1912) after the injection of pituitary extracts and was attributed principally to oxytocin by Gaddum (1928). The development of an assay method on this basis was due to Coon (1939); the method produces results very close to those of the older guinea pig uterus method and is quicker and technically more simple. Coon described the following technique which has proved very satisfactory and is the basis of the assay method of the British Pharmacopeia (1958).

White Leghorn chickens are used weighing 1.8–2.2 kg., although owing to difficulties of supply, the author has used Light Sussex birds, of a similar weight, satisfactorily, whereas Rhode Island Reds proved of little use. The bird is anesthetized by intravenous injection of 200 mg. per kilogram of sodium phenobarbital via the brachial vein and arranged for recording blood pressure from the ischiadic artery. The ischiadic artery is exposed by removing the feathers from the outer surface of the left thigh, an incision 7–8 cm. long is made in the skin, parallel to and about 1.5 cm. below the femur, exposing the gluteus primus muscle. The lower edge of this incision is retracted to expose the edge of the gluteus primus muscle overlying the semitendinosis muscle. This edge is then freed for the length of the incision, and when the free edge is lifted, the ischiadic artery, ischiadic vein, and crural vein can be seen lying along the edge of semitendinosus muscle. The gluteus primus muscle is cut at right angles near the proximal end of the incision and the resulting flap deflected and secured to the upper thigh. Lengths of the ischiadic artery and crural vein are dissected free and the artery cannulated.

For recording blood pressure a mercury manometer may be used with an inside diameter of 2.5 to 3 mm. using a hollow ebonite float to operate the recorder pointer, as anticoagulant a 5–8.5% solution of sodium citrate is employed to fill the manometer. The blood pressure recorded should be approximately 105 mm. Hg and will quickly settle down to a constant level. It is convenient to use a slow-moving recording drum with a surface speed of approximately 1 cm. per minute, since injections are made every 3–5 minutes. Injections are made directly into the crural vein by means of a 1-ml. tuberculin syringe and fine needle, using the same puncture hole for subsequent injections, covering it with a pledget of absorbent cotton between each pair of injections. The standard posterior pituitary extract (2 units per milliliter) is diluted 1 in 10 with 0.9% saline and such injections made that a graded fall in blood pressure results from graded doses. The illustration of Fig. 3 from Coon's paper shows the effects observed in a good preparation. The fall in blood pressure should be between 20 and 40 mm. Hg. A suitable dose for preliminary trial should be 0.2 ml. of the diluted extract. After a suitable dose has been determined, doses of the test and standard can be injected at 3- to 5-minute intervals according to the suitability of the bird. The doses can be injected in any suitably arranged sequence. Coon endeavored to produce matched responses and to obtain the potency of the unknown sample by direct comparison, but a suitable experimental arrangement is a random block design with 2 doses of the test and standard preparations as used in the rat uterine assay.

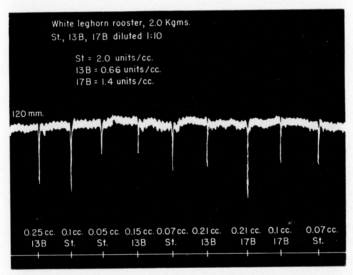

FIG. 3. A typical tracing of the assay of 2 unknown samples of posterior pituitary extract by the chicken depressor method. Injections were given at intervals of 3 to 4 minutes (Coon, 1939).

Further work on this method has been reported by Smith (1942) and Smith and Vos (1943) and most recently by Thompson (1944). Smith and Vos showed that the depressor response in the chicken increases linearly with the logarithm of the dose of pituitary extract given, and they used a randomized arrangement similar to that referred to above. Since this arrangement eliminates the variations in sensitivity over long periods of time, but is still subject to influence by changes in sensitivity within the period of an individual group of 4 doses, Thompson (1944) made use of an experimental design developed by Vos (1943) for use in the assay of ergonovine upon the rabbit uterus. In this arrangement, the dose of the standard preparation is kept constant and administered alternately with three varied doses of the test sample giving responses above, below, and equivalent to that of the standard. The dose of the test preparation giving a response greater than that of the standard should not be more than twice as great as the dose producing the smallest response. This assay must be run to an accurate time schedule and an interval of 3 minutes between doses is recommended unless this allows insufficient time for the blood pressure to return to normal between doses. The accuracy obtained by Smith and Vos was such that a mean error of 6.9% was obtained using "unknown" dilutions from a standard preparation, and results obtained by Thompson showed even better agreement.

Coon found that the presence of large amounts of vasopressin caused a secondary rise in blood pressure, after the initial fall, but this did not introduce appreciable errors with pressor to oxytocic ratios of less than 4:1. In addition to this secondary pressor action, however, the presence of large amounts of the pressor principle was shown to produce some degree of enhancement of the oxytocic depressor response. A slightly higher apparent potency would therefore be obtained in comparison with the isolated uterus preparation. In practice it was found that ratios of pressor to oxytocic principle of less than 2.5:1 did not produce significant deviation from the uterine value. As the assay continues, the animal becomes tolerant to the depressor response, and it may be advisable to leave the bird to recover for an hour or so, if the sensitivity becomes greatly reduced. If the blood pressure falls to an undesirably low level the injection of 4 to 8 mg. per kilogram of ephedrine sulfate frequently restores the pressure to a useful level. A chicken prepared in this way can constitute a stable preparation for 6 to 12 hours and may be used to assay several unknown samples, and approximately 90% of these preparations prove suitable for assay purposes.

C. Other Methods for Oxytocic Activity

For estimation of oxytocin in extracts rich in this hormone the methods just described are very suitable, but since vasopressin has quite a strong oxytocic effect as shown by van Dyke and his colleagues (1955) (see Table I) allowance must be made for this where the quantity of vasopressin is likely to be appreciable. Robertson (1960) uses the rat uterus assay for the estimation of oxytocin in hypothalamic and pituitary extracts and is able to estimate 0.25 mU. added to a 5-ml. bath using uteri from rats pretreated with stilbestrol.

1. Superfusion Preparation of Isolated Rat Uterus

Gaddum (1953) described a process of superfusion of the rat uterus suitable for the assay of oxytocin in which the effective dose is about 0.02 mU. This method consisted of suspending a segment of rat uterus

TABLE I

POTENCY OF PURIFIED OXYTOCIN AND VASOPRESSIN IN TERMS
OF INTERNATIONAL STANDARD[a]

(All figures are U.S.P. units per milligram)

	Oxytocic (rat uterus)	Avian depressor (fowl)	Milk-ejecting (rabbit)	Pressor (rat)	Antidiuretic (dog)
Oxytocin	500	500	500	7	3
Vasopressin	30	85	100	600	600

[a] van Dyke *et al.* (1955).

in a warmed bath similar to the arrangement used by Holton (1948) but without the saline solution bathing the tissue. Down the thread attaching the muscle to the writing lever a steady flow of 1 to 5 ml. per minute of solution (Gaddum *et al.*, 1949) was arranged from a glass tube having a spoon-shaped tip and to this tip is added the substance under test in a volume of 0.2 ml. The flow of saline solution is turned off during the period (10–60 seconds) in which the drug is allowed to act on the muscle. The uteri which Gaddum used were taken from rats prepared by the injection of stilbestrol (0.1 mg. per kilogram) the day before the experiment.

2. Milk-Ejection in the Lactating Rabbit

Another sensitive method for the estimation of oxytocin makes use of the milk-ejecting property of oxytocin in the lactating rabbit but in this test vasopressin also shows appreciable activity and is approximately one-sixth as active as oxytocin (Cross and van Dyke, 1953) so that content of vasopressin must be known.

This method is very specific and a dose of 0.5 mU. can be detected after intravenous injection into an anesthetized lactating rabbit weighing 1.8 kg.

The method is fully described by van Dyke and his colleagues (1955) and makes use of rabbits in lactation anesthetized with urethan and pentobarbital. One of the ducts in the rabbit's nipple is cannulated with a hypodermic needle connected to a condenser manometer of high sensitivity. The apparatus used by these workers was such that 1 mm. on the record corresponded to a pressure of 0.4 mm. of water at maximum sensitivity. Figure 4 shows a record obtained in such an assay and illustrates the degree of discrimination which is given between doses of 0.5, 0.75, and 1.0 mU. of standard posterior pituitary extract.

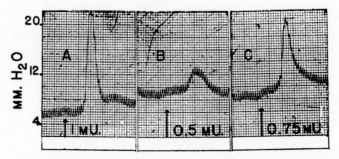

Fig. 4. The effect of intravenous injection of standard posterior pituitary extract on the pressure in the lactating mammary gland of the rabbit which weighed 1.8 kg. and was in the eighth day of lactation. The small regular waves represent respiratory movements. 1 mm. on the abscissa = 2 seconds; 1 mm. ordinate = 0.4 mm. water pressure.

3. Sources of Error in Oxytocic Assays

It has been shown by a number of workers that the concentration of magnesium in the saline solution bathing isolated organs used for the assay of preparations of oxytocin can influence the result obtained when the preparation also contains vasopressin. Stewart (1949) showed that the guinea pig uterus assay for oxytocic activity could give results which were quite erroneous when the concentration of vasopressin in the mixture was high. He examined mixtures in which the oxytocin:vasopressin ratio varied from 4:1 to 1:4 but in each case the oxytocic potency was known. When Stewart used the Ringer's solution (British Pharmacopeia, 1948) prescribed for the assay he obtained very good agreement between the assay result and the known values but when extra magnesium was added to the Ringer's solution errors up to 25% high were observed when the ratio of oxytocin:vasopressin was less than 1:1.

The effect of magnesium concentration upon the rat uterus preparation has recently been examined by Munsick (1960) who, using pure oxytocin and vasopressin provided by du Vigneaud *et al.* (1953), showed that arginine vasopressin which has an oxytocic potency of 9 U. per milligram in the absence of magnesium, 15 U. per milligram in 0.5 mM per liter of magnesium, 42 U. per milligram in the chicken depressor assay and 51 U. per milligram by the rabbit milk-ejection reaction gave the least oxytocic action in the absence of magnesium. Munsick recommends that the rat uterus preparation under these circumstances is the most specific assay for oxytocin. In these experiments Munsick (1960) showed that valyl oxytocin was most potentiated by magnesium but since this sample was an impure analog he did not attach great importance to this result. He also pointed out that assays performed with and without magnesium added to the bath could provide a useful qualitative tool since oxytocin is the only octapeptide not showing increased potency in the presence of this ion.

D. Methods for the Determination of Pressor Activity

For the assay of vasopressin by its pressor properties 3 animal preparations may be used; the spinal cat, the anesthetized dog, and the anesthetized or spinal rat. The rat preparation is the most economical, sensitive, and reliable of these and this forms the basis of the official methods described in the British Pharmacopeia (1958) and the U. S. Pharmacopeia (XVI revision) and is the method of choice today.

In view of the expense and protracted nature of assays upon cats or dogs, attempts have been made to use the rat for this purpose, and this work has largely been described by Landgrebe et al. (1946). These workers used anesthetized male rats and in some cases spinal animals and found the following procedure to be the most satisfactory.

Rats weighing more than 380 gm. and preferably above 450 gm. should be used and are anesthetized with 0.3 ml. per kilogram of "Dial" liquid intraperitoneally ("Dial" Ciba, or a liquid prepared by taking 0.4 gm. monoethyl urea, 0.4 gm. urethan, 0.1 gm. diallylbarbituric acid and making up to 1 ml. with water). The animal is kept warm and given a total of 400 to 500 mg. of urethan in doses of 100 mg. after an interval of 1 or 2 hours. After a further 30 minutes the animal is prepared for operation on a warm table, keeping the rectal temperature at 33°C. The trachea is cannulated and the pharyngeal extremity plugged with cotton wool, and the vagi and associated spinal nerves are cut. The central nervous system is next pithed caudally from the anterior tip of the pelvic girdle to eliminate fluctuations of the blood pressure when injections are made via the femoral vein. The femoral vein is then cannulated for injection and 1–2 mg. of heparin is injected. One carotid artery is next ligated, and the second is cannulated and arranged for recording the blood pressure by means of a narrow-bore mercury manometer, using 3.8% sodium citrate as an anticoagulant. The preparation is next given 12–18 mg. of soluble pentobarbitone by the venous cannula, and artificial respiration is given at 40 strokes per minute. Pentobarbitone in that dosage causes cessation of normal respiration without increasing the degree of general anesthesia or lessening the blood pressure. The pituitary preparation is injected at 15-minute intervals via the venous cannula, and the authors suggest the arrangement illustrated in Fig. 5, which ensures that the whole of a dose of a hormone is washed into circulation.

Animals prepared in this way have a relatively steady blood pressure

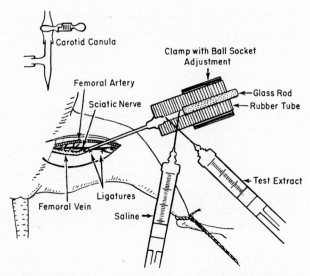

Fig. 5. Details of the apparatus and femoral cannulation in the pressor assay of vasopressin on the rat. The external and internal diameters of the carotid cannula are 1.0 and 0.7 mm., respectively (Landgrebe *et al.*, 1946).

baseline and survive for 12 to 15 hours. Figure 6 from this paper shows the pressure difference produced by 30% changes in dose, and a 10% difference is usually easily discriminated even in the less sensitive preparations. Figure 7 shows the dose-response relationship for this preparation,

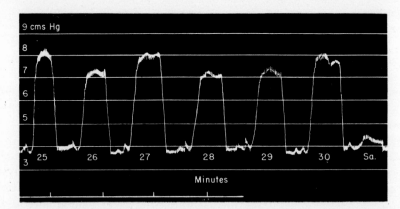

Fig. 6. Pressor responses to injection of posterior pituitary lobe extracts using the rat preparation (Landgrebe *et al.*, 1946).

KEY: 25 = 8 mU. posterior pituitary extract; 26 = 6 mU. posterior pituitary extract; 27 = 8 mU. posterior pituitary extract; 28 = 6 mU. posterior pituitary extract; 29 = 6 mU. posterior pituitary extract; 30 = 8 mU. posterior pituitary extract; Sa = 0.2 ml. saline.

and it will be seen that the best discrimination occurs between 6 and 8 mU. of posterior pituitary lobe extract. When much larger doses are given, up to 32 mU., irregular responses are produced but this effect is not normally serious since it only occurs with 4 to 5 times the most suitable dose.

The response of the rat preparation to histamine is small and hence the amount normally present in commercial powders is insufficient to interfere with the pressor assay. In fact, histamine contamination up to

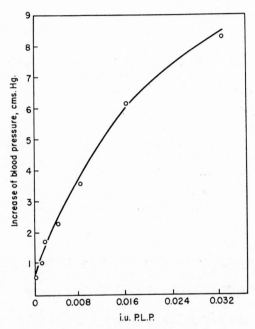

Fig. 7. Dose-response curve obtained for the pressor response in the rat using posterior pituitary lobe extract (Landgrebe *et al.*, 1946).

2% by weight in a posterior pituitary lobe powder has no effect upon the pressor assay. The rat preparation is normally 15–20 times as sensitive as a good spinal cat and will often detect 10% and certainly discriminate 20% dose intervals, which is again, as good or better than, the cat.

Dekanski (1952) has shown that the rat need not be pithed but that equally good results may be obtained by treatment with dibenzylamine ("Dibenamine"). For this modification the rat is anesthetized with urethan (175 mg. per kilogram) and the trachea is cannulated, the femoral vein is also cannulated for injection and heparin (2000 units per kilogram) is then given. The carotid artery is cannulated for the recording of blood pressure by means of a narrow-bore mercury manometer. Dibenzylamine is then injected in 2 doses of 100 μg./100 gm. of body weight at intervals of 10 minutes. The pressor effect of an injection of saline of 0.3 to 0.5 ml. should then be very reduced and if this does not occur a third dose of dibenzylamine should be given. Dekanski showed that doses of posterior pituitary standard ranging from 1 to 38 mU. gave a linear relationship between log dose and the increase in blood pressure. He suggests that doses of 4 to 12 mU. be given at intervals of 6 to 10 minutes and that the preparation can be used for up to 40 injections. An experimental arrangement such as the (2 + 2) assay design is again applicable to this preparation.

The procedure described in the U. S. Pharmacopeia is similar except that an injection of 10 mg. per kilogram of phenoxybenzamine hydrochloride is made about 18 hours previously. This injection is prepared by dissolving 5 mg. of phenoxybenzamine hydrochloride in 0.1 ml. of alcohol, adding one drop of sulfuric acid and diluting to 5 ml. with saline. The British Pharmacopeia has also adopted the rat blood pressure method as the official pressor assay but in this case hexamethonium is used to produce a level blood pressure of about 50 mm. Hg. and to abolish the volume effect of injected solutions. Doses of 6 to 10 mU. are suggested as a suitable range of dose of pituitary extract to be tried at the commencement of the assay.

E. Methods for the Determination of Antidiuretic Activity

The first attempt to utilize the antidiuretic activity of preparations from the posterior pituitary lobe as a method of biological assay was described by Gibbs (1930), using mice. Groups of 8 mice were used for these experiments and each animal was placed in a glass funnel on a gauze mesh disk and covered with a second funnel. Beneath each was placed a graduated cylinder for the collection of the urine. Each mouse was given an injection of warm tap water intraperitoneally and then 4 of the mice were given a dose of pituitary extract by subcutaneous injection. The actual dose Gibbs used is not exactly described but was presumably 0.1 ml. of a 10-unit per milliliter preparation. Gibbs indicated the flow of urine by one or more "+" signs and noted that after about 2 hours the control mice were excreting increasing quantities of urine whereas there was a marked delay in the urinary excretion of the pituitary treated mice.

Burn (1931) followed up this work and first suggested the use of rats instead of mice since the former animals could be used in a cross-over test, and also because they produce an easily measurable volume of urine, thus converting the method from a quantal to a continuous variate one.

The technique used by Burn employed a group of 16 male rats each weighing 120–240 gm. housed in gauze-floored cylindrical cages supported over large funnels with 4 rats in each cage. The rats were starved at least 12 hours before the test was commenced, although free access to water was still permitted. This procedure results in a greater change in the delay in diuresis with a given incremental change in dose, than is the case with rats fed up to the time of the experiment.

The rats were weighed for the test and given 5 ml./100 gm. of warm tap water by stomach tube. They were then given the dose of posterior pituitary extract by subcutaneous injection, placed in the cages, and the urine collected in 10-ml. graduated cylinders placed below the funnels. Time was recorded for each group from the mean time of injection of the pituitary preparation, and when the excretion of urine was first observed the amount produced was recorded every 15 minutes until it became consistently small.

Burn recorded these amounts in tabular form and determined the time of maximum water excretion by adding together the separate volumes, with the exception of the first collection, dividing by 2, and obtaining the corresponding time interval to this volume from the table. The first collection was rejected because it often occurred as an isolated urine excretion and not the forerunner of the main diuresis. The test was repeated 2 or 3 days later with the same group of animals in a crossover arrangement so that those which received the standard received the test and vice versa. This was done to compensate for any inherent difference in sensitivity between groups.

The relative potency of the unknown sample Burn determined from a graph for that particular colony of rats, by previous determinations of the time of diuresis delay with several known doses.

During the ensuing years many other workers have used and modified Burn's antidiuretic assay. Gilman and Goodman (1937) found that a more consistent response was obtained after the administration of a preliminary hydrating dose of water. This consisted of tap water in a volume equal to 2.5% of the body weight given by mouth, and, 3 hours later, at the commencement of the test, all urine previously collected was rejected and twice this dose of water was given at the same time as the dose of posterior pituitary lobe extract. Silvette (1940) gave a single dose of 10 ml. of 0.2% saline/100 gm. by intraperitoneal injection but used a method of calculation based upon the measurement of the total volume of urine excreted per 100 gm. of body weight during a period of 6 hours after the fluid intake. Krieger and Kilvington (1940) used a different method of interpretation again and actually plotted the amounts of urine after intervals of 15 minutes against time for a period of 6 hours from the fluid intake. They then measured the area enclosed by the curve with a planimeter and used this as the response criterion. They gave less water, using only 12 ml. for a rat weighing 200 gm. Robinson and Farr (1940) measured the time taken to excrete 2.5% of the original body weight of water.

It will be seen therefore that, at this time, there was a diversity of slight modifications but there was little evidence as to which was the most accurate.

Burn's method was re-examined by Ginsburg (1951) who pointed out that it had disadvantages in that the cross-over test could not be completed in less than 2 or 3 days and also the error of a single assay could not easily be calculated. Ginsburg modified the method so that it could be completed in 4 to $4\frac{1}{2}$ hours and described a statistical procedure for the calculation of the fiducial limits of the assay. The doses of the test material were given subcutaneously but Ginsburg and Heller (1953) then showed that intravenous injection is more satisfactory since it is free from tissue reactions and more sensitive. These workers inserted a cannula of polythene tubing into the right external jugular vein 18 hours before the test and externalized the end of the cannula between the ears of the rat. When the test was to be performed the rats were placed singly in metabolism cages and the cannula was extended to permit injections to be made without disturbing the animals. Each rat was next given 2 doses of water (5% of the body weight) by stomach tube at intervals of 50 minutes and the urinary output was measured at intervals of 10 minutes thereafter. For rats to be included in the test these workers required the urinary excretion to be at least 1.5 ml./10 minutes, and if this were so doses of vasopressin were given and washed in with 0.2 ml. of heparin solution in saline (10 U./ml. in 0.9% NaCl). The first injection was usually heparin solution alone and this should produce no antidiuresis. For the subcutaneous injection route Ginsburg (1951) found that 0.4 mU. of vasopressin would normally produce a satisfactory response whereas by the intravenous route Ginsburg and Heller (1953) state that significant antidiuretic responses were frequently observed with 12.5 μU./100 gm. of body weight. They usually gave doses greater than this and with a series of doses between 50 and 200 μU./100 gm. a graded response was obtained.

In these antidiuretic assays a most important point is to maintain a constant rate of urine flow during the control periods and although this is usually done by the repeated oral administration of water whenever the urine flow decreases this results in the assay being performed against a background of a gradually decreasing water load. Boura and Dicker (1953) therefore devised a very ingenious method whereby the water load could be maintained constant by using the urinary output to control the administration of water by stomach tube automatically and employing a correction for the extrarenal water loss. In this method records are made on a kymograph of each 0.1 ml. of urine excreted, the number of drops of urine flowing from the bladder catheter perunit time, and the deviation of body weight of the rat during the experiment. They showed a very level urinary output in their results and also a very clear antidiuretic effect with a dose of 5 μU./100 gm. of body weight.

Dicker in a subsequent paper (1953) described the use of this apparatus in the assay of small amounts of antidiuretic activity and showed that the useful range of the method was 3.5–50 μU./100 gm. of body weight. They also added ethanol to the water given to the rat since van Dyke and Ames (1951) had shown that ethanol suppresses the excretion of endogenous antidiuretic hormone. By using this technique the same dose of vasopressin produced a similar response each time, not only in the same animal, but in all the animals these workers used. This method is extremely elegant and undoubtedly represents a major advance in the assay of vasopressin. It forms the basis of the British Pharmacopeia (1958) assay for this hormone which follows:

A male rat weighing about 200 gm. is deprived of food but not water overnight. Next morning it is given by stomach tube 3 ml. of water per 100 gm. of body weight and, an hour later, 5 ml. of a 12% v/v solution of ethyl alcohol per 100 gm. of body weight. One hour after the dose of ethyl alcohol, a cannula is inserted in one of the jugular veins and a catheter in the bladder and a volume of water equal to the volume of urine excreted from the time the water was administered to the completion of the insertion of the catheter is given by the stomach tube, which is left in position. The rat is placed on the pan of a balance and the urine excreted is replaced by administering a 2.5% v/v solution of ethyl alcohol so as to maintain a constant water load throughout the assay. When the flow of urine has become steady, a dose of the standard preparation is injected into the jugular vein and the antidiuretic effect is calculated from the expression $100(a - b)/a$, where a is the volume of urine excreted in the 10 minutes lasting from the eighth minute before injection to the second minute after injection and b is the volume excreted in the 10 minutes lasting from the second to the twelfth minute after injection. The injection of the standard preparation is repeated several times if necessary until similar antidiuretic effects are obtained for equal doses. The rat is then ready for the assay.

Two dose levels of the standard preparation and 2 of the preparation being tested are used, the ratio of the high dose to the low dose being the same for each. Suggested doses are 0.01 and 0.02 mU./100 gm. of body weight.

A (2 + 2) dose assay of up to 3 groups may be conveniently run on the same animal provided that the volumes injected do not exceed 0.1 ml./100 gm. of body weight. The result is calculated by standard statistical methods.

F. CHROMATOGRAPHIC METHODS FOR THE SEPARATION OF OXYTOCIN ANV VASOPRESSIN PRIOR TO ASSAY

Recently studies have been made on the chromatography of hypophyseal polypeptides and Heller and Lederis (1958) reported a technique of paper chromatography using butanol/acetic acid/water in the ascending manner on Whatman No. 1 paper. After location of the spots by chlorination and spraying with potassium iodide-starch solution, (Reindel and Hoppe, 1954) these workers cut out and eluted spots from parallel chromatograms and assayed the extracts biologically using the isolated rat uterus method for oxytocin and the pressor response in the rat for vasopressin. They showed that 10 mU. of oxytocic or pressor activity could be eluted or assayed in this way.

Arimura and Dingman (1959) described an improved technic of chromatography for these substances which is complete in 30–50 minutes. They used glass-fiber paper strips (6 × 15 cm.) impregnated with silica acid according to the method of Dieckert *et al.* (1958), but with double the concentration of potassium silicate. The papers were dried at 150–200°C. and stored in a desiccator prior to use. Two different solvent mixtures were used, one for vasopressin comprising butanol, ethanol, and ammonium hydroxide in a ratio 60:30:10 (solvent A) and a second of *n*-amyl alcohol and acetic acid, 80:5, saturated with water (solvent B) for oxytocin.

The chromatograms were run by the ascending method in closed glass jars without previous equilibration and then dried by means of a fan and sprayed on the reverse side with Folin's phenol reagent which detects as little of 0.5 μg. of a polypeptide.

With solvent A synthetic oxytocin runs to the solvent front and lysine vasopressin gives a clear spot at R_f 0.71. With solvent B synthetic oxytocin showed two spots, one very faint at the solvent front and one very strong at R_f 0.71. "Pitressin" did not move at all and the spot remained at the starting line.

When 1.0-mU. spots of "Pitressin" or of synthetic oxytocin were applied to the paper and the appropriate areas eluted into Ringer solution for biological assay 93% of the activity of the "Pitressin" was recovered from the spot at R_f 0.71 corresponding to the lysine vasopressin, and 99% of the activity of synthetic oxytocin was recovered from the chromatogram in solvent B again at position R_f 0.71.

The biological assays were performed using Gaddum's superfused rat uterine strip for oxytocic assays and Dicker's antidiuretic method (1953) for vasopressin.

These authors conclude that quantities less than 1.0 mU. of each substance could be estimated after minor modifications of the method in view of the great sensitivity of the biological assays they employed.

REFERENCES

Arimura, A., and Dingman, J. F. (1959). *Nature* **184,** 1874.
Berde, B. (1959). "Recent Progress in Oxytocin Research," pp. 6–20. C. C. Thomas, Springfield, Illinois.
Boissonnas, R. A., Guttmann, S., Jaquenoud, P. A., and Waller, J. P. (1955). *Helv. Chim. Acta* **38,** 1491.
Boura, A., and Dicker, S. E. (1953). *J. Physiol. (London)* **122,** 144.
British Pharmacopeia (1958). Pharmaceutical Press, London.
Burn, J. H. (1931). *Quart. J. Pharm. and Pharmacol.* **4,** 517.
Coon, J. M. (1939). *Arch. intern. pharmacodynamie* **62,** 79.
Cross, B. A., and van Dyke, H. B. (1953). *J. Endocrinol.* **9,** 232.
Dekanski, J. (1952). *Brit. J. Pharmacol.* **7,** 567.
Dicker, S. E. (1953). *J. Physiol. (London)* **122,** 149.
Diekert, J. W., Carney, W. B., Ory, R. L., and Morris, N. J. (1958). *Anal. Chem.* **30,** 1442.
du Vigneaud, V., Ressler, C., Swan, J. M., Roberts, C. W., Katsoyannis, P. G., and Gordon, S. (1953). *J. Am. Chem. Soc.* **75,** 4879.
Gaddum, J. H. (1927). *Pharm. J.* **119,** 580.
Gaddum, J. H. (1928). *J. Physiol. (London)* **65,** 434.
Gaddum, J. H. (1938). *Quart. J. Pharm. and Pharmacol.* **11,** 697.
Gaddum, J. H. (1953). *Brit. J. Pharmacol.* **8,** 321.
Gaddum, J. H., Peart, W. S., and Vogt, M. (1949). *J. Physiol. (London)* **108,** 467.
Gibbs, O. S. (1930). *J. Pharmacol. Exptl. Therap.* **40,** 129.
Gilman, A., and Goodman, L. (1937). *J. Physiol. (London)* **90,** 113.
Ginsburg, M. (1951). *Brit. J. Pharmacol.* **6,** 411.
Ginsburg, M., and Heller, H. (1953). *J. Endocrinol.* **9,** 267.
Heller, H., and Lederis, K. (1958). *Nature* **182,** 1231.
Holton, P. (1948). *Brit. J. Pharmacol.* **3,** 328.
Kamm, O., Aldrich, T. B., Grotte, I. W., Rowe, L. W., and Bugbee, E. P. (1928). *J. Am. Chem. Soc.* **50,** 573.
Krieger, V. I., and Kilvington, T. B. (1940). *Med. J. Australia* **1,** 575.
Landgrebe, F. W., Macaulay, M. H. E., and Waring, H. (1946). *Proc. Roy. Soc. Edinburgh* **B62,** 202.
Livermore, A. H., and du Vigneaud, V. (1949). *J. Biol. Chem.* **180,** 365.
Munsick, R. A. (1960). *Endocrinology* **66,** 451.

Paton, D. N., and Watson, A. (1912). *J. Physiol. (London)* **44**, 413.

Reindel, F., and Hoppe, W. (1954). *Chem. Ber.* **87**, 1103.

Robertson, P. A. (1960). Personal communication.

Robinson, F. H., Jr., and Farr, L. E. (1940). *Ann. Internal Med.* **14**, 42.

Silvette, H. (1940). *Am. J. Physiol.* **128**, 747.

Smith, M. J., and McClosky, W. T. (1924). *Hyg. Lab. Bull.* **138**.

Smith, R. B., Jr. (1942). *J. Pharmacol. Exptl. Therap.* **75**, 342.

Smith, R. B., Jr., and Vos, B. J., Jr. (1943). *J. Pharmacol. Exptl. Therap.* **78**, 72.

Stewart, G. A. (1949). *J. Pharm. and Pharmacol.* **1**, 436.

Thompson, R. E. (1944). *J. Pharmacol. Exptl. Therap.* **80**, 373.

U. S. Pharmacopeia (1960). Sixteenth Revision. Mack Publ. Co., Easton, Pennsylvania.

van Dyke, H. B., and Ames, R. G. (1951). *Acta Endocrinol.* **7**, 110.

van Dyke, H. B., Adamsons, K., Jr., and Engel, S. L. (1955). *Recent Progr. in Hormone Research* **11**, 1.

Vos, B. J., Jr. (1943). *J. Am. Pharm. Assoc., Sci. Ed.* **32**, 138.

Chapter 15

Melanophore-Expanding Activity

F. W. LANDGREBE AND H. WARING

I. Introduction

In the normal physiological process of color change in some amphibia there is complete evidence for the role of a pituitary hormone. This was originally called the melanophore-expanding hormone. The same term is used by some authors to denote pharmacologically active extracts of pituitary glands from other species. This has led to a certain confusion in terminology, most authors making the tacit assumption that any substance which evokes melanophore expansion in fish and amphibia is necessarily a hormone. Various authors have used such terms as

517

melanocyte-stimulating hormone, melanophore-stimulating hormone, intermedin, to designate the activity.

We have previously suggested the use of the term "B-hormone" for that hormone which causes the physiological blackening of amphibia, and the term "B" for material of pituitary origin which causes this same pharmacological action in our test animals. In this article we propose the use of the term "melanophore-expanding substance" (MES) for materials which will cause melanophore expansion in test animals but for which we have as yet no evidence as to their pituitary origin.

Other physiological responses are also believed to be evoked by this hormone in certain animals, such as the production of skin melanin in amphibia and fish and of erythrophores in the fish *Phoxinus*. Different workers have used various methods for the assay of extracts from a variety of sources, including melanophore expansion in amphibia and fish, skin transparency or reflectance, and the production of ventral reddening in *Phoxinus*. The active polypeptide extractable from pituitaries of different species is species specific. Thus there could be a variation in response to each of these polypeptides according to the technique of assay. The actual test animal and method of assay defines the activity.

II. Historical Résumé

The following brief selection from the literature indicates the major lines of attack on the problem of assaying "B." Abel in 1924 ligated the posterior limbs of the frog and compared changes in skin color after injection of pituitary extract. McLean (1928) perfused the hind legs of the frog and compared the gross color change produced by different concentrations of pituitary extract. Jores (1933) removed skin from the back of pale frogs and macroscopically observed the color change in a piece of skin when it was immersed in different concentrations of extract. Hogben (1923) used a minimal effect dose method combined with direct microscopic reading of the melanophores in the web.

Methods of assay proposed between 1930 and 1948 were all based on intact or hypophysectomized amphibia, on hypophysectomized *Anolis* and on intact *Phoxinus*. Methods using amphibians have employed a variety of species, the commonest being *Rana temporaria, Rana pipiens, Hyla arborea* and the South African clawed toad, *Xenopus laevis*. Zondek and Krohn in 1932 introduced the *Phoxinus* method for the assay of their "B"-containing extract which they called intermedin. The method using hypophysectomized *Anolis* (Kleinholz and Rahn, 1940) was introduced later than the test using amphibia and its authors claimed that it was more sensitive.

In retrospect it would be easy to criticize early efforts. Among other things, all predated the general appreciation that an agreed stable reference standard should be used. The work of Hogben and his collaborators between 1922 and 1930 prepared the field for the assays now in current use. Hogben and Winton as early as 1922 were expressing the strength of extracts in quantitative terms after determining the minimal dose of extracts that would evoke a certain degree of melanophore expansion and also recognized that greater discrimination between doses could be attained by following the complete sequence of melanophore behavior after an injection.

Methods now in use are based on these solid advances. Landgrebe and Waring (1944) determined and recorded practical minutiae for accurate assays and expressed their results in "international units." The *in vitro* assays now in use are based on the same principles and are, in practice, refinements of Jores' (1933) early efforts with excised skin. In short, advances during the last two decades have been chiefly in technique.

III. Theoretical Considerations

In designing an assay for "B" there are two primary considerations— the existence of a satisfactory international reference standard and the choice of a suitable animal preparation.

A. REFERENCE STANDARD

Simple extracts of posterior lobe have pressor, antidiuretic, oxytocic, and "B" properties. The first three are derived from the pars nervosa and the last from the pars intermedia where this is discrete. When extracts are processed so that the neural lobe activities are removed, the extract has only one certain property and that is chromatophore activation (Landgrebe and Mitchell, 1954). There is no international reference standard for "B" alone but there is one for the posterior lobe. This standard preparation is dried bovine posterior pituitary. The first international standard powder established was all used up about 1939, a second powder was substituted for it in the same year, and a third powder again in 1956. We have found that the three vary little in their "B" content. In terms of the third international standard powder, the second is 100% and the first 96% (Tables I and II). An international unit of

TABLE I

ASSAY TO DETERMINE THE RELATIVE "B" CONTENT OF THE SECOND AND THIRD INTERNATIONAL STANDARD POWDERS

Date	Second international standard powder					Third international standard powder					Second international standard as percentage of third international standard
	Group of 12 toads	Dose (µg.)	Max. m.i.	Average max. m.i. from 24 toads	Relative dose read from Fig. 7	Group of 12 toads	Dose (µg.)	Max. m.i.	Average max. m.i. from 24 toads	Relative dose read from Fig. 7	
Feb. 3, 1960	C	1.4	2.95			D	1.4	2.85			
Feb. 4, 1960	D	1.4	2.85	2.90	0.875	C	1.4	2.9	2.87	0.85	$\dfrac{0.875}{0.85} \times 100 = 103$
Feb. 5, 1960	C	1.2	2.65			D	0.625	2.7			
Feb. 6, 1960	D	1.2	2.7	2.67	0.66	C	0.625	2.7	2.7	0.69	$\dfrac{66}{69} \times 100 = 95$

TABLE II

Assay to Determine the Relative "B" Content of the First and Second International Standard Powders

	First international standard powder					Second international standard powder					First international standard as percentage of second international standard
Date	Group[a] of 12 toads	Dose (mu.)	Max. m.i.	Average max. m.i. from 24 toads	Relative dose read from Fig. 7	Group[a] of 12 toads	Dose (mu.)	Max. m.i.	Average max. m.i. from 24 toads	Relative dose read from Fig. 7	
May 18, 1943	A	5.0	4.1	4.05	3.5	B	5.0	4.0	4.0	3.2	$\frac{3.5}{3.2} \times 100 = 109$
May 19, 1943	B	5.0	4.0			A	5.0	4.0			
May 20, 1943	A	2.5	3.2	3.2	1.25	B	2.5	3.2	3.15	1.2	$\frac{1.25}{1.2} \times 100 = 104$
May 21, 1943	B	2.5	3.2			A	2.5	3.1			
May 22, 1943	A	1.25	2.4	2.4	0.5	B	1.25	2.6	2.45	0.53	$\frac{0.5}{0.53} \times 100 = 94$
May 23, 1943	B	1.25	2.4			A	1.25	2.3			

[a] Two groups (A and B) of 12 intact Xenopus.

pressor, oxytocic, or antidiuretic activity is defined as that amount of activity present in half a milligram of the international powder. Landgrebe and Waring (1944) examined the effect of the neural lobe excitants on the measurement of "B" by their method and found that these other activities had no effect on the assay of "B" in the quantities encountered and that different posterior lobe powders have very different proportions of the several activities (Table III). It follows that it is perfectly sound

TABLE III

ACTIVITY RECORDED AS PERCENTAGE OF INTERNATIONAL STANDARD POWDER[a]

Powder	Pressor	Oxytocic	"B"
First international standard	87	87	103
Second international standard	100	100	100
Canadian standard	100[b]	100[b]	40[c]
Our substandard used for routine pressor assays	90	80	17
Commercial (Oxo)	65	50	15
Commercial (Duncan Flockhart)	70	70	60
F.G.Y.[d]	60	50	18

[a] From Landgrebe and Waring (1944).
[b] Assumed.
[c] Calculated from Stehle's (1936) figures.
[d] A powder kindly supplied by Dr. F. G. Young of the British Medical Research Council.

practice to use one ox powder as the local laboratory substandard for both neural lobe activities and "B," provided always that its content of each is separately labeled after comparison with international standard powder. On this basis we recommended in 1944 that an international unit of "B" activity be defined as the activity in half a milligram of the international posterior lobe powder. This has never been formally recognized but we have continued to use this international unitage with every satisfaction. The chemical composition of three different active polypeptides extractable from pituitary tissue is now known, but, as yet, not enough can be prepared for us to use the pure materials as international standards. The practice of using a commercially available preparation labeled "ACTH" as a reference standard is to be deprecated. Different batches vary in the relative content of "B" and the activity (adrenal ascorbic acid-depleting substance) for which the material is extracted. These could be used as laboratory substandards after each batch had been assayed against the international standard, but we do not yet know whether they are stable indefinitely. Hudson and Bentley (1957a) have found that both samples they have used as reference standards remained stable over a period of 4 years.

Even though there are theoretical objections to the use of a bovine standard when measuring "B" from other species, we have not, in practice, so far encountered any difficulty (see reference to Main *et al.*, 1960, in Section III, B).

B. Animal Preparation

Chromatically active cold-blooded vertebrates may have one or all of the following color cells: dermal and epidermal melanophores, erythrophores and xanthophores containing, respectively, black, red, and yellow pigment. With the exception of Zondek and Krohn's method which is based on the activation of erythrophores in *Phoxinus,* all proposed methods of assay have used melanophores of amphibia or reptiles.

Specificity is an important consideration in any method of assay. There is good information regarding amphibia using melanophores but, so far as we are aware, none with regard to those of the other proposed test animals. Hogben's pioneer work (1924), followed by that of Shen (1937) and Teague *et al.* (1939), has shown that whereas melanophores of the intact frog can be caused to expand by a few non-pituitary substances, full melanophore response in the hypophysectomized frog is specific to pituitary "B." A personal communication from Dr. Shen in 1939 informed us that he had found *Xenopus* to behave similarly. By 1943 we too had reached the general conclusion that "B" alone would in sufficient dose fully darken a hypophysectomized *Xenopus.* Burgers (1956) following up his observation that disturbed intact and hypophysectomized *Xenopus* exhibited a measure of melanophore expansion, showed that adrenaline, *Xenopus* skin secretion, and a large number of phenylalkylamines will cause partial melanophore expansion in the whole animal.

We have tested many of these agents and find that none of them will produce full melanophore expansion when injected into the whole animal. For example, doses up to 100 μg. of adrenaline have little or no effect on melanophore expansion; doses from 200 to 500 μg. give a partial response (to a Hogben melanophore index of 3.0) and larger doses than this produce no further effect, 1000 μg. usually causing the death of the animal. In other words, with these agents, unlike pituitary extracts, a dose-response curve is unobtainable. In isolated skin, however, Burgers found that urine from pregnant women will sometimes give a full expansion of at least some melanophores. Similar results were found with phenylalkylamines.

Main *et al.* (1960) have investigated pituitary extracts made from glands of different species including ox, pig, and man and found that using both *Xenopus* and *Hyla* as test animals the dose-response lines in all cases are parallel to one another. This is interesting since there is evidence that we are not dealing with identical chemical substances in the various extracts. We know, for example, that the porcine polypeptide responsible for this activity differs chemically from the bovine one.

When a "B"-containing extract is injected into pale test animals the melanophores expand and the skin appears darker; the skin then gradually gets paler as the melanophores contract again. To use this sequence of events for assay purposes we must decide on a method of measuring melanophore expansion or skin darkening, select a suitable preparation, and adopt a criterion for estimating relative potencies of extracts.

C. Measurement of Melanophore Expansion

This can be done by naked eye estimation of skin color, by microscopic observation of melanophores, or by photoelectric measurement of reflection or absorption of light. Macroscopic estimation, of course, is based upon the total picture of all chromatophores. In contrast with experiments in which it is desired to know the precise separate contribution of all effectors this is probably not a very important shortcoming under standardized conditions. The overriding objection is that it is far less accurate than either microscopic observation of melanophores or photoelectric measurement. In experiments involving groups of animals the variation in melanophore density may be so great, for example, in the animals used in Fig. 1, that an animal with few but fully expanded melanophores is paler than an animal with abundant contracted ones.

Hill *et al.* (1935) seemed to be the first to introduce photoelectric measurement, although they used it for plotting background reversal times and not for assay purposes. Smith (1936) described a photoelectric method for measuring melanophore expansion in teleost scales in response to drugs and changes in ionic concentration. Thing (1952) also using whole animals, reinvestigated the method but abandoned it in favor of microscopic melanophore reading which he found to be as accurate and, of course, simpler. Photoelectric determination shared the disadvantage of macroscopic observation in giving the over-all result of the activity of several effectors, and it would appear also that with methods so far devised they offer no compensating advantages when

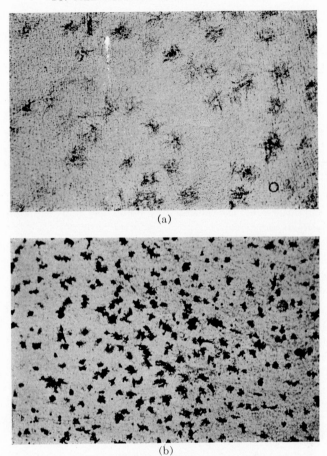

(a)

(b)

FIG. 1. Shows how a combination of reduced melanophores per unit area and melanin per melanophore may result in a skin (b) with melanophores equilibrated at melanophore index (m.i.) = 2 being macroscopically darker than skin (a) at m.i. 5. Magnification of both photographs the same. [We have *Xenopus* with less melanin than in (a) but these do not photograph well with the melanophores expanded.] (From Landgrebe and Waring, 1944.)

applied to whole animals. They do, however, offer some advantage when applied to isolated skin preparations.

Bentley and Hudson (1957) found that the method using visual estimation is not sufficiently sensitive to measure quantities of activity normally present in the circulation even after procedures for concentrating it had been used, and Hudson and Bentley (1957a) found estimation of pigment change in isolated skin by photoelectric means more sensitive because areas of skin can be selected where the melanophore density is so high that a very small dispersion of pigment which is insufficient to permit accurate visual estimation will substantially affect the amount of light either reflected or passing through the skin.

Main (1960) has developed a useful technique using a binocular microscope, the eyepiece of which is fitted with a photoelectric cell, the other being available for microscopic examination. Using isolated skin from *Rana temporaria,* he found that the amount of light transmitted through the skin and measured photoelectrically varies inversely as the microscopically observed expansion of the melanophores but that changes in the photoelectric readings can be observed before any definite change can be seen in the melanophores themselves. In other words, for very low concentrations of the activity it could be that the photoelectric method is more sensitive.

So, in essence, the increased sensitivity is achieved by using the lower ranges in the scale of melanophore expansion. This may have certain disadvantages. Earlier workers and ourselves have found that nonspecific substances will evoke a small measure of expansion in isolated skin melanophores. Further work on the specificity of isolated skin would be rewarding.

The third method of assessing melanophore expansion is by direct visual estimation of the state of the melanophores and recording the value in terms of the arbitrary melanophore index (m.i.) (Fig. 2).

FIG. 2. Melanophore index (m.i.). (From Landgrebe and Waring, 1944.)

Hogben was the first to introduce this method and his first index appeared in 1923. In 1930 Hogben and Gordon published an improved one which has subsequently been used by many workers. After a few hours' practice, a novice with the figure for reference can read the middle portion of the web of 12 *Xenopus* without his average m.i. differing by more than 0.1 from that of an experienced operator.

D. CRITERIA FOR A SUITABLE ANIMAL PREPARATION

The choice of the animal preparation will be determined by whether the *in vitro* or *in vivo* method of estimation is to be employed. For *in vitro* estimations the only two animal species that have been recommended are the frog and the lizard *Anolis*. Isolated skin from the latter is said to be more sensitive but the local distribution of the lizard is likely to preclude its general adoption. For a certain specialized purpose we have found dogfish skin (Landgrebe and Waring, 1949) a more satisfactory *in vitro* preparation than frog skin but it has not been examined for its assay possibilities. *Rana, Hyla, Xenopus,* or *Anolis,* either intact or hypophysectomized, have been used by many workers. Kleinholz and Rahn in 1940 advocated the use of *Anolis* because of its greater sensitivity, but the animal has no webs and assessments have to be made on macroscopic color. Thing (1952) advocated the use of *Xenopus* tadpoles which are more sensitive, but it is unlikely that they will replace adults for routine work because of their fragility.

IV. Methods Using the Whole Animal

Satisfactory assays can be made using *Rana, Hyla, Xenopus,* and probably other frogs and toads. *Xenopus* seems the most satisfactory.

A. ADVANTAGES OF XENOPUS OVER *Rana temporaria* OR *Hyla arborea*

1. Ease of Access

Xenopus can be easily imported from South Africa and if necessary be bred in the laboratory (Landgrebe and Samson, 1944).

2. Ease of Reading

Xenopus have a much larger web and can more rapidly be positioned on a microscope stage. Chromatophores other than melanophores are either absent or nonobtrusive. The apparent change of shape of the melanophore in transition from 1 to 5 on the melanophore scale is smoother and more uniform throughout the web.

3. Ease of Maintaining Standardized Conditions

Temperature, humidity, and light have profound effects on chromatic function of amphibia. All three are easily standardized in an aquatic animal such as *Xenopus*. A serious objection to the use of the British *Rana temporaria* is the dominant role played by humidity. In up to 50% of intact specimens, melanophores are always expanded in the presence of water. If *Rana temporaria* are kept dry, survival is low.

4. Length of Life

Xenopus live indefinitely in the laboratory and maintenance is easy (Landgrebe, 1939). *Rana temporaria* can sometimes be kept alive for a few months but only with considerable attention.

Other advantages of *Xenopus* are that under conditions to be specified their response to a given dose is consistent for long periods (Fig. 3).

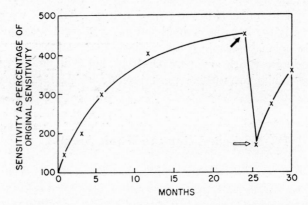

Fig. 3. Graphic representation of the effect of background on the sensitivity of *Xenopus* to injection of "B"-containing extracts. All animals kept on a black background for several weeks before experiment. For the first 24 months of the experiment toads were kept on a white "background." At → they were transferred to a black background. At ⇒ they were transferred to a white background. Points are the average sensitivity figures from the same 12 toads. Sensitivity estimated at intervals shown by injecting each toad equilibrated on a white background with same dose of freshly made extract from the same sample of posterior lobe pituitary powder kept in a desiccator at 0°C. (From Landgrebe and Waring, 1944.)

Thus a rapid rough assay can be made and the appropriate dose chosen. Accurate reading of animals with many melanophores is difficult; this is one of the chief obstacles to accurate assay with the *Rana* available to us. *Xenopus* kept for long periods on a white background have fewer melanophores (Fig. 1).

Hyla arborea are relatively easy to import and are more suitable test animals than *Rana temporaria*. The melanophores in the skin of the hindlimb can fairly easily be read microscopically (Fig. 4) and they can be kept alive for many months in the laboratory without too much difficulty. They are smaller than the *Xenopus* usually used and, partly for this reason, they are more sensitive. They are not sensitive enough to assay minute quantities such as occur in some samples of blood and urine, for which isolated skin may be sufficiently sensitive.

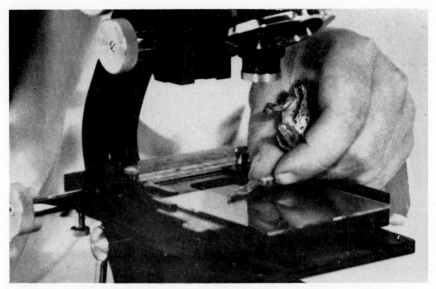

Fig. 4. Reading of melanophores in *Hyla arborea*.

B. Criterion for Comparing Potency of Extracts

With *in vitro* preparations immersed in solutions of the activity un-likely to decay during the period of observation, the criterion is the peak m.i., i.e., the maximum darkening, or the modification adopted by some workers (Hudson and Bentley, 1957a) of reading at a fixed arbitrary time after application of the activity. With *in vivo* assays where injected material is slowly destroyed, either the peak m.i. or the duration of response have been used and these two criteria, of course,

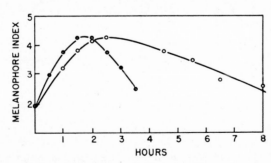

Fig. 5. Completely hypophysectomized *Xenopus*. Responses to ox posterior lobe extracts. All injections 1 ml. at 15°C.

Key: ——●—— Untreated aqueous extract; ——○—— Same extract treated with caustic soda. One half the above dose.

TABLE IV

Effect of Caustic Soda Treatment on a Selection of Original Glandular Materials[a]

Extract[b]	Percentage potentiation	Percentage protection
Ox I.S.P. (P.L.P.)	110	80
Ox commercial (P.L.P.)	100	80
Ox commercial (A.L.P.)	20	160
Dogfish (P.L.P.)	220	80
L.R.W. (Landgrebe et al., 1943)	0	0

Note: 1 ml. of 0.25% acetic acid extract + 0.14 ml. N NaOH, boiling water bath 2 minutes, 0.1 ml. N HCl (neutralizes to litmus). Original extracts approximately equivalent in "B" activity to that of a standard extract of I.S.P.

[a] From Landgrebe et al. (1950).

[b] I.S.P. = International standard posterior lobe powder.

P.L.P. = Posterior lobe of the pituitary.

A.L.P. = Anterior lobe of the pituitary.

measure different things. But with a standard extract of good pituitary material they give approximately the same result. We do not use the second, i.e., duration of response, for the following reasons. The time-response curve is very flat toward the end and there is room for considerable error, especially when this method is combined with macroscopic estimation of the response. Secondly, it is not applicable to extracts

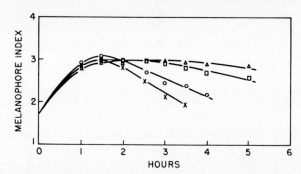

Fig. 6. Responses of same group of intact *Xenopus* to extracts of whole gland and posterior lobe alone. Doses adjusted to give approximately same peak m.i. Each point is the average reading from 6 toads. White background; 15°C. All doses 0.25 ml./D.L.S. (From Landgrebe and Waring, 1944.)

Key: ○ = Whole gland extracted by standard procedure with 0.25% acetic acid; × = Posterior lobe alone extracted by standard procedure with 0.25% acetic acid; △ = Whole gland extracted by standard procedure with 0.25% acetic acid, neutralized, adjusted to 0.1 N NaOH, heated in boiling water bath for 10 minutes, and then neutralized; □ = Posterior lobe alone, as above.

treated with caustic soda because this treatment flattens the time-response curve (Fig. 5). The degree of flattening is not directly proportional to the "B" content of the original material (Table IV). Thirdly, inert protein such as that present in anterior lobe extracts, flattens the time-response curve even when extraction is made by the standard method (British Pharmacopeia, 1932) (Fig. 6). Fourthly, the second method takes longer than the first. Landgrebe and Mitchell (1954) show that the time the animal has been on a white background also alters the degree of duration of flattening.

C. FREQUENCY OF USE

We have previously recommended that *Xenopus laevis* be used only once daily. Ketterer and Remilton (1954) investigated the possibility of speeding up the procedure by administering 2 doses per day but found a fall in sensitivity after even only 3 days. So only one injection per day should be made into each animal and two groups of animals are used to obtain adequate control. Toads from one group receive the reference standard and those from the other the unknown on the first day. The groups are reversed on the second day. The following description is taken from Landgrebe and Waring (1944). The description is for *Xenopus* but *Rana* or *Hyla* can be substituted with obvious modifications.

D. SELECTION OF ANIMALS

In choosing animals it is important to make certain that they are capable of a maximum response because a few animals exhibit no greater melanophore expansion than is represented by a m.i. of 4.0 even when injected with several times the minimal dose necessary to evoke this index. The error that this can introduce needs no emphasis when looking for a peak m.i. attained. In practice, however, lower dose levels than this are employed. We have used animals weighing from 10 to 200 gm., the smaller ones being more sensitive; but most workers find toads weighing about 30 gm. easiest to handle.

If, in spite of its relative insensitivity, this method is used for assaying materials such as extracts of blood or urine, a test should first be done on intact animals. These have a far higher resistance to toxic substances than hypophysectomized ones, though the latter must be used to obtain final results with such extracts not derived from the pituitary. Removal of the pituitary in *Xenopus laevis* is simple (Hogben, 1923).

The sensitivity of intact animals depends on the previous background history. In its incipient stages the loss or gain of sensitivity when the background is changed is not the same for all melanophores in one web so that an animal with a varied background history spread over a week or so may react to an injection of "B" by some of the melanophores expanding to 2 and others to 5. It is obviously difficult to get high accuracy with such animals, though a useful result can be obtained by a skilled worker. Stability of sensitivity and with it equality of sensitivity between different melanophores can be obtained in a number of ways: (1) by keeping the animal on a white background for a long period prior to assay when the curve of increasing sensitivity has flattened (Fig. 3), or (2) by keeping up a regular small daily injection of "B" while the animal is on a white background (Ketterer and Remilton, 1954), or (3) by using the animals for a period of a few days, resting them on a black background for a day or two with feeding, and then using them again for a few days in such a way that the sensitivity remains stable (Karkun, 1960). Hypophysectomized animals are more sensitive than intact ones and the sensitivity of operated animals increases more or less consistently for a few months. Hudson and Bentley (1957b) confirm this fact and record a fivefold increase in sensitivity but they do not indicate the time interval between operation and test.

E. Care of Animals

Xenopus should be kept separately in white containers about 6 inches in diameter, 8 inches high, half-full of water, and fitted with wire mesh lids. They must be kept in overhead illumination—artificial light is adequate for this. One 100-watt lamp 6 feet above 20 containers seems to be adequate. Even at 16°C. (the usual temperature for test purposes) *Xenopus* will rarely eat when being handled as in assays. Every 6 months or so we rest the animals at 20°–25°C. when they feed voraciously and rapidly regain any loss of condition. Feeding once or twice a week is sufficient and the containers should be cleaned out the following day. We have always prescribed separate containers for the animals and the soundness of this advice is reinforced by the following observations of Ketterer and Remilton (1954). When a number of pale *Xenopus* in a trough were consistently disturbed they became macroscopically slightly darker. This was investigated further by taking a group of 6 *Xenopus* in use for assay, disturbing them manually, and reading the m.i. regularly. At 15 minutes all recorded a m.i. of 2 and the effect disappeared 1 hour after cessation of excitation. The effect of excitement combined with injections of "B" was tried; disturbed animals reached the peak of the curve more quickly than controls. These findings emphasize the importance of keeping *Xenopus* singly and under minimal disturbance during the course of an assay.

F. MISCELLANEA WITH REGARD TO ASSAY

1. We have used dorsal lymph sac (D.L.S.), intraperitoneal (I.P.), subcutaneous, and intravenous injections. Intravenous injections are extremely tedious and quite impracticable for routine work. *Xenopus* skin does not readily close over a skin puncture, so subcutaneous injections are unreliable. Intraperitoneal injections may give erratic results. Sometimes one or two of a group do not respond (probably due to the extract entering the viscera). If, however, large numbers of test animals are used, fairly consistent results can be obtained. The response curve after I.P. injection differs from that after D.L.S. injection (Fig. 7) and varies con-

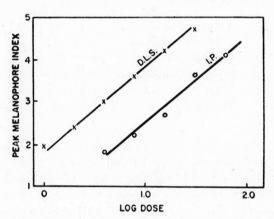

FIG. 7. Dose-response curve of 18 *Xenopus* similar to those used to collect data for Table II.

KEY: ✕—✕ Dorsal lymph sac injection; ◯—◯ Intraperitoneal injection.

siderably for different groups of animals. Four to ten times the dose is required and the results are not so consistent. The most satisfactory route for injection is the dorsal lymph sac.

2. Dermal melanophores only are used. Animals kept on a white background for some months will have a convenient number of dermal melanophores, and few toads will have any epidermal melanophores. Those with many epidermal melanophores should be discarded.

3. A dose that will give a peak m.i. around 3.0 should be used.

4. There is a slight gradient of melanophore expansion from the tip

of the web proximally, so readings should be taken from the central portion of the large web to obtain a figure approximating to the average m.i. of the whole web. This is facilitated by covering the microscope stage with a glass plate blackened except for a central hole ⅛ inch in diameter.

5. Reading is best done with ⅔ inch objective and 10× eyepiece. Strength of microscope illumination must be adequate and constant.

6. Injections are made with a 2-inch needle through the thigh muscles. This point of entry is used both for D.L.S. and I.P. injections.

7. As many as 20 D.L.S. injections can be made with water as a solvent. More than this often results in the skin of the back appearing black (jacketing) while the m.i. in the web does not rise. This is because the injected activity does not leave the lymph sac owing to inactivation of the lymph heart. The incidence of jacketing can be reduced by using the following saline as a solvent:

Sodium chloride	8.3	gm.
Potassium chloride	0.33	gm.
Calcium chloride	0.12	gm.
Sodium bicarbonate	0.1	gm.
Magnesium chloride	0.1	gm.
Dextrose	0.5	gm.
Water to	1	liter

Animals that jacket in spite of the use of this saline have damaged lymph hearts and, if used, must be given I.P. injections.

8. Claims have been made that the volume of fluid used as a solvent for injected activity affects the response (Calloway *et al.*, 1942). We cannot confirm this. Nevertheless, it is advisable to standardize the volume injected. We find that 1 and 0.25 ml. give identical responses and suggest the use of 0.25 ml.

V. Performance of an Assay

A. PRELIMINARIES

1. Select a large sample of ox posterior lobe powder preferably prepared from fresh glands and stored according to standard procedure (Burn, 1937). Use this as a substandard. There is no reason to suppose that such a preparation deteriorates even over a period of 13 years (Table I).

2. Prepare a standard extract of substandard powder with dilute acetic acid (British Pharmacopeia, 1932, 1948). Such extracts unsealed

are stable for a few hours and then sometimes deteriorate rapidly. Stehle (1936) also noted this instability of some extracts. Solutions store well if ampoules containing up to 1 ml. are placed in boiling water bath for 1 minute, sealed while hot, and kept in the dark. At room temperature they are stable for at least 3 months and at 0°C. for at least 6 months.

3. Divide 12 to 24 toads into 2 equal groups, A and B.

B. STANDARDIZATION OF SUBSTANDARD POWDER

Inject suitable doses (refer for guidance to Tables I and II) of the standard into test animals of group A and substandard into those of group B. On the next day inject the same dose of standard into B and of substandard into A. Repeat this procedure at three dose levels. This will yield data that can be used for (1) constructing a skeleton dose-response curve and (2) calculating the potency of substandard to about 10%. To construct an accurate dose-response curve several dose levels must be used. Figure 8 shows the kind of discrimination to expect between different doses.

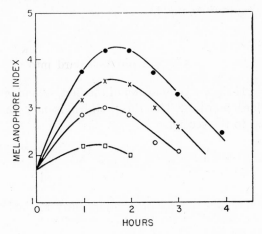

FIG. 8. Illustrates the response of intact animals to graded doses of the same "B"-containing extract (supplied by Professor Stehle). 15°C.; white background. All injections ¼ ml. D.L.S.

KEY: ● = 0.2 μg., × = 0.1 μg., ○ = 0.05 μg., □ = 0.025 μg. Stehle's powder.

If a large number of routine assays are not contemplated and a figure corrected to about 20% is sufficient, a simpler procedure can be adopted. Inject group A with standard and group B with the unknown extract at one dose level, preferably estimated to raise m.i. to about 3. Calculate the result, using Fig. 7 of this paper. Experience shows that the sensitivity of toads varies considerably, but the log dose-response curve of any group after D.L.S. injections is not significantly different from that illustrated. This is strikingly demonstrated by comparison of graph 6 in Waring and Landgrebe (1941), which is based on observation of hypophysectomized toads by Waring in 1940, and which conforms to Fig. 7 shown here, based on normal animals read by Landgrebe in 1942.

C. Assay of Unknown Extract

It must again be emphasized that hypophysectomized animals must be used for the final assay of extracts of nonpituitary origin.

Prepare 3 or 4 trial doses of the unknown and inject each into one toad. At 16°C. read at $1\frac{1}{2}$ hour (peak rise). From the figures so obtained estimate a dose that will raise the average m.i. of a group to about 3.0. Avoid doses that raise the index above 4. Inject the unknown extract into group A and a comparable dose of substandard into group B. Reverse the groups next day. The response to substandard shows whether the toads are behaving true to form. If they are, the potency of the unknown extract can be read off on the dose-response curve.

VI. Sample Assays

Tables I and II show a comparison of the first, second, and third international standard powders. The third, which is now the standard, is almost identical to the second.

VII. Accuracy to Be Expected

There are two main sources of error in assay methods of this kind: (1) mistakes in reading and (2) inconsistency of response over the period (2 or 3 days) necessary to a complete assay. The first has already been mentioned, and the error from this source has been estimated in the following experiment:

A worker was trained to read melanophore indices to 0.5 on the scale, so that an index between, say, 3 and 4 was recorded as 3.5. A group of 10 toads which had been equilibrated on a black background were then transferred to a white background and the melanophores of each toad were read 12 hours later. The melanophores were then re-examined and 5 successive records taken for each toad. In the period of time necessary for these observations the melanophores of the animals contract very little on the white background, as the natural color change of the animal at this stage is fairly slow. The grand mean for the 50 readings was 2.72, and the maximum probable error calculated for the group means was only 0.08. This error taken in conjunction with the dose-response curve (Fig. 7) would produce a maximum final error of only about 10% for a reading of 10 toads. So, in a usual assay using 24 animals, the error from this source is much less than 10%.

The second source of error, consistency of response, can best be illustrated by three examples:

(*a*) *Over short periods.* The consistency of response by *selected* toads over short periods of time is illustrated by groups A and B (Table II) at 3 dose levels spread over 6 days.

(*b*) *Over long periods.* See Fig. 3.

(*c*) *With toads taken at random.* Two groups of 6 were taken at random from a tank of 30 used for pregnancy diagnosis. Each animal received 0.25 ml. of a 1 in 200 dilution of standard extract of International standard posterior lobe powder (I.S.P.P.) into the D.L.S. with the results shown in the following tabulation:

Time (hours):	0	1	1½	2	3
Group 1 (average m.i.):	1.7	2.7	3.1	3.2	2.3
Group 2 (average m.i.):	1.5	2.9	3.5	3.5	2.8

A smooth curve drawn through these points shows the maxima to be 3.2 and 3.5, respectively. By taking these as the criteria of potency and assuming the dose-response curve, the ratio of the doses recorded from this test is 1:1.3.

The same dose was administered the next day with the following result:

Time (hours):	0	1	1½	2	3
Group 1 (average m.i.):	1.5	3.0	3.3	3.2	2.4
Group 2 (average m.i.):	1.4	3.0	3.6	3.4	2.7

The maxima, 3.3 and 3.6, are almost the same as those of the previous day. The maximum of group 1 first day averaged with that of group 2 second day is 3.4. The maximum of group 2 first day averaged with that of group 1 second day is 3.45. On the dose-response curve these figures give a difference between the equal doses of about 10%.

The data show remarkable consistency of response, but it must be emphasized that the background history of all these toads had been the same for at least a year, so one of the greatest potential sources of inaccuracy was eliminated.

Ketterer and Remilton (1954) have applied statistical methods to results obtained by this assay method. In order to evaluate their results statistically they have used stock animals, i.e., unselected test animals, and have randomly grouped them on each day of the test. They used 6 animals per group and the allotment of the groups to dose level was random and was changed on each day of the assay. They evaluated the expression obtained for 95% fiducial limits of prediction of potency for response corresponding to a m.i. of about 3 and found that the true potency may be expected to lie between 0.92 and 1.09 of the calculated. In other words, they have obtained statistical evidence that our own estimate of the accuracy of the method using groups of 12 selected animals in a cross-over test, i.e., 10%, is, if anything, an overestimate.

VIII. Assay of Material Subjected to Heat at pH 12-13

Considerable work has been done with glandular extracts subject to caustic soda treatment. On using ox material, alkali treatment destroys the pressor and oxytocic properties and increases "B" potency. When unfractionated extracts of ox posterior lobe are heated in a boiling water bath for 2 minutes at pH 13.0, two things happen: (1) a greatly increased melanophore-expanding potency as judged by peak m.i. attained (potentiation) and (2) a pronounced increase in duration of response (protection) when judged on submaximal responses (Fig. 5). These two effects have been analyzed (Landgrebe and Waring, 1950). On the other hand, when crude extracts made from pig material are subjected to treatment with alkali there is a greatly decreased melanophore-expanding potency and a pronounced increase in duration of response.

As will be apparent from previous work, the exact mechanism of potentiation and protection are not understood, but the following items are relevant to assay procedure: (a) It is reasonably certain that during the heating process some activity is being destroyed and some activity is being activated (or freshly created); (b) with different species, and even with the same species, subject to different lighting conditions previous to death, glandular material has different potentials with regard to potentiation and protection; (c) test animals freshly adapted to a white background exhibit the potentiated nature of the extract; those adapted for long periods do not unless they have been injected daily.

Bearing (a), (b), and (c) in mind, we can say that a full assay must involve figures both from untreated and treated extracts, in which the treatment is rigidly controlled and furthermore the previous background and injection history of the test animals must also be suitable. The index of potentiation and protection can be expressed as shown in Fig. 9.

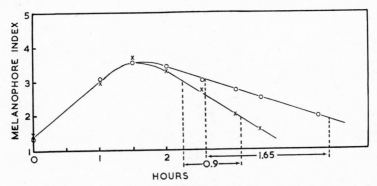

Fig. 9. $\times$ = average m.i. 12 *Xenopus* injected with I.S.S.E. untreated—diluted 1 in 120 and 0.2 ml. injected. $\bigcirc$ = average m.i. same 12 *Xenopus* injected with I.S.S.E. (International standard, standard extract) treated—diluted 1 in 240 and 0.2 ml. injected. Treatment = adjustment to pH 13 and boiling water bath for 2 minutes.

Since the same peak m.i. is attained after injection of half the dose of treated extract, the *potentiation = 100%*. Since the time taken for m.i. to fall from 3 to 2 is 0.9 hours after untreated extract and 1.65 hours after treated, protection = [(1.65 − 0.9)/0.9] × 100 = 83%. (From Landgrebe *et al.*, 1950.)

In view of the information set out in this section we need not bother to criticize in detail schemes to measure potency that involve caustic soda treatment of extracts (Chen and Geiling, 1943), when estimates of alleged potentiation are made by measuring duration of response. Furthermore, although gross macroscopic color determination is to be deprecated in assay work at any time, it is here seen at its worst because (a) the end point is so prolonged by this method, and (b) it is quite impossible to be certain that one is dealing with a submaximal response. In any case most workers who have employed alkali treatment alone without parallel assays of untreated material have heated it for varying periods up to 10 minutes after adding variable amounts of caustic soda. The pH and time of heating are critical for optimum results (Tables V and VI). No potentiation or protection occurs with ox material if the extracts are heated at a pH below 12, and although we have no exact data about what happens at higher pH than 13 it seems likely from information given in Table VI that destruction of activity would mask

TABLE V

EFFECT OF HEATING A STANDARD EXTRACT OF INTERNATIONAL STANDARD POWDER
IN A BOILING WATER BATH FOR DIFFERENT TIMES AT pH 13
(pH Adjusted with N Caustic Soda)

Duration of treatment in minutes	Potentiation	Protection
1	1.0	0.8
2	1.0	0.8
3	0.8	0.8
7	0.5	0.75
10	−0.2[b]	0.6

[a] From Landgrebe et al., 1950.
[b] Loss of potency.

TABLE VI

POTENTIATION AND PROTECTION AT DIFFERENT pH VALUES

pH	Potentiation	Protection
8.0–12.0	0	0
12.5	0.3	0.5
12.6	0.5	0.5
12.8	1.0	0.7
13.0	1.0	0.8

NOTE: Standard extract of international standard powder 0.1 + 0.9 ml. buffer (glycine) adjusted to pH as noted (with cation correction) on Marconi glass electrode meter, followed by 2 minutes in boiling water bath, and neutralized. No loss or gain of activity was detectable after boiling water bath treatment within the pH range 8–12 ·

any potentiation. In the absence of evidence to the contrary, it seems likely that, from the start of heating with caustic soda, potentiation and destruction are proceeding simultaneously.

IX. Methods Using Isolated Skin

The effector time of the melanophore is short. In perfusion experiments the frog melanophore can expand completely in 30 minutes. Consequently isolated skin offers the possibility of repetitive serial tests with the advantage of internal control provided conditions allow of melanophore contraction once the expanded state has been reached.

Early workers found that the melanophores of isolated pieces of pale skin could be expanded by immersion of the skin in a pituitary extract (Trendelenburg, 1926; Hogben and Slome, 1931; Jores, 1933). Subsequent immersion of the skin in fresh saline resulted in contraction of the melanophores. This observation showed that the action was directly on the melanophores but the assessment of the result on the macroscopic appearance of the piece of skin was not otherwise very useful. More recently, workers have used microscopic examination of melanophores as well as photoelectric methods based on those of Hill *et al.* (1935) and Smith (1936). Hill *et al.* used a method of reflectance by which they measured the amount of a beam of light reflected from the back of a fish (*Fundulus heteroclitus*) by focusing it onto a photoelectric cell and recording on a galvanometer. Smith used a method of light transmission and passed a light through an isolated fish scale onto the surface of a photoelectric cell. Belehradek (1937) contributed to the technique by supporting a piece of frog skin in a frame for test purposes. Subsequent workers, notably Wright (1948), Frieden *et al.* (1948), Shizume *et al.* (1954), Hudson and Bentley (1957a, b) modified and improved on these techniques.

A. Methods Using Light Absorption

Wright in 1946 published a note on the measurement of melanophore expansion in isolated frog skin using an absorptiometer, and followed this

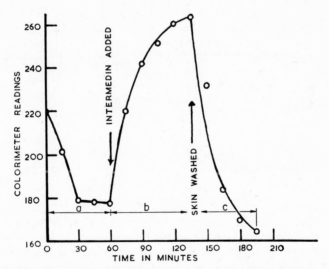

Fig. 10. Changes in light transmission of frog skin following: (a) spontaneous melanophore contraction; (b) melanophore expansion under influence of pituitary extracts; and (c) contraction following removal of extract. (From Frieden *et al.*, 1948.)

with a detailed description in 1948. The latter paper does not describe an assay method but contains some very pertinent material. Wright has provided a series of photographs of the melanophores corresponding to various colorimeter readings. These are important since they show that clearly readable degrees of melanophore expansion correspond with his colorimeter readings.

Frieden *et al.* (1948) have examined the possibility of using Wright's method for assay purposes. Figure 10 shows the responses to Ringer and pituitary solutions. This cycle can be repeated 2 or 3 times with the same piece of skin.

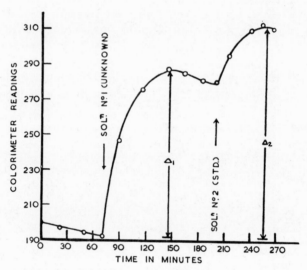

Fig. 11. Changes in light transmission of frog skin effected by unknown (Δ_1) and by standard pituitary extract (Δ_2). (From Frieden *et al.*, 1948.)

Two experimental designs were investigated and are discussed below.

(1) Attempts on the basis of relationship between concentration and response (or rate of response). Nowhere within the range covered did there seem to be a consistent, reproducible relation between response and concentration, nor was a regular relation discernible between the rate of response to concentration. This is ambiguous but probably means that different skin did not give comparable responses to the same dose of reference standard. If this is the correct interpretation it is common experience. It is obviously more convenient if the reference standard and the unknown can be compared on the same test object.

(2) A series of skins were treated with various dilutions of pituitary extract (Fig. 11) and the change in transmission (Δ_1) recorded. The skins

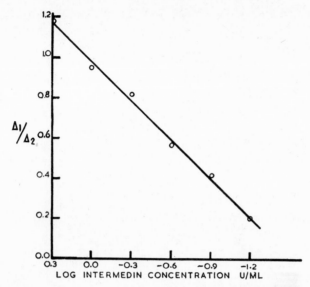

FIG. 12. Relation between relative response (Δ_1/Δ_2) and intermedin concentration. (From Frieden *et al.*, 1948.)

were then subjected to a fixed dose of reference standard and the difference between the second maxima and the original base line is recorded as Δ_2. No reason is advanced for this unusual procedure which involves comparing the response to unknown extract on the lower scale of melanophore expansion with the response to reference standard on the more expanded part of the scale; one would have expected a direct comparison over the same part of the scale as is done by other workers. Frieden *et al.* (1948) mention scattering of data but the data reproduced show a very good fit to a straight line plotting Δ_1/Δ_2 against log concentration of

TABLE VII

CONCENTRATION-RESPONSE DATA FOR FROG SKINS *in Vitro*[a]

Solution No. 1 (U./ml.)	Solution No. 2 (U./ml.)	No. of determinations	Average Δ_1/Δ_2	Range of Δ_1/Δ_2
2.0	1.0	4	1.18 ± 0.10	0.98–1.35
1.0	1.0	7	0.95 ± 0.04	0.92–1.02
0.50	1.0	14	0.82 ± 0.06	0.74–0.92
0.25	1.0	9	0.57 ± 0.06	0.49–0.63
0.125	1.0	11	0.42 ± 0.05	0.35–0.50
0.0625	1.0	5	0.21 ± 0.02	0.17–0.26

[a] From Frieden *et al.* (1948).

pituitary extract (Table VII and Fig. 12). A sample assay is shown in Table VIII. They concluded that their method was slow and expensive but was consistent.

Thing (1952) compared assay methods based upon photoelectric measurement and microscopic observation. Using both techniques simultaneously but on different areas of skin, he obtained almost identical results. He concluded that there is no reason for preferring the photoelectric method.

Main (1960) has now developed a technique that has the great advantage that both microscopic examination of the melanophores and

TABLE VIII

INTERMEDIN ASSAY OF U.S.P. POSTERIOR LOBE POWDER[a]

(Reference Standard B3801)

Sample No.:	1	2	3	4	5	6
Equiv. powder conc.						
(μg./ml.)	0.025	0.0125	0.00625	0.025	0.0125	0.00625
Δ_1	49	28	26	82	37	10
Δ_2	107	96	121	141	111	75
Ratio, Δ_1/Δ_2	0.46	0.29	0.22	0.58	0.33	0.13
Log C	-0.80	-1.06	-1.17	-0.62	-1.00	-1.31
C (U./ml.)	0.16	0.087	0.068	0.24	0.10	0.049
Intermedin content of						
powder (U./μg.)	6.4	7.0	10.9	9.6	8.0	7.8

Average (U./μg.): 8.3 $\pm$ 1.5

[a] From Frieden et al. (1948).

photoelectric records of the transmissibility of the same piece of skin can be recorded. He designed a cell (Fig. 13) which held the skin in a stretched and fixed position enabling it to be immersed in saline or test solution. It was placed in position on the stage of a binocular microscope (see Fig. 14). One eyepiece was used for visual observation and to the other was attached a photoelectric cell (Weston Photronic) connected directly to a sensitive galvanometer (2000 mm. per microampere).

Many workers have attempted such *in vitro* methods without much success and Main has discovered a number of important points of technique using the skin of *Rana temporaria* which make the difference between success and failure. Before killing the donor animal and dissecting the isolated skin, it is important to submit the living animal to varying white and black backgrounds under overhead illumination so that the melanophores can expand and contract before operation. These preliminary changes serve three purposes: first, it allows observation of areas of skin which show maximal alteration in color indicating a good melanophore response; second, the sensitivity of the chosen piece of skin is increased in this way; third, if the previous history of the animal is controlled in this way the sensitivity of different pieces of skins are more similar. The areas of skin most suitable for using in this technique are from the thighs, avoiding the surface marking areas. Another important

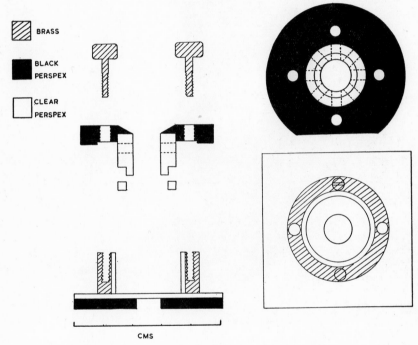

FIG. 13. Diagram of cell used to hold the skin. (Main, 1960.)

point seems to be that before using the skin for an actual assay, each piece should first be immersed in a sufficient concentration of pituitary extract to expand the melanophores almost but not quite fully. The skin is then washed with saline and left immersed in saline until the melanophores are fully contracted again and in a suitable condition for test. This usually takes about 45 minutes. Skin treated in this way from *Rana temporaria* remains viable for at least 10 hours and can be subject to 6 or 7 different concentrations of extract. A concentration of 0.1 mU. of "B" in the 2 ml. of saline contained in the cell usually gives a reasonable response. Galvanometer readings and readings of the m.i. are taken simul-

FIG. 14. Binocular microscope fitted with photoelectric cell with skin holder placed on the stage. (Main, 1960).

taneously every 10 or 15 minutes until the maximum response is elicited, usually in 30 to 45 minutes. Assessment of potency is made from (a) the readings of the m.i. in the usual way and (b) from the amount of light absorbed which is recorded as a percentage of the light originally passing through the skin and is plotted against the log concentration (Fig. 15).

A great deal of individual variation occurs in the response of different pieces of skin to the same low concentration of extract and only the more sensitive are used. Both standard and unknown solutions are tested on each sample of skin and fairly accurate results can usually be obtained using only three samples. Up to 4 pieces of skin can be handled together by one worker, so that the method is not too time consuming. It does, however, take much more skilled time than the *in vivo* method.

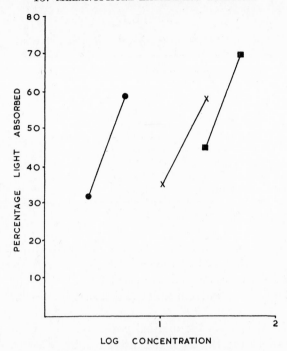

FIG. 15. Dose-response curve of isolated skin (*Rana temporaria*) to extracts of activity from different sources. (Main *et al.*, 1960.)

KEY: ● = Ox posterior lobe pituitary extract (international standard); ✕ = human anterior lobe pituitary extract; ■ = normal human blood extract.

B. METHODS USING LIGHT REFLECTION

Shizume *et al.* (1954) describe their method as a modification of that described by Frieden *et al.* (1948), and they used quantitative photoelectric measurement of light reflected from the skin to determine the darkening of isolated frog skin.

Skin is removed from frogs' thighs, cleaned of larger vessels, clamped between two frames, and placed in a beaker containing 20 cc. saline (NaCl 6.50 gm. per liter, KCl 0.14 gm. per liter, CaCl₂ 0.12 gm. per liter, NaHCO₃ 0.20 gm. per liter). The search unit is placed with its opening uppermost and the beaker placed over it so that the skin corresponds with the opening. Room light is kept constant. After the skin is placed in the saline, there is a contraction of its melanophores and increased reflectance which reaches its maximum in an hour. The recommended procedure, to avoid change of pH and salt concentration in the saline bathing the skin, is to make appropriate dilutions of the unknown so

TABLE IX

VALUES OF Δ_1/Δ_2 OBTAINED WITH VARIOUS CONCENTRATIONS OF MSH

0.125 U./ml.	0.25 U./ml.	0.5 U./ml.	1.0 U./ml.	2.0 U./ml.
0.35	0.59	0.76	1.18	1.23
0.39	0.31	0.81	0.96	1.26
0.24	0.57	0.90	0.94	1.32
0.24	0.58	0.79	1.12	1.13
0.15	0.38	0.63	1.00	1.34
0.21	0.49	0.69	0.95	1.21
0.13	0.54	0.63	0.90	1.31
0.30	0.61	0.78	0.83	1.20

^a *a* From Shizume *et al.*, 1954.

that only 0.1–0.2 ml. of a neutral extract is put into the 20-cc. beaker holding the skin. After addition of "B" solution the reflectance decreases and the reading on the meter is taken at 60 minutes. The skin is then washed for 30 minutes in fresh saline and then a further "B" sample can be tested.

Table IX, taken from the original paper, records responses to different concentrations of "B." Δ_1 is the meter reading after 60 minutes immersion in the saline containing from 0.125–2.0 U. per milliliter of the unknown "B" extract; the skin is then washed in saline for 30 minutes.

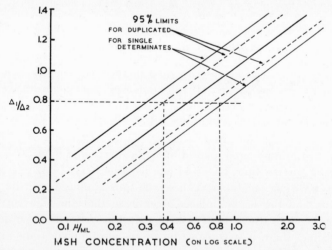

FIG. 16. Regression of response (Δ_1/Δ_2) on log of "B" (MSH) concentration, with 95% confidence limits for single and duplicate determinations. (From Shizume *et al.*, 1954.)

Twenty units[1] of the reference standard are then introduced so that the saline contains 1 U. per milliliter, and Δ_2 is the increment reading after 60 minutes. It is not stated how often a single piece of skin can be activated reliably but we are told that "twenty duplicates (can be) performed easily in a day." Figure 16 "represents the regression of response Δ_1/Δ_2 versus the logarithm of concentration with approximately 95% confidence limits. This graph may be used as a nomogram of the mean Δ_1/Δ_2 between 0.26 and 1.26. Thus, with a two-skin assay two determinations of Δ_1/Δ_2 on the same solution of MSH in Ringer's solution is 0.80, the concentration of MSH may be estimated to be between 0.39 and 0.82 unit per ml." From their results it is clear that the method could be fairly accurate if a sufficient number of pieces of skin were used.

Experiments were made to test the response to variations in osmotic activity, ionic strength, pH, temperature, heavy metals, and a variety of organic compounds. These showed the salt concentration should be kept between 0.75 and 1.25 × that of Ringer, the pH must be kept above 6.5, and the temperature at 20–25°C. Solutions of a number of metallic salts, steroids, and pressor amines were found to have an effect but no information is given on the effect of the likely contaminants in glandular extracts. The authors conclude that the method is "particularly useful for the isolation and identification of MSH" and that "possible interference by other substances could be eliminated easily by using dilutions of 10^5 or greater."

Hudson and Bentley's procedure (1957a) is similar to that of Shizume *et al.* (1954) and differs mainly in that hypophysectomized *Xenopus* were used as skin donors. The skin is placed in a special container holding 2 ml. of solution and designed so that both surfaces of the skin are bathed in the fluid under test. Reflection from the skin is measured by a reflectance head placed on top of the supports shown (Fig. 17).

1. Assay Procedure

Three pieces of skin taken from the same animal are fixed in the frames and allowed to stand in *Xenopus* Ringer for 30 minutes. The saline solution is then replaced by saline containing pituitary extract, either reference standard or unknown, for 45 minutes. The skin is then flushed with another sample of the test solution and 45 minutes later a reading is taken of reflectance. This means the skin has been subjected to the pituitary solution for 90 minutes before the reading is taken. The difference between initial and final galvanometer readings is recorded.

[1] Unfortunately these authors chose their own reference standard powder and defined a unit as the effect produced by 0.04 μg. of it. We find 1.33×10^4 of these units equivalent to 1 international unit.

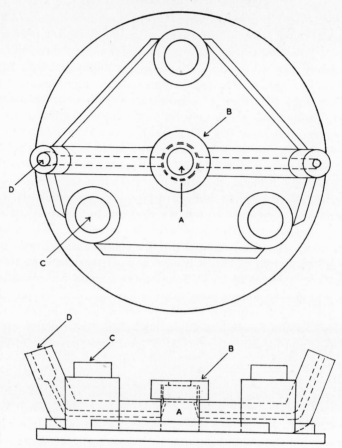

FIG. 17. Sectional drawing of Hudson and Bentley's skin bath (1957a). (A) Small well containing fluid under test; (B) Ring to clip skin on to well; (C) Supports for reflectance head; (D) Attachment for syringe to introduce solution under test.

The chamber is then flushed with Ringer and the skin allowed to return to its initial level of reflectance. Once this has been reached, usually within 30–40 minutes, the procedure can be repeated. Hudson and Bentley (1957b) arranged their assay so that the response to an unknown solution lay between the responses to 2 different concentrations of standard; sometimes 4 doses were applied to a single piece of skin.

Table X shows the responses to a ninefold dose range of the reference standard. Regression analysis of these responses shows that a reasonably good linear relationship exists between log dose and response. Table XI shows the responses of skin from hypophysectomized *Xenopus* to doses

TABLE X

SKIN RESPONSES FROM NORMAL, LIGHT-ADAPTED TOADS TO DOSES
OF P.60 CORTICOTROPIN[a]

Dose (μg./ml.)	Change in reflectance (galvanometer readings)		
	Skin 1	Skin 2	Skin 3
0.044	3.0	0.5	4.5
0.133	14.5	17.0	15.0
0.4	21.5	24.5	15.5
0.044	3.0	3.5	1.0
0.133	13.5	14.5	14.5
0.4	23.5	31.0	25.5
0.044	0.0	3.5	2.0
0.133	21.0	16.5	18.5
0.4	22.0	24.0	25.5

[a] From Hudson and Bentley, 1957a.
P.60 = Commonwealth Serum Laboratories Batch No.

of the same reference standard; this skin is plainly much more sensitive. No information is given on the effect of likely contaminants.

Like Shizume *et al.* (1954), Hudson and Bentley chose a reference standard (a corticotropin) of their own, so their figures cannot be related directly to the results of other workers. They have, however, in a subsequent communication (Bentley and Hudson, 1957) recorded that their

TABLE XI

SKIN RESPONSES FROM HYPOPHYSECTOMIZED TOADS TO DOSES
OF P.60 CORTICOTROPIN[a]

Dose (μg./ml.)	Change in reflectance (galvanometer readings)		
	Skin 1	Skin 2	Skin 3
0.02	4.0	7.5	2.5
0.06	17.5	17.0	16.5
0.18	21.0	28.0	31.0
0.02	8.5	4.5	6.5
0.06	12.0	19.0	17.5
0.18	23.5	21.5	25.5

[a] From Hudson and Bentley (1957a).

corticotropin was 1.04 times as potent as Lerner's so that 1 μg. of their reference standard contains about 26 Lerner units.

Since they also worked with intact and hypophysectomized *Xenopus* using the same reference standard, they can say with confidence that their isolated skin preparation is much more sensitive than is the whole animal method. They comment that the isolated skin method "is by no means as simple, reliable or precise" as that using the whole animal.

Extravagant claims have been made for the comparative sensitivity of the *in vitro* test. Hudson and Bentley (1957a) for example, claim that theirs is 100–150 times as sensitive as the test using the whole animal. They base this, not on the relative *amount* of activity required, but on a comparison between the concentration of active substance needed to produce an effect when 2 ml. is used in an isolated skin technique and 0.25 ml. is used by injection into the whole animal. Up to 1 ml. of a nontoxic extract can be injected into the whole animal and this would bring the ratio down to about 30. If test animals are selected for sensitivity a further reduction in the ratio can be obtained.

Main *et al.* (1960) compared the same extracts on isolated skin of *Rana temporaria* and on whole *Xenopus* and found (1) most isolated skin samples respond to a degree suitable for assay purposes when immersed in 2 ml. saline containing 0.1 mU. of "B," and (2) selected normal *Xenopus* respond adequately to an injection of 0.2 ml. containing 1.0 mU. In other words, this *in vitro* technique seems to be only about 10 times as sensitive as the *in vivo* method.

X. Assay of Melanophore-Expanding Substance in Urine and Blood

Neutralized urine is often toxic when injected into amphibia. Even when no toxic signs are apparent after the injection of urine, *Xenopus* usually respond erratically to subsequent doses of "B" extracts. In any case, the urine of normal amphibia and mammals does not appear to contain enough MES for assay by direct injection. Therefore urine samples should be purified and concentrated before testing.

Landgrebe and Waring (1941) used carbon adsorption and phenol elution in an attempt to detect the activity in normal urine, most samples of which produced a slight macroscopic darkening of the test animals. While 60% of the activity of added pituitary extract was recoverable by their method, yet they could not demonstrate the presence of "B" activity in normal human urine. They concluded that the darkening substance was not "B." Shizume and Lerner (1954) also suggested a method using adsorption onto benzoic acid, solution of the benzoic acid in acetone, and extraction with hot 80% alcohol. Only 20% of added "B" extract could be recovered and the authors pointed out that there was no absolute proof that the MES in pregnancy urine is "B." It seems likely, however, that some of the methods (outlined below) for blood would also be useful for urine.

Blood from amphibia and fish can be assayed after injection directly into a test animal of the same species (Fig. 18). Difficulties arise, how-

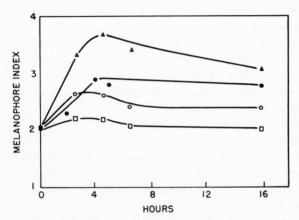

Fig. 18. Responses of hypophysectomized eels to doses of pressor-free posterior lobe extract and serum removed from black-adapted eels; all injections 3 ml. (From Waring and Landgrebe, 1941.)

Key: —●—●— Serum from donor fish; —△—△— 0.01% pituitary extract; —○—○— 0.005% pituitary extract; —□—□— 0.0025% pituitary extract.

ever, when measuring the MES in the circulation of one species by injecting blood into test animals of another species. It is probable, too, that mammalian blood contains less MES than that of fish and amphibia. So assays of blood also require processing and concentration procedures.

Procedures to concentrate the activity using either adsorption or precipitation techniques have not yet been put on a proper quantitative basis. One cannot hope to get 100% recovery of the original activity, but in the absence of this ideal, a reasonable objective would be an assessment of the yield. We still wait for someone to provide this kind of data by trying various procedures on say *Xenopus* blood, where a good estimate of initial concentration can be obtained by injecting blood direct from donor to test animal. Methods effective for *Xenopus* worked out in this way will not necessarily be suitable for mammalian blood, but would be worth testing.

The earliest recorded effort to extract MES from mammalian blood seems to be that of Jores (1933, 1935). He precipitated blood protein with acetone, made a dilute acetic acid extract from the precipitate and evaporated this to dryness. The active principle was then taken up in hot ethanol, the solution evaporated to dryness, and an aqueous solution made from the residue and tested on isolated skin. By this method Jores claimed not only to have detected MES in blood from intact rabbits but to have detected quantitative differences according to whether the donor had been in light or darkness. Landgrebe *et al.* (1943), using an *in vivo* method of assay, could not confirm Jores' finding of the activity in the blood of untreated animals, but showed that with the addition of known amounts of "B" extract to the blood before extraction there was a yield of about 60%. Modifications of Jores' technique might yet prove useful. Apart from Levinson's (1940) work, which is of unknown significance because he used heat treatment with alkali, interest in the problem seems to have flagged for many years.

The advent of the therapeutic use of ACTH extracts and the skin pigmentation produced by prolonged treatment with this material (Sprague *et al.*, 1950) encouraged renewed interest in the measurement of "B" in human blood. Johnsson and Högberg (1952) and Sulman (1952) claimed to have detected MES in blood. Johnsson and Högberg precipitated allegedly inert protein from serum with trichloroacetic acid and then threw down the activity with phosphotungstic acid. The solid was dissolved in decinormal sodium hydroxide, treated with Amberlite IRA-400, and injected into hypophysectomized *R. temporaria* and *esculenta*. Serum from normal individuals produced a slight rise of m.i. but trebling the dose produced no further effect. On the other hand, serum from patients with Addison's disease produced a maximum melanophore expansion in some of the test animals which indicates that, here at least, he might have been estimating "B."

Sulman treated whole blood with acid-acetone to precipitate allegedly inert protein and then threw down the MES by adding further quantities of acetone. The solid was dissolved in dilute sodium hydroxide, neutralized and injected into *Hyla arborea*. Macroscopic change of color from bright green to dark olive was considered a positive reaction. No evidence that he was dealing with "B" was presented, however.

Shizume and Lerner (1954) investigated the matter further and used a new method of extracting blood:

Twenty milliliters of venous blood was drawn and immediately mixed with 80 ml. of glacial acetic acid. The mixture was stirred gently at 70°–80°C. for 30 minutes in a water bath, transferred to a 2-liter Erlenmeyer flask, and then diluted with 1300 ml. of distilled water; 2 gm. of washed oxycellulose was added, and the mixture shaken overnight mechanically. The activity was adsorbed on the oxycellulose. The mixture was filtered through a coarse sintered glass, and the oxycellulose was washed with 0.1 N acetic acid until the washings became colorless. The MES was eluted from the oxycellulose by suspending the oxycellulose in 20 ml. of 80% acetic acid. The material was stirred gently at 70°–80°C. for one hour in a water bath and filtered through a sintered glass. The precipitate was treated in the same manner again with approximately 10 ml. of 80% acetic acid. All the filtrates were combined and diluted with an equal volume of water and lyophilized. A brown-colored solid was obtained which was dissolved in 2 ml. of distilled water and neutralized with a small amount of 1 N sodium hydroxide. This was tested on isolated frog skin by the method outlined under Section IX, B.

The authors have produced good evidence that the activity extracted from the blood of an adrenalectomized dog might be of pituitary origin. The preoperative level of about 0.25 mU. per milliliter (3 Lerner units) was increased to about 1.8 mU. per milliliter by adrenalectomy and this was again reduced to normal by treatment with deoxycorticosterone acetate.

Bentley and Hudson (1957) compared some of the different methods of extraction of blood using *in vivo* assay methods and evolved a method which they found much more efficient than those previously used. Protein is removed from whole blood by the addition of an equal volume of acetone, the acetone is evaporated under reduced pressure at 45°C., the residual aqueous extract is acidified to decinormal with acetic acid, and the activity adsorbed to oxycellulose. The MES was eluted from the oxycellulose with decinormal hydrochloric acid, neutralized, and tested. By this means they could recover between 80 and 85% of added "B." They found (Table XII) that their method gave a higher yield than the others tested and that there is a greater yield with whole blood than with plasma or serum. This they thought was due to adsorption of activity to the blood cells. Hudson and Bentley (1957b), using this method of extraction and using isolated skin from hypophysectomized *Xenopus* as a more sensitive test, found that patients with Addison's disease had more MES circulating than normal.

A finding by Landgrebe *et al.* (1943) seems to have escaped the notice of more recent workers: "In our experiments (with whole animals using Jores' method of extracting blood) a very noticeable local darkening frequently occurred and persisted for various periods, even though the melanophore index did not rise above 2.5. The reason why we are doubtful as to whether we ever detected "B" in the blood of normal animals is that if the equivalent of 3 ml. raised the index to 2.5, twice the dose had no

TABLE XII

RECOVERIES OF ADDED AMOUNTS OF MSH TO BLOOD, PLASMA, AND SERUM YIELDED
BY DIFFERENT METHODS[a]

MSH added to	MSH recovered from	MSH added (μg.)	% Recovery	Method and author
Plasma	Plasma	500	23	Acetone extraction, ether precipitation
Plasma	Plasma	500	58	Sulman (1952)
Plasma	Plasma	500	45	
Plasma	Plasma	500	39	
Blood	Blood	500	25	
Blood	Blood	500	36	
Blood	Plasma	500	<5	
Blood	Serum	500	<5	
Blood	Serum	1000	<5	
Blood	Serum	500	<5	Phosphotungstic acid precipitation
Blood	Serum	1000	<5	Johnsson and Högberg (1952)
Blood	Serum	1000	<5	
Blood	Blood	250	12	
Blood	Blood	500	20	
Plasma	Plasma	500	10	
Blood	Blood	500	25	Acetic acid extraction, oxycellulose con-
Blood	Blood	500	45	centration Sydnor and Sayers (1952)
Blood	Blood	500	56	
Blood	Blood	250	76	
Blood	Blood	250	68	
Blood	Plasma	500	20	
Blood	Serum	500	<5	
Plasma	Plasma	500	60	
Blood	Blood	500	63[b]	Acetone extraction, oxycellulose concen-
Blood	Blood	500	71[b]	tration (Currently described)
Blood	Blood	500	83	
Blood	Blood	500	78	
Blood	Blood	500	84	
Plasma	Plasma	500	55	
Plasma	Plasma	500	80	
Plasma	Plasma	500	62	
Serum	Serum	500	70	
Blood	Plasma	500	10	
Blood	Plasma	500	15	
Blood	Serum	500	<5	

[a] From Bentley and Hudson (1957).
[b] Acid-acetone extraction.

greater effect. This does not happen with graded doses of pituitary." The relevance of this is the possibility that the reflectance scale in isolated skin techniques for low amounts of activity is measuring differences associated with only slight melanophore expansion.

Main *et al.* (1960) have produced results which avoid this criticism. They used simple acid-acetone precipitation of blood proteins and subsequent precipitation of the MES with further acetone. An extract made from blood of a hyperpigmented patient, when injected into whole *Xenopus, Hyla,* or tested on isolated skin of *Rana* gives dose response curves which are parallel to those obtained with international standard extract (Fig. 15). They also found that their method using isolated skin was about 10 times as sensitive as that using the whole animal.

It would seem then that without more knowledge of the specificity of isolated skin, further work should be directed toward methods which will more efficiently extract mammalian blood to overcome the relative insensitivity of the *in vivo* technique.

REFERENCES

Abel, J. (1924). "Physiological, Chemical and Clinical Studies on Pituitary Principles." Lippincott, Philadelphia, Pennsylvania.

Belehradek, J. (1937). *Compt. rend. soc. biol.* **126,** 119.

Bentley, G. A., and Hudson, B. (1957). *Australian J. Exptl. Biol. Med. Sci.* **35,** 157.

Burgers, A. C. J. (1956). "Investigations into the Action of Certain Hormones and other Substances on the Melanophores of the South African Clawed Toad, *Xenopus laevis.*" G. W. Van der Wiel and Co., Arnhem.

Burn, J. H. (1937). "Biological Standardisation." Oxford Univ. Press, London and New York.

Calloway, N. O., McCormack, R. M., and Singh, N. P. (1942). *Endocrinology* **30,** 423.

Chen, G., and Geiling, E. M. K. (1943). *J. Pharmacol. Exptl. Therap.* **78,** 222.

Frieden, E. H., Fishbein, J. W., and Hisaw, F. L. (1948). *Arch. Biochem.* **17,** 183.

Hill, A. V., Parkinson, J. L., and Solandt, D. Y. (1935). *J. Exp. Biol.* **12,** 397.

Hogben, L. (1923). *Quart. J. Exptl. Physiol.* **13,** 177.

Hogben, L. (1924). "Pigmentary Effector System." Oliver & Boyd, Edinburgh.

Hogben, L., and Gordon, C. (1930). *J. Exptl. Biol.* **7,** 286.

Hogben, L., and Slome, D. (1931). *Proc. Roy. Soc.* **B108,** 10.

Hogben, L., and Winton, F. A. (1922). *Proc. Roy. Soc.* **B93,** 318.

Hudson, B., and Bentley, G. A. (1957a). *Australian J. Exptl. Biol. Med. Sci.* **35,** 45.

Hudson, B., and Bentley, G. A. (1957b). *Australasian Ann. Med.* **6**(2), 98.

Johnsson, S., and Högberg, B. (1952). *Nature* **169,** 286.

Jores, A. (1933). *Klin. Wochschr.* **11,** 1293.

Jores, A. (1935). *Klin. Wochschr.* **14,** 1713.

Karkun, J. N. (1960). Unpublished.

Ketterer, B., and Remilton, E. (1954), *J. Endocrinol.* **11,** 14.

Kleinholz, L. H., and Rahn, H. (1940). *Anat. Record* **76,** 157.

Landgrebe, F. W. (1939). *J. Exptl. Biol.* **16**, 89.

Landgrebe, F. W., and Mitchell, G. M. (1954). *Quart. J. Exptl. Physiol.* **39**, 11.

Landgrebe, F. W., and Samson, L. (1944). *J. Obstet. Gynaecol. Brit. Empire* **51**, 133.

Landgrebe, F. W., and Waring, H. (1941). *Quart. J. Exptl. Physiol.* **31**, 31.

Landgrebe, F. W., and Waring, H. (1944). *Quart. J. Exptl. Physiol.* **33**, 1.

Landgrebe, F. W., and Waring, H. (1949). *Australian J. Exptl. Biol. Med. Sci.* **27**, 331.

Landgrebe, F. W., and Waring, H. (1950). *In* "The Hormones" (G. Pincus and K. V. Thimann, eds.), Vol. 2. Academic Press, New York.

Landgrebe, F. W., Reid, E., and Waring, H. (1943). *Quart. J. Exptl. Physiol.* **32**, 121.

Landgrebe, F. W., Munday, K., and Waring, H. (1950). *Australian J. Exptl. Biol. Med. Sci.* **28**, 619.

Levinson, L. L. (1940). *Proc. Natl. Acad. Sci. U.S.* **26**, 257.

McLean, A. J. (1928). *J. Pharmacol. Exptl. Therap.* **33**, 301.

Main, R. A. (1960). Unpublished.

Main, R. A., Karkun, J. N., Mitchell, G. M., Landgrebe, F. W. (1960). *J. Physiol. (London)* **152**, 459.

Shen, T. C. R. (1937). *Arch. intern. pharmacodynamie* **57**, 289; *Compt. rend. soc. biol.* **126**, 433.

Shizume, K., and Lerner, A. B. (1954). *J. Clin. Endocrinol. and Metabolism* **14**, 1491.

Shizume, K., Lerner, A. B., and Fitzpatrick, T. B. (1954). *Endocrinology* **54**, 553.

Smith, C. D. (1936). *J. Cellular Comp. Physiol.* **8**, 83.

Sprague, R. G., Power, M. H., Mason, H. L., Albert, A., Mathieson, D. R., Hench, P. S., Kendall, E. C., Slocumb, C. H., and Polley, H. F. (1950). *A.M.A. Arch. Internal Med.* **85**, 199.

Stehle, R. L. (1936). *Am. J. Pharm.* **57**, 1.

Sulman, F. G. (1952). *Lancet.* **i**, 1161.

Sydnor, K. L., and Sayers, G. (1952). *Proc. Soc. Exptl. Biol. Med.* **79**, 432.

Teague, R. S., Noojin, R. O., and Geiling, E. M. K. (1939). *J. Pharmacol. Exptl. Therap.* **65**, 115.

Thing, E. (1952). *Acta Endocrinol.* **10**, 295.

Trendelenburg, P. (1926). *Arch. Exptl. Pathol. Pharmakol. Naunyn-Schmiedeberg's* **114**, 255.

Waring, H., and Landgrebe, F. W. (1941). *J. Exptl. Biol.* **18**, 80.

Wright, P. A. (1946). *Anat. Record* **96**, 540.

Wright, P. A. (1948). *J. Cellular Comp. Physiol.* **31**, 111.

Zondek, B., and Krohn, H. (1932). *Klin. Wochschr.* **11**, 405.

Chapter 16

Relaxin

Bernard G. Steinetz, Vivian L. Beach, and Robert L. Kroc

I. Introduction

Increasing international interest in the nonsteroidal hormone, relaxin, has underscored the need for a practical and reproducible method of bioassay, and for a well-characterized reference standard.

Although all available evidence indicates that relaxin activity is associated with a water-soluble polypeptide structure, the hormone has not yet been isolated as a chemical entity. Thus, the quality of much relaxin research is directly dependent upon the adequacies (or inadequacies) of the bioassay methods used by the investigator or his suppliers. The most common method of assay employs subjective evaluation of increased flexibility of the pelvic girdle of guinea pigs. With careful control and adequate numbers, reproducibility and statistical validity may be obtained. However, most workers have been content to use the assay in a qualitative sense.

Relaxin extracts are generally prepared from pregnant sow ovaries, which have high activity and are commercially available frozen or acetone dried. However, relaxin is not restricted to the pregnant mammal. Relaxin-like activity has been found in elasmobranch ovaries, in the ovaries and testes of birds, in pregnant and nonpregnant mammalian ovaries, in placentas, and in blood serum of female mammals including man (for reviews see Hisaw and Zarrow, 1950, and Steinetz *et al.*, 1959a). Recently, definite relaxin activity was detected in mammalian testes (unpublished data 1960).

Experimental studies have established several roles of relaxin in mammalian reproduction. In addition to the softening action of relaxin upon the ligaments of the pelvis, effects on the motility and composition of the uterus, on the distensibility of the cervix, on parturition, and on mammary gland growth have been described (for reviews and recent literature see Hisaw and Zarrow, 1950; Kroc *et al.*, 1959; Steinetz *et al.*, 1959a; Wada and Turner, 1959; Wiqvist, 1959a, b).

The dramatic softening effects of relaxin on the connective tissue of the pubic symphysis have stimulated investigations of its actions on peripheral and vascular connective tissues (Casten *et al.*, 1956; Boucek, 1958; Casten and Gilmore, 1958; Reynolds and Livingood, 1959).

Progress in the field has been hampered by the lack of standardization of relaxin extracts used by different investigators. To date, no bioassay method has been universally accepted, and no United States Pharmacopeia (U.S.P.), British Pharmacopeia (B.P.), or international standard has been established.

It is the purpose of the present communication to describe the various relaxin assay methods which have been published, and to propose a simple and reliable method which may be reproduced easily in any laboratory.

In the absence of a national or international standard, an appropriate "house" or "lab" standard may be designated on rather firm criteria, so that potency estimates obtained by various laboratories, using the proposed assay method, should not differ by more than 2- to 3-fold. At present, discrepancies of 25- to 50-fold are not uncommon when ill-defined standards are employed in different assay designs, or investigators rely on response units.

II. A Standard Preparation

In 1955, a 130-gm. lot of purified relaxin extracted from selected pregnant sow ovaries (Kroc and Phillips, 1958) was set aside as a house reference standard. This material, laboratory number B37-348/8alα, was designated Warner-Chilcott Relaxin Reference Standard W1164-A, Lot 8. Repeated assays against an experience curve by guinea pig pubic symphysis palpation (Kroc *et al.*, 1956a, b, 1959) revealed a potency of approximately 150 guinea pig units per milligram. The activity of 1 mg. of standard is roughly equivalent to the relaxin activity of 15 to 20 ml. of rabbit serum obtained on the twenty-eighth day of pregnancy, or to the activity of 250 mg. of fresh pregnant sow ovaries obtained when the fetal crown-rump length is 5 to 7 inches.

Standard W1164-A, Lot 8 is a fine white powder, moisture content 6.5%, nitrogen 16.55%, ash 1.6%; it is soluble up to 6% in 0.85% saline or distilled water at pH 5 or lower.

For those readers who wish to establish a provisional standard in their own laboratory, an extract of frozen or fresh pregnant sow ovaries, of acetone-dried sow ovaries, or of pregnant rabbit serum may be made according to published methods (Albert and Money, 1946; Albert *et al.*, 1947; Frieden and Hisaw, 1950; Frieden and Layman, 1957; Kroc and Phillips, 1958). The extracts may then be tested at several dose levels using the mouse interpubic ligament method described in Section IV. The useful portion of the dose-response curve (2-fold dose increments) for interpubic ligament growth in estrogen-primed mice should occupy the ranges as shown in the following tabulation.

Dose of relaxin	Mean ligament length (10–20 mice)
No relaxin	0.4–0.8 mm.
Low dose	1.0–1.6 mm.
Intermediate dose	1.7–2.2 mm.
High dose	2.3–3.0 mm.

The slope (b) of the dose-response line should be in the range 1.5–2.5 or greater, and $\lambda(s/b)$ values should be less than 0.4.

If these criteria are met, the investigator may assume that the doses of his standard are roughly equivalent to 1.7, 3.3, and 6.7 μg. Standard W1164-A, Lot 8.

The use of appropriate standards will be discussed further in Sections III–VI.

III. Guinea Pig Pubic Symphysis Methods of Assay

A. SURVEY OF GUINEA PIG METHODS

1. Pubic Symphysis Palpation and X-Ray Measurement of Pubic Separation

Experimental relaxation of the symphysis pubis of the spayed guinea pig was described as early as 1929 by Hisaw. A relaxin assay using ovariectomized estrogen-primed guinea pigs was published by Abramowitz and associates (1944). The Abramowitz unit was defined as the dose of relaxin required to induce unmistakable "relaxation" of the pubic symphysis of two-thirds of a group of 12 guinea pigs. "Relaxation" or mobility was determined subjectively by manual palpation of the pubic symphysis. The assay was thus based upon "all-or-none" criteria. Frieden and Hisaw (1950) added a graded scoring system to Abramowitz' assay. Talmadge and Hurst (1950) described a revised method using a combination of palpation and roentgenographic measurement of the symphysis pubis. A few experiments of this type were attempted in this laboratory (Beach and Kroc, unpublished, 1953) but X-ray measurement of pubic separation did not correlate with relaxin dose or palpation score. A quantitative palpation procedure using intact guinea pigs and a relaxin reference standard was summarized by Kroc and associates (1956a, b, 1959). This method will be described in detail:

B. A PUBIC SYMPHYSIS PALPATION ASSAY PROCEDURE EMPLOYING A REFERENCE STANDARD

1. Materials

Guinea pig colony: Virgin female guinea pigs (mixed strains) weighing 300–400 gm. are housed in aluminum cages on wood shavings. They are maintained on Rockland or Purina Guinea Pig diet and fresh lettuce, one head lettuce per 5 guinea pigs per day. No supplementary water is necessary.

2. Methods

Estrogen priming consists of one subcutaneous injection per week of 5 μg. estradiol cyclopentylpropionate (Depo®-Estradiol, Upjohn) in 0.1 ml. sesame or corn oil.

Relaxin priming (this procedure was proved necessary) is accomplished by administering 20 μg. relaxin standard (Warner-Chilcott Relaxin Reference Standard W1164-A, Lot 8) in 1 ml. saline subcutaneously once a week on the fifth day after the estrogen injection.

Six hours after relaxin administration the symphysis pubis of the animal is palpated. The animal is held head down, ventral side away, between the thighs of the seated examiner. The ischial crests and symphysis pubis are firmly grasped between the thumbs and forefingers so that the two halves of the pelvis may be moved back and forth alternately. If the pubic symphysis is rigid at this time, the estrogen and relaxin priming are continued weekly until marked mobility of the symphysis is observed. The increased flexibility is transient, the peak response occurring at 6 hours and subsiding 12–24 hours after injection.

Mobility responses are estimated subjectively and scored on an arbitrary scale of 0 to 6. "Zero" indicates no detectable flexibility of the pubic symphysis, whereas "6" represents extreme softening of the ligament separating the pubic bones. Scores of 4 or higher are regarded as "positive" responses.

During the priming period approximately 5% of the guinea pigs give positive responses to the first dose of relaxin, 33% to the second dose, and the remaining animals require 3–4 weeks of relaxin priming. (Occasionally an animal does not respond during 8 weeks of priming.) Positively responding animals are usually reliable for assay for several weeks (range = 2–16 weeks).

Experimental relaxation does not usually result in the magnitude of spread or softness observed at the pubic symphysis of the late-pregnant guinea pig. Scoring gradations can be learned only by experience, but if a beginner starts by gently palpating a pregnant guinea pig once or twice a week from mid-pregnancy on, some concept of degree of relaxation can be learned during this transitional period.

One week after an animal has responded positively to 20μg. of relaxin standard it is added to the assay colony. Before assay time all eligible animals, new and old, are mixed and divided into groups of 10 to 20 guinea pigs each.

On the day of assay the relaxin extracts are dissolved or suspended in saline in graded dilutions (usually 2-fold apart) and coded. "Unknown" preparations are administered in parallel with relaxin standard, generally in 1-ml. doses. All animals are palpated before injection. Only those with no symphyseal movement are used. Two operators palpate and score each animal at the sixth hour after injection. Guinea pigs with scores of 4 or higher may be used for assay the following week. Negative animals must be reprimed with relaxin. Pigs which fail to score positively on two consecutive weeks are discarded.

The loss of sensitivity to relaxin described by Noall and Frieden

(1956) was noted during the work described here. In an isolated group of 20 guinea pigs the response to 20μg. relaxin standard fell from 100% positive to 44% positive in 7 weeks and the drop in response to 3.3 μg. was even greater: 50 to 10% in 3 weeks. This observation points out the need for randomization of new and old guinea pigs.

Figure 1 shows variability of absolute response to Warner-Chilcott relaxin standard over a period of 3 months and 95% confidence limits for different sized groups of guinea pigs.

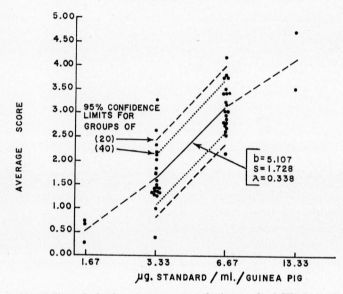

FIG. 1. Variability of absolute response to relaxin standard W1164-A, Lot 8 over a period of 3 months and 95% confidence limits for different sized groups of guinea pigs.

The scores are averaged, and if desired, a median score and per cent positive may be calculated (Kroc *et al.*, 1956a). The activity of an unknown is determined by comparison with the dose response to concomitantly administered relaxin standard.

3. Statistical Evaluation

Statistical analyses are based on scores alone and calculated according to the methods of Bliss (1952) and Snedecor (1940) for a 4- or 6-point balanced assay.

Table I shows two typical bioassays of a relaxin (Releasin®)-vialed preparation. The two assays did not differ significantly from the theoretical potency of 20 mg. S per milliliter. The combined results showed a

TABLE I

BioAssay of Releasin W1164-3, Lot 017, Vialed Solution (U)[a]

Preparation	No. of pigs	Dose/pig	Average score	S.E.	Median score	% Positive
1st Assay						
S	20	3.33 μg.	1.36	0.35	0.5	15
S	20	6.67 μg.	3.21	0.42	4.0	63
U	20	1/6000 ml.[b]	1.38	0.36	1.1	10
U	20	1/3000 ml.[b]	2.93	0.44	4.0	65
2nd Assay						
S	20	3.33 μg.	0.91	0.35	0.0	13
S	20	6.67 μg.	3.13	0.44	4.3	65
U	20	1/6000 ml.[b]	1.93	0.42	1.0	35
U	20	1/3000 ml.[b]	3.01	0.44	4.1	60

Statistical Analysis (based on scores only)

	N^c	Slope b	mg.S/ml.	Range mg.S/ml. at $P = 0.95$	Limits of error at $P = 0.95$
1st Assay	80	5.65	19.0	13.8–26.2	73–138%
2nd Assay	80	5.48	24.2	17.0–34.6	70–143%
Combined:	160	5.56	21.4	17.0–27.0	79–126%

Conclusion: The observed relative potencies did not differ significantly from the reference standard potency.

[a] Guinea pig pubic symphysis palpation method. Reference standard, S (Lab. No. W1164-A, Lot 8) tested concomitantly on 4 assay days within a 9-day period. All doses administered subcutaneously in volume of 1 ml.

[b] Assumed *activity* equivalents to 3.33 and 6.67 μg. reference standard, respectively, based on previous bioassays of constituent purified stock powders.

[c] Total number of animals in completed assay with $N/2$ animals receiving standard (S) and unknown (U), respectively.

potency of 21.4 mg S per milliliter and limits of error of 79–126% at the 95% confidence level.

Despite the subjective element of scoring, the use of coded materials and the averaging of the scores of two operators reduce this inherent error. With as few as 20 guinea pigs at each of two dose levels of unknown and standard, the limits of error at $P = 0.95$ are generally within minus 33 to plus 50% of the observed potency. The error may be further reduced by increasing the number of animals per group.

The above-described relaxin assay has advantages over methods previously reported in the literature. The elimination of ovariectomies, the establishment of a relaxin standard, and the reduction in the number of estrogen injections to one per week make the method practical for laboratory routine.

IV. Mouse Pubic Symphysis Methods of Assay

A. SURVEY OF MOUSE METHODS

Interpubic ligament formation in relaxin-treated mice has been studied by many investigators (Hall, 1956; Crelin, 1957; Storey, 1957; Horn, 1958). Several workers have devised bioassay procedures utilizing dose-proportional increases in interpubic ligament length as a measure of potency of relaxin-containing extracts.

1. X-Ray Measurement of Pubic Separation

Hall and Newton (1947) and Hall (1948) described a qualitative assay in which mice were primed with estrone (1.5 μg. daily for 2 to 9 days) and then injected with relaxin. Pubic symphyses were X-rayed before and 24 hours after relaxin injection and the distance between pubic bones was measured following development of the dental X-ray plates. Response was evaluated in terms of increase in width of the pubic gap. The effects of graded doses of relaxin were not investigated. Dorfman et al. (1953) proposed a quantal assay employing X-ray of the pubic symphysis in ovariectomized adult or intact immature female mice. Using a 4-point assay design with 16 mice at each dose level of "standard" and "unknown," the authors reported limits of error of 65 to 155% at $P = 0.95$, and a λ value of 0.375. The chief drawbacks in the assay design of Dorfman and co-workers were the 5 daily estrogen-priming injections and the 4 injections of relaxin per mouse required to produce a significant response. Subsequent work has shown that this group was using the lower segment of the potential dose-response curve.

Kliman et al. (1953) and Kliman and Greep (1958) also adopted a roentgenographic technique for the measurement of pubic separation in mice. In their study, mice were primed with 1 μg. 17β-estradiol daily for 7 days, and, after obtaining a control X ray of the pelvis, animals were injected subcutaneously with graded doses of relaxin, and X-rayed again 24 hours later.

Kliman and associates (1953) made use of the long dose-response curve and obtained good precision with their method.

An important contribution to relaxin research was the discovery of Kliman and Greep (1955, 1958) that relaxin activity was markedly enhanced by the use of repository vehicles for injection of the hormone.

Thus relaxin, injected as a suspension in beeswax-oil was 65 times more potent than the identical preparation injected in saline solution. The depot principle has been confirmed by a number of investigators (Hall, 1957; Horn, 1958; Kroc et al., 1959; Steinetz et al., 1959a), and will be referred to in Sections VI and VII.

2. Direct Measurement of Interpubic Ligament

Several investigators have reported direct measurement of the interpubic ligament of mice (Crelin, 1954; Kroc et al., 1956b; Steinetz et al., 1957; Horn, 1958).

Kroc et al. (1956b, 1959) and Steinetz et al. (1960) proposed a direct measurement technique involving transillumination of the exposed pubic symphysis. Measurements of ligament lengths were made at $13\times$ magnification using a binocular dissecting microscope fitted with an ocular micrometer. These authors also drastically reduced the total number of injections required for priming and dosing, thus permitting a large increase in the number of animals which could be handled in each assay. Kroc et al. (1959) proposed a single subcutaneous injection of 5 μg. estradiol cyclopentylpropionate for estrogen priming. Seven days later, the mice received single subcutaneous injections of relaxin in 1% aqueous benzopurpurine 4-B. This vehicle was found to be twice as effective as beeswax-oil, and offered the usual advantages of making up and injecting a solution rather than a suspension (Steinetz et al., 1959a).

3. Measurement of Flexibility of the Pelvic Girdle

Crelin (1955) proposed an elegant technique for quantitating changes in the flexibility of the sacroiliac joints and pubic symphyses of mice. The method depends upon the amount of joint flexion produced by a known weight load under standardized conditions of time and positioning of the innominates. Flexion is accurately measured with a protractor viewed through a peep sight. The author has not as yet published bioassay data obtained with the method.

B. A SIMPLE MOUSE INTERPUBIC LIGAMENT DIRECT MEASUREMENT ASSAY EMPLOYING A REFERENCE STANDARD (AFTER KROC et al., 1956b, AND STEINETZ et al., 1960)

1. Materials

a. Mice. Virgin female mice weighing 18–20 gm. are used for assay. In the experience of the authors, many commercially available strains of mice have proven satisfactory for relaxin assay. Docile, rapidly growing animals appear superior to inherently nervous or slow growing mice.

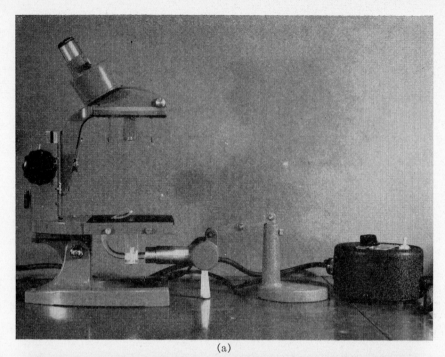

(a)

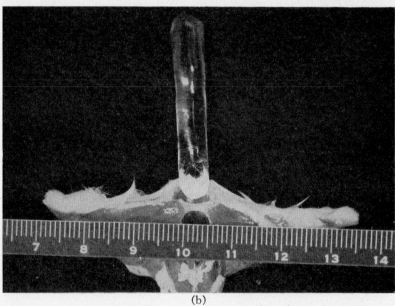

(b)

Fig. 2. (a) Dissecting microscope equipped with transilluminating device and ocular micrometer for measuring interpubic ligament length in mice. (b) The ventral view of a dissection of the mouse pelvis, and the interpubic ligament positioned on the transilluminator (Kroc *et al.*, 1959).

Mice are housed in groups of 10 in boxes sufficiently large to prevent crowding. Rockland Mouse Diet is supplemented with whole oats twice per week, and tap water is allowed *ad libitum*.

b. Solutions for injection. Estradiol cyclopentylpropionate (Depo-Estradiol, Upjohn) is diluted with peanut oil to a concentration of 5 μg./0.1 ml.

Relaxin extracts may be dissolved in 0.9% saline at 10 times the desired concentration and then diluted 1:10 with 1.11% aqueous benzopurpurine 4-B (Dykem). Alternatively, relaxin preparations may be dissolved and diluted with distilled water, and 1% (w/v) benzopurpurine 4-B added as a powder. Final pH should be 4.5–7.2.

c. Special equipment. Binocular dissecting microscope fitted with calibrated ocular micrometer. The transilluminating device consists of a "U-shaped" Lucite rod affixed to the microscope stage as illustrated in Fig. 2. The beveled tip of the rod directs light vertically through the objective. A standard Nicholas illuminator is used as light source.

2. Method of Assay

a. On day 0 each assay mouse is primed with a single subcutaneous injection of 5 μg. estradiol cyclopentylpropionate in 0.1 ml. peanut oil. As 20 mice are generally employed for each of three dose levels of "standard" (S) and "unknown" (U), a minimum of 120 mice are primed for each assay. In practice, it is feasible to prime an additional 60 or 120 mice so that 2 or 3 unknowns may be run concomitantly with the standard on a given assay day.

b. On day 7, the relaxin standard and unknowns are injected, 20 mice per dose level.

c. Eighteen to twenty-four hours later, the mice are killed (in groups of 10) by exposure to an atmosphere of CO_2 (insulated "dry ice" in a closed jar). Mice must weigh at least 20 gm. to be eligible for assay.

d. The abdominal cavities are opened, and uteri examined for evidence of estrogen priming. Mice exhibiting threadlike uteri ("priming failure") are discarded (Steinetz *et al.*, 1960).

e. The anal and vulval areas are cut away with scissors, and the upper half of the body is cut off to prevent subsequent bleeding at the pubic symphysis. The bony birth canal is freed of skin, vagina, and rectum, and fascia is cleaned off the pubic symphysis.

f. The pelvis is positioned on the transilluminator so that the tip of the Lucite rod passes a beam of light vertically through the exposed pubic ligament. The feet are grasped between the thumbs and index fingers, applying a very slight lateral traction. Ligaments do not stretch, but may tear if too much traction is used.

g. The shortest distance between the edges of the pubes is measured, using the ocular micrometer. Micrometer readings are converted to millimeters. When practiced, an operator can dissect and measure at a rate of 2 to 3 mice per minute.

3. Statistics

Data may be handled statistically according to any conventional method. The authors have employed the methods of Bliss (1952) and Snedecor (1940) for 6-point balanced assays. Potencies of unknowns are expressed in milligram equivalents of the reference standard. In acceptable assays, the limits of error at $P = 0.95$ must fall within minus 33 and plus 50% of the observed potency. Usually, the limits of error at $P = 0.95$ are minus 26 to plus 35% or smaller (Steinetz *et al.*, 1960).

4. Results

Figure 3 shows dose-response curves of a typical mouse assay. Table II illustrates statistical evaluation of results of a completed mouse assay.

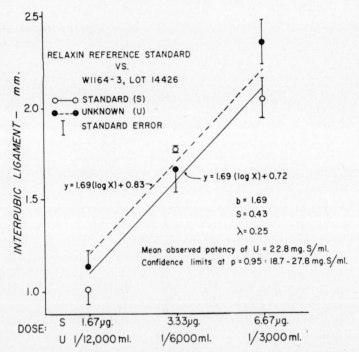

FIG. 3. Mouse interpubic ligament assay of sterile-vialed Releasin solution W1164-3, Lot 14426 against reference standard W1164-A, Lot 8. The unknown was vialed at a theoretical activity of 20 mg. standard/ml. (Steinetz *et al.*, 1960).

TABLE II

MOUSE PUBIC LIGAMENT BIOASSAY OF RELEASIN REPOSITORY SUSPENSION W1164-35, LOT 0729 (U) VERSUS RELAXIN REFERENCE STANDARD W1164-A, LOT 8 (S)[a]

Preparation	No. of mice	Dose (mg. or ml./mouse)	Average ligament length (mm. ± S.E.)
S	20	1.67 mg.	1.25 ± 0.12
S	19	3.33 mg.	1.88 ± 0.11
S	20	6.67 mg.	2.81 ± 0.13
U	21	1/12000 ml.	1.16 ± 0.10
U	21	1/6000 ml.	1.73 ± 0.12
U	19	1/3000 ml.	3.14 ± 0.13

Mean observed potency of U: 20.4 mg.S/ml.
Range of potency (at $P = 0.95$):   17.5–23.7 mg.S/ml.
Limits of error (at $P = 0.95$):   86–116%

$S = 0.527$ $b = 2.95$ $\lambda = 0.179$

[a] From Steinetz *et al.* (1960).

Figure 4 illustrates the distribution of λ values in 21 mouse assays. In two thirds of the assays λ was 0.3 or less. Loss of precision is almost invariably due to a decrease in slope, as the error, "s," remains remarkably constant.

When a high slope value is obtained, fewer observations are required

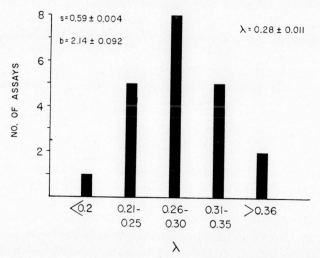

FIG. 4. Distribution of λ values in 21 mouse assays (Steinetz *et al.*, 1960).

to attain satisfactory limits of error. The predictions in Table III were based on a slope of 2.5 (which is frequently observed). Limits of error as low or lower than those predicted in Table III, were obtained in approximately 33% of assays up to 1958. Failure to achieve these limits was generally due to low slope values. Since 1958, the limits shown in Table III have been observed approximately 67% of the time. The improvement is correlated with an increase in slope obtained with

TABLE III

RELATIONSHIP OF EXPECTED LIMITS OF ERROR TO THE TOTAL NUMBER OF OBSERVATIONS IN THE MOUSE ASSAY ASSUMING A CONSTANT SLOPE OF 2.5

Expected % limits of error[a]	Approximate total number of observations
95–105	2745
91–110	686
87–115	308
83–120	177
80–125	116
77–130	82
71–140	48
67–150	32

[a] At $P = 0.95$. At $P = 0.99$ the corresponding limits at each level would naturally cover a greater range.

mice from a new supplier. It is unwise, however, to attribute the difference solely to strain. Steinetz et al. (1960) observed extreme seasonal shifts in slope and dose-response curves of several commercial strains of mice.

According to Steinetz et al. (1960) agreement between 9 replicate mouse assays averaged 91%, and the greatest difference between potency estimates was a nonsignificant 16%. Their data are reproduced in Table IV.

5. Other Uses or Applications of the Mouse Assay

Hall (1949) and later Kliman (personal communication, 1955) and Crelin and Honeyman (1957) described an inhibitory effect of progesterone and certain other steroids on relaxin-induced growth of the pubic ligament in mice. Steinetz et al. (1959a, b) obtained quantitative data on the inhibitory phenomenon, and showed that 19-nortestosterone derivatives were extremely potent in preventing ligament formation due to relaxin treatment. The assay design and results obtained with a number of

TABLE IV

RESULTS OF DUPLICATE MOUSE ASSAYS OF RELAXIN-CONTAINING EXTRACTS
AGAINST REFERENCE STANDARD W1164-A, LOT 8[a]

Type of preparation	Total mice	Potency of U (mg.S/ml. or mg.)	Limits of error, % at $P = 0.95$	λ
Sterile vialed solutions				
Lot 22907				
(a)	113	24.2	79–127	0.28
(b)	112	20.6	81–124	0.24
Lot 25367				
(a)	120	23.8	82–123	0.24
(b)	120	26.0	76–131	0.32
Lot 24757				
(a)	119	21.2	71–141	0.41
(b)	120	19.3	80–125	0.27
Lot 35-0729				
(a)	118	19.3	84–119	0.21
(b)	120	20.4	86–116	0.18
Powders				
M-9714				
(a)	121	1.43	74–135	0.36
(b)	117	1.51	78–129	0.31
M-8630				
(a)	117	0.88	80–124	0.25
(b)	115	0.74	77–131	0.30
M-43 (low potent)				
(a)	153	0.13	81–124	0.29
(b)	89	0.12	71–141	0.33
Relaxin reference standard				
W1164-A, Lot 8				
(a)	123	1.12	77–130	0.31
(b) As above, but with added nonpregnant sow ovarian tissue (2.5 mg./0.2 ml.)	139	0.97	80–125	0.26

[a] From Steinetz et al. (1960).

steroids are illustrated in Figs. 5 and 6. This technique was also found
suitable for evaluating activity of ACTH and gonadotropins, as removal
of adrenals or gonads abolished the inhibitory activity of the tropic
hormones (Steinetz et al., 1959a, b).

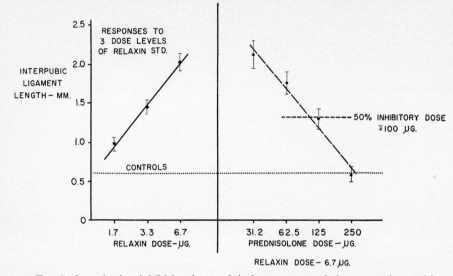

Fig. 5. Quantitative inhibition by prednisolone acetate of the mouse interpubic ligament response to relaxin. All mice were primed with 5 μg. estradiol cyclopentylpropionate on day zero. On day 7, groups of 10 to 20 mice were injected subcutaneously with graded doses of relaxin (left side of figure) or 6.7 μg. relaxin plus graded doses of prednisolone acetate (right side of figure). Controls received only vehicle. Interpubic ligament lengths were measured 24 hours after injection (Steinetz et al., 1959a).

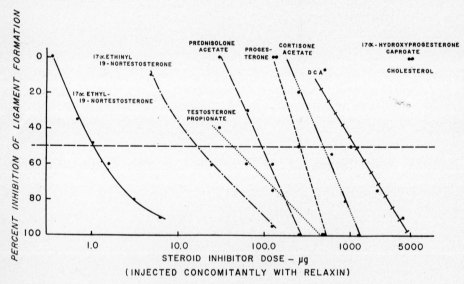

Fig. 6. Acute steroid inhibition of interpubic ligament formation in relaxin-treated estrogen-primed mice. The various inhibitors were evaluated by the method illustrated in Fig. 5. The data are summarized here plotting inhibition of interpubic ligament formation against steroid dose (Steinetz et al., 1959a).

V. Assay of Relaxin by Inhibition of Uterine Motility

Relaxin-containing extracts specifically inhibit the spontaneous motility of the estrogen-dominated uterus *in vivo* and *in vitro* (Felton *et al.*, 1953; Sawyer *et al.*, 1953; Wada and Yuhara, 1956; Miller *et al.*, 1957; Wiqvist and Paul, 1958; Wiqvist, 1959a, b). Several investigators have suggested that there exist marked species differences in uterine response to relaxin (Miller *et al.*, 1957; McGaughey *et al.*, 1958). Progestin domination and pregnancy also importantly modify the effects of relaxin on uterine motility patterns (Posse and Kelly, 1956; Kelly and Posse, 1956; Wiqvist and Paul, 1958; Wiqvist, 1959a, b).

Several workers have proposed methods of relaxin assay based upon inhibition of spontaneous uterine contractions.

In general, neither the assay designs nor the expenditure of time required for execution make this type of assay attractive for routine use. However, the 4-point balanced assay designed by Wiqvist and Paul (1958) and the screening procedure described by Kroc *et al.* (1959) are well standardized and useful for correlating the uterine motility-inhibiting effects of relaxin with its very different action on the pubic symphysis.

A. *In Vivo* METHODS

Krantz and associates (1950) first described the uterine motility-inhibiting activity of aqueous extracts of sow corpora lutea. In this and a subsequent publication by Felton *et al.* (1953), activity was evaluated *in vivo* in anesthetized guinea pigs. The animals were primed with massive doses of estradiol benzoate (80–100 μg. daily for 7 to 10 days). One uterine horn was exposed and attached to a recording lever, and after a satisfactory contractile pattern had been established, the test preparation was injected intravenously, and the decrease in amplitude of contractions observed. Potency was estimated as the minimum dose required to induce a 90% reduction in amplitude of contractions for a period of 10 minutes. No reference standard was employed and no statistically analyzable data have been published to date. This method has been evaluated in our laboratory, and although qualitatively similar results were observed, variations in sensitivity between guinea pigs were so extreme that no quantitation was possible.

This intravenous test in guinea pigs is routinely used for estimation of potency of a commercial extract of sow ovaries marketed for oral use (Bryant, 1959).

B. *In Vitro* METHODS

1. Wiqvist and Paul (1958) proposed a relaxin assay based on inhibition of motility of the rat uterus *in vitro*. They carefully explored the effects of various environmental variables and set up standardized conditions and criteria which may be duplicated by any laboratory. Ovariectomized rats were primed with 2 μg. estradiol daily for 3 days. On the fourth day, uterine horns were removed, bisected, and suspended in Locke's solution with 1% CO_2 in O_2 (pH 7.57–7.60) and a temperature of $37.5 \pm 0.5°C$. Recording was effected with a heart lever (1.5 gm. tension) writing on a smoked drum. A symmetrical 4-point assay design was adopted with twofold dose increments of standard and unknown.

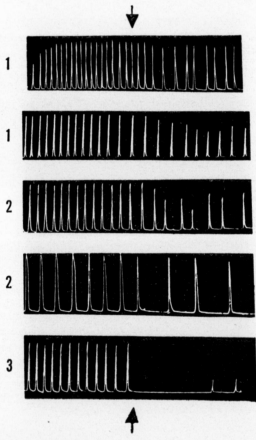

FIG. 7. Uterine motility inhibition scoring system of Wiqvist and Paul (1958). Visual responses are apportioned values of 1 to 3.

Responses were classified visually and assigned values of 1 to 3 according to the scheme represented in Fig. 7. The subjective element in scoring did not seriously influence potency estimates when 8 examiners independently classified the tracings obtained in a particular assay.

Since all 4 test doses (2 doses each of standard and unknown) were run simultaneously on the 4 uterine segments obtained from each rat, good precision was obtained with small numbers of rats. A sample assay is illustrated in Table V and results and statistical evaluations of this and three other assays are shown in Table VI. Standard preparation number 3 is Standard W1164-A, Lot 8, described in Section II. Test preparation number 4 is W1164-A, Lot 36, which assayed 0.067 mg. standard per milligram by the mouse interpubic ligament procedure (Section IV).

The indices of precision (λ) obtained by Wiqvist and Paul (1958) compare favorably with those generally observed in the mouse interpubic ligament assay.

2. Kroc *et al.* (1959) described a relaxin assay utilizing inhibition *in vitro* of motility of uteri obtained from mice in spontaneous estrus. Mice exhibiting cornified vaginal smears were sacrificed and uteri removed. Segments of mate horns were suspended in 25 or 50 ml. modified

TABLE V

SAMPLE ASSAY: 4-POINT ASSAY NUMBER 2 WITH VISUAL CLASSIFICATION OF RESPONSE IN SCORES[a]

Animal No.	Standard preparation No. 3 Dose (μg.)		Test preparation No. 4 Dose (μg.)		Totals
	2	4	32	64	
1	0.5	1.0	0	1.5	3.0
2	0	1.0	1.5	1.0	3.5
3	1.0	2.0	3.0	3.0	9.0
4	0.5	2.0	0.5	1.0	4.0
5	0.5	2.5	0	2.5	5.5
6	2.0	2.5	1.0	2.5	8.0
7	0.5	0.5	0	0.5	1.5
8	1.5	3.0	2.0	2.0	8.5
Totals	6.5	14.5	8.0	14.0	43.0
No. of curves	8	8	8	8	32
Means	0.81	1.81	1.0	1.75	—

[a] From Wiqvist and Paul (1958).

TABLE VI

EXAMPLES OF 4-POINT ASSAYS[a]

[Slopes significant according to validity tests with no significant deviation from parallelism ($P = 0.05$)]

Assay No.	Standard preparation	Unknown preparation	Relative potency (%)	Confidence limits ($P = 0.05$)	Precision (λ)
1	1	1	1.30	0.84– 2.02	0.24
2	3	4	0.066	0.046–0.096	0.22
3	3	2	0.49	0.31– 0.76	0.22
4	3	2	0.40	0.27– 0.60	0.22

[a] From Wiqvist and Paul (1958).

Ringer's solution aerated with oxygen or 5% CO_2 in oxygen, at a temperature of 37°C. Contractions were recorded via a heart lever writing on a smoked drum. After a control period of 10–15 minutes, doses of standard and unknown were added to baths containing mate segments. Doses were added to the baths at 5-minute intervals in increments that doubled the concentration, for example, 0.1, 0.1, 0.2, 0.4 ml. Optimal concentrations of standard and unknowns did not influence motility patterns until after the second or third addition. Thus, in the majority of tests, Standard W1164-A, Lot 8 was used at a concentration of 6.7 μg. per milliliter, and unknowns, after preliminary test, were adjusted to approximate the activity of this concentration of standard. Under these conditions a graded response is obtained for standard and unknown (Fig. 8). By calculating the minimal total dose required for similar degrees of motility inhibition (preferably 50%) by S and U, the ratio S/U times the concentration of S per milliliter yields the relative potency of U per milliliter.

This method has been useful for screening purposes, as only 2 or 3 tests are required to obtain a reasonably good (semiquantitative) potency estimate. This method was not practical for quantitative assay, as only 12–14 segment pairs could be run in one day by a single operator, permitting accurate assessment of only 1 or 2 unknowns.

VI. Comparison of Relaxin Assay Methods

The mouse interpubic ligament direct measurement method offers the most practical means for relaxin bioassay. The direct measurement

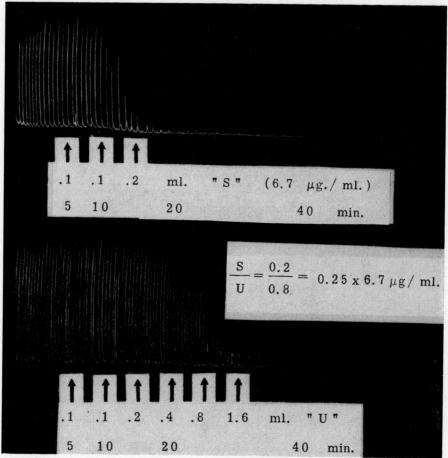

FIG. 8. Kymographic tracing of paired horns of mouse uterus treated with increasing doses of standard (S) and unknown (U) relaxin preparations. Potency ratio was estimated from the 50% inhibiting doses of S and U (Kroc *et al.*, 1959).

mouse method is simple, objective, and rapid, and easily learned by laboratory personnel. In contrast to this, the guinea pig pubic symphysis palpation method is subjective, requiring coded samples and independent observations of at least two investigators, and presents the added burden of maintaining a large guinea pig colony. One month of intensive training is generally required for technicians to become adept at classifying the gradations of mobility of the guinea pig pubic symphysis.

Roentgenographic pubic symphysis methods offer the possible advantage of pretreatment measurements of pubic separation, but this problem can be circumvented in the direct measurement method by sacrificing a representative control sample of the mouse population. The difficulties encountered in anesthetizing mice, X-raying, and measuring pubic separation from developed plates versus the simplicity of direct measurement recommend the latter method.

Uterine motility inhibition methods are tedious and difficult. The *in vivo* method of Felton *et al.* (1953) does not permit comparison with a reference standard, and no statistically analyzable data obtained with this method have been published to date. *In vitro* methods offer the obvious advantages of a population of segments or strips obtained from the same uterus, thus permitting evaluation of unknowns in terms of a standard. Wiqvist and Paul (1958) proposed a satisfactory 4-point assay design based on inhibition of uterine motility, but the authors, themselves, called attention to the dangers in subjective scoring of degrees of inhibition. The possibility of nonspecificity of *in vitro* methods has been recognized (Wiqvist and Paul, 1958; Bryant, 1959), but discreet use of this type of assay during fractionation and purification procedures has been justified by experience (Kroc *et al.*, 1959).

There has been a question as to whether the mouse pubic symphysis method measures the same activity as the classic guinea pig palpation method. Thus, Kliman and co-workers (1953) observed that highly purified relaxin of good potency by guinea pig test, was relatively ineffective in inducing pubic ligament formation in mice. Conversely, crude preparations, which assayed low in potency by the guinea pig method, were extremely effective in mice. Kliman and Greep (1955, 1959) subsequently showed that the rate of absorption of relaxin from the injection site was critical in the mouse, and that crude preparations were only slowly mobilized, giving a repository effect. The activity of highly purified relaxin was greatly enhanced in mice by use of appropriate retardant vehicles, whereas activity of crude preparations was not influenced by adjuvants.

Kroc *et al.* (1956a, b, 1959) assayed various relaxin preparations against the *same* reference standard by the guinea pig and mouse methods. Potency estimates obtained by the two methods were in good agreement (Table VII). Essential agreement was likewise obtained between guinea pig and mouse pubic symphysis methods and *in vitro* uterine motility inhibition methods (Kroc *et al.*, 1959; Wiqvist and Paul, 1958).

Thus, postulates of various different "relaxins" and "uterine relaxing factors" obtained from sow ovaries do not have substantiative evidence in their support. In fact, the proponents of a "uterine-relaxing factor" distinct from relaxin did not assay their materials against a reference standard, but relied on end-point units in their respective uterine motility

TABLE VII

BIOASSAYS OF RELAXIN EXTRACTS AGAINST A REFERENCE STANDARD,
BY MOUSE AND GUINEA PIG PUBIC SYMPHYSIS METHODS

Material and method of bioassay	Total animals (S + U)	Potency of U (mg.S/ml. or mg.)	Limits of error, % at $P = 0.95$	λ
Vialed sterile solutions				
Lot 016 (prepared from S)				
Guinea pig	120	17.4	73–137	0.40
Mouse	120	21.6	79–127	0.28
Lot 017				
Guinea pig	80	19.0	73–138	0.41
Mouse	97	22.2	78–128	0.26
Lot 14296				
Guinea pig	108	17.1	70–142	0.40
Mouse	117	17.2	76–132	0.32
Lot 14286				
Guinea pig	88	18.7	70–142	0.36
Mouse	107	14.5	82–122	0.22
Lot 018 (low potent control)				
Guinea pig	60	1.72	70–144	0.40
Mouse	140	1.70	76–132	0.30
Powders				
M30-31				
Guinea pig	85	0.74	77–131	0.27
Mouse	107	0.74	78–128	0.26
M66				
Guinea pig	120	1.06	76–131	0.33
Mouse	140	0.99	72–140	0.33
M36 (low potent control)				
Guinea pig	110	0.07	66–151	0.47
Mouse	69	0.07	81–123	0.21
Commercially available relaxin:				
Cervilaxin® (list No. 19852)				
(control No. 13891) (stated to				
contain 20 mg. standard				
(4000 guinea pig units)/ml.				
Guinea pig	80	0.31	69–144	0.29
Mouse	117	0.32	80–125	0.27
Releasin Lot 13216 (stated to				
contain 20 mg. Warner-Chilcott				
standard/ml.)				
Guinea pig	80	23.0	70–142	0.34
Mouse	116	20.6	76–132	0.33
Crude relaxin:				
Saline homogenates of pregnant				
sow ovaries				
Guinea pig	156	4 mg./gm. fresh	69–144	0.48
Mouse	92	5 mg./gm. fresh	75–134	0.30

inhibition and pubic symphysis palpation tests (Felton *et al.*, 1953; Frieden and Layman, 1957).

VII. Assay of Repository Forms of Relaxin

A. POTENTIATION OF RELAXIN

Kliman and Greep (1955) first reported that the action of relaxin on the mouse pubic symphysis was markedly enhanced by suitable repository vehicles. Relaxin activity may be potentiated by mechanical retardation of absorption (beeswax-oil mixtures, protein precipitants) or by biochemical alteration of the injection site (antihyaluronidases). Figure 9 illustrates the potentiating effects of various types of vehicles on the response of the mouse interpubic ligament to single doses of relaxin. Benzopurpurine 4B (L-390) and beeswax in oil are remarkable potentiators as the minimum effective dose of relaxin in these vehicles is 1/150th to 1/300th of the dose required in saline solution.

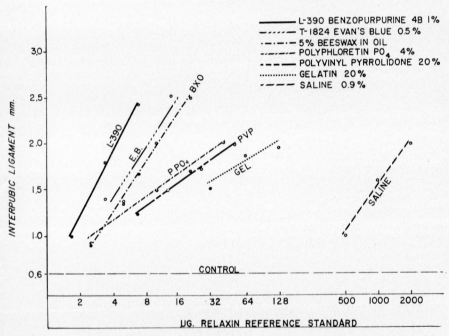

FIG. 9. Influence of vehicle on the 24-hour response of the mouse interpubic ligament to a single subcutaneous injection of relaxin. The curve illustrating relaxin in saline represents a composite of several assays. It is atypical; usually no dose response is obtained (Steinetz *et al.*, 1960).

The relative efficiency of a repository vehicle may be assessed by comparing dose-response curves obtained with the standard relaxin preparation injected in the unknown vehicle and in benzopurpurine 4-B. Otherwise the standardized procedure described under Section IV is followed.

B. DURATION OF PELVIC RELAXATION IN GUINEA PIGS

In contrast to the mouse, the guinea pig will not show potentiation of low doses of relaxin administered in repository vehicles. The doses for the guinea pig duration test must be approximately 500 times greater than the relaxin priming dose, i.e., 10 versus 0.02 mg. After administration of a single large dose of relaxin in saline solution to guinea pigs, marked relaxation is observed at 6–24 hours, but this is followed by rapid retrogradation of the interpubic ligament so that little or no innominate mobility is detectable at 48 hours. In contrast, an identical dose injected in an effective repository vehicle will maintain strong relaxation for 1 to 3 weeks. (The mouse pubic ligament does not regress and therefore cannot be used for a duration test.)

The phenomenon of prolonged relaxation of the pubic symphysis made possible a semiquantitative assay procedure for evaluating long-acting relaxin preparations.

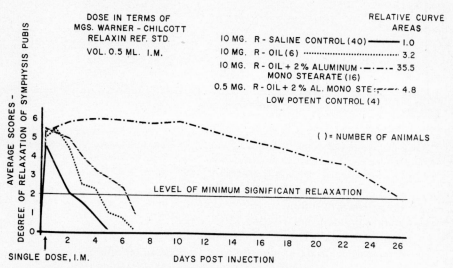

FIG. 10. Effect of relaxin repository preparation on duration of relaxation of the guinea pig symphysis pubis. Semi-quantitative estimate of effectiveness was obtained from calculated relative areas under the curve assigning a value of 1 to the area observed with a single injection of relaxin in saline.

Young responsive guinea pigs (estrogen- and relaxin-primed as in Section III) are isolated from the regular colony and injected intramuscularly with a single dose of relaxin in depot form. The animals are palpated 6 hours later and daily or every other day until scores reach zero. (The scoring system is the same as described in Section III.) The palpation scores are recorded and averaged. The level of minimum significant relaxation is arbitrarily an average score of 2.

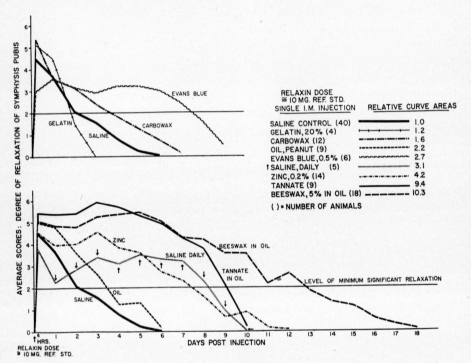

FIG. 11. Effect of relaxin repository preparations on duration of relaxation of the guinea pig symphysis pubis. Multiple injections of relaxin in saline failed to maintain the degree of relaxation observed when animals were treated with effective repository preparations (Steinetz et al., 1959a).

The estrogen priming is discontinued when the assay is started. The guinea pigs are not re-used after a test.

Figure 10 is a graphic representation of the duration effect of a vialed repository preparation of relaxin (relaxin in oil plus 2% aluminum monostearate; Anschel, 1960) at 10 mg. equivalent relaxin standard activity. For purposes of comparison, 10 mg. of a low potent powder (equivalent to 0.5 mg. relaxin standard activity) suspended in the same vehicle were injected in another group of pigs. These preparations are compared to single doses of 10 mg. relaxin standard in sesame oil and in saline. The 10 mg. standard dose in aluminum monostearate produced a significant level of relaxation for 26 days, whereas an equivalent dose in oil or saline or a low dose (0.5 mg. standard activity) in aluminum monostearate did not maintain relaxation after 4, 2, or 6 days, respectively.

Figure 11 depicts the sustained action of single injections of relaxin in different repository forms. In contrast, even repeated daily injections of relaxin in saline solution failed to duplicate the effects of the depot.

This test has been useful and reliable in estimating duration of effect for clinical trial repository preparations.

VIII. Other Actions of Relaxin Potentially Suitable for Bioassay Work

A. Effects of Relaxin on the Uterus

Zarrow and Brennan (1959) first demonstrated an effect of relaxin on the water content of uteri of weanling rats. Increase in water content was proportional to dose of relaxin administered, and the peak effect was observed 6 hours after injection.

Steinetz et al. (1957) investigated the effects of relaxin on the composition of uteri of estrogen-primed, ovariectomized rats. Uterine weight, nitrogen, and water content were markedly increased in 6 to 12 hours, and glycogen concentration was doubled 12–24 hours following relaxin injection. All these effects were of sufficient magnitude to warrant exploration of a dose-response curve.

B. Effects of Relaxin on the Cervix

A softening effect of relaxin upon the uterine cervix has been reported by several investigators (Graham and Dracy, 1952; Zarrow et al., 1956; Steinetz et al., 1957; Crelin, 1958; Cullen and Harkness, 1958; Kroc et al., 1959). Kroc et al. (1959) succeeded in obtaining dilatability increments proportional to relaxin dose in spayed, pregnant rats maintained on estrogen and progesterone. Only in such animals was the magnitude of the effect sufficiently great to permit the establishment of a dose-response curve.

C. Miscellaneous Effects

Many other actions of relaxin have been reported in the literature (i.e., induction of mammary gland growth, Hamolsky and Sparrow,

1945; Smith, 1954; Wada and Turner, 1959; influences on parturition, Smithberg and Runner, 1956; Steinetz *et al.,* 1957; effects on subcutaneous connective tissue, Casten and Boucek, 1956; Casten and Gilmore, 1958). Techniques for the demonstration of such effects, however, are in all probability too difficult or time consuming to be adapted to bioassay procedures.

IX. Notes on the Stability of Relaxin

An important application of the mouse assay of relaxin described in Section IV has been its use in evaluating the stability of preparations manufactured for human use.

Whereas, relaxin activity is lost during incubation with proteolytic enzymes or reducing agents (Frieden, 1951), the hormone is very stable under less drastic conditions.

Relaxin is relatively thermostable, and may be autoclaved for 20 to 30 minutes without significant potency loss. Sterile saline solutions of relaxin are likewise stable, but refrigeration is desirable to prevent "shedding." Table VIII illustrates the stability of 4 lots of sterile-vialed

TABLE VIII

STABILITY OF STERILE RELEASIN SALINE SOLUTIONS

Preparation	Original potency, mg.S/ml. (range at $P = 0.95$)	Potency after storage at 4°C. 1–2 years, mg.S/ml. (range at $P = 0.95$)
W1164-3		
Lot 07547	18.5 (14.1–24.4)	19.1 (15.3–24.1)
Lot 244482	19.9 (13.9–28.5)	20.2 (16.2–24.8)
Lot 153782	18.1 (14.1–22.8)	19.0 (16.2–22.4)
Lot 13216	20.6 (15.7–27.2)	19.8 (14.7–26.7)

relaxin solutions stored at 4°C. for 1 to 2 years. The preparations were in each instance assayed against reference standard W1164-A, Lot 8, by the mouse pubic ligament direct measurement method.

Table IX demonstrates the stability of relaxin repository suspensions stored at room temperature and 45°C. for 1 to 6 months.

Relaxin solutions continuously subjected to a temperature of 100°C. undergo a gradual potency loss which is linearly related to the logarithm of the heating time (Table X). Addition of 20% gelatin delays the loss

TABLE IX

STABILITY OF STERILE RELEASIN REPOSITORY SUSPENSIONS

Preparation W1164-35:	Lot 002088, mg.S/ml. (range at $P = 0.95$)			Lot 003108, mg.S/ml. (range at $P = 0.95$)		
Storage temperature:	45°C.	Room temp.	4°C.	45°C.	Room temp.	4°C.
Original assay:	—	19.3	—	—	19.9	—
Months stored		(15.5–24.1)			(17.5–22.7)	
1	23.7 (18.0–31.0)	25.4 (19.0–34.0)	24.4 (19.5–30.7)	21.4 (17.3–26.5)	18.0 (14.4–22.7)	18.7 (15.5–22.4)
3	18.5 (14.4–23.8)	18.4 (13.8–24.5)	18.3 (14.3–23.6)	20.0 (15.6–26.6)	25.6 (18.9–34.3)	—
6	16.3 (12.5–21.5)	18.9 (14.7–24.2)	—	—	—	—

of potency until the eighth hour of heating (Table X). This finding is curious, inasmuch as simple addition of gelatin to relaxin solutions is often accompanied by an apparent reduction (20–30%) in potency, which becomes a statistically significant 50% after heating at 100°C.

TABLE X

RELEASIN HEAT STABILITY TEST (MOUSE INTERPUBIC LIGAMENT ASSAY)
POWDER W1164-A, LOT 30-31
(27.3 mg./ml. $\cong$ 20 mg.S/ml.)

	In 0.9% saline solution			In 20% gelatin solution		
Hours heated at 100°C.	Observed potency mg.S/ml.	(range at $P = 0.95$)	% 0 Hour potency	Observed potency mg.S/ml.	(range at $P = 0.95$)	% 0 Hour potency
0	22.7	(17.0–30.3)	100	15.8	(12.6–19.8)	100
1	22.0	(17.0–28.6)	97	11.4	(7.8–16.6)	72
2	16.0	(11.0–23.0)	70	10.6	(7.4–15.4)	67
4	7.8	(5.0–12.4)	34[a]	9.4	(6.8–13.1)	60
8	2.0	(1.2– 3.2)	9[a]	3.6	(2.6– 5.0)	23[a]
16	0.6	(0.4– 0.8)	3[a]	1.4	(1.0– 2.0)	9[a]
32	<0.1		<0.4[a]	<0.1		<0.4[a]
	$Y = 1.05 - 0.94 \log X$			$Y = 0.61 - 0.45 \log X$		

[a] Potency loss significant ($P < 0.01$).

for 1 hour. Whether this represents true inactivation or reversible binding, remains an unanswered question.

REFERENCES

Abramowitz, A. A., Money, W. L., Zarrow, M. X., Talmage, R. V. N., Kleinholz, L. H., and Hisaw, F. L. (1944). *Endocrinology* **34**, 103.

Albert, A., and Money, W. L. (1946). *Endocrinology* **38**, 56.

Albert, A., Money, W. L., and Zarrow, M. X. (1947). *Endocrinology* **40**, 370.

Anschel, J. (1960). U.S. Patent 2,964,448.

Bliss, C. I. (1952). "The Statistics of Bioassay." Academic Press, New York.

Boucek, R. J. (1958). *Southern Med. J.* **51**, 825.

Bryant, H. H. (1959). Discussion: Part IX. *Ann. N.Y. Acad. Sci.* **75**, 1037.

Casten, G. G., and Boucek, R. J. (1958). *J. Am. Med. Assoc.* **166**, 319.

Casten, G. G., and Gilmore, H. R. (1958). *Circulation* **18**, 702.

Casten, G. G., Boucek, R. J., Noble, N., and Scotti, T. M. (1956). *Am. J. Med.* **20**, 943.

Crelin, E. S. (1954). *Am. J. Anat.* **95**, 47.

Crelin, E. S. (1955). *Proc. Soc. Exptl. Biol. Med.* **90**, 236.

Crelin, E. S. (1957). *Science* **125**, 650.

Crelin, E. S. (1958). *Anat. Record* **130**, 401.

Crelin, E. S., and Honeyman, M. S. (1957). *Anat. Record* **127**, 407.

Cullen, B. M., and Harkness, R. D. (1958). *J. Physiol. (London)* **140**, 46P.

Dorfman, R. I., Marsters, R. W., and Dinerstein, J. (1953). *Endocrinology* **52**, 204.

Felton, L. C., Frieden, E. H., and Bryant, H. H. (1953). *J. Pharmacol. Exptl. Therap.* **107**, 160.

Frieden, E. H. (1951). *Arch. Biochem.* **30**, 138.

Frieden, E. H., and Hisaw, F. L. (1950). *Arch. Biochem.* **29**, 166.

Frieden, E. H., and Layman, N. W. (1957). *J. Biol. Chem.* **229**, 569.

Graham, E. F., and Dracy, A. E. (1952). *J. Dairy Sci.* **35**, 499.

Hall, K. J. (1948). *Endocrinology* **5**, 314.

Hall, K. J. (1949). *Quart. J. Exptl. Physiol.* **35**, 65.

Hall, K. J. (1956). *J. Endocrinol.* **13**, 384.

Hall, K. J. (1957). *J. Endocrinol.* **15**, 108.

Hall, K. J., and Newton, W. H. (1947). *J. Physiol. (London)* **106**, 18.

Hamolsky, M., and Sparrow, R. C. (1945). *Proc. Soc. Exptl. Biol. Med.* **60**, 8.

Hisaw, F. L. (1929). *Physiol. Zoöl.* **2**, 59.

Hisaw, F. L., and Zarrow, M. X. (1950). *Vitamins and Hormones* **8**, 151.

Horn, E. H. (1958). *Endocrinology* **63**, 481.

Kelly, J. V., and Posse, N. (1956). *Obstet. and Gynecol.* **8**, 531.

Kliman, B., and Greep, R. O. (1955). *J. Clin. Endocrinol. and Metabolism* **15**, 847.

Kliman, B., and Greep, R. O. (1958). *Endocrinology* **63**, 586.

Kliman, B., Salhanick, H. A., and Zarrow, M. X. (1953). *Endocrinology* **53**, 391.

Krantz, J. C., Jr., Bryant, H. H., and Carr, J. (1950). *Surg. Gynecol. Obstet.* **90**, 372.

Kroc, R. L., and Phillips, G. E. (1958). U. S. Patent 2,852,431.

Kroc, R. L., Beach, V. L., and Stasilli, N. R. (1956a). *Federation Proc.* **15**, 113.

Kroc, R. L., Steinetz, B. G., Beach, V. L., and Stasilli, N. R. (1956b). *J. Clin. Endocrinol. and Metabolism* **16**, 966.

Kroc, R. L., Steinetz, B. G., and Beach, V. L. (1959). *Ann. N. Y. Acad. Sci.* **75,** 942.

McGaughey, H. S., Jr., Corey, E. L., and Thornton, W. N. (1958). *Am. J. Obstet. Gynecol.* **75,** 23.

Miller, J. W., Kesley, A., and Murray, W. J. (1957). *J. Pharmacol. Exptl. Therap.* **120,** 426.

Noall, M. W., and Frieden, E. H. (1956). *Endocrinology* **58,** 659.

Posse, N., and Kelly, J. V. (1956). *Surg. Gynecol. Obstet.* **103,** 687.

Reynolds, H., and Livingood, C. S. (1959). *A.M.A. Arch. Dermatol.* **80,** 407.

Sawyer, W. H., Frieden, E. H., and Martin, A. C. (1953). *Am. J. Physiol.* **172,** 547.

Smith, T. C. (1954). *Endocrinology* **59,** 54.

Smithberg, M., and Runner, M. N. (1956). *J. Exptl. Zool.* **133,** 441.

Snedecor, G. W. (1940). "Statistical Methods." Iowa State College Press, Ames, Iowa.

Steinetz, B. G., Beach, V. L., and Kroc, R. L. (1957). *Endocrinology* **61,** 271.

Steinetz, B. G., Beach, V. L., and Kroc, R. L. (1959a). *In* "Recent Progress in The Endocrinology of Reproduction" (C. W. Lloyd, ed.), pp. 389–427. Academic Press, New York.

Steinetz, B. G., Beach, V. L., and Kroc, R. L. (1959b). *Program of 41st Meeting Endocrine Soc.* p. 102.

Steinetz, B. G., Beach, V. L., Kroc, R. L., Stasilli, N. R., Nussbaum, R. E., Nemith, P. J., and Dun, R. K. (1960). *Endocrinology* **67,** 102.

Storey, E. (1957). *J. Pathol. Bacteriol.* **74,** 147.

Talmadge, R. V. and Hurst, W. R. (1950). *J. Endocrinol.* **7,** 24.

Wada, H., and Turner, C. W. (1959). *Proc. Soc. Exptl. Biol. Med.* **102,** 568.

Wada, H., and Yuhara, M. (1956). *Sci. Repts. Fac. Agr. Okayama Univ.* **9,** 21.

Wiqvist, N. (1959a). *Acta Endocrinol.* **31,** 391.

Wiqvist, N. (1959b). *Acta Endocrinol. Suppl.* **46,** 3 and 15.

Wiqvist, N., and Paul, K.-G. (1958). *Acta Endocrinol.* **29,** 135.

Zarrow, M. X., and Brennan, D. M. (1959). *Ann. N. Y. Acad. Sci.* **75,** 981.

Zarrow, M. X., Neher, G. M., Sikes, D., Brennan, D. M., and Bullard, J. F. (1956). *Am. J. Obstet. Gynecol.* **72,** 260.

Chapter 17

The Gonadotropins

ALBERT SEGALOFF

I. Historical Introduction

The gonad-stimulating hormones are those pituitary or placental mucoproteins that produce growth and secretion of the gonads of both sexes. This characteristic function is manifested in both the hypophysectomized and the intact animal. General custom names these hormones by their activity on the ovary as the follicle-stimulating hormone (FSH), producing follicular growth, and the luteinizing hormone (LH), converting the follicle to the corpus luteum. There is evidence, in the rodent at least, that the lactogenic hormone, prolactin, may have an effect on the corpus luteum leading to secretion of the natural progestational hormone and this might be considered as a gonadotropin. However, this will be treated in a separate chapter.

It is generally conceded that the materials which stimulate follicular growth in the ovary are responsible for spermatogenesis in the male, whereas those which transform ovarian follicles to corpora lutea are responsible for the morphologic stimulation of the interstitial cells of the testis and for their hormonal secretion.

A. Site of Gonad-Stimulating Hormone

Gonad-stimulating hormones have been found in the pituitaries of all species of animals and in the placentas of human beings and of horses. The human placental gonadotropin, chorionic gonadotropin, is also found in the plasma and urine of pregnant women. In the pregnant mare, the gonadotropin is found in the blood but does not spill over into the urine.

The literature is replete with claims for the isolation of pure, specific gonad-stimulating hormones showing only follicle-stimulating or luteinizing activity and devoid of other hormonal activity. At present these claims must be regarded as interesting but unproved. Only when the exact chemical nature of the gonadotropins is known and these hormones have been prepared synthetically will it finally be known if the activities are indeed separable.

B. Luteinizing Hormone (LH)

The recent introduction of new methods of purifying and separating proteins has not led to luteinizing preparations of substantially greater activity or purity. The demonstration that a luteinizing hormone preparation is free from follicle-stimulating activity is an undertaking of great magnitude, and indeed it may be an impossible one in light of what is presently known of LH action.

Even the best available luteinizing hormone preparations do not just stimulate the Leydig cells in the hypophysectomized male rodent. There is also an increase in testis weight due to growth and differentiation of the tubules. However, this cannot be construed as proof that the LH is stimulating the tubules directly, since this is a well-recognized effect of androgenic steroids (Nelson, 1937). Biologic differentiation of effect might be possible if a good antiandrogen were available or if we had an enzyme inhibitor which would prevent the formation of androgenic steroids.

The situation in the female is even more difficult because without the prior action of FSH and a follicle to act upon, there is no site for the LH to display its activity! Demonstration that estrogen has an effect on ovarian maintenance after hypophysectomy (Simpson *et al.*, 1941) only muddies the water still further. Indeed, there are those who believe that LH is necessary for full follicular development, so that there is a 1:2 type of action making real demonstration of separability difficult. Despite these biologic problems and contradictions, it is refreshing to realize that much progress has been made in resolving the problem of preparation of LH from various species.

Evaluation of highly active preparations from various laboratories is difficult because of lack of uniformity in assay procedures and because results are often not expressed in terms of any available reference preparation. Biologic units are also particularly difficult to interpret when they are obtained in different strains or even different species of animals and by widely varying methods of administration.

The most enlightening work has been done on ovine-luteinizing hormone. Squire and Li (1958) fractionated their highly purified material on IRC-50 resin and reported two fractions with LH activity. One of these fractions was further purified by starch zone electrophoresis. This they designated as β-ICSH. Ward and co-workers (1959) developed a method for isolation of both fractions from carboxymethylcellulose (CMC) columns and designated the fractions as LH_1 and LH_2. LH_2 and β-ICSH appear to be the same material. β-ICSH is estimated to have a molecular weight of 30,000 while the molecular weight of LH_2 is estimated at 28,000. These values agree within the experimental error.

Ward and co-workers (1959) showed that LH_1 and LH_2 had equal ability to stimulate the ventral prostate of the hypophysectomized immature male rat and that they both equaled the activity of the Armour LH standard SL 227-80. LH_1 appears to be the less stable component. Indeed, further attempts at purification of LH_1 resulted in conversion to LH_2 but the converse was not observed.

C. LH in Human Pituitary

The human pituitary is particularly rich in LH. Indeed, a moderately purified preparation of gonadotropins from this source has several times the ventral-prostate-stimulating activity of the above preparations (Steelman *et al.*, 1958). Starting with this preparation it has been possible to obtain a highly purified potent LH preparation from human pituitaries. The LH fraction is retained on CMC and is separated from the FSH fraction which is not retained. Further workup of the retained fraction on CMC columns yielded two separate components, only one of which (CMC-B-1) had substantial LH activity. This material has little or no FSH activity and approximates ten times the Armour standard in ventral-prostate-stimulating activity, but it still does not appear to be homogeneous.

Although it was my opinion that the LH activity of human urine was only that inherent in the HMG (gonadotropin of human menopausal urine) (Segaloff, 1954–1955), it has been possible to separate LH material from male urine essentially free of FSH (Segaloff and Steelman, 1959). The separable urinary LH is not retained on DEAE cellulose. The crude LH preparation from the DEAE cellulose column can be purified by the use of CMC columns. The reported material is not homogeneous and has 2 to 3% of the ventral-prostate-stimulating activity of the Armour standard.

Although equine pituitaries have been said to predominate in FSH activity, they have also been reported to be high in LH (Steelman and Segaloff, 1959). However, I am not aware of any purification procedures for equine LH.

D. FOLLICLE-STIMULATING HORMONE (FSH)

In contrast to the situation with LH, application of the newest methods of purification of proteins has produced FSH preparations of considerably greater potency than those previously obtained. Since this material is not dialyzable and appears to be a mucoprotein, one must conclude that this does not represent a small active molecule of FSH which had been separated from a large molecular weight protein carrier.

The first of these highly active FSH's was prepared from porcine FSH which had been digested with pancreatin. It had been demonstrated many years ago by McShan and Meyer (1938) and by Chow and co-workers (1939) that pancreatin would destroy LH activity but did not destroy FSH activity. Pancreatin-digested porcine FSH could be fractionated with alcohol, yielding a product ten or twelve times as active as the Armour reference standard (Steelman et al., 1952). The concentrated FSH prepared by alcohol fractionation could be further purified by column chromatography on DEAE cellulose (Steelman et al., 1956). Repeated chromatography on such columns yielded a fraction which was nondialyzable and which assayed thirty to forty times the activity of the Armour standard in the Steelman and Pohley augmentation assay (1953). It was impossible to show ventral prostate stimulation when adequate amounts of this product were given to hypophysectomized immature male rats for as long as 3 weeks. A total dose of 1 to 2 μg.

produced a significant increase in ovarian weight in hypophysectomized female rats, while larger doses gave a good log dosage-response curve. It was possible to double the ovarian weight without significant increase in uterine weight. However, larger doses invariably resulted in uterine weight increases (Steelman and Segaloff, 1959). It would appear noteworthy that previous workers who claim that their FSH would not cause estrogen secretion did not give doses in excess of that which would produce doubling of the ovarian weight (Greep et al., 1942). This material is reported to be homogeneous chromatographically and by ultracentrifugal and paper electrophoretic measurements. The sedimentation constant of the single component ($S_{20\omega}$) was 2.49, the diffusion constant ($D_{20\omega}$) was 7.43×10^{-7}, and when one assumes a partial specific volume of 0.72, the molecular weight was calculated to be 29,000. The material appears to have an isoelectric point of 5.1 to 5.2. The material has 7.4% of total carbohydrate, 3.7% of which is hexosamine, the other identified carbohydrates being galactose, mannose, and fucose.

E. METHODS OF PURIFICATION OF LH AND FSH

Non-pancreatin-digested porcine FSH can be processed in the same manner (Steelman and Segaloff, 1959) to yield a product which appears to be similar in its FSH activity and purity but which still retains LH activity when measured in the hypophysectomized immature male rat. However, this highly purified material from nondigested extracts is unstable, even in the lyophilized state in the deep freeze.

Ellis (1958) reported essentially the same findings for FSH of ovine origin. He attributes the instability of these preparations to a specific proteolytic enzyme present in pituitaries which can be concentrated separately from the FSH but which cannot be removed entirely from the FSH fractions.

F. HUMAN MENOPAUSAL GONADOTROPIN

Application of similar methods to the gonadotropin of human menopausal urine, which we will designate as the HMG, has resulted in the isolation of a fraction which predominates in FSH activity but which, like the nondigested pituitary gonadotropins from porcine and ovine sources, retains some LH activity (Segaloff et al., 1959). This material, which approximates the Armour standard in FSH activity, appears to be homogeneous by chromatographic behavior on DEAE cellulose, paper electrophoresis over a pH range from 6.8 to 8.6, and ultracentrifugation. It appears to have a molecular weight of 30,000 when analyzed by the Archibald method (1947).

Preparation of a gonadotropin concentrate from acetone-dried human pituitaries has already been mentioned. When this gonadotropin concentrate is passed once through a CMC column to remove the separable LH activity the FSH fraction is not retained (Segaloff and Steelman, 1959). The FSH fraction is then further purified on DEAE cellulose columns and eluted with appropriate buffers. It was found that greater recoveries of activity could be obtained with the use of appropriate volatile buffers. The FSH fraction thus obtained has about twenty-five times the FSH activity (Steelman and Pohley, 1953) of the urinary HMG or of the Armour reference standard. This material from human pituitaries has not been reported as completely homogeneous although preparations which are largely one component have been obtained. Unfortunately, like the native undigested pituitary materials from the other species, this highly purified material is also unstable. The luteinizing hormone activity of this preparation is about 70 to 100% of the activity of the Armour LH standard when assayed on the hypophysectomized male rat ventral prostate.

II. Reference Standards

A wide variety of reference substances is available for assays of gonadotropic hormone activity. As in all other assays, it is wise to prepare a large laboratory standard and carefully test it against well-recognized standards. It would help greatly if more data were given in terms such that preparations and results could be compared and assessed.

An excellent standard for LH activity is the international standard preparation of human chorionic gonadotropin. This preparation gives good dosage-response curves in the hypophysectomized immature male rat ventral prostate assay. The international unit is 0.1 mg. (100 μg.) of the international standard preparation (*League of Nations Bull. Health Organisation*, 1938a).

A pituitary reference material with LH activity has been prepared from sheep pituitary glands and is available through the Endocrinology Study Section of the National Institutes of Health, U.S. Public Health Service. No unit has been established.

The Armour house standard—SL 227–80—is of sheep origin and is said to be about 80% pure.

HMG–20–A is a kaolin extract of human menopausal urine and has been widely used as an unofficial reference material for both LH and FSH assays of preparations from human menopausal urine. Unfortunately, supplies of this material are essentially exhausted.

The international reference preparation of human menopausal gonadotropin (HMG 24) contains both LH and FSH activity and can be employed as a standard for either activity. This is also a kaolin extract of human menopausal urine. No unit has been assigned to this material (International Reference Preparation for Human Menopausal Gonadotropin, 1959).

The international reference standard of pregnant mare serum also has both LH and FSH activity. However, it is suggested only as a standard for pregnant mare serum preparations. The international unit is 0.25 mg. (250 μg.) of the standard preparation (*League Nations Bull. Health Organisation*, 1938b).

The Endocrine Study Section of the National Institutes of Health, U.S. Public Health Service, has made a standard preparation of sheep pituitary FSH available. No unit has been assigned to this material.

The Armour house standard FSH (264–151–X) has been widely employed. The Armour FSH unit is the biologic activity in the Steelman and Pohley assay (1953) of 1 mg. of this material.

It has been proposed (Rosemberg *et al.*, 1957) that estrone yields curves in the mouse uterine weight assay which parallel those with gonadotropic hormone preparations and that crystalline estrone may therefore be employed as a readily available standard for this assay.

III. Use of Gonadotropin Assays

The widest clinical use of gonadotropic hormone assays is in the detection of pregnancy. The same crude assays are also employed to detect the neoplasms that secrete chorionic gonadotropin, particularly chorioepithelioma. These determinations present the simplest of the clinical gonadotropin assays because the hormone content of the urine is high and the accuracy of the estimate of the hormone titer need not be great.

A. Pregnancy Tests

A commonly used pregnancy test is the Friedman test. We believe that the rabbit is not a good animal for the quantitative bioassay of gonadotropins since it is expensive, gives no differentiation of gonadotropin activities, and lacks sensitivity; also, it is difficult to get standard animals in adequate numbers. However, when employed for the diagnosis of pregnancy where only 1 or 2 test animals are employed and where sensitivity is not a problem, it has the advantage of yielding an answer in 24 hours where needed.

The procedure is as follows: 10–20 cc. of the first morning specimen voided is filtered if necessary and then injected intravenously into an estrous female rabbit. A test is positive when there is evidence of ovulation 24 hours after the injection. Some people prefer to wait 48 hours since corpora lutea are better formed at that time and more readily seen.

The Kupperman test (Kupperman et al., 1943) can be completed in 2 hours. This test requires somewhat more experience with the end point than the Friedman test and 1 or 2 litter-mate controls should be killed simultaneously with the test animals. It is important to know the sensitivity of the animals at the available age for testing. Two or more immature female rats are injected intraperitoneally with 1.5 ml. of the first morning specimen voided. This should be given as two separate 0.75 ml. injections in each of the lower abdominal quadrants. Two hours later the animals and the controls are killed with ether and the color of the ovarian capsule is compared with that of the controls. In a positive test the ovarian capsules have a reddish hyperemic appearance as compared with the white or light pink color of the controls.

Another rapid pregnancy test utilizes male toads and frogs. This test depends upon extrusion of sperm by the animal and frequently yields a result within 2 hours. However, the wide variety of available frogs and toads prevents specific directions. The animals can be used repeatedly.

In patients taking Promazine® or Chlorpromazine® the results may be falsely positive in the male frog tests but not in tests employing rabbits or mice. This is opposite to the effect on urinary excretion of pituitary gonadotropins (Brillhart, 1959).

The Hogben test employs the female *Xenopus laevis* which is readily available commercially. This animal will extrude ova within 24 hours in a positive test. The animals can be used repeatedly. However, they are relatively insensitive and some method like the nondialysis alcohol precipitation method mentioned below must be used to concentrate the urine activity.

The oldest of the pregnancy tests is the Aschheim-Zondek test. Three or four immature female mice are injected with 0.5 ml. of the first morning urine specimen twice daily for 4 days. The mice are killed on the fifth day and the ovaries are examined for the presence of hemorrhagic follicles and corpora lutea. Here also it is necessary to have control animals until one is well acquainted with the end point.

For further detailed information there are several excellent reviews of pregnancy testing (Cowie, 1948; Hobson, 1955; Robbins and Parker, 1948; Thorberg, 1950).

B. Male Hypogonadism Test

Clinical interest in the quantitation of urinary gonad-stimulating hormones has continued to increase. Their usefulness in such instances as male hypogonadism is great. Here, for example, the gonadotropic hormone determination will enable one to decide whether a given testicular dysfunction is of testicular or pituitary origin, the former requiring therapy with steroids and the latter responding best to gonadotropic hormone preparations.

IV. Method of Urine Collection

Most clinical assays for gonadotropic hormone must start with urine, since the hormonal titer in blood is low and is difficult to concentrate. It is sheer folly to erect an edifice of difficult biologic assay upon a urine specimen unless one is as certain as he can be that it has been adequately collected, refrigerated if at all possible, and is of a relatively standard volume. Although many investigators say that the urine volume does not affect recovery of gonadotropin or other materials from the urine, I believe that disregarding urine volume gives one a false sense of security and adds difficulty and uncertainty to the interpretation of results. It frequently gives the patients an unwarranted sense of security about the collection and, I believe, may tend to make them considerably more careless than if they were properly instructed, with careful attention to fluid intake. I feel strongly that, on every urine specimen on which a gonadotropin assay is carried out, one should always do a creatinine determination to serve as a further check on the collection.

It is our custom to instruct our patients carefully in urine collection. When possible we start to dehydrate them 48 hours before the actual collection of urine and restrict fluids sufficiently so that the urine volume will be one liter or less in 24 hours. We also supply them with suitable bottles and a portable ice chest, if needed, where the bottles can be kept on ice during the 24-hour collection period. It is of the utmost importance to make sure that the urine collection is started at a specific time with an empty bladder. Many nurses and physicians fail to recognize the crucial importance of discarding the urine voided at the time the 24-hour collection is started so that one starts collecting with an empty bladder at a specific time. Then all urine passed up to and including this same time the next day is put into a single container and refrigerated. This constitutes the 24-hour urine. There are many things to remember about the urine collection and about the patient from whom one is collecting the urine. Changes in environmental temperature, such as coming into an air-conditioned hospital to stay during the summer time when the weather is extremely warm, cut down on the insensible water loss and since the patients do not usually alter their drinking habits immediately, this results in a tremendous increase in urine volume during the early days in such an environment.

It should also be recognized that many sulfonamides and some antibiotics are excreted in such a form as to make the extract toxic to the assay animals. Patients should discontinue the use of these drugs for at least 24 hours before starting urine collections. In addition, it should be recalled that many tranquilizing agents and other central nervous system active drugs have a suppressing effect on the hypothalamus and have been reported to lower the gonadotropin excretion measurably in most patients. Therefore, one should be careful to see that these agents are stopped as long a time as possible before gonadotropic hormone determinations are undertaken; otherwise the assays will show spuriously low values.

Finally, for completeness, it must be noted that in patients who are taking potent hormonal agents, these preparations will be reflected in the level of urinary gonadotropic hormones.

V. Clinical Assay

Many different methods for the routine assay of the gonadotropic hormone titer of urine in the nonpregnant patient have been proposed. Each has its staunch supporters and opponents. For routine measurement of urinary gonadotropin, I know of no real reason for advocating any particular method or combination of methods. I will give details of two methods of extraction and two of bioassay. I would suggest strongly that a choice be made as to which combination of these will be employed, basing the choice upon facilities, animal supply, and the skill of the technicians who will carry out the procedures.

A recent observation would suggest that some low values may be due to the existence of an antagonist to human urinary gonadotropin. Such activity has been demonstrated in the urine of some children. Extracts of children's urine have been reported to prevent the response to potent extracts of adult urine (Landau *et al.*, 1960). We have been unable to confirm this and are not aware of anyone else who has.

A. KAOLIN ABSORPTION METHOD

For the routine clinical gonadotropin assay either a kaolin absorption or an alcohol precipitation method should be used for the preparation of the concentrate for bioassay. The ultrafiltration methods are not recommended.

The kaolin procedure we prefer is that of Albert (1950). Automatic equipment is commercially available for this procedure but it can be employed without this. The extract is prepared as follows:

(1) Adjust a 24- to 48-hour urine specimen to pH 4.5. A glass electrode, pH meter, and glacial acetic acid should be employed.

(2) Add 20 gm. of dry kaolin (Oxford-English) to the urine and stir briskly for 5 seconds.

(3) Pour the mixture into a suitable pressure chamber for filtration and filter off the urine. Either discard the filtrate or save for steroid determination.

(4) Wash the residual cake with 2 liters of water containing 1 ml. of glacial acetic acid. Discard the washing.

(5) Elute the gonadotropin with 100 ml. of 2 N NH$_4$OH passed through the kaolin cake twice. Follow this with 50 ml. of distilled water. The second run through of NH$_4$OH and the distilled water are combined.

(6) Adjust the combined eluate to pH 5.5 with glacial acetic acid.

(7) Add 2 volumes of acetone to the pH 5.5 solution, stir it, and place in the cold room or refrigerator for $\frac{1}{2}$ hour.

(8) Centrifuge the acetone suspension and discard the supernatant.

(9) Take up the precipitate in distilled water immediately for assay or dry it overnight in the desiccator.

B. ALCOHOL PRECIPITATION METHOD

For alcohol precipitation we prefer the method of Klinefelter *et al.* (1943). This method tests for either elevated or normal levels of gonadotropin separately.

The nondialysis method can be used only when the titer is high (above 100 mouse units per 24 hours). These levels occur in patients with gonadal failure and rarely in normal individuals. This extract is prepared as follows:

(1) Make a 90-minute aliquot of urine acid to litmus with glacial acetic acid. Filter if cloudy.

(2) Add 8 volumes of cold 95% ethyl alcohol and leave the mixture undisturbed in the cold room overnight.

(3) Siphon off the clear supernatant, transfer the rest to a centrifuge tube, and centrifuge.

(4) Discard all supernatants.

(5) Dry the precipitate twice with 10 cc. of absolute alcohol and twice with ether. Centrifuge each time and discard the supernatant.

(6) Dry overnight in a vacuum desiccator. This dry extract is stable at room temperature.

If it is desired to assay gonadotropin and low or normal values are expected, then the alcohol procedure is as follows:

(1) Make a 16-hour urine equivalent acid to litmus and filter if cloudy.

(2) Add 1 gm. of NaCl per 100 ml. of urine.

(3) Add 4 volumes of cold 95% ethyl alcohol and let stand undisturbed in the cold room overnight.

(4) Siphon off the clear supernatant, transfer the rest to a centrifuge bottle, and centrifuge.

(5) Discard the supernatants.

(6) Wash the precipitate once with 50 to 60 cc. of ether.

(7) Dry the precipitate and stirring rod overnight in the desiccator.

(8) Extract the precipitate with 15 cc. of distilled water for 30 minutes after carefully breaking up the precipitate with the glass rod.

(9) Transfer the supernatant to an osmosis membrane bag. Dialysis should be either for 4 hours against running cold tap water or for 16 hours against several changes of distilled water in the cold room. Whichever method is chosen should be used consistently.

(10) Transfer the solution remaining in the bag, with the aid of a small amount of distilled water, to an appropriate flask or beaker. Add 0.1 gm. NaCl and then 4 volumes of cold 95% ethyl alcohol.

(11) Allow the solution to stand overnight in the refrigerator.

(12) Siphon off the supernatant and centrifuge down the precipitate.

(13) Wash the precipitate twice with 15 to 20 cc. of ether and dry in the desiccator overnight.

The same bioassays can be carried out with any of these extracts, adjusting the volume of extracting fluid to the levels at which it is desired to test the material.

The assay solution can be prepared by overnight extraction in the cold of the finely ground precipitate with an appropriate volume of distilled water. It has been my experience that results are more uniform if only the water-soluble extract is used and the insoluble material is removed by centrifugation.

VI. Bioassay

A. MOUSE AND RAT UTERINE WEIGHT

The most widely used assay is the uterine weight of the immature female mouse. Weanling mice from a single source should be used. If they come from outside the laboratory they should not be used on the day of arrival. The total material for injection into each mouse should be contained in 2.5 ml. of solution. The mice are given 5 subcutaneous injections of 0.5 ml. each; one the first day, 2 (one in the morning and one in the late afternoon) the second day, and 2 the third day. The mice are killed with a lethal dose of an anesthetic on the afternoon of the fourth day. The uteri are dissected free of fat and extraneous tissue. The vagina should be severed just below the cervix and grasped in a fine forceps and the uterus freed of ligaments and other tissue with a fine scissors, starting at the cervix and dissecting to the ovaries. The uterotubal junction is then cut and the uterus incised; any fluid present is expressed and blotted on filter paper or on paper towels. The uteri are then weighed on a torsion balance.

There are several means of interpreting the results in the bioassay and of setting up the injection in terms of percentage of the 24-hour urine injected. When a mouse unit is to be employed it should be based both on the uterine weight of control animals injected with saline alone and on the ability of the technician to increase the uterine weight with urine extracts. Our unit on this basis requires 20 mg. uteri since our control uterine weights average about 10 mg.

The commonest experimental setup for this assay is to use 2 mice on each dosage level and to inject the mice being tested for the lowest level with 3.6 hours' equivalent of extract, thereby testing for 6.6 mouse uterine units per 24 hours. Successive groups of 2 mice are injected with half the dose of the previous groups up to 100 units. In the case of the alcohol precipitation methods, titers of greater than 100 mouse uterine weight units should be tested with the nondialysis technique, and the lower levels with the dialysis method. The single kaolin extract, on the other hand, can be used for all dilutions. One can also inject the mice with 2 or 3 levels of extract at an interval previously determined for the extraction procedure and the mice, and compare the potency of the extract with a simultaneously injected reference material. The activity of the extract can then be expressed in terms of the reference material and related to the original urine in terms of equivalent per 24 hours of the reference standard.

The other animal that can be employed for clinical bioassay is the immature female rat. As suggested for the mouse uterine weight assay, animals should be of uniform age and from a single source. It is even more important for rats to be tested for sensitivity to the extract prepared by your method than for mice. Indeed, there is so much variation in the sensitivity of the rat ovary to gonadotropin that one cannot reasonably use a biologic unit unless it is one carefully determined in the rats and with the urine extract used in your bioassay method.

The rats should have daily subcutaneous injections for 4 days and autopsy should be performed on the fifth day. Since the rat ovary is less responsive than the mouse uterus, each rat should be injected with extract equivalent to 12 hours of urine. Thus, only 2 rats can be injected with the extract of one 24-hour urine. However, since the rat ovary has a great potential response, the weight attained can be compared to the previously determined curve and expressed in terms of the standard. If well-standardized rats of a sensitive strain are available, the results on 2 rats give reasonable clinical precision (Albert, 1950).

The adequate assessment of the gonad-stimulating hormone (GSH) activity of pituitary tissue, extracts and body fluids presents many problems. As pointed out early in this chapter, we are not even sure that we can completely separate the various activities. Indeed, we are not certain how many different mucoproteins with gonad-stimulating properties exist. Thus, we are in the position where we must prepare extracts and characterize them as well as possible by many physical measurements. Further, in view of the multiple biologic activities and even the apparent overlap of these activities in various preparations, it is wise to apply a series of biologic "yardsticks" to all GSH preparations.

Several assays do not discriminate between the various gonadotropic activities and are utilized as "total gonadotropic" measures. As mentioned previously, the estrous rabbit is such a test object, but for the reasons already given we do not recommend it as an assay animal of choice. The uterus of the immature mouse also fails to discriminate between preparations of human origin which greatly predominate in either LH or FSH activity by other bioassay procedures (Segaloff and Steelman, 1959). Similar lack of true discrimination is also found in the ovary of the intact rat and mouse and the rat uterus. Indeed, it can be said that the rat ovary and uterus, or the mouse ovary and uterus, can be employed interchangeably as end points varying only in sensitivity. Mouse uterus is the most sensitive, followed by the mouse ovary, rat uterus, and rat ovary.

There is often a marked variation in sensitivity in different animal colonies, the variation between mice being less than between rats. Therefore, for all accurate assays of these types, one should always employ a reference standard and either a 4-point (2 levels of standard and 2 levels of unknown) or a 6-point (3 levels of standard and 3 levels of unknown) assay procedure.

B. Uterine and Ovarian Weight

In the procedure which we employ, weanling mice or rats are used for the best results. They should be assigned to the treatment groups in an acceptable statistical randomization fashion and each group should contain 5 or more animals.

The preparation should be dissolved in a saline solution and divided into 5 portions so that each portion can be removed for injection at one time. It is our practice to inject the animals once on the first day, twice each on the second and third days, with autopsy on the afternoon of the fourth day. All animals are inspected to determine whether the vagina is canalized. The animals are killed with ether and the uteri and ovaries are dissected free of extraneous tissue (see instructions above under clinical assays). The uteri are incised and after the fluid has been expressed are weighed on a torsion balance without the fluid, note being made of the presence or absence of such uterine fluid. The ovaries should then be dissected free of the tube, capsule, and fat, and weighed on a torsion balance. The potency of the unknown is then calculated by the usual methods in terms of the reference standard employed.

The schedule of one daily injection recommended for the rat assay in the clinical method is adequate for crude preparations but we find that the injection described in the preceding paragraphs is better for extracts of greater purity. Indeed, with preparations of high activity it is best to employ inert protein material, such as 0.5% gelatin, as the vehicle rather than saline.

C. FSH Assay

The method for measurement of follicle-stimulating hormone which I believe most suitable employs the rat. A sufficiently high dose of human chorionic gonadotropin is given together with the unknown extract, so that the amount of luteinizing hormone which may be contained in the extract does not interfere. It has been our experience that the method described by Steelman and Pohley (1953) is the most suitable for this.

The amount of human chorionic gonadotropin necessary for optimal results with this method varies in many rats. In our hands it has generally been 40 I.U. per rat rather than the 20 I.U. recommended in the original method. Here again it is always necessary to inject the control with a reference standard. It is our custom to use a 4-point assay design, most commonly using 0.1 and 0.2 mg. of the Armour reference FSH material and 2 doses of the unknown after a preliminary assay at a single-dose level.

D. LH Assay

The ventral prostate of the hypophysectomized male rat appears to be the best end organ for the measurement of LH. The great problem with this assay is that in many strains of rats other pituitary hormones, particularly prolactin and growth hormone, synergize the effect of either androgen or LH on the ventral prostate (Segaloff et al., 1956). The length of time elapsed between hypophysectomy and initiation of treatment has an important bearing both on sensitivity and on the effect of prolactin. The longer the period after hypophysectomy, the less the sensitivity and the greater the effect of the other pituitary fractions. Therefore we find it best to use animals 24 hours after hypophysectomy. Testicular weight in these animals can be employed as a rough measure of FSH. It should be pointed out that with extracts rich in LH the weight increase of the testis may be due to the LH, since androgens and the best preparations of LH both increase testis weight.

Thus, for this assay we employ immature male rats (c. 75 gm.) and give them their first injection 24 hours after hypophysectomy. They are then injected twice on the second and third days, making a total of 5 injections of 0.5 ml. of solution during a period of 3 days. They are killed with ether on the afternoon of the fourth day. The ventral prostate, seminal vesicles, and testes are dissected out and weighed on a sensitive torsion balance. As in the other assays a standard should be employed and either a 4- or 6-point assay design. The potency is calculated as usual.

E. Ovarian Hyperemia

Ovarian hyperemia, suggested previously as a pregnancy test, is said to be a measure of LH. However, this is a quantal assay with a difficult end point which does not give adequate results in some animal colonies. This has been reviewed by Loraine (1958).

A new method of assessing the end point which may obviate these difficulties has recently been suggested (Ellis and Porter, 1957; Ellis, 1961). However, neither the literature nor our own experience is extensive enough to recommend this without reservation as a measure of LH, although I would recommend it because of its sensitivity and rapidity. In this method immature female rats are given an intravenous injection of 0.2 ml. of the hormone-containing solution. Two hours later they are given 0.2 ml. of a solution of I^{131}-labeled human serum albumin. One microcurie is given to each animal. Fifteen minutes after the isotope is injected, the animals are killed with chloroform. Great care must be taken to have the animals dead before removal of the ovaries. Removal of the ovaries of anesthetized animals results in failure of the ovarian radioactivity to increase. The ovaries are removed with the capsule, tubes, and a small amount of fat. The radioactivity is then measured in a suitable counter. We have found, in a preliminary fashion, that if one then dissects the capsules, tubes, and fat away from the ovary, weighs the ovary and expresses the radioactivity per milligram of ovary, the best curves are obtained. It must be emphasized that these are only preliminary results which are being included for completeness.

REFERENCES

Albert, A. (1950). *Recent Progr. in Hormone Research* **12**, 227.
Archibald, W. J. (1947). *J. Phys. Colloid Chem.* **51**, 1204.
Brillhart, J. R. (1959). *Obstet. and Gynecol.* **14**, 581.
Chow, B. F., Greep, R. O., and van Dyke, H. B. (1939). *J. Endocrinol.* **1**, 440.
Cowie, A. T. (1948). *Commonwealth Agr. Bur. (Gt. Brit.) Joint Publ.* **13**.
Ellis, S. (1958). *J. Biol. Chem.* **233**, 63.
Ellis, S. (1961). *Endocrinology* **68**, 334.
Ellis, S., and Porter, J. (1957). *Federation Proc.* **16**, 34.
Greep, R. O., van Dyke, H. B., and Chow, B. F. (1942). *Endocrinology* **30**, 635.
Hobson, B. M. (1955). *J. Obstet. Gynaecol. Brit. Empire* **62**, 354.
International Reference Preparation for Human Menopausal Gonadotrophin. (1959). *World Health Organization Tech. Rept. Ser.* **172**.
Klinefelter, H. F., Jr., Albright, F., and Griswold, G. C. (1943). *J. Clin. Endocrinol.* **3**, 529.
Kupperman, H. S., Greenblatt, R. B., and Noback, C. R. (1943). *J. Clin. Endocrinol.* **3**, 548.
Landau, B., Schwartz, H. S., and Soffer, L. J. (1960). *Metabolism* **9**, 85.
League Nations Bull. Health Organisation (1938a). **8**, Ext. 16, p. 884.
League Nations Bull. Health Organisation (1938b). **8**, Ext. 18, p. 899.
Loraine, J. A. (1958). "Clinical Application of Hormone Assay." E. and S. Livingstone, Edinburgh and London.
McShan, W. H., and Meyer, R. K. (1938). *J. Biol. Chem.* **117**, 111.
Nelson, W. O. (1937). *Cold Spring Harbor Symposia Quant. Biol.* **5**, 123.
Robbins, S. L., and Parker, F. (1948). *Endocrinology* **27**, 37.
Rosemberg, E., Smith, F., and Dorfman, R. I. (1957). *Endocrinology* **61**, 337.
Segaloff, A. (1954–55). *Year Book Endocrinol.* p. 266.
Segaloff, A., and Steelman, S. L. (1959). *Recent Progr. in Hormone Research* **15**, 127.
Segaloff, A., Steelman, S. L., and Flores, A. (1956). *Endocrinology* **59**, 233.

Segaloff, A., Steelman, S. L., Everett, C., and Flores, A. (1959). *J. Clin. Endocrinol. and Metabolism* **19**, 827.

Simpson, M. E., Evans, H. M., Fraenkel-Conrat, H. L., and Li, C. H. (1941). *Endocrinology* **28**, 37.

Squire, P. G., and Li, C. H. (1958). *Science* **127**, 32.

Steelman, S. L., and Pohley, F. M. (1953). *Endocrinology* **53**, 604.

Steelman, S. L., and Segaloff, A. (1959). *Recent Progr. in Hormone Research* **15**, 115.

Steelman, S. L., Lamont, W. A., and Baltes, B. J. (1952). *Acta Endocrinol.* **22**, 186.

Steelman, S. L., Kelly, T. L., Segaloff, A., and Weber, G. F. (1956). *Endocrinology* **59**, 256.

Steelman, S. L., Segaloff, A., and Mays, M. G. (1958). *Arch. Biochem. Biophys.* **78**, 262.

Thorberg, J. V. (1950). *Acta Endocrinol.* **4**, 163.

Ward, D. N., McGregor, R. F., and Griffin, A. C. (1959). *Biochim. et Biophys. Acta* **32**, 305

Chapter 18

Prolactin

ALBERT SEGALOFF

I. Historical Introduction

Prolactin is one of the most interesting pituitary factors. It has undergone several cycles of popularity with a great deal of work being done, then very little, then a great deal of work being done again. It was one of the earliest pituitary principles to be highly purified. Indeed, it was the first pituitary protein hormone to be crystallized (White, 1949). The lactogenic hormone (which hereafter will be used interchangeably with prolactin) has a long history of claims and counterclaims with regard to its various activities.

There seems to be little question, however, that there is an essentially homogeneous protein, obtained most readily from the pituitaries of sheep, which does play a key role in initiation of lactation in properly prepared mammals. Lyons first conclusively demonstrated the direct action of lactogenic hormone on suitably prepared mammary tissue in 1942, when he injected a lactogenic hormone concentrate into the collecting ducts of pseudopregnant rabbits and obtained localized lactation only in the ducts so injected. However, there is not universal agreement that this is proof that lactogenic hormone is the sole pituitary factor involved in initiation of lactation. Folley and Malpress (1948) pointed out that in hypophysectomized animals other than the rabbit it is impossible to induce lactation with such pituitary extracts. Another point that they bring up, which I feel is not necessarily pertinent to the problem of initiation of lactation, is that lactogenic hormone is not the most potent agent in increasing established lactation, but that crude pituitary extracts or extracts particularly rich in growth hormone are more effective in this regard than the lactogenic hormone. This, of course, is an entirely separate problem.

In 1931 Riddle and Braucher showed that secretion of "crop milk" by pigeons and doves is initiated and maintained by a factor from the anterior pituitary of these birds. Riddle and Bates (1939) later demonstrated that this factor is identical with the lactogenic hormone. This work formed the basis for the most widely utilized assays for lactogenic hormone, which will be discussed later.

A. Lactogenic Hormone and Growth Hormone

The possible identity of lactogenic hormone with growth hormone has a long and honored history of dispute. Indeed, one of the classic feuds in endocrinology was the one between H. M. Evans and Oscar Riddle, the former insisting that there is a growth hormone and that it is not lactogenic hormone; the latter insisting that there is a growth hormone and that it is lactogenic hormone. Riddle's arguments were based on the effects of hypophyseal lactogenic hormone preparations in doves, whereas Evans maintained that a separate hormone with only growth-promoting activity can be prepared from pituitaries. This entire question seems to swing full circle, for there are indeed many areas of overlapping activities. Retention of nitrogen, the so-called "anabolic effect" of growth hormone, usually seen in man only after administering growth hormone from primates, is also produced by sheep prolactin (Bergenstal and Lipsett, 1958). Both preparations seem capable of initiating and/or sustaining lactation, and both sensitize the ventral prostate of the hypophysectomized male rat to androgens (Segaloff et al., 1956). Whether this overlap of properties is due to the inadequacy of present preparations, or whether this is indeed an overlap of properties, as in the case of oxytocin and vasopressin, remains an open question.

B. Luteotropic Properties

The luteotropic properties of prolactin are also a subject of some debate. We define luteotropic properties as those needed to induce secretion of progestational hormone from preformed corpora lutea. This property has been demonstrated conclusively only in some rodents. In fact, this may actually be due to a pituitary principle separable from prolactin.

There has been much controversy as to whether this material is identical with the lactogenic hormone and whether such effects of lactogenic hormone actually can be demonstrated in the human ovary. The only unequivocal demonstration of luteotropic effects in women is with large doses of chorionic gonadotropin (Sternberg *et al.*, 1953). All attempts with lactogenic hormone alone have failed, but one study has been reported to show that lactogenic hormone lowers the requirements of chorionic gonadotropin for luteotropic effects in man (Fried and Rakoff, 1952). Unfortunately, even in animals, there are series of experiments in reliable hands which seem to be completely contradictory: some investigators say that the lactogenic hormone can maintain pregnancy in rats following hypophysectomy; some point out that they are unable to do this. In addition to this, there are those who believe that induction of pseudopregnancy in normal-cycling rats is a reliable assay for this activity, and others who believe that this can be shown by pituitary principles other than lactogenic hormone. Luteotropin also has the ability to maintain enough corpora luteal function, even after hypophysectomy, to produce decidua by traumatization of the uterus. This is possible in animals previously treated with gonadotropin for the induction of large corpora lutea, then hypophysectomized, given lactogenic hormone to maintain the corpora lutea, and subsequently having their uteri traumatized. To the best of our knowledge, there is no satisfactory assay for this property. It may or may not be a property of lactogenic hormone.

II. Assay Methods

The most suitable assay methods for lactogenic hormone are those based on the pigeon crop or dove crop (Cowie and Folley, 1955). These crop sacs are thin, transparent membranes at all times except during the latter half of the incubation period of a clutch of eggs. At this time, in both males and females, they increase in weight, become thickened, and secrete so-called "crop milk," which desquamates from the surface of the crop sac and which the birds feed to their young. This apparently occurs through stimulation from the animal's pituitary and has been widely employed as an assay procedure for lactogenic hormone in non-incubating pigeons. This method has many advantages over the methods employing mammals. Pigeons are exquisitely sensitive to lactogenic hormone, and the assay can be done with considerably less material than the mammalian assays. Second, the assay birds require no preliminary build-up of their mammary tree. Third, there is no sex difference in their response. Fourth, pigeons are more readily available in standardized size and strain than either rabbits or guinea pigs. Finally, the assays are more reproducible in pigeons than in other experimental animals. Many studies have been done on the effect of different types of pigeons, season, route of injection, and injection volume on lactogenic hormone assaying in pigeons. Clark and Folley (1953) feel that it is most important to take the weight of the bird into account and to employ young pigeons.

Bahn and Bates (1956) have done extensive studies on the specificity of the pigeon crop response to human urine. They showed that when pigeons are injected with lactogenic extracts of sheep or human pituitaries cytoplasmic basophilia developed in the proliferated crop sacs. On the other hand, this did not develop in those birds injected with extracts of human urine. In addition, they noted nonspecific substances in urine capable of increasing crop weight in pigeons. However, until it is demonstrated that crop-weight-increasing extracts of human urine fail to show the lactation-inducing properties of sheep extracts, this must be looked upon as an interesting observation of questionable value.

A. Pigeon Assays—Micro Method

The most sensitive assay method is the so-called micro method of local intracutaneous injections of the crop sac. The following procedure is recommended. Pigeons of a uniform strain (we use white Carneaux pigeons) are selected and divided into groups. The feathers are plucked over the crop and in the area for each injection. Each bird should be injected with two different preparations on opposite sides of the crop, one injection with a standard and the other with the unknown. It is our custom to inject an extremely small bleb of India ink to mark the area for the repeated intradermal injections. Intradermal injections raising a bleb are made by inserting the needle into a follicle from which a feather has been plucked. We use a $\frac{1}{2}$-inch-long 27 or 28 gauge hypodermic needle on a $\frac{1}{4}$-cc. tuberculin syringe and inject 0.1 cc. of solution each time. The animals are killed by decapitation on the fifth day, 24 hours after the fourth intradermal injection. The crops are cleaned and removed, and the degree of proliferation for the experimental material is compared with that for the control.

We have found it impossible to estimate the response consistently against a scale, since crop stretching and drying are most important and vary greatly from time to time. We therefore feel that it is absolutely necessary to use a comparison with a standard in the same bird's crop for each bird. We have found that the best way to observe the crops is under diffuse light, and we try to have 2 independent observers estimate the response of each bird.

Larger quantities of lactogenic hormone activity in extracts of pituitary tissue can best be estimated in groups given the hormone systemically. The birds should be of uniform age and strain. They are injected subcutaneously once daily for 4 days and decapitated on the fifth day. Crops are then carefully dissected out, cleaned, and weighed. We believe that for preliminary assays a 4-point design should be used with 4 birds on each point. For more precise assays larger numbers of birds and more points are a necessity.

B. MAMMALIAN ASSAYS

Although several mammalian assays are available, based on the various principles of physiology which we have outlined above, we do not believe that any of them has sufficient sensitivity or reproducibility to be recommended as a means for measuring lactogenic hormone. The assay of lactogenic hormone by its property of induction of lactation in the rabbit is difficult and the animals are expensive and insensitive. However, since ultimate proof of the identity of the two properties is lacking, one may wish to employ such methods on occasion.

The most sensitive of such methods is the local injection method of Lyons (1942). The modification of Meites and Turner (1950) has the advantage of not requiring the surgical hysterectomy and castration of the Lyons method. It is carried out as follows: mature rabbits are made pseudopregnant by intravenous injection of 50 to 75 I.U. of human chorionic gonadotropin (HCG). Fifteen days later the rabbits are anesthetized, the nipples are cleaned, and the hair shaved around the mammary gland area. The solution is injected with a nonbeveled 27 gauge needle. One milliliter of solution is injected into a single sector of the mammary gland. The solvent should be injected into a control gland. It is usually necessary to use a binocular dissecting microscope for the injections. After the second day attempts are made to express milk from the nipple. The result is considered positive if milk can be expressed from the nipple by the fifth day after the injection. If the animals are killed, the milk can be seen distending the ducts of the injected sector of mammary glands.

The systemic method of Bergman et al. (1940) is the easiest to employ. Mature estrous rabbits are made pseudopregnant by intravenous injection of 50 I.U. of chorionic gonadotropin. Fourteen days later the animals are carefully examined to be sure that they have the characteristic well-developed mammary glands of pseudopregnancy. If they have, subcutaneous injections of the assay solution are begun. They are given 6 daily injections and killed on the seventh day. The mammary glands are then rated as to response on a scale of 1 to 4+. I am not aware of any extensive comparison of standards by this method so that it can at best be referred to as semiquantitative at present.

III. Assay of Prolactin in Human Urine

Prolactin activity in human urine can be estimated after suitable concentration procedures (Coppedge and Segaloff, 1951). The assay is carried out on 24-hour urine samples collected with the precautions given under the gonadotropin assay. To the total 24-hour urine 1% by weight of sodium chloride is added, the urine is acidified to litmus with glacial acetic acid if necessary, and then 4 volumes of 95% alcohol, kept in the cold room, are added to the urine in a container of suitable size; the urine is stirred vigorously and then put in the cold room to settle overnight. The supernatant is syphoned off and decanted and the precipitate is concentrated by centrifugation. The precipitate is washed twice with 95% alcohol, twice with ether, and then it is permitted to dry overnight at room temperature. The dry precipitate, which is stable, can be extracted with three 15 ml. extractions of distilled water. The precipitate should be finally comminuted and extracted 30 minutes at room temperature for each extraction. The material is centrifuged out and the extract decanted off. The combined extracts are placed in dialysis casings and dialyzed in the cold room against 6 hourly changes of 0.5% sodium chloride.

To the solution remaining within the membrane, 100 mg. of sodium chloride (0.5 cc. of a 20% solution) and 4 volumes of 95% alcohol are added. The material is stirred and then allowed to settle overnight in the cold room. The supernatant is syphoned off, the precipitate is dried as before, and the extract can be stored at room temperature for assay since it is stable.

The extract is ground and extracted with 40 ml. of distilled water for 2 hours, the material is centrifuged, the supernatant is decanted and used for injection into suitable pigeons.

The pigeons are all given a daily subcutaneous injection of 2.5 I.U. of a standard preparation of sheep prolactin in order to boost their crop response to the steep portion of the curve. Then 2 ml. of each of the extracts, the supernatants previously mentioned, are injected intravenously into each of 4 pigeons daily for 4 days. Thus, each bird gets 20% of the 24-hour urine.

One group of pigeons is given only the 2.5 I.U. by subcutaneous injection. Another group of pigeons is given the 2.5 I.U. by subcutaneous injection plus 40 I.U. intravenously. From these two groups a comparison is made with the crop weight obtained when the pigeons are injected with the unknown extract. Results can be calculated as shown in Table I (Segaloff, 1953).

TABLE I

CALCULATION OF RESULTS OF ASSAY

y = average crop weight/body weight for each group of 4 birds

It is assumed that the ratio of y varies linearly between 2.5 and 40 + 2.5 I.U. This implies

$$\frac{u}{y - y_{2.5}} = \frac{40}{y_{40} - y_{2.5}}$$

where u = units of urinary prolactin received by each bird

Hence

$$u = \left(\frac{40}{y_{40} - y_{2.5}}\right)(y - y_{2.5})$$

and

$$\text{I.U.} = 5\left(\frac{40}{y_{40} - y_{2.5}}\right)(y - y_{2.5})$$

Let

$$C = 5\left(\frac{40}{y_{40} - y_{2.5}}\right) = \frac{200}{y_{40} - y_{2.5}}$$

calculated from control data for each assay group

$$\text{I.U.} = C(y - y_{2.5})$$

REFERENCES

Bahn, R. C., and Bates, R. W. (1956). *J. Clin. Endocrinol. and Metabolism* **16**, 1337.

Bergenstal, D., and Lipsett, M. B. (1958). *J. Clin. Invest.* **32**, 877.

Bergman, A. J., Meites, J., and Turner, C. W. (1940). *Endocrinology* **26**, 716.

Clark, P. M., and Folley, S. J. (1953). *Ciba Foundation Colloquia Endocrinol.* **5**, 90.

Coppedge, R. L., and Segaloff, A. (1951). *J. Clin. Endocrinol.* **11**, 465.

Cowie, A. T., and Folley, S. J. (1955). *In* "The Hormones" (G. Pincus and K. V. Thimann, eds.) Vol. 3, p. 345. Academic Press, New York.

Folley, S. J., and Malpress, F. H. (1948). *In* "The Hormones" (G. Pincus and K. V. Thimann, eds.), Vol. 1, Chapts. 15, 16. Academic Press, New York.

Fried, P. H., and Rakoff, A. E. (1952). *J. Clin. Endocrinol. and Metabolism* **12**, 321.

Lyons, W. R. (1942). *Proc. Soc. Exptl. Biol. Med.* **51**, 308.

Meites, J., and Turner, C. W. (1950). *In* "Hormone Assay" (C. W. Emmens, ed.), p. 237. Academic Press, New York.

Riddle, O., and Bates, R. W. (1939). "Sex and Internal Secretions," 2nd ed., p. 1088. Williams & Wilkins, Baltimore, Maryland.

Riddle, O., and Bates, R. W. (1939). "Sex and Internal Secretions," 2nd ed., p. 1088.

Segaloff, A. (1953). *Ciba Foundation Colloquia Endocrinol.* **5**, 109.

Segaloff, A., Steelman, S. L., and Flores, A. (1956). *Endocrinology* **59**, 233.

Sternberg, W. H., Segaloff, A., and Gaskill, C. J. (1953). *J. Clin. Endocrinol. and Metabolism* **13**, 139.

White, A. (1949). *Vitamins and Hormones* **7**, 253.

Chapter 19

Thyrotropic Hormone

C. W. TURNER

I. Introduction

It is interesting to note the lack of references to the use of radioactive iodine (I^{131}) as a tool in the assay of thyrotropin in the volume "Hormone Assay" (Turner, 1950). During the past 10 years, by the use of I^{131}, many of the intimate details of thyroid gland function have been elucidated. As a by-product of this research, the role of the anterior pituitary hormone, thyrotropin (TSH), in the regulation of thyroxine secretion has been greatly increased. That the thyroid gland may function autonomously, to a slight extent, is indicated by the limited trapping of I^{131} in hypophysectomized animals and by the slight release of hormonal-I^{131}. However, the major functional activity of the thyroid gland has been shown to be under pituitary control. The question whether the major function of TSH is concerned with the iodine-trapping phenomenon or with the thyroidal hormone release mechanism has not been resolved.

It is generally accepted that the rate of secretion (or release) of TSH and the rate of release of thyroxine into the blood in individual animals is in equilibrium under standard conditions of environment. Injection of TSH increases I^{131} trapping and thyroxine release rate, whereas injection of thyroxine depresses TSH secretion (and release) and inhibits thyroidal-I^{131} release.

Methods of assay of TSH using I^{131} are thus based upon the functional activity of the thyroid gland either in the I^{131} trapping or releasing mechanisms. It is interesting to note that primary study during the past few years has been devoted to thyroxine secretion rate rather than to a study of TSH secretion rate. This is based upon the tacit assumption that thyroxine secretion rate indirectly measures TSH secretion rate. It is quite possible, however, that species and individual thyroid glands vary in their responsiveness to TSH. It is possible to measure in the same animal at the same time TSH and thyroxine secretion rates. Data of this type will indicate the variation in sensitivity of the thyroid glands to TSH. While such data are not currently available, a technique for the simultaneous determination of thyroxine and TSH secretion rates will be presented.

In addition to the use of I^{131} in the assay of TSH, Borell and Holmgren (1949) suggested the use of P^{32} uptake by the thyroid gland. Its value has been explored and methods using several species of experimental animals have been outlined. Lamberg (1955) reviewed the usefulness of P^{32} methods in detail.

For the older methods of TSH assay the reader is referred to Chapter IX, Thyrotropic Hormone (Turner, 1950) in "Hormone Assay." Tala (1952) also reviewed the earlier methods and presented extensive data on the relative sensitivity of the methods. Lamberg (1955) compared the earlier methods with those using radioactive indicators. Brown (1959) recently presented a critical review of the assay methods available.

For an extensive review of the chemistry and physiology of TSH, the reader is referred to Sonenberg (1958). The chemistry and physiology of the thyroid gland has been reviewed by Rawson *et al.* (1955).

A. TERMINOLOGY

The thyroid-stimulating hormone of the anterior pituitary has been called thyrotropin, thyrotrophin, thyrotropic hormone, and thyrotrophic hormone. In this chapter the abbreviation TSH will be used.

B. Two Thyrotropic Hormones?

Greer (1952) postulated that there are two thyrotropic principles secreted by the pituitary. One, a "metabolic factor" is independent of the hypothalamus and enables the thyroid to concentrate and bind iodine. Second, a "growth factor" regulates thyroid cell height and gross thyroid size. Hypothalamic lesions interfere with the secretion of this factor. The level of circulating thyroid hormone is believed to govern, in part, the secretion of this factor (see also Greer *et al.*, 1953). No evidence of a chemical separation of two factors has been presented.

C. Isolation and Purification of Pituitary TSH

A review of the older methods of purifying pituitary TSH has been presented by Sonenberg (1958). Recently, chromatographic purification of TSH has been reported by Heideman (1953), Pierce and Nyc (1956), and Condliffe and Bates (1956) using the carboxylic cation exchange resin, Amberlite IRC-50. In addition, Fels *et al.* (1955) reported the use of oxycellulose, Condliffe and Bates (1956) the use of carboxymethylcellulose and later the use of diethylaminoethylcellulose (Condliffe and Bates, 1957).

D. Exophthalmos-Producing Substance (EPS)

Dobyns (1946) reported that some TSH preparations were more effective in producing exophthalmos than others. These observations were further confirmed by Dobyns and Steelman (1953). They were able to separate two fractions by their differential solubility in trichloracetic acid, one of which contained TSH and the second EPS.

Smelser and Ozanics (1955) suggested from studies with guinea pigs that ACTH may be acting synergistically with TSH to produce exophthalmos. Adams and Purves (1957b) suggested that this explanation avoided the necessity of postulating a specific pituitary ophthalmotrophic factor which would serve no function other than to explain an obscure human disease. An abnormal type of response to the sera of the thyrotoxic patients has been reported by Adams (1958), McKenzie (1958b), and Munro (1959). Its cause has not been explained.

Querido and Lameyer (1956) concluded that there is no relation between exophthalmos and serum TSH level. Gilliland, in a discussion (same paper), reported high levels of serum TSH in most patients with spontaneous myxedema, in induced myxedema, and in cretinism, all unassociated with exophthalmos making it unlikely that TSH alone is the cause of exophthalmos.

E. Assay of Exophthalmos-Producing Substance

Albert (1945) method. Fundulus heteroclitus, Linn. (the common Atlantic minnow), 3–4 inches in length are kept in a tank of running tap water at 10°C. in winter and 18°C. in summer. To avoid loss of fluids by the intraperitoneal injection route, the needle is inserted into the cloaca, through the rectum, over the pelvic girdle, and into the peritoneal cavity for a distance of about $\frac{1}{2}$ inch. The volume of fluid injected should be 0.1–0.5 ml. The effect of the hormone is to cause protrusion of the eyeballs (exophthalmos). A unit of EPS has been defined as that amount of substance which induces proptosis in 25% of a group of 20 fish 6 hours following injection.

F. Standard Preparation

The lack of a reference standard of thyrotropin referred to in "Hormone Assay" (Turner, 1950) was finally remedied in 1952 by the preparation of a provisional U.S.P. thyrotropin reference substance in tablets of 20 mg. each containing 1 U.S.P. thyrotropin unit. One milligram of this substance contains 0.05 U.S.P. unit. The material was a lyophilized preparation of thyrotropin obtained from bovine anterior pituitary glands. Minimal amounts of other anterior and posterior pituitary hormones were present.

An international standard for thyrotropin was authorized by the World Health Organization Expert Committee on Biological Standardization at its 7th session held in Geneva in 1953. The Department of Biological Standards at the National Institute for Medical Research, London, prepared the new standard. Two 60-gm. lots of thyrotropin were pooled, diluted with lactose, and made into tablets. The tablets were put into ampules filled with pure dry nitrogen and stored at −10°C. Ten laboratories from 8 countries, using 8 methods of assay, joined in a collaborative standardization of the new lot against the provisional U.S.P. thyrotropin reference substance. The description of the assay methods employed and the results of the assays were described by Mussett and Perry (1955). After a thorough analysis of the results, a figure of 0.074 units per milligram was accepted as the potency of the new international standard. Thus, 1 unit of the international standard represents the activity of 13.5 mg. of the provisional U.S.P. standard and 20 mg. of tablet equals 1.48 units. The present U.S.P. and the international units are identical. Thus, 1 U.S.P. unit = 1 I.U.

In the assay of body fluids it has been suggested that the results be expressed in terms of international milliunits (I.mU. or mU.) per milliliter of fluid.

II. Factors Influencing the Sensitivity of the Thyroid Gland

In the choice of animals in the assay of TSH it is of great importance to understand the factors influencing endogenous secretion unless hypophysectomized animals are used. In normal animals, the sensitivity of response to exogenous TSH will be related to the endogenous secretion rate. Species with low endogenous TSH secretion are preferred. Further, the time in the life span when TSH secretion is low should be selected. Environmental factors such as temperature and nutrition also markedly influence TSH secretion. Finally, substances which may partially or completely block TSH secretion or discharge are of interest.

Of the normal animals, the baby chick and young guinea pig have been used most extensively in the assay of TSH, due, it is believed, to their low endogenous secretion of TSH. The use of normal mice and rats in TSH assay has not been successful.

In normal animals, the reduction of TSH secretion by underfeeding may be helpful in increasing their sensitivity. Similarly, the use of high environmental temperature will tend to reduce TSH secretion to a minimum.

With our increasing knowledge of thyroid physiology, the use of normal animals in assay procedures has gradually been replaced by the use of hypophysectomized animals or by the complete block of TSH secretion by use of thyroxine or thyroprotein.

A. HYPOPHYSECTOMY

Leblond and Sue (1941) and Morton et al. (1942) early reported upon the reduced capacity of the thyroid gland of the hypophysectomized animal to take up I^{131}. Ghosh et al. (1951) showed a gradual decline in the capacity of the thyroid gland of the rat to trap I^{131} up to about 5 or 7 days after hypophysectomy, at which time only 3 to 4% of the injected dose was trapped.

Vanderlaan and Greer (1950) noted that hypophysectomy not only greatly decreased the ability of the thyroid gland to trap I^{131}, but showed that its capacity to bind iodine to protein and to discharge thyroidal-I^{131} is decreased. TSH restores all of these functions and thus the measurement of either the uptake or release of I^{131} serves as excellent indices of TSH response.

B. Administration of Thyroid Hormone

Indirect evidence for the effect of graded levels of thyroxine upon the discharge of TSH was obtained by the method of estimating thyroxine secretion rate by the use of goitrogens. When thyroxine secretion is blocked by the goitrogens, the secretion of TSH is believed to be increased, resulting in thyroid hyperplasia. Increasing levels of thyroxine administered to animals fed goitrogens reduced the thyroid hyperplasia to normal or below. This effect was assumed to be due to blockage of TSH discharge.

Overbeek *et al.* (1953) showed the effect of oral thyroprotein or injected thyroxine upon the capacity of the thyroid gland of the rat to trap I^{131} (Table I). These data show thyroprotein at level of 50

TABLE I

Effect of Thyroid Hormone on I^{131} Uptake in Rat

Thyroprotein diet (mg./kg.)	I^{131} Uptake (%)		Thyroxine (µg./day)	I^{131} Uptake (%)	
	7 days	14 days		7 days	14 days
0	34.5	28.1	0	29.6	35.8
25	3.3	3.3	2.5	3.0	15.0
50	0.8	1.2	5.0	2.1	1.9
100	0.6	0.8	10.0	2.4	1.8
200	0.5	0.5	20.0	1.4	1.5
400	0.4	0.3	40.0	1.6	1.5

mg./kg. feed to block I^{131} uptake very effectively, in fact, slightly better than thyroxine. The above observations have been utilized in the method of assay of TSH proposed by Overbeek *et al.* (1953).

III. Methods of Assay of Pituitary TSH

The earlier methods of assay of TSH described in "Hormone Assay" were primarily indices of direct action of TSH upon thyroid anatomy, including weight (gravimetric response), general histological changes, cell height, mitotic index, and intracellular droplets. The assay methods to be described are primarily indirect indices of TSH activity depending upon the uptake or release rate of radioactive isotopes (I^{131} and P^{32}).

The assay methods have been classified first on the basis of uptake or release of the isotope, and second, on the basis of the use of normal, hypophysectomized, or TSH-blocked animals.

A. METHODS DEPENDENT UPON I^{131} UPTAKE

1. Normal Animals

The guinea pig, newborn rat, chick, and tadpole have been studied as to their adaptability as assay animals. The following methods utilize normal animals.

a. Guinea pig. Henry (1951) method. Normal immature guinea pigs weighing 150–200 gm. were injected twice daily with increasing levels of TSH for 3 days. The I^{131} uptake was determined 6 hours after its administration. The maximum increase over control uptake was observed when 0.75 Heyl-Laqueur units were administered. The thyroid glands were hydrolyzed prior to counting.

b. Rat. Reiss and Wyatt (1956) method. Young rats aged 6–9 days, weighing 10–15 gm. were used as assay animals. Members of each litter were distributed at random among the groups. The total dose was given daily in 3 fractions and the animals killed on the fourth day. On the fourth day each animal was injected subcutaneously with 5µc. I^{131} in 0.1 ml. N saline, exactly 1 hour before death. The thyroids were dissected, dissolved in NaOH, and counted. The uptake of I^{131} by the thyroids was expressed as the percentage uptake of the total I^{131} injected. The index of precision (λ) of a number of assays had a mean value of 0.240.

c. Day-old chick. Keating *et al.* (1945) studied the influence of TSH upon the uptake and release of I^{131} in the thyroid of the chick. It was reported that while mean acinar cell height was apparent within 24 hours after TSH injection, collection of I^{131} occurred only after 48 hours. I^{131} collected in the thyroid was promptly released by TSH.

Wahlberg (1955) reported an extensive study of untreated White Leghorn chicks maintained at 35–36°C. for their usefulness in the assay of TSH. Maximum uptake of I^{131} was observed after 24 hours in normal chicks.

Postel (1956) method. Day-old cockerels, maintained at temperature of 85–90°F. were given tap water and a chick starter containing 1.6 µg. iodide per gram. One milliliter of TSH solution was injected at 24-hour intervals for 3 days. Fifteen hours after the last injection, 0.2 µc. I^{131}

was injected intramuscularly. Four hours later, thyroids were removed and radioactivity measured in a well-type scintillation detector. The uptake was expressed as per cent of administered dose. An eight- to tenfold increase in I^{131} uptake was shown by TSH over the range of 0.005 to 0.05 U.S.P. units per milliliter.

d. Tadpoles. D'Angelo (1956) reported that *Rana* tadpoles showed a progressive increase in I^{131} uptake in the isolated gland (estimated weight 50–200 μg.) throughout normal development, whereas increased P^{32} uptake occurred only in advanced development. Exogenous TSH increased I^{131} and P^{32} accumulation in the thyroids of young tadpoles (*Rana clamitans*). The dose-response curves obtained with a single injection of the hormone did not display a range of proportionality which could lead to precise estimations of TSH in blood and pituitary compared to measurement of thyroid cell height in the stasis tadpole.

Brown and Dodd (1956) investigated the usefulness of *Xenopus laevis* tadpole in the assay of TSH using I^{131}. Tadpoles weighing about 500 mg. and having hindlegs between 4–6 mm. in length were starved for 8 days. They were placed in jars containing water to which 10 μC. I^{131} per liter had been added. The tadpoles were injected once daily for 5 days into the submental lymph sac with 0.02 ml. solution containing TSH. The thyroids were removed and I^{131} counted. The limit of detection was about 10 mU./ml.

2. Hypophysectomized Animals

Since the uptake or trapping of I^{131} by the thyroid gland is primarily under the influence of the pituitary, the use of hypophysectomized animals is indicated, since, in such animals, I^{131} uptake is minimal.

Ghosh, Woodbury, and Sayers (1951) method. Male rats were hypophysectomized 5 days prior to the beginning of the assay. The TSH was injected in 4 equal parts at 12-hour intervals. Twelve hours after the last injection 30 μc. of I^{131} was administered. The thyroid glands were removed 24 hours later, suspended in 10 ml. of 1.0% solution of sodium iodide made alkaline to 2 N NaOH. The tissue was dissolved in 12 hours, a 0.1-ml. aliquot was evaporated in a planchet, and its radioactivity measured.

Purified TSH containing 13 Junkmann-Schoeller (J-S) units per milligram produced a graded response in the dosage range of 0.1 to 0.5 mg. The slope of the log-dose-response curves for purified TSH and crude hog pituitary were not significantly different.

Brimblecombe *et al.* (1952) reported success in use of hypophysectomized rat in routine assay of TSH.

Levey *et al.* (1956) compared hypophysectomized 100–150-gm. rats with intact animals either thyroxine-treated or thyroid powder prefed. The hypophysectomized rats responded linearly over the range of 0.625–2.5 mμ (U.S.P.) thyrotropin.

3. TSH Secretion Blocked by Thyroxine or Thyroprotein

When thyroxine is injected or thyroprotein (thyroactive iodinated casein) is fed in excess of the thyroxine secretion rate, the secretion and discharge of TSH is blocked and I[131] uptake reduced to levels comparable to those of hypophysectomized animals. The advantage in the use of such animals in comparison with hypophysectomized animals might reside in their normality in respect to other hypophyseal hormones. Investigators using these methods should be cautioned not to use a thyroxine-blocking

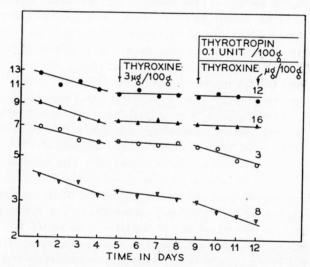

FIG. 1. It is shown that 3 μg. thyroxine/100 gm. body weight/day blocks release of thyroidal-I[131]. The injection of 0.1 U.S.P. unit TSH/100 gm. will stimulate release of thyroidal-I[131] when 3 or 8 μg. thyroxine are administered. When 12 to 16 μg./day were administered, the higher metabolic rate is believed to increase the metabolism of TSH resulting in reduced response (Premachandra and Turner, unpublished).

dose much in excess of the normal thyroxine secretion rate or the thyroxine may stimulate increased metabolism of exogenous TSH.

In a study of rats by Premachandra and Turner (unpublished data) it was shown that 3 μg. thyroxine/100 gm./day blocked thyroidal-I[131] discharge (Fig. 1). When this level of thyroxine (or 8 μg.) was continued, 0.1 U.S.P. unit-TSH/100 gm. caused a discharge of thyroidal-I[131] equal to the pre-blockage rate. However, when 12 to 16 μg. thyroxine/100 gm./day was administered as the blocking dose, the above level of TSH failed to cause release of the thyroidal-I^{131}. It is suggested that the higher levels of thyroxine increased the rate of metabolism of TSH. The sensitivity of the method would thus be reduced.

Querido et al. (*1953*) *method*. Female mice weighing 20–23 gm. are used. A diet containing 25 mg./kg. of thyroprotein is fed for 9 days. The TSH was injected intraperitoneally in 4 equal doses at 12-hour intervals. At 36 hours after the first injection, 1 μc. I^{131} was administered by the same route and 24 hours later the thyroids were removed, digested, and radioactivity measured as in the Overbeek method. During the 24-hour I^{131} uptake period, the animals may be fasted. The sensitivity of the method using mice appears to be similar to that of the comparable method using rats, but great strain differences were encountered. TSH in amounts equivalent to 10–250 μg. of provisional U.S.P. units may be estimated.

Overbeek et al. (*1953*) *method*. Male and female rats, 3 weeks old and of 50–100 gm. body weight were used. These animals were kept for about 12 days on a diet containing 30–50 mg. of thyroprotein per kilogram feed. As the animals consume about 10 gm. of feed daily, they received about 0.3–0.5 mg. of thyroprotein daily. The animals were divided into groups of equal total body weight and variability no greater than 20 gm. within groups. The animals then received 2 subcutaneous injections of TSH, diluted with saline, at 9 A.M. and 5 P.M., respectively. Next day at 9 A.M., 0.5 ml. of a carrier-free solution of I^{131} with an activity of 1–5 μc. was injected intraperitoneally. The animals were then placed for 24 hours on wire netting in glass vessels, during which period they received neither food nor water. At the end of this period the animals were killed by giving chloroform or ether. The entire gland was taken out and put into 10 ml. of 2 N NaOH containing 1% KI. The tissue dissolves entirely if kept for 24 hours at room temperature. The solution was then put into a Geiger-Müller tube and radioactivity was measured in the usual way. The radioactivity in the thyroid gland, in counts per minute, was expressed as a percentage of the radioactivity of the injected I^{131}. These percentage values are linearly related to the log dose of TSH.

Sensitivity of the method has been indicated by following comparisons. The difference between the controls and 10 μg. (0.01 units) provisional U.S.P. units TSH was barely significant, whereas 20 μg. (0.02 units) produced highly significant differences in I^{131} uptake. By this method it was shown that 1 Heyl-Laqueur unit was equal to 0.11 provisional U.S.P. units.

Levey *et al.* (1956) reported the use of thyroid powder added to rat feed to be more effective than thyroxine injection in the pretreatment of 100–150 gm. intact rats in assay of TSH.

Tissue slices. Bakke and Lawrence (1956) studied the capacity of cattle thyroid tissue *in vitro* to collect and release I^{131} under the influence of TSH. A definite method of assay was not suggested.

Botari (1957) method. The thyroid glands of 200 gm. male guinea pigs or 10–12-week-old calves were dissected under sterile conditions. Each lobe of the guinea pig was divided into quarters sliced into small fragments. The calf thyroid may be divided into many parts. The fragments were cultured for 48 hours at 37°C. by means of a roller tube technique (without coagulum). The culture medium (2 ml. per tube) was composed of Gey's solution 60%, horse serum 30%, and antibiotics 10% (5 mg. dihydrostreptomycin and 6 mg. potassium penicillin in 10 ml. Gey's solution). The pH of the medium was 7.4–7.6. After 48 hours, the TSH dissolved in 0.2 ml. Gey's solution was introduced and incubation continued for 2 hours. The medium was then replaced by an equal volume of fresh medium containing 1 μc. I^{131} per milliliter and incubation continued for 1 hour. After removal of the medium the cultures were washed twice in 10.0 ml. N saline, dried on filter paper, and weighed. The radioactivity of the culture was measured by a well-type scintillation counter after an overnight digestion in 2 N NaOH. The results were expressed in terms of counts per minute per milligram tissue. In plotting the log-dose-response curve, either the T/M ratio (T = counts per minute per milligram; M = specific activity of an equivalent amount of medium) or the specific activity of the thyroid tissue may be used. The first method is useful in standardizing the assay technique, whereas the second is reliable for the routine 4-point assay procedure.

Bottari and Donovan (1958) method. A more accurate modification of the above method has been described. It is based upon the effect of TSH upon the release of I^{131}-labeled protein-bound iodine from the thyroid gland. The thyroid gland slices were incubated in a nutrient medium containing I^{131}. After 18 hours sodium iodide was added to the tubes to prevent recirculation of labeled iodine and a sample of the medium removed for measurement of its radioactivity. Comparison with control solutions then permitted the calculation of the amount of I^{131} picked up by the thyroid tissue. The fluid to be assayed was added and a second portion of incubating medium removed after 2 hours for estimation of radioactivity. The percentage release of labeled iodine was then calculated from the change in I^{131} concentration in the medium. A linear log-dose-response curve was obtained from serial dilution of a standard preparation of TSH and spans a range of sensitivity between 0.001 and 10 mU. I.S. Separated plasma or serum may be used without treatment.

Hart et al. *(1959) method.* This is based upon the concept that the iodine-concentrating ability of thyroid slices is not homogeneous. It is suggested that tissue variability may be reduced to a minimum by mincing several glands together. *In vitro* uptake of I^{131} by minced cattle thyroid glands was found to be proportional to TSH content of the incubation medium, but not in the form of homogenates. After 2 hours' incubation in 4.0 ml. Krebs-Ringer-phosphate buffer containing 10 to 20 μc. NaI^{131}, 800 mg. of minced thyroid showed a mean I^{131} uptake of 22.6%. When TSH concentration was plotted against per cent uptake there was a rectilinear response between 1 and 10 mU./ml. TSH with a mean uptake of 40.2%.

Bakke et al. (*1957*) *method*. The observation that TSH influences the osmoregulation of cattle thyroid slices incubated 21 hours at 38°C. was used as an index of response. TSH has been shown to induce higher final weights compared to the control group due to the swelling of the follicles resulting from the entry of fluid from the incubation medium. The reader is referred to the original paper for the details of the method. The method is said to be specific, of adequate range, sensitive to < 0.01 U.S.P. mU. of TSH per milliliter, with a median λ of 0.28.

B. METHODS DEPENDENT UPON I^{131} RELEASE

After I^{131} is trapped by the thyroid gland, it becomes associated with thyroglobulin. The thyroglobulin is then hydrolyzed, and thyroxine and variable amounts of triiodothyronine are released into the blood. The trapping and release are both under the control of TSH. The release rate may be measured by the change in amount of thyroxine-like I^{131} present in the blood under the influence of TSH. The release rate may be measured also by successive *in vivo* counts of I^{131} in the thyroid gland. However, these measurements are influenced by the recycling (uptake) of I^{131} resulting from the metabolism of thyroxine. However, by the use of a goitrogen, the recycling of metabolized I^{131} can be prevented and a true rate of release of thyroidal-I^{131} may be obtained.

Basic data on factors influencing the release rate of thyroidal-I^{131} in the rat were presented by Wolff (1951). Control rats lost I^{131} from the thyroid with a biological $T_{1/2}$ of 3.3 days. Addition of 0.03% propylthiouracil to the diet increased $T_{1/2}$ to 1.6 days. Hypophysectomy resulted in prolongation of $T_{1/2}$ to 24 days. Subsequent treatment with TSH increased the release rate to normal or greater in 24 hours. Treatment with 15 μg. L-thyroxine had an effect similar to hypophysectomy, $T_{1/2}$ decreasing to 26 days.

When rats fed propylthiouracil showed a $T_{1/2}$ of 1.6 days, the addition of TSH increased the $T_{1/2}$ to 8 to 10 hours after a latent period of 2 to 3 hours.

A number of methods of assay of TSH based upon the thyroidal-I^{131} release rate have been proposed.

1. Guinea Pig

Adams and Purves (1953, 1955, 1957a) method. Young guinea pigs, weighing 250–350 gm. were given twice daily subcutaneous injections of 10 μg. L-thyroxine throughout the assay period. On the second day each animal was given 2 μc. I^{131} intraperitoneally. Three days later a blood sample was taken and the TSH was injected subcutaneously or intravenously. Five hours after subcutaneous, or three hours after intravenous, injection, a second blood sample was obtained. The blood plasma of the two samples was measured for radioactivity and the difference constituted the response. To facilitate blood sampling and intravenous injection, the animals were warmed and the ear veins illuminated with a Perspex rod. A marginal vein was nicked and 0.6 ml. of blood was collected in a tube containing a drop of heparin solution. Injection of TSH and measurement of response can be repeated on at least 5 successive days in the same animal. It was observed that the response between animals was much greater than that between days. The response appears to be directly proportional to dose of TSH up to threefold. On using the provisional U.S.P. reference substance, 100–300 μg. injected subcutaneously or 10–60 μg. injected intravenously fall within this response range. A good response is obtained by 10 μg. provisional U.S.P. standard with limits of detection about 2 μg. when given intravenously.

In the 1957 paper it was reported that 200 gm. animals of either sex were most sensitive. Three microcuries I^{131}/100 gm. body weight were administered. If uptake was less than 20%, 1 μc./100 gm. was then given. A single injection of 40 μg. daily was administered. No advantage was observed in use of PBI^{131} (protein-bound iodine) response as compared to plasma.

2. Mouse

McKenzie (1958a) method. Swiss-Webster female mice weighing about 15 gm. were used. Eight microcuries I^{131} were injected to ensure maximum uptake. Ten micrograms thyroxine was then administered, followed by the addition to the ration of 0.066% thyroid powder (U.S.P.). After 3 days allowed for clearance of blood iodine, TSH was injected intravenously. Maximum blood I^{131} was reached in 2 hours. The I^{131} in blood was counted by plating 0.1 ml. on aluminum planchets using either a gas flow or an end-window counter. The lower limit of detection was 0.025 mU. with a volume of injection of 0.2 to 0.5 ml. of serum. The average index of precision (λ) was 0.24. A 4-point assay technique was suggested with 6 observations for each of 2 doses of the standard and of the unknown preparations. The error of an assay was calculated to be about 25%.

3. Chick

Observations on the release of I^{131} from the thyroid gland of the chick as stimulated with TSH have been reported by Keating *et al.* (1945). It was observed that during the first 24 hours after stimulation, 77% of the activity was released from the thyroid. Rawson (1949) also noted a loss after 6 hours of TSH stimulation and a maximal loss after 24 hours.

Gilliland and Strudwick (1953) method. This method is based on the release of I^{131} from the thyroid glands of baby chicks treated with thyroxine to minimize endogenous secretion of TSH. However, the recycling of metabolized thyroidal-I^{131} was not prevented by the use of a goitrogen. Twenty microcuries of I^{131} was administered on day 2, and 8 μg. of thyroxine given daily on 3 days following. The TSH was then administered at the end of the 3-day preparatory period in 2 doses at 24-hour intervals. The radioactivity was measured *in vivo* before TSH was injected and after 48 hours. The percentage discharged measures the activity of TSH. The method can detect 0.003 mg. U.S.P. units.

Gilliland and Fraser (1953) presented a preliminary report using essentially the same procedure.

Bates and Cornfield (1957) method. New Hampshire chicks, one-day-old were kept in a brooder with water available, but no food. They were injected subcutaneously with 2–3 μc. I^{131}. I^{131} uptake was measured in *in vivo* 24 hours later. Only chicks with at least 15% uptake were included. A solution containing 8 μg. thyroxine and 0.5 mg. propylthiouracil was then injected daily to block endogenous TSH secretion and I^{131} recycling. The TSH solution to be assayed was injected subcutaneously in a volume of 0.2 ml. daily for 2 or 3 days. Daily thyroidal-I^{131} counts were made. The end point is the relative per cent of I^{131} remaining (RPR) at the end of 1, 2, or 3 days. A linear relation between log dose and the extent of depletion was found with an index of precision, λ, of about 0.20.

Frey and Albert (1959) suggested that chicks having a low I^{131} uptake (8%) could be used by introducing a "tail count" as a correction factor for the extra thyroidal radioactivity in the neck (the background). The difference between the count obtained over the neck and the count over the tail may be taken to represent the true thyroidal radioactivity.

Comment on methods using I^{131}. In the use of methods employing I^{131} either in uptake or release studies, the presently available counting systems are sufficiently sensitive to make possible *in vivo* observations rather than to require dissection of the thyroid glands. Further, the prescribed amount of I^{131} which is administered may be reduced in some cases.

In assays employing the release of thyroidal-I^{131}, it is important to administer an iodine-blocking agent (goitrogen) to prevent the recycling of metabolized I^{131}.

C. METHODS DEPENDENT UPON P^{32} UPTAKE

Borell and Holmgren (1949) were the first to make use of P^{32} in the assay of TSH. It was shown that TSH stimulated an increased P^{32} uptake by the thyroid gland. It has been suggested that the uptake is due to increased metabolism of the gland and need of phosphorus in phosphorylated compounds. Increased need of phosphorus by growing cells may also play a role in the phenomenon.

1. Normal Immature Guinea Pig

Borell and Holmgren (1949) method. Normal male guinea pigs weighing about 150 gm., and kept at a temperature of 30–32°C. were used. TSH was administered daily for 2 days, then 0.05 μc. P^{32} was injected intraperitoneally 40 minutes before sacrifice. One thyroid lobe was weighed and P^{32} and total P determined, the second lobe was histologically studied in regard to cell height. From ½ to 12 Heyl-Laqueur GP (guinea pig) units of TSH were administered. The P^{32} uptake increased linearly in relation to the log dose.

It is interesting to note that Tala (1952) observed a maximal response 2 hours after a single dose of TSH but response did not increase when stimulation was repeated. Later Tala *et al.* (1955) reported maximum uptake of P^{32} within 1 hour, then diminished only to reach another maximum at 8 hours.

2. Day-Old Chick

Besford et al. (1952) method. Two-day-old chicks were injected with TSH intraperitoneally in 1 ml. of saline, 4 hours later the chicks were injected with 10 μc. of P^{32} in 0.5 ml. H_2O by the same route. Two hours later the chicks were killed, the thyroids dissected out and weighed, and radioactivity counted at a fixed geometry. Chicks receiving only P^{32} served as controls and chicks receiving graded amounts of TSH showed a log-dose-response curve. At 6 hours a straight line response was observed between 2 and 16 μg. TSH. The method is said to be sensitive to 0.02 J-S units.

In further study of the method by Crooke and Matthews (1953), it was indicated that a breed difference in sensitivity exists, that intraperitoneal and subcutaneous injections are equally effective and that a single dose is more effective than divided doses of the same amount of TSH.

Lamberg (1953a, b) reported maximal P^{32} uptake in chicks 8 hours after TSH injection and $\frac{1}{2}$ to 1 hour after P^{32} is injected parenterally. Lamberg and Olin-Lamberg (1955) reported that acinar cell height and nuclear volume reached a maximum 8 hours after TSH injection and only a slight or no decline after 24 hours. P^{32} uptake, however, showed a rapid decline after 24 hours. Lamberg et al. (1955) studied, also, the effect of repeated doses of TSH.

Greenspan et al. (*1956*) *method.* Day-old White Leghorn cockerels, with feed and water withheld, were used. TSH dissolved in 0.1 ml. of isotonic saline was injected directly into the heart and 25 μc. of P^{32} in 0.5 ml. of saline was injected intraperitoneally. Six hours later, the thyroid lobes were removed, placed on small copper disks, dried in air, and β-radioactivity was determined by an end-window Geiger counter. The response was expressed as the square root of T where $T =$ time in seconds to count 1024 counts per chick thyroid. Three dose levels of unknown were compared with three dose levels of standard TSH with a three-fold step increase between each dose. A dose of 0.5 mU. U.S.P. hormone is easily detected.

3. Hypophysectomized Rat

Dedman et al. (1953) reported results of a study of factors influencing P^{32} uptake by the thyroid glands of female hypophysectomized rats, 6–7 weeks of age (100–120 gm.). After hypophysectomy the drop in P^{32} uptake was maximal by the fifth day. TSH was then given in 4 doses at 12-hour intervals. The maximum uptake of P^{32} was found at 40 minutes after injection with a decrease by 160 minutes. The rats are killed and the thyroid glands removed and counts made under standard geometry.

Mussett and Perry (1955) reported that international standard thyrotropin was assayed by the following method. Female Wistar rats 105–123 gm., 42–50 days old, were hypophysectomized. Five days later they were injected subcutaneously with the test material in 0.5 ml. of saline. Approximately 20 μc. of carrier-free P^{32} was injected intraperitoneally 70 minutes before autopsy which was carried out 5 hours after the single injection of TSH. The animals were killed with chloroform, the thyroids dissected out and weighed, and the P^{32} determined by direct counting of the thyroids. The P^{32} content of the injection solution is determined by dilution and direct counting. The results are expressed as uptake per milligram of thyroid per gram of body weight of rat and measures relative, not absolute, uptake. There is a linear relationship between this ratio and the log dose of TSH.

4. Tissue Slices

Morton and Schwartz (1953) showed that the addition of TSH stimulated the incorporation of P^{32} into the lipid fraction of surviving cattle thyroid slices in vitro. Florsheim et al. (1956) investigated the use of this effect in the assay of TSH. Only thyroid tissue and neoplasms of thyroidal origin are affected by TSH. Lecithin turnover is stimulated, but sphingomyelin is unaffected. The specific activity of lecithin-P is related to the amount of TSH added by a log-dose-response curve which is linear from 2 to 100 mU.

IV. Determination of TSH Secretion Rate

Crenshaw et al. (1957) blocked the secretion of TSH by the administration of thyroprotein to a dwarf beef animal. Iodine^{131} uptake in the animal was greatly reduced. TSH was then administered in increasing amounts until I^{131} uptake was restored to normal. It was estimated that the TSH secretion rate of this animal was about 40 U.S.P. units/100 lb. body weight.

A modification of this method has been suggested by Premachandra and Turner (1960) in which both the thyroxine secretion and TSH secretion could be estimated concurrently. In the determination of thyroxine secretion rate (see Chapter 10), the thyroidal-I^{131} release rate with recycling blocked is first determined. Then increasing levels of thyroxine are administered to block TSH secretion and thyroidal-I^{131} release. This level is considered the estimated thyroxine secretion rate. By maintaining the block of endogenous TSH secretion, the injection of TSH in amounts sufficient to restore the initial rate of release of thyroidal-I^{131} is then considered the estimated TSH secretion rate.

If one wishes to determine only the estimated TSH secretion rate, the following procedure is suggested. The biological $T_{1/2}$ of thyroidal-I^{131} release under administration of a goitrogen is determined (time required for $\frac{1}{2}$ of thyroidal-I^{131} to be released). Then a level of thyroxine is administered slightly in excess of thyroxine secretion rate to block TSH. TSH is injected for 4 days and the $T_{1/2}$ is again determined. If $T_{1/2}$ is less than original $T_{1/2}$, the amount of TSH is increased, if greater, the amount of TSH is reduced.

By this technique, a group of mature chickens were shown to have estimated TSH secretion rates ranging between 0.05 and 0.075 U.S.P. units/100 gm. body weight.

V. Bioassay of TSH in Blood Serum

In the study of the TSH level of the circulating blood, most investigators have used whole serum. It has been claimed by several students of the problem (Fellinger, 1936; De Robertis, 1948) that acetone precipitation of the blood increased the apparent activity. In this technique 10 to 20 ml. blood was hemolyzed by adding distilled water to a volume of 50 ml.; 45 ml. of acetone was added and the mixture filtered after standing a few hours in the refrigerator. Acetone was then added to bring the concentration to 85%. The precipitate was separated by centrifugation and dried *in vacuo* at 40°C. For injection, the precipitate was redissolved in water at pH 6.0.

Lameyer (1956) assayed human serum concentrated by the method of Cohn *et al.* (1946). Fractions II, III, and IV contained activity.

Postel (1956) described a zone electrophoresis method in a starch-supported phosphate buffer medium at pH 7.4 which was hoped to separate serum TSH. While his observations indicated a non-iodine-containing inhibitor of I^{131} uptake in the chick, the method did not concentrate blood TSH sufficient to measure by his chick assay method.

McKenzie (1958a) used starch block electrophoresis of blood serum described by Kunkel and Slater (1952). The TSH was shown to travel on electrophoresis with γ-globulin.

Evidence of a TSH-inhibiting factor has been reported by Adams (1958) and McKenzie (1958b) in serum and in urine by Greenspan and Lew (1959).

A. TSH IN NORMAL SERUM

With TSH assays of increased sensitivity available, several workers have reported studies of its content in normal serum. D'Angelo *et al.* (1951) reported a range of 0.0–0.001 J-S units in 9 normal patients assayed by the stasis tadpole.

Querido and Lameyer (1956) reported serum TSH levels in the range of 0.0–2.0 μg./ml. Gilliland and Strudwick (1956) measured the TSH in the serum of 2 normal individuals and in the pooled serum of 6 others. The average for these 3 tests was 39 μg./100 ml. This is the equivalent of 0.165 mU. TSH per milliliter. No TSH was observed in 2 other subjects.

Di George *et al.* (1958) reported a mean TSH value of 0.2 μg. per milliliter and a range of 0–0.5 μg. in 3 normal individuals. Greenspan and Lew (1959) were unable to detect TSH in the serum of normal subjects, patients with Graves' disease or with malignant exophthalmos. They are of the opinion that the level of TSH is below 0.5 mU./per milliliter in agreement with the above reports.

Bottari (1958) assayed the serum of 120 men ranging in age between 20 to 60 years. The mean TSH was 22 mU./100 ml. with a 95% fiducial limit of 20–25 mU. and a range of 10 to 45 mU./100 ml. In women before the menopause, the mean TSH was 37 mU./100 ml. with a fall into the male range later. Aging in both sexes resulted in a fall to a mean value of 5 mU./100 ml.

B. TSH in Serum in Hypothyroidism

Hypothyroidism may result from insufficient TSH secretion or from a lack of or failure of the thyroid gland to function. If hypothyroidism is due to a deficiency of TSH secretion, the serum TSH would be expected to be low, whereas, if the thyroid gland is at fault, the serum TSH would be expected to be high.

D'Angelo et al. (1951) reported there was no TSH in the serum of 5 out of 10 hypothyroid patients with a range of 0–0.005 J-S units per milliliter of serum. In five other cases, the TSH was either normal or excessively high. Gilliland and Strudwick (1956) reported that patients with myxedema of recent origin and young cretins showed a high level of serum TSH, as did most patients with spontaneous myxedema. The pituitary may ultimately fail to secrete TSH in myxedema, but this may be reversed by treatment.

McKenzie (1958a) reported TSH estimations in 4 patients with myxedema to vary from 0.12 mU. per milliliter of serum to 0.64 mU. He reported that TSH activity was present solely with the γ-globulin fraction of the serum. Bottari (1958) reported that hypophysectomy was followed by the disappearance of TSH from the blood, while primary myxedema showed TSH values ranging from 200 to 800 mU./100 ml. Treatment induced a return toward normal levels.

C. TSH in Serum in Hyperthyroidism

D'Angelo (1951) et al. observed in 10 cases of hyperthyroidism that excessively high thyroid hormone levels in the blood coexisted with a normal TSH content. Gilliland and Strudwick (1956) reported 2 of 5 patients with thyrotoxicosis without severe eye signs showed a raised serum TSH level comparable to that of spontaneous myxedema. Three patients with severe eye signs without thyrotoxicosis showed normal levels of TSH. It was concluded that TSH alone is not the cause of exophthalmos, but that some other factor which may also be of pituitary origin is involved. Bottari (1958) reported that thyrotoxicosis was usually associated with an increase in serum TSH, although in some cases it was normal.

D. ABNORMAL FACTOR IN SERUM IN HYPERTHYROIDISM

In the assay of TSH by methods of Adams and Purves (1957a) and McKenzie (1958a) guinea pigs and mice previously injected with I^{131} show a maximum increase in serum I^{131} after an interval of 2 to 3 hours when TSH is administered. In the assay of serum from thyrotoxic patients Adams (1958) noted that the maximum response did not occur until after 16 hours. When U.S.P. thyrotropin is added to serum which elicits the abnormal TSH response, the time course of the response induced by the mixture indicates that the 2 components act independently. It was suggested that the abnormal responses only to sera from cases of thyrotoxicosis makes it seem likely that the abnormal TSH has relationship to this disorder.

McKenzie (1958b) noted a delayed response in mice with sera from 9 of 11 thyrotoxic patients and with sera from 3 patients not thyrotoxic. Sera from 4 myxedematous, 2 euthyroid, and 2 thyrotoxic individuals gave no delayed response.

Munro (1959) assayed the serum from 32 patients by the McKenzie method. The 2-hour response was observed in 3 of 6 patients with hypothyroidism, in 1 of 3 patients with simple or non-toxic goiter, and in 1 of 9 normal subjects. Six of 11 patients with hyperthyroidism gave the delayed response and 1 of 9 normal subjects. Serum from 7 normal subjects did not give either response.

McKenzie (1960) reported that mice administered thyroid to block TSH secretion showed an increased thyroidal-I^{131} by sera from patients with hyperthyroidism when given 12 hours before I^{131} injection. TSH produced a maximal increase in I^{131} uptake when administered 4 hours before I^{131}. Thus a delayed response both in I^{131} uptake and release is shown by the sera in hyperthyroidism.

VI. Bioassay of TSH in Urine

Gorbman (1945) described a method for the ultrafiltration of urine to recover excreted hypophyseal hormones. After filtration, the 2% collodion membrane is dissolved in alcohol-ether and the dried residue taken up in saline for assay. Kriss and Greenspan (1954) further purified the extract by precipitation with 40% alcohol and reprecipitated with 80% alcohol.

Greenspan and Lew (1959), using the Gorbman (1945) method, reported that the ultrafiltrate residue contained a nonhypophyseal factor which stimulated P^{32} uptake by the chick thyroid as well as a factor which interferes with the effect of TSH on the release of thyroidal-I^{131} in the chick. They suggested that data on urine levels of TSH reported by Henry and Bloche-Michel (1955) and Currie *et al.* (1956) may have to be corrected for the presence of the interfering substance.

TSH in urine. The estimation of TSH in urine of normal and pathological cases appears to be of doubtful value at this time. Students of the problem include Savoie (1952), Kriss and Greenspan (1954), Henry and Bloche-Michel (1955), Bloche-Michel and Henry (1955), Currie *et al.* (1956), and Greenspan and Lew (1959).

REFERENCES

Adams, D. D. (1958). *J. Clin. Endocrinol. and Metabolism* **18**, 699.
Adams, D. D., and Purves, H. D. (1953). *Proc. Univ. Otago Med. School* **31**, 38.
Adams, D. D., and Purves, H. D. (1955). *Endocrinology* **57**, 17.
Adams, D. D., and Purves, H. D. (1957a). *Can. J. Biochem. and Physiol.* **35**, 993.
Adams, D. D., and Purves, H. D. (1957b). *Metabolism, Clin. and Exptl.* **6**, 26.
Albert, A. (1945). *Ann. N. Y. Acad. Sci.* **50**, 466.
Bakke, J. L., and Lawrence, N. L. (1956). *Endocrinology* **58**, 531.
Bakke, J. L., Heideman, M. L., Jr., Lawrence, N. L., and Wiberg, C. (1957). *Endocrinology* **61**, 352.
Bates, R. W., and Cornfield, J. (1957). *Endocrinology* **60**, 225.
Besford, H., Crooke, A. C. and Matthews, J. D. (1952), *J. Endocrinol.* **8**, xv.
Bloche-Michel, H., and Henry, R. (1955). *Ann. endocrinol. (Paris)* **16**, 268.
Borell, U., and Holmgren, H. (1949). *Acta Endocrinol.* **3**, 331.
Bottari, P. M. (1957). *Ciba Foundation Colloquia Endocrinol.* **11**, 52.
Bottari, P. M. (1958). *J. Endocrinol.* **17**, xix.
Bottari, P. M., and Donovan, B. T. (1958). *J. Physiol. (London)* **140**, 36.
Brimblecombe, R., Haigh, C. P., Halkerston, I. D. K., Reiss, M., and Warledge, J. (1952). *J. Endocrinol.* **8**, v.
Brown, J. R. (1959). *Acta Endocrinol.* **32**, 289.
Brown, J. R., and Dodd, J. M. (1956). *J. Endocrinol.* **14**, xxix.
Cohn, E. J., Strong, L. E., Hughes, W. L., Jr., Mulford, D. J., Ashworth, J. N., Melin, M., and Taylor, H. L. (1946). *J. Am. Chem. Soc.* **68**, 459.
Condliffe, P. G., and Bates, R. W. (1956). *J. Biol. Chem.* **223**, 843.
Condliffe, P. G., and Bates, R. W. (1957). *Arch. Biochem. Biophys.* **68**, 229.
Crenshaw, W. W., Pipes, G. W., Ruppert, H. L., Jr., and Turner, C. W. (1957). *Missouri, Univ. Agr. Expt. Sta. Research Bull.* **621**.
Crooke, A. C., and Matthews, J. D. (1953). *Ciba Foundation Colloquia Endocrinol.* **5**, 25.

Currie, A. R., Cruickshank, B., Dekanski, J. B., Hewett, C. L., and McGirr, E. M. (1956). *Scot. Med. J.* **1**, 355.

D'Angelo, S. A. (1951). *Endocrinology* **48**, 249.

D'Angelo, S. A. (1956). *Proc. Soc. Exptl. Biol. Med.* **92**, 693.

D'Angelo, S. A., Paschkis, K. E., Cantarow, A., and Gordon, A. S. (1951). *J. Clin. Endocrinol.* **11**, 761.

De Robertis, E. (1948). *J. Clin. Endocrinol.* **8**, 956.

Dedman, M. L., Mason, A. S., Morris, P., and Morris, C. J. (1953). *Ciba Foundation Colloquia Endocrinol.* **5**, 10.

Di George, A. M., D'Angelo, S. A., and Paschkis, K. E. (1958). *J. Clin. Endocrinol. and Metabolism* **17**, 842.

Dobyns, B. M. (1946). *Surg. Gynecol. Obstet.* **82**, 290.

Dobyns, B. M., and Steelman, S. L. (1953). *Endocrinology* **37**, 389.

Fellinger, K. (1936). *Wien. Archiv. inn. Med.* **29**, 375.

Fels, I. G., Simpson, M. E., and Evans, H. M. (1955). *J. Biol. Chem.* **213**, 311.

Florsheim, W. H., Moskowitz, N., and Morton, M. E. (1956). *J. Clin. Endocrinol. and Metabolism* **16**, 927.

Frey, H. M., and Albert, A. (1959). *Endocrinology* **64**, 304.

Ghosh, B. N., Woodbury, D. M., and Sayers, G. (1951). *Endocrinology* **48**, 631.

Gilliland, I. C., and Fraser, R. (1953). *Ciba Foundation Colloquia Endocrinol.* **5**, 20.

Gilliland, I. C., and Strudwick, J. I. (1953). *Clin. Sci.* **12**, 265.

Gilliland, I. C., and Strudwick, J. I. (1956). *Brit. Med. J.* **i**, 378.

Gorbman, A. (1945). *Endocrinology* **37**, 177.

Greenspan, F. S., and Lew, W. (1959). *Endocrinology* **64**, 160.

Greenspan, F. S., Kriss, J. P., Moses, L. E., and Lew, W. (1956). *Endocrinology* **58**, 767.

Greer, M. A. (1952). *J. Clin. Endocrinol. and Metabolism* **12**, 1259.

Greer, M. A., Scow, R. O., and Grobstein, C. (1953). *Proc. Soc. Exptl. Biol. Med.* **82**, 28.

Hart, K. T., Druet, D., and Mack, R. E. (1959). *Endocrinology* **64**, 857.

Heideman, M. L., Jr. (1953). *Endocrinology* **53**, 640.

Henry, R. (1951). *Ann. pharm. franc.* **9**, 724.

Henry, R., and Bloche-Michel, H. (1955). *Ann. endocrinol. (Paris)* **16**, 258.

Keating, F. R., Jr., Rawson, R. W., Peacock, W., and Evans, R. D. (1945). *Endocrinology* **36**, 137.

Kriss, J. P., and Greenspan, F. S. (1954). *J. Clin. Endocrinol. and Metabolism* **14**, 770.

Kunkel, H. G., and Slater, R. J. (1952). *Proc. Soc. Exptl. Biol. Med.* **31**, 677.

Lamberg, B.-A. (1953a). *Acta Endocrinol.* **13**, 145.

Lamberg, B.-A. (1953b). *Acta Med. Scand. Suppl.* **279**.

Lamberg, B.-A. (1955). *Acta Endocrinol.* **18**, 405.

Lamberg, B.-A., and Olin-Lamberg, C. (1955). *Acta Endocrinol.* **19**, 249.

Lamberg, B.-A., Wahlberg, P., and Olin-Lamberg, C. (1955). *Acta Endocrinol.* **19**, 263.

Lameyer, L. D. F. (1956). Thesis, Leiden University, Leiden; *Proc. Roy. Soc. Med.* **49**, 209.

Leblond, C. P., and Sue, P. (1941). *Am. J. Physiol.* **134**, 549.

Levey, H. A., Cheever, E., and Roberts, S. (1956). *Endocrinology* **58**, 420.

McKenzie, J. M. (1958a). *Endocrinology* **63**, 372.

McKenzie, J. M. (1958b). *Endocrinology* **62**, 865.

McKenzie, J. M. (1960). *J. Clin. Endocrinol. and Metabolism* **20**, 380.

Morton, M. E., and Schwartz, J. R. (1953). *Science* **117**, 103.

Morton, M. E., Pearlman, I., Anderson, E., and Chaikoff, I. L. (1942). *Endocrinology* **30**, 495.

Munro, D. S. (1959). *J. Endocrinol.* **19**, 64.

Mussett, M. V., and Perry, W. L. M. (1955). *Bull. World Health Organization* **13**, 917.

Overbeek, G. A., Fokkens, J., Querido, A., de Visser, J., and Canninga, P. V. (1953). *Acta Endocrinol.* **14**, 285.

Pierce, J. G., and Nyc, J. F. (1956). *J. Biol. Chem.* **222**, 777.

Postel, S. (1956). *Endocrinology* **58**, 557.

Premachandra, B. N., and Turner, C. W. (1960). *Poultry Sci.* **39**, 1286.

Querido, A., and Lameyer, L. D. F. (1956). *Proc. Royal Soc. Med.* **49**, 209.

Querido, A. Kassenaar, A. A. H., and Lameyer, L. D. F. (1953). *Acta Endocrinol.* **12**, 335.

Rawson, R. W. (1949). *Ann. N. Y. Acad. Sci.* **50**, 491.

Rawson, R. W., Rall, J. E., and Sonenberg, M. (1955). *In* "The Hormones" (G. Pincus and K. V. Thimann, eds.) Chapter 10. Academic Press, New York.

Reiss, J. M., and Wyatt, A. F. (1956). *J. Endocrinol.* **13**, 412.

Savoie, I. C. (1952). *Ann. endocrinol (Paris)* **13**, 81.

Smelser, G. K., and Ozanics, V. (1955). *Am. J. Ophthalmol.* **39**, 146.

Sonenberg, M. (1958). *Vitamins and Hormones* **16**, 205.

Tala, P. (1952). *Acta Endocrinol. Suppl.* **9.**

Tala, P., Lamberg, B.-A., and Uotila, U. (1955). *Acta Endocrinol.* **19**, 255.

Turner, C. W. (1950). *In* "Hormone Assay" (C. W. Emmens, ed.) Chapter 9. Academic Press, New York.

Vanderlaan, W. P., and Greer, M. A. (1950). *Endocrinology* **47**, 36.

Wahlberg, P. (1955). *Acta Endocrinol. Suppl.* **23.**

Wolff, J. (1951). *Endocrinology* **48**, 284.

Chapter 20

Adrenocorticotropin

Joseph D. Fisher

I. Introduction

The procedures to be outlined are not in any way intended to avoid the noble efforts (Emmens, 1950) of those investigators who, in previous years, have attempted to obtain adequate standardization with impure preparations. The methods to be emphasized are those which have withstood the rigors of extensive use. The specificity and ease of handling in large numbers have been proven adequate for quantitative purposes.

II. Standard Preparations and Definition of Unit

The first international standard was established by using the standard preparation against which most of the preparations utilized in obtaining much of the initial clinical experience with ACTH had been evaluated (1947–1949). This preparation, termed La-I-A, was one obtained by a modification of the Lyons (1937) procedure, followed by a series of isoelectric precipitation steps (Munson, 1946). An arbitrarily assigned potency of 1.0 unit per milligram was established. Ampoules containing about 1.3 mg. and some containing 4.8 mg. were distributed as a primary standard.

The first provisional U.S.P. reference standard was a mixture of crude preparations which was evaluated against La-I-A [the intravenous (I.V.)-Sayers *et al.* (1948) and/or Munson *et al.* (1948) procedure]. This preparation was diluted with lactose, tableted, and found to contain 0.005 international units (I.U.) (and by agreement, 0.005 U.S.P. units) per milligram.

The second international and U.S.P. standard is a crude corticotropin (one step prior to oxycellulose purification) isolated by the Astwood *et al.* (1951) procedure. The preparation was assigned a potency of 1.14 I.U. (U.S.P.) per milligram after evaluation by the I.V.-Sayers *et al.* (1948) (and/or Munson *et al.* 1948) modification, the subcutaneous (S.C.) ascorbic acid method (U.S.P. XV), a thymus involution assay (Bruce *et al.*, 1952) and compared against the first international standard. The international unit was, therefore, redefined as 0.88 mg. of the new standard. Ampoules containing 28 mg. were distributed. Twelve collaborating laboratories in five different countries with a total of 61 assays contributed data to this evaluation.

As of the present writing, an attempt at establishment of the third international and U.S.P. standard is underway by collaborative effort. The proposed standard is constituted exclusively by one preparation. This latter preparation is an oxycellulose-purified porcine pituitary (all previous standards are also of porcine origin) corticotropin with the following approximate potencies and ratios:

S.C. approx. 100 units/mg.
I.V. approx. 30 units/mg.

This preparation has been put into ampoules containing approximately 50 μg. and about 5 mg. of lactose as a stabilizer. Each vial will, therefore, contain approximately 5 units (S.C.).

It was recommended (International Conference on the Standardization of Corticotropin, 1957) that to avoid undue change in the labeling of potency of commercial clinical preparations, the unitage of the new standard should be based on its subcutaneous potency in terms of the second international existing standard. The unit once defined in this manner does not indicate the potency or "purity" as measured by the alternate route of administration (I.V.) or by an *in vitro* test. A particular experimental preparation may have, because of its history of isolation and purification, widely different potencies for these latter assay procedures. It was also assumed that the commercial preparations currently available would nearly all be of a particular history of isolation (corticotropin-A type) and purity. These preparations would, therefore, contain only about one third of the amount of the hormone specified by one unit of the existing standard.

Corticotropin has been classified into several different chemical entity forms. The classification system generally agreed upon consists of the following:

Corticotropin A: The "native" polypeptide form not subject to degradation.

Corticotropin B: The "native" polypeptide form subjected to enzymic degradation.

A third category which could be added to the above would include any additional degradation or chemical modification beyond that obtainable by exposure to enzymes.

III. *In Vitro* Assay Procedure (Saffran and Schally, 1955)

A. MATERIALS

1. Krebs-Ringer 0.025 M bicarbonate (Umbreit *et al.*, 1949) containing 200 mg. % glucose and with a Ca^{++} concentration of not less than 0.5 mM. Bicarbonate is preferred over phosphate in order to avoid precipitation of calcium. No significant differences can be shown within a Ca^{++} (Birmingham *et al.*, 1953) concentration range of between 0.5–10 mM. Ca^{++} appears to be directly involved as an intercedent to ACTH stimulation. The need for KCl (Peron and Koritz, 1958) and glucose (Schonbaum *et al.*, 1956) in the above formulation appears to be nonspecific, yet when present, augments the stimulatory response to ACTH in terms of corticoid output. If the concentration of potassium is increased, the requirement for calcium is no longer present (Peron and Koritz, 1958).

2. Methylene chloride—washed with an equal volume of water, dried with anhydrous sodium sulfate, and decolorized with charcoal. The solvent is kept over sodium hydroxide flakes for approximately 24 hours and is distilled. Only the fraction boiling between 40° and 41°C. is utilized. Absorption characteristics are checked against water at 230, 240, 250, 255, and 265 mμ in a spectrophotometer, preferably with a photomultiplier attachment.

3. Warburg manometric respiratory apparatus or Dubnoff metabolic incubator or the equivalent.

4. Spectrophotometer, preferably with a photomultiplier attachment (Beckman DU or its equivalent).

5. Ninety-five per cent O_2—five per cent CO_2 gas.

6. Glass-stoppered centrifuge tubes (or fitted with plastic caps), 2, 3, or 5 ml.

B. Method

Critical adherence to the timing of each step is a factor in the extent of reproducibility of the assay. Therefore, many of the steps call for operations which are necessary to adhere to a critical schedule.

1. Rats of either sex, body weight 90–200 gm. The latter, if possible, to be held to a minimum variation, for example, ±15 gm., maintained in a constant temperature-controlled environment for approximately 48 hours before use. Overbeek (1957) has stressed the point of rigid environmental control for the animals. Maintaining the animals for 1 week in their normal environment and/or anesthetization in the animal room before removal to the surgery area has been considered. If such precautions are not taken, the adrenals often appear soft and the slope of the dose-response curve decreases.

2. Intraperitoneal injection of 4 to 5 mg. of Nembutal/100-gm. body weight, while avoiding unusual sensory stress. Under some laboratory conditions, it would appear advisable to decapitate the animals rather than to utilize the method of administering Nembutal prior to surgery.

3. Pipet 1.5 ml. of medium (previously equilibrated with 95% O_2—5% CO_2) into semimicro Warburg flasks.

4. The removal of the adrenals within 15 minutes postanesthetization, or immediately following decapitation. The glands are carefully separated from all fat and connective tissue, weighed on a microtorsion balance to the nearest 0.05 mg., and placed into a Petri dish containing Krebs-Ringer bicarbonate glucose medium cooled on crushed ice. The pair of adrenals from each rat is kept together.

5. Careful dissection into quarters is accomplished with a fine scissors. The eight quarters from each pair of glands are then distributed onto eight numbered sectors of a filter paper moistened with Krebs-Ringer bicarbonate glucose medium and placed in a Petri dish in a humidor which is kept over crushed ice.

6. The adrenals of all the rats constituting a group are handled as above and distribution made into each of the numbered sectors in a

way that each sector would contain a quarter of an adrenal from each of the animals in the group.

7. The quartered adrenal sectors from each numbered sector are then weighed and placed into the Warburg flasks containing 1.5 ml. of the Krebs-Ringer bicarbonate glucose medium. The flasks are mounted on the Warburg manometer, flushed with 95% O_2—5% CO_2 and shaken for approximately 1 hour at a bath temperature of 38°C. The Dubnoff metabolic incubator will suffice when a Warburg apparatus is not available; the adrenal sectors being placed into 10-ml. beakers containing buffer and the unit flushed with a gas phase of 95% O_2—5% CO_2 at a temperature of 38°C. The time of this preincubation period may be varied, but within the explored limits of 0.5 to 1.5 hours.

8. The corticotropin samples to be assayed are prepared during the preincubation period in such a way that nearly a constant volume may be added regardless of dose. The samples are weighed, dissolved in 0.025 N acetic acid to a concentration of 900 milliunits (mU.) per milliliter and diluted with either saline or buffer medium to a concentration of 300 and 100 mU. per milliliter. A 0.1 ml. volume would, therefore, represent 30 and 10 mU., respectively.

9. The flasks are removed from the bath. The preincubation buffer medium is drawn off as completely as possible by suction, and a new charge of medium, 1.4 ml., is added to each flask. The preincubation medium is discarded. There is enhanced sensitivity to added ACTH resulting from the preincubation step. Only preincubated gland sections produce significant amounts of corticoids in the absence of ACTH stimulation, therefore, reducing one major variable. Substitution of saline-bicarbonate for the Krebs-Ringer bicarbonate glucose medium in the initial incubation step resulted in a distinct requirement for KCl, $CaCl_2$, and glucose in the final incubation stage (Peron and Koritz, 1958). The significant corticoid response to ACTH, obtained in the presence of the Krebs-Ringer bicarbonate glucose medium, is dependent upon the critical concentrations of the various ionic species present in that medium.

10. The volume of corticotropin added to each flask is adjusted to compensate for the difference of weight in adrenal present so that an almost constant ratio of volume to weight is established. Approximately 0.1 ml. of the assay standard dose concentrations is required. A random assignment is made of standard and unknown to be added to flasks. Two of the flasks receive the low dose of standard (S_1), two receive the high dose of standard (S_2) and the remaining two flasks, the low and high dose of unknown (U_1 and U_2, respectively).

11. The flasks are mounted on the manometer, flushed with a gas

mixture and again placed into the water bath at a temperature of 38°C. and shaken for 2 hours as the final incubation period.

12. To each of eight glass-stoppered 2-ml. centrifuge tubes is added 1.0 ml. of previously purified methylene chloride.

13. At the termination of the final incubation period, 1.0 ml. of the incubated medium is withdrawn, added to the 1.0 ml. of methylene chloride and the tubes shaken vigorously for approximately 30 seconds. The emulsion which occurs may be separated into two phases by centrifugation at 2000–3000 r.p.m. If incomplete separation is obtained upon the initial centrifugation, inversion of the tube contents is repeated and the material again centrifuged.

14. A part of the lower phase is transferred by means of a long

TABLE I

SAMPLE PROTOCOL[a]

S_1 3 mU./0.1 ml.; S_2 9 mU./0.1 ml.
U_1 28.7 μg./0.1 ml.; U_2 86.0 μg./0.1 ml.

Flask number:	1	2	3	4	5	6	7	8
Adrenal weight (mg.):	34.7	33.8	30.0	33.5	33.8	32.6	30.0	33.0
Sample:	U_1	U_2	S_1	S_2	S_1	U_1	S_2	U_2
Sample volume (μl.):	115	115	100	110	115	110	100	110
Medium volume (ml.):	1.4	1.4	1.4	1.4	1.4	1.4	1.4	1.4
Optical densities × 1000								
230 mμ	510	660	370	590	460	530	480	610
240 mμ	650	880	472	800	590	680	630	820
250 mμ	440	605	308	525	390	450	420	560
255 mμ	260	360	178	300	220	260	240	320
260 mμ	120	165	75	125	90	110	92	140
240–255 mμ	390	520	294	500	370	420	390	500
Response								
$= \dfrac{240-255}{\text{adrenal wt.}} \times 10$	112	153	98	149	109	128	130	151

Slope, $b = 71.3$

Root mean square for experimental error, $s = 9.59$

Index of precision, $s/b = 0.134$

Log potency ratio $M = 0.203$; Antilog $M = 1.595$

Standard error of $M = s_m = 0.1014$

Per cent error $= 100$ (antilog $s_m - 1$) $= 26\%$

Limits of error at $P = 0.05 = 0.203 - (2.776 \times 0.1014)$ and $0.203 + (2.776 \times 0.1014)$
$= \bar{1}.923$ and 0.483. Antilogs $= 0.84$ and 3.04

Therefore, 1 mg. contains $(9 \times 1.595/86) \times 1000 = 167$ mU. of corticotropin activity, with limits of 88 and 318

[a] Saffran and Schally (1955).

needle and syringe to a quartz microcuvette and readings taken at 230, 240, 250, 255, and 260 mμ in a spectrophotometer. The control blank contains methylene chloride which had been previously equilibrated with the incubation medium. The centrifuge tubes which are to be subsequently read are kept capped. The lamp housing of the spectrophotometer must be cooled to avoid loss of the solvent.

15. The response at each dose is estimated by

$$\frac{O.D._{240} - O.D._{255}}{Mg.\ adrenal} \times 10$$

Table I is a sample protocol indicating the approximate character of volumes and units utilized and recorded; O.D.$_{240}$ represents the maximum absorption of the corticoid extract. Spectral scan of adrenal incubate extracts indicate coincidental characteristics with cortisol from 230 to 265 mμ and a 240 mμ maximum. Except for an incidence of turbidity which develops in the methylene chloride extracts, direct reading at a wavelength at 240 mμ could be used for estimation of corticoid level. The turbidity necessitates a correction at the higher wavelength of 255 mμ. The difference between the values obtained at the two wavelengths is a measure of the error that the interference causes. The use of methylene chloride reduces to a minimum the variation and degree of background that is obtained when chloroform, for example, is used as the extracting solvent.

This ultraviolet (UV) method essentially measures the availability

TABLE II

STEROID VALUES OF ADRENAL INCUBATION MEDIA MEASURED BY THE UV AND TETRAZOLIUM METHODS[a]

	Preincubation media	No added ACTH	With added ACTH	Calculated effect of ACTH
	(μg./100 mg. adrenals)			
TET. method				
No. of tests	(9)	(10)	(18)	(10)
Mean	8 ± 3.2 (S.D.)	7 ± 1.3	19 ± 5.2	11 ± 5.0
UV method				
No. of tests	(9)	(10)	(18)	(10)
Mean	15 ± 5.5	14 ± 3.7	32 ± 7.7	17 ± 8.5
TET./UV ratio				
No. of tests	(9)	(10)	(18)	(10)
Mean	0.52 ± 0.05	0.53 ± 0.03	0.61 ± 0.06	0.73 ± 0.11

[a] Elliott et al. (1954).

of ring A-Δ^4-3-ketosteroids. Comparison with other methods (Elliott *et al.*, 1954), such as the tetrazolium chloride derivatives method which measures steroids with an α-ketol side chain, indicated that the UV method resulted in higher values than that obtained for the chemical procedure (Table II). It has been concluded that the isolated rat adrenal produces substances with an α, β-unsaturated keto group, but without the characteristic α-ketol-reducing side chain. Investigation of the lipid-soluble, UV-absorbing, Porter-Silber chromagens secreted by the isolated rat adrenal tissue (Birmingham and Kurlents, 1958, 1959) has indicated that they are located in the X region (Heard *et al.*, 1954) of the toluene, propylene glycol chromatogram and not found in the cortisone or cortisol zone (Koritz and Peron, 1958). ACTH stimulation causes an increase in Porter-Silber chromagens of up to 9 times the control level and constitutes approximately one third the amount eluted from the corticosterone zone.

The number of rats per assay is limited only by the necessity of sufficient adrenal tissue being present to produce a measurable amount of corticoid. The response to ACTH is dependent upon the amount of ACTH added per unit weight of tissue and is independent of the concentration of ACTH in the medium. Incubated rat adrenals respond to ACTH for a limited time only with an increased rate of corticoid formation (Birmingham *et al.*, 1953; Saffran and Schally, 1955). ACTH incubated with adrenal tissue disappears from the medium, strongly suggesting the possibility that this hormone is being bound and inactivated (Birmingham *et al.*, 1956; Fortier, 1958; Macchi and Hechter, 1954).

Readings taken at wavelengths other than those utilized in the calculation of estimated activity are necessary as additional evidence of the homogeneity of the substances extracted by methylene chloride. Elliott *et al.* (1954) have critically evaluated the estimation of steroid values from their UV absorption curve characteristics. A comparison of the absorption curves in the 240-mμ region for the effect of various impurities and the means by which correction for and contribution to optical density at this wavelength are made. McKerns and Nordstrand (1955) has directly applied the suggestion of Birmingham *et al.* (1954) and of Allen (1950) in utilizing the formula

$$C.D._1 = O.D._{240} - \frac{(O.D._{225} + O.D._{255})}{2} \quad \text{(C.D. = calculated density)} \quad (1)$$

in conjunction with a second formula,

$$C.D._2 = O.D._{240} - O.D._{260} \quad (2)$$

as an estimate of adrenal steroids measured in the presence of interfering substances having an absorption curve concave to the wavelength axis. The above correction appears nonessential when methylene chloride is used as the extracting medium rather than chloroform. Saffran and Schally (1955) have reported a mean index of precision of 0.15 ± 0.007 from a series of 24 assays. Rerup (1958b) has confirmed this degree of precision from a series of 130 assays. However, the difference in slope between standard and unknown frequently occurs within an assay; the day-to-day variations in the variance of the single responses resulted in a wide range of λ values. A shift in mean responses from assay to assay has been observed in spite of all attempts at rigid control. Relative potency estimates based upon replicate assay for the same material are very reproducible (Table III), however. From a comparison of

TABLE III

MULTIPLE ASSAYS OF AN ACTH SAMPLE AGAINST THE PROVISIONAL
U.S.P. STANDARD PREPARATION[a]

Assay number	M	S_M	Potency (units/mg.)	s/b	% Error
1	−0.010	0.087	1.76	0.12	22
2	0.013	0.084	1.85	0.12	21
3	−0.109	0.092	1.40	0.13	24
4	−0.328	0.090	0.84	0.11	23
5	−0.076	0.142	1.51	0.19	38
6	−0.215	0.095	1.10	0.13	24
7	−0.015	0.159	1.74	0.22	44
8	−0.008	0.133	1.77	0.19	36
Unweighted mean	−0.0986	0.110	1.50	0.15	29
Semi-weighted mean	−0.105	0.039	1.42	—	9

[a] Saffran and Schally (1955).

mean λ values it had been calculated (Rerup, 1958b) that approximately 25 rats would be required in this test in order to obtain identical values which would require approximately 120 rats in the Sayers test.

After continued use of the specified test procedure, Saffran (1957) indicated that the mean index of precision in some additional 543 assays was 0.117 and even less in later assays, about 0.06–0.09. The total number of observations for any desired standard error was calculated by the formula

$$N = \frac{4(\lambda + ts\lambda)^2}{S_M^2} \tag{3}$$

TABLE IV

CONVENIENCE OF AN ASSAY[a]

| | λ (nearest whole number) | | | | | |
	0.15	0.125	0.10	0.075	% Error	S_M
No. of rats:	144	100	64	33	10	0.0414
No. of assays:	(18)	(13)	(8)	(5)		
No. of rats:	39	27	18	9	20	0.0792
No. of assays:	(5)	(4)	(3)	(2)		
No. of rats:	19	13	9	5	30	0.1139
No. of assays:	(3)	(2)	(2)	(1)		
No. of rats:	9	6	4	2	50	0.1761
No. of assays:	(2)	(1)	(1)	(1)		

$$N = 4 \, (\lambda + ts\lambda)^2/S_M{}^2, \text{ assuming } S\lambda \text{ is } 23.3\% \text{ of } \lambda \text{ and } t = 0.05 = 2.776$$

[a] Saffran (1957).

The per cent error is calculated by 100 (antilog $S_M - 1$). Table IV was used to illustrate the per cent error and the number of observations required to obtain that error at several values.

Each assay consists of 8 observations and a team of 2 can carry out 4 assays per day. The error, as expressed by λ, in the series averaged 23.3% of λ. The number of degrees of freedom for S^2 in an assay is 4. Therefore, $t_p = 0.05 = 2.776$ in a 28-assay single sequence, S_M averaged 0.127, an error of 34%.

TABLE V

RELATION BETWEEN DOSE AND CORTICOID OUTPUT[a,b]

| | Doses ACTH/100 mg. adrenals | | | | |
Series	0.005 I.U.	0.015 I.U.	0.045 I.U.	0.135 I.U.	Total
1	7.08	8.40	9.73	13.17	38.38
2	9.40	9.17	11.43	15.18	45.18
3	6.95	9.46	10.54	11.82	38.77
4	6.42	8.56	9.75	10.47	35.20
Total	29.85	35.59	41.45	50.64	—
Mean	7.46	8.90	10.36	12.66	—

$$s = 0.88; \; \bar{b} = 3.63; \; s/b = 0.242$$

[a] The corticoid output is expressed as micrograms per milliliter and as the means of two stimulations.

[b] McKerns and Nordstrand (1955).

The linear portion of the dose-response curve has been shown most reproducible in the range 30–90 mU. of ACTH. Table V is descriptive of the relation between dose and corticoid output (McKerns and Nordstrand, 1955). Saffran and Schally (1955) have shown that the responses of preincubate rat adrenals to increasing amounts of ACTH reach a maximum in 2 hours with production of 40 to 50 μg. of corticoids per 100 mg. adrenal tissue. The measurement of less than 10 μg. of corticoid is uncertain. The range of effective response appeared between 0.04–0.1 U.S.P. units per 100 mg. adrenal tissue.

C. Validation

Comparison with other assay procedures has indicated a high degree of correlation with results obtainable by the I.V.-Sayers procedure (Saffran and Bayliss, 1953; Saffran and Schally, 1955; Rerup, 1958b; McKerns and Nordstrand, 1955; Fortier, 1958); the correlation is greatest with corticotropins of low potency.

Birmingham et al. (1956) have shown what appeared to be a major discrepancy in the assay of rat hypophyseal corticotropin by the two methods and suggested that the steroidogenic/ascorbic-acid-depleting activity ratio might be higher in native pituitary extracts than in the more purified preparations, exemplified by the corticotropin reference standard. Guillemin et al. (1959a) and Fortier (1958) have further evaluated this problem by assay of in vivo steroidogenic (plasma and adrenal) and adrenal ascorbic acid effects of such material compared with the in vitro procedure. The different rates of ACTH absorption in vitro and the more rapid activation in vivo than in vitro would appear to explain the marked discrepancy between the estimates of rat hypophyseal ACTH concentration indicated by the in vivo and in vitro assays.

Roberts (1957) has also raised the point of nonspecificity of the in vitro (Saffran procedure), since rat plasma and serum samples are capable of evoking an increased production of corticoids. However, it would appear that, in part, a differential sensitivity of the I.V.-Sayers estimate of ACTH present (oxycellulose adsorbable) in the plasma and serum when compared with the in vitro estimates can be explained by the adsorption and inactivation rate differences which appear to play a major role (Fortier, 1958). The in vitro method does not differentiate between samples with different dose-response slopes as does the assay involving subcutaneous administration of ACTH and measurement of adrenal ascorbic acid depletion in the 24-hour hypophysectomized rat. Potency assignments to different preparations may, therefore, carry with them the inherent error of possible dissimilarity when comparison is made by extravascular administration. In addition, the considerable experience of at least one investigator (Rerup, 1958b) leads one to recommend that at least two 4-point assays be carried out on a single sample in spite of the narrow confidence limits of a single assay. This latter point is made because of the possible variation in λ value between assays which could appear more in one laboratory than another.

IV. Measurement of Corticosterone in Plasma and Adrenal Gland

A number of procedures have been suggested for the assay of microgram concentrations of corticosterone and hydrocortisone in plasma and the adrenal gland. Among these procedures are:

1. The fluorometric analysis of sulfuric acid inducing fluorescence devised by Sweat (1954).

2. An isotope dilution procedure as a modification of the Sweat method (Peterson, 1957).

3. A fluorometric measurement in concentrated acid (Kalant, 1958).

4. A procedure designed as a more practical, although less specific, analysis method requiring as little as 0.5 ml. of plasma for analysis (Silber et al., 1958).

Guillemin et al. (1957, 1958a, b, 1959c), using essentially the procedure outlined by Silber, applied the method to a number of test situations involving a variation in a number of stress procedures and the effect of ACTH administration. Background or residual fluorescence which appeared in the analysis as reported by Silber et al. (1958) and Guillemin et al. (1959) appeared to be constant. Because this background varied between groups, it was maintained in the calculations of corticosterone concentrations by Guillemin et al. (1959c). Silber proposed a correction involving two different concentrations of sulfuric acid. Moncloa et al. (1959) have proposed a simple method wherein this residual fluorescence is eliminated from the data, resulting in a determination of absolute corticosterone. The background fluorescence appears to be a linear function of the amount of plasma or tissue aliquot used in the determination.

A. REAGENTS

1. Iso-octane—reagent grade.
2. Methylene chloride—reagent grade.
3. Sodium hydroxide—0.1 N solution.

4. Sulfuric acid—30 N (8 volumes of reagent sulfuric acid and 2 volumes of distilled water).

5. Corticosterone—free alcohol—as a standard.

6. Ethyl alcohol redistilled from 2,4-dinitrophenylhydrazine.

B. INSTRUMENT AND EQUIPMENT

1. Fluorometer or spectrophotofluorometer or a comparable instrument.

2. The filter system as used by Guillemin *et al.* (1959c) (fluorometer) was that described by Sweat (1954)—a primary filter, $\lambda = 436$ mμ; Corning filters 3389 + 5113; secondary filter, $\lambda = 530$–545 mμ. Kodak Wratten gelatin numbers 16–74. The system used by Silber *et al.* (1958) (Aminco-Bowman spectrofluorometer) called for the Wratten K 2–8 filter.

3. Centrifuge tubes, 50-ml. glass-stoppered or plastic cap; 15-ml. glass-stoppered or plastic cap; clinical centrifuge tubes, 12-ml., and Teflon plastic caps No. 0.

4. Blunt-tip needles about 7 inches long, 16 or 18 gauge.

C. METHOD

1. Three-fourths milliliter of a stock solution containing 2 μg. of corticosterone per milliliter in absolute alcohol is placed into a 50-ml. centrifuge tube and carefully evaporated to dryness in a stream of air. Two milliliters of distilled water is added and this aliquot carried through the procedure to follow.

2. Plasma, an aliquot of 1 ml. or more, is placed in a 50-ml. centrifuge tube to which is added 3 volumes of iso-octane. The tube is capped and shaken vigorously for 15 to 30 seconds. After centrifugation, the iso-octane phase is discarded.

Five milliliters of distilled water is added and an additional 15 ml. of methylene chloride (Silber *et al.*, 1958) [chloroform—Guillemin *et al.* (1959b); (ligroine—Peron and Dorfman (1959)]. The tubes are capped, shaken for 30 seconds, and centrifuged for about 3 minutes at 2000 r.p.m. The aqueous layer is removed by aspiration and discarded.

3. One milliliter of 0.1 N NaOH is added; the tubes are shaken for 10 to 15 seconds and centrifuged. The alkaline wash is discarded and 10-ml. aliquots of methylene chloride are transferred to 50-ml. centrifuge tubes. To the alkaline-washed methylene chloride [chloroform—Guillemin *et al.* (1959c)] is added 2 ml. of 30 N sulfuric acid. The tube is capped and shaken vigorously for 30 seconds. Pressure is released slowly

because of danger of resultant spray (the time of exposure of acid is critical because of instability of the steroid). The tube is centrifuged for 1 to 3 minutes. The solvent layer is removed by aspiration.

4. The acid layer is kept at room temperature for 30 to 90 minutes. An aliquot is transferred into the cuvettes or fluorometer tubes. The fluorometer is set at 80 for 1.5 μg. of corticosterone standard. For the spectrophotofluorometer fluorescence, the sample is read at an excitation wavelength of 470 mμ and an emission wavelength of 530 mμ [525 mμ—Peron and Dorfman (1959)]. Continuous scan from 500 to 560 mμ might be advisable. Fluorescence is proportional to the amount of standard [0.02 to 0.08 μg.—Peron and Dorfman (1959); 0.1 to 0.5 μg.—Silber *et al.* (1958)] after correction for the low reading obtained with the blank carried through the same procedure.

The method has been scaled down to the use of 0.2 ml. of plasma sample (Guillemin *et al.*, 1959c).

Intravenous injection (Guillemin *et al.*, 1958a) of ACTH (0.05–1.0 mμ) into 24-hour hypophysectomized rats increases plasma-free corticosteroid with a maximum level found at 15 minutes postadministration. The responses obtained appear as a linear function of the log of the dose between 0.2 and 1.0 mμ. The response is linear at the several time intervals studied, 15, 30, and 60 minutes, following ACTH administration.

The time relationships are similar to those found by Nelson and Hume (1955) in their study on the hypophysectomized dog.

Average plasma control values reported by Peron and Dorfman (1959) are 19.4 $\pm$ 6.3 μg./100 ml.; Silber *et al.* (1958) 17 μg. corrected, 23 μg. uncorrected; Guillemin *et al.* (1959c) 9–15 μg.

The procedure outlined by Guillemin *et al.* (1958a, 1959c) appears to be reproducible.

The method for estimation of adrenal gland steroid level is as follows. One adrenal gland, trimmed and weighed, is placed in a 12-ml. centrifuge tube containing 4 ml. saline plus 1 ml. absolute ethanol and a few grains of sand. The gland is ground with a glass rod or equivalent procedure. Four milliliters of iso-octane is added. The tube is capped, shaken for 30 seconds, and centrifuged for 3 minutes. The iso-octane layer is discarded. Four milliliters of the ethanol-saline extract is transferred to a 50-ml. centrifuge tube. The conditions cited for plasma above are then followed.

D. Calculations (Guillemin *et al.*, 1959c)

Standard curves are plotted for each technique on linear graph paper. The curves are of the type $y = a + bx$, where a (due to the minimal background fluorescence found within the reagents when a water blank is run through the procedure) is of the order of +1.0 for A, +4.0 for B, and +1.5 for C. The amount of fluorescent steroids in a sample is read from this graph. It is usually expressed in micrograms of corticosterone per 100 ml. of plasma or per gram of adrenal tissue.

Resting levels of rat plasma-free corticosteroid are subject to nychthemeral variations. The highest concentrations of steroid appear between 4 P.M. and midnight (Guillemin *et al.*, 1959c). A plateau normally occurs between the early morning hours, 8 A.M.–11 A.M. A difference of twofold may occur between 11 A.M. and 1 P.M., with the highest concentrations appearing in the later afternoon hours. A similar pattern has been shown to appear in mice (Halberg *et al.*, 1959).

V. Adrenal Ascorbic Acid as an End Point

The dichotomy between adrenal ascorbic acid and corticosterone response to a variety of stimuli [adequately shown through lesioned intervention in the hypothalamus (Slusher, 1958)] has its counterpart in the dynamics of adrenal response where the separation in rate and magnitude of response of these two indices has been demonstrated (Slusher and Roberts, 1957; Munson and Toepel, 1958; Guillemin *et al.*, 1959a; Lipscomb and Nelson, 1960).

The initial significant finding by Sayers *et al.* (1944) of the fall in adrenal ascorbic acid as an index of adrenal stimulation has been extensively elaborated upon in the intervening years (Sayers *et al.*, 1948; Munson *et al.*, 1948; Greenspan *et al.*, 1950; Thompson and Fisher, 1953; Rerup, 1958a, b, c, 1959; Loraine, 1957).

Detection and quantitation of corticotropic hormone activity by measurement of the effect on adrenal venous ascorbic acid has been detailed by Briggs and Toepel (1958), Slusher and Roberts (1957), Munson and Toepel (1958), Lipscomb and Nelson (1960).

Although adequately standardized by way of the I.V.-Sayers procedure, differences between preparations were apparent following extravascular administration clinically. Experimental animal (Fisher and Thompson, 1952; Bates, 1953; Thompson and Fisher, 1953; Liddle *et al.*, 1954) and clinical studies (Wolfson, 1953) established conclusively that extravascular potency differences could be specifically related to differences in the ACTH preparations isolated and purified by a variety of methods. The biological differentiation was augmented by the chemical and physical characterization of different ACTH forms (White, 1953; Shepherd *et al.*, 1956; Li *et al.*, 1955; Bell, 1954). Avoidance of hydrolytic conditions during the isolation procedures resulted in a preparation, which, at the purity level obtainable by the Astwood *et al.* (1951) oxycellulose procedure or at a greater level of purity, showed the highest subcutaneous/intravenous potency ratio. Preparations of lesser potency or those exposed to varying degrees of hydrolytic conditions, either acid or enzymic, were shown to possess decreasing potency ratios (S.C./I.V.) when compared to the U.S.P. corticotropic reference standard (assumed 100% or 1/1). Potency ratios were shown to vary from 3/1 to 0.25/1 (Wolfson, 1953).

Brodish and Long (1960), in an exacting study, have discussed the reliability and limitation of adrenal ascorbic index for quantitative determination of ACTH. They indicated the following major points:

1. The rate of ascorbic acid depletion is approximately 120 times the rate of recovery.

2. For doses up to 5 mU., a linear log dose-response relationship occurs at the 1-hour response times (Sayers *et al.*, 1948).

3. Extending the dose beyond 5 mU. increases the time of achieving maximum responses so that a 2-hour interval would extend the dose-response curve.

In an earlier study Brodish and Long (1956), through the use of a cross-circulation technique, indicated the quantitative reliability of the adrenal ascorbic acid depletion index in hypophysectomized rats.

The depletion of adrenal ascorbic acid is without question highly specific. Although there have been questions raised as to a possible alteration in effect, no other substance other than ACTH has been shown to affect comparably this depletion. There have been reports (Stacke-Dunne, 1957) that impurities such as bovine plasma albumin or protamine may alter the intravenous effect. Saffran (1957), however, had utilized purified serum albumin as a nonspecific protein control in the *in vitro* test without indication of measurable interference (Roberts, 1957).

A. SUBCUTANEOUS ASSAY METHOD (U.S.P. XV and/or XVI; Thompson and Fisher, 1953; Rerup, 1957, 1959)

1. Reagents and Standards

a. Metaphosphoric acid solutions

(1) 6%. Sixty grams of C. P. metaphosphoric acid is added to one liter of distilled water and stirred until complete solution is obtained. This concentrate must be stored at refrigerator temperature and prepared fresh every 2 weeks if continuous use is planned.

(2) 2.5%. Prepared fresh when required by dilution of 250 ml. of 6% to 600 ml. with distilled water.

b. Ascorbic acid standards

(1) Stock solution (1.00 mg./ml.). Ten milligrams of U.S.P. reference standard ascorbic acid is dissolved in and diluted to 10 ml. with 2.5% metaphosphoric acid. The stock solution may be stored in a deep freeze without significant deterioration.

(2) Concentrated standard solution (0.1 mg./ml.). The stock solution is diluted 1:10 with 2.5% metaphosphoric acid. The concentrated standard may also be stored in a deep freeze.

(3) Dilute standard solutions. Aliquots of the concentrated standard solution are diluted to the following three concentrations: 2.0, 4.0 and 6.0 μg./ml., respectively, at the time of assay. These concentrations represent that amount necessary for preparation of the standard concentration-absorbance curve.

c. 2,6-Dichlorophenolindophenol solution

Fifteen milligrams of sodium 2,6-dichlorophenolindophenol, which has been stored in a desiccator over soda lime, is dissolved in distilled water at 85°–95°C., filtered, cooled, and diluted to 500 ml. This solution must be stored in the cold and prepared fresh every 2 weeks.

d. Sodium acetate solution

Dissolve 22.65 gm. NaAc·3H₂O analytical grade, in 500 ml. distilled water and adjust pH to 7.0 with 0.5 M acetic acid. Store in cold and prepare fresh each week.

e. Indophenol-acetate solution

Mix equal volumes of 2,6-dichlorophenolindophenol solution and sodium acetate solution. This solution must be stored in the cold and may be used for not longer than 2 days.

2. Standard Preparation

Dissolve a sufficient amount of the second U.S.P. or international corticotropin reference standard in 0.5% phenol or acid saline (0.01 N HCl) to result in a concentration of 20 units per milliliter. The third U.S.P. or international standard may be dissolved directly in 15% gelatin. Using 15% gelatin as a diluent, three standard dilutions are made in such a manner that the various concentrations are in a geometric series of 1:2:4 or 1:3:9 and the quantity of corticotropin in each 0.5 ml. falls within the range of 10 to 300 mU.

3. Unknown Preparation

Prepare in a manner identical to that of the standard and dilute to concentrations conforming to estimated standard unit equivalent at three dose levels.

4. Assay Animals

a. Rats of either sex may be used, but select animals from the same sex for each assay. Size of animals does not appear to be critical. Weights between 80 and 120 gm. would be preferred although animals weighing from 90 to 200 gm. have been used. Restrict weight to ±15 gm. if possible. Maintain in a constant temperature environment for approximately 48 hours before use. Anesthetize with ether and hypophysectomize via the parapharyngeal approach utilizing gentle suction via a fine-tipped glass tube.

b. Approximately 16–48 hours after surgery, select rats weighing between 80 and 120 gm., but restrict to groups such that no rat is more than 30% heavier than the lightest. Randomly select and separate rats into six groups. The groups should be equal in size and consist of between 6 and 8 animals. Random assignment is made of the standard and unknown doses to be administered to the various groups.

5. Assay Procedure

Standard and unknown solutions are injected subcutaneously to the previously assigned groups. The animals are then kept in their cages for 3 hours. At the end of the 3-hour delay, the rats are anesthetized with ether, both adrenals removed, the adrenals carefully trimmed free of adhering tissue and promptly weighed on a torsion balance to the nearest 0.1 mg. The weighed glands from each rat are then submerged in 0.5 ml. to 5.0 ml. of 2.5% metaphosphoric acid in a vessel suitable for comminution by grinding. A small quantity of washed sand may be used. Heavy wall Pyrex ignition test tubes may be used and the glands plus 2.5% metaphosphoric acid stored at −5°C. if necessary. If the latter storage procedure is used, the tubes are removed from the freezer and while partially frozen may be ground with a tissue grinder pestle attached to the chuck of an air-driven stirrer. An additional amount of 2.5% metaphosphoric acid is added both to wash the pestle and to increase to a final volume of 10.0 ml. Each vessel or tube is then set aside until all of the series has been completed. The suspension is mixed thoroughly and filtered. A clear colorless filtrate is obtained.

6. Analytical Procedure

Equal volumes (5 ml.) of each 2.5% metaphosphoric acid filtrate and indophenol acetate solution are added to colorimeter tubes or suitable cuvettes. The solution is mixed and absorbance is read in a electrophotometer fitted with a 520 mμ filter, within 30 seconds after the addition of the 2.5% metaphosphoric acid. To 5 ml. of ascorbic acid dilute standard solutions containing 2.0, 4.0, and 6.0 μg. per milliliter is added 5 ml. of indophenol acetate solution. Within the same time period as for the adrenal gland extracts absorbance is read in the same instrument. Absorbance values are plotted against ascorbic acid concentration on arithmetic graph paper. A line of best fit is plotted for the three readings. The total amount of ascorbic acid in the glands is obtained by multiplying the equivalent value obtained from the standard curve by the total volume of 2.5% metaphosphoric acid solution used. The ascorbic acid concentration is expressed as micrograms of ascorbic acid per milligram adrenal weight.

B. INTRAVENOUS ASSAY METHOD

Proceed as for the S.C. method except use normal saline or 0.5% phenol in preparing dilutions of both the standard and unknown. The dose to be administered should be within the range of 1–10 mU. in 0.5 ml. of the appropriate vehicle. Inject the rats intravenously, and 1 hour after the injection sacrifice all animals of each group. The remaining steps are identical to those of the previous procedure.

Rerup (1959) has shown that in a study where standard and unknown were compared in either equivalent volumes of saline or in gelatin that the dose-response slopes were identical. It was suggested, therefore, that since equivalent values could be obtained when using either medium, that saline would be the preferred vehicle because of ease of handling. This suggestion is being put to test during the current collaborative study in an attempt to establish the new international standard.

C. ADRENAL VENOUS ASCORBIC ACID METHODS

Slusher and Roberts (1957), Briggs and Toepel (1958), Munson and Toepel (1958), and Lipscomb and Nelson (1960) have described the characteristics of changes in either ascorbic acid or corticosterone or both in adrenal venous blood after ACTH administration. Specific methods, based upon these responses, were proposed for the assay of ACTH in blood by Munson and Toepel (1958) and Lipscomb and Nelson (1960).

Munson and Toepel (1958) used hypophysectomized plateaued 210- to 310-gm. female rats. The postsurgery interval varied from 12 to 20 hours. The increase in adrenal venous ascorbic acid concentration was measured during the period of cannulation, an average of 9 minutes' duration. The following assay characteristics were tentatively ascribed to the procedure: (1) linearity to the log dose of ACTH over the range 0.01–0.10 mU./100 gm.; (2) a standard deviation (s) of 2.12; (3) a slope (*b*) of 20.0; and (4) an index of precision (λ) of 0.106. The minimum dose requirement of this procedure was contrasted to that of the standard I.V.-Sayers assay which required approximately 0.25 mU. Under the conditions of this procedure only a minimum or even an undetectable change in adrenal gland ascorbic acid concentration occurred while a significant increase in venous effluent level could be shown. Additional analysis of changes in systemic blood ascorbic acid concentrations was made as a control. The assay characteristics cited were those obtained from a limited number of observations ranging from 2 to 5 animals per dose with a total number of observations of 14. The increase in adrenal venous ascorbic acid was from approximately 2 μg. to 18 μg. per milliliter from a dose range of 0.02 to 0.1 mU. The method of Roe and Kuether (1943) was used to determine the ascorbic acid concentration in the blood samples and adrenal glands. Additional data would have to be acquired before the reliability of the above-cited characteristics can be more rigidly established.

Lipscomb and Nelson (1960), in a continuation of an earlier study (Lipscomb and Nelson, 1959), evaluated the effect of ACTH on adrenal venous effluent by concommitant measure of both corticosterone and ascorbic acid. They reported that (1) ascorbic acid release precedes corticosteroid release; (2) ascorbic acid levels fall as steroid levels rise; (3) no significant ascorbic acid release was observed in the absence of steroid release. The above data confirm the report by Slusher and Roberts (1957) of the order of release of these constituents. In an earlier study (Lipscomb and Nelson, 1959) using hypophysectomized 200- to 220-gm. rats and measuring corticosterone exclusively showed that this procedure was also usable as a measure of ACTH in plasma. Utilizing a dose range of ACTH between 0.01 and 1.0 mU., they showed that there exists a linear function of log of dose and response between 0.05 and 1.0 mU.

VI. Other Assay Procedures

The following assays have been designed to overcome the differences in extravascular as compared to intravenous potency estimates for ACTH.

A. Guinea Pig Steroid Assay

Liddle *et al.* (1954) have described a guinea pig assay in which ACTH is injected subcutaneously and its effectiveness is accessed in terms of urinary 17-hydroxy corticoids. Each animal received its total dose in three equal portions at different time intervals with pretreatment and posttreatment urinary samples taken. In a later modification of this procedure (Liddle *et al.*, 1955), the effects of a single administration of ACTH was measured. Lambda values of 0.2 were reported and a log dose-response rectilinear in character within a dose range of approximately sixteen-fold.

B. Thymus Involution Assay

Based upon the observation by Jailer (1950) that very young rats are markedly insensitive to nonspecific stress reactions, Bruce *et al.* (1952) outlined the following thymus involution procedure as an assay method:

1. Rats, 7–10 days of age, of either sex and weighing from 10 to 15 gm., are used as the test animals. The test groups preferably should be limited to as homogeneous a weight group as possible. Litter mates are used.

2. The animals are selected at random. Each of the doses is given to one member of each litter. Usually nine litters, consisting of nine rats each, are treated with 3 doses of the standard preparation and 5 doses of the unknown sample (Rerup, 1958c). The remaining animal group serves as a control and is injected with the beeswax medium alone. The ACTH is suspended in a 5% beeswax-arachis oil mixture. The beeswax-oil mixture is warmed in a water bath (70°–80°C.) and the suspension is made in a glass homogenizer. The suspension is rewarmed and stirred thoroughly before each injection; 0.1 ml. is given subcutaneously, once daily, for 3 days. Twenty-four hours after the last injection the animals are sacrificed, the thymus removed and immediately dissected and weighed to the nearest 0.1 mg. The response, as recorded, is expressed as the average of the individual values for each dose level. Thing (1953) and Rerup (1958), in contrast to Bruce *et al.* (1952), have found a linear relationship of the thymus weight of the log dose in the upper portion of the dose-response curve. A rectilinear dose-response relationship has been established in the dose range 0.05–0.2 U.S.P. units per day (Rerup, 1958c). This technique, in which there is an inversion in thymic weight, has been shown to correlate, as does the S.C. ascorbic acid depletion assay, with the expected clinical potencies obtained upon extravascular administration. This procedure has been adopted by the "British Pharmacopeia" (1953) along with both the I.V. and S.C. ascorbic acid methods.

VII. Methods Other Than Ascorbic Acid

A. SURVIVAL TIME OF ENDOTOXIN-TREATED RATS
(Gass and Umberger, 1959)

The mean survival (in minutes) response of hypophysectomized rats weighing 80–150 gm., given 0.5 mg. of endotoxin (*Escherichia coli* and lipopolysaccharide) I.P. (intraperitoneally) followed immediately by intravenous injection of ACTH. A linear dose response was shown with 0.5–4.5 mU. of ACTH.

B. A GENERAL SUMMARY OF OTHER CORTICOTROPIN EFFECTS

In a very complete review (Li *et al.*, 1957) of the various biological properties of the pure peptide hormone of α-corticotropin (A) of sheep origin with a stated potency of 150 I.U. per milligram, a description was made of the following quantitative characteristics for a variety of assays.

1. The Effect on Adrenal Weight

a. Utilizing the beeswax suspension form suggested by Bruce *et al.* (1952), the hormone was administered once daily (0.1 ml.) I.P. for 4 days to 28-day-old rats. Twenty-four hours after the last injection the animals were autopsied. The increment of adrenal weight was expressed as a function of the daily dose in the following manner: $A = 51.3 \log D - 9.4$ in which A represents adrenal weight in milligrams and D, the daily dose in micrograms. A daily dose range of 4 to 75 μg. was used. An index of precision of 0.31 was reported for the procedure.

Concomitant measure of thymus weight indicated a greater sensitivity for this index than that for adrenal weight, as shown previously by Hayashida and Li (1953) and Thompson and Fisher (1953).

b. Utilizing hypophysectomized rats (40 days of age), the beeswax medium, and assay conditions identical to that above, they found that the weight of adrenal to dose relationship could be expressed in the following manner: $A = 13.7 \log D + 12.8$. The index of precision was calculated to be 0.26. A daily dose of 1.0 I.U. was shown to elicit a 100% increase in adrenal weight.

2. Effect on Circulating Eosinophils in the Hypophysectomized Rat

By utilizing dose ranges from 1 to 10 μg., the maximum response occurred with 10 μg. and a rectilinear dose-response curve could be established (Spiers *et al.*, 1953).

3. Muscle Glycogen in the Hypophysectomized Rat

With and without hydrocortisone there appeared an elevation of muscle glycogen proportional to the dose which ranged from 1.5 to 37.5 μg.

4. Effect on Growth in the Hypophysectomized and Hypophysectomized-Gonadectomized Rat

The reversal of response to growth hormone when utilizing a concentration of ACTH of 18 μg. per day, as compared with a growth hormone dose of 0.3 mg. for 10 days. The end measures were body weight, cartilage width, thymus involution, and adrenal and spleen weights.

5. Fat-Mobilizing (Adipokinetic) Activity in Mice

By utilizing the method of Campbell (1938), it was found that in the dose range 0.5–10 μg., the effect was more evident (8–16 times) than that for growth hormone in the same assay.

6. Effect on Accessory Sex Glands

The following effects were shown on accessory sex glands of castrated hypophysectomized rats when α-corticotropin was administered in a concentration of 22.5 μg. per day; the weight increase of the ventral prostate was insignificant but there was evidence, however, of histological improvement. A daily dose of 15 μg. gave no evidence of androgen secretion, histologically.

Pharmacologic blocking agents. Many attempts have been made with the use of a fairly wide series of pharmacologic agents in an attempt to create a pharmacologic hypophysectomy. The degree of blockade was determined by response to agents such as histamine, adrenaline, noradrenaline, acetylcholine, serotonin, and vasopressin. Blockade was attempted with either single principles or combinations thereof. The following agents were most extensively explored: hydrocortisone blockade (Porter and Jones, 1956) and a comparison of other steroids such as the 9α-fluoro-hydrocortisone (Casentini *et al.*, 1959). The latter preparation was shown to be 10 times as potent as hydrocortisone in blocking ACTH discharge as evidenced after ether anesthesia and unilateral adrenalectomy. Sodium pentobarbital alone and in conjunction with morphine (Briggs and Munson, 1955); nalorphine; reserpine; Dibenzyline; and chlorpromazine were the most extensively studied (Wells *et al.*, 1956; Olling and de Wied, 1956; Briggs and Munson, 1955; Ohler and Sevy, 1956; Sevy *et al.*, 1957; Van Pieenen and Way, 1957; Holzbauer and Vogt, 1958; Kitay *et al.*, 1959; de Wied and Mirsky, 1959; Nowell, 1959; Hamburger, 1955; Mahfouz and Ezz, 1958).

The problem of breakthrough following exposure to a series of controlled stressor agents, the reduction in adrenal sensitivity, and response variation within groups have made the above approach unsatisfactory to date. Some investigators (Overbeek, 1957, p. 42) have reported some measure of success with steroid blockade when utilizing modifications of the original Porter and Jones (1956) procedure.

VIII. Choice of Procedure

Analysis of the collaborative data for the second international standard utilizing the three major assay procedures submitted by twelve laboratories of five different countries represented the best opportunity to judge the intra-laboratory qualifications of these procedures for standardization purposes. A total of 61 assays were done, of which 15 are the thymus involution procedure, 19 the I.V.-Sayers or Munson and 27 the S.C. modification of this procedure (Thompson and Fisher, 1953; U.S.P. XV). All three assay procedure values reported encountered invalid data based upon the following characteristics:

1. Nonlinearity of the dose-response lines so that analysis was not possible.

2. Estimates of potency within a series that were heterogeneous.

3. Significant curvature (curvilinear) of the dose-response lines which occasionally allowed $3 + 3$ assay design to be analyzed as a $2 + 2$.

The relative accuracy of the above methods of assay were judged by the average weight contributed by one animal in each of the types of assays (Table VI).

TABLE VI

WEIGHT PER ANIMAL[a]

Method	No. of animals	Total weight	Weight/animal
Thymus (rat only)	522	5438	10.42
Subcutaneous	736	1895	2.57
Intravenous (Sayers)	1101	2882	2.62

[a] Mussett and Perry (1956).

It was pointed out that the thymus test is some 4 times as efficient as the Sayers test when judged by this criterion (Miles and Perry, 1950). If the mean weight per assay is used as the criterion of efficiency, for the thymus test, it is 453 as compared with 111 for the Sayers test. (The weighted mean potency was calculated from the equation $M = \Sigma WM/\Sigma W$, where $W = 1/V_m$.)

The selection of one or another precedure cannot be totally judged from the above data. The far greater experiences of some laboratories which have reported analysis for some of these techniques would indicate considerably greater uniformity and precision than would be inferred from this cross-section analysis. Overbeek (1957) has reported from a summary of 98 assays (S.C.) using 6000–7000 rats, that the average value b_s was 94.2 and for b_u 96.5 ($t = 0.77$, $P = 0.1$). In contrast to these data, the unpublished data covering the S.C. assay experience of the author's (Fisher) laboratories indicate that the average b_s is approximately 200 and that the s/b is approximately 0.15. These latter values were obtained from a summary of some 300 assays involving some 18,000 rats. Perry (1957) has indicated that there appeared bigger inter-laboratory variations than intra-laboratory variations; but in the latter case, there is still a bigger variation than would be expected from the fiducial limits. The U.S.P. collaborative studies (Miller, 1957) have resulted in the conclusion that higher λ values for the I.V. assay are nearly always obtained than for the S.C. assay procedure. Generally, only half as much confidence can be placed in the I.V. procedure as compared with the S.C. procedure. Concurrence with the report (Rerup, 1958a) that the I.V.-Sayers procedure has a relatively low precision due to a high experimental variation of the responses between animals, has been great. The day-to-day variation in responses, in spite of rigid control, has also been high.

Rerup (1959) has suggested the use of a triple cross-over design [as used by Smith (1950) for insulin] by both the I.V. (Rerup, 1959) and the S.C. assay (Rerup, 1958) procedures which reduces the high variations in response between animals (Table VII), thereby leaving only the variation, in the same animals, due to time.

Advantages of this procedure as compared with the 6-point assay were shown in essentially more consistent responses. The use of small groups of four or five rats did lead to large deviation of mean responses as compared to the expected dose-response curve. Parallel precedence is cited for the use of the cross-over design (Smith *et al.*, 1944; Smith, 1950; Burn *et al.*, 1952; Finney, 1952 for insulin).

Far greater experience with this assay structure would have to be gained in order to achieve the validation of the proposed advantages. There would appear to be a need for expressing purity in a manner similar to what the intravenous or *in vitro* method is capable of giving with results expressed as units per milligram nitrogen or protein. The subcutaneous assay procedure is probably influenced by variables which

TABLE VII

DISTRIBUTION OF DOSES TO ANIMAL GROUP AT DIFFERENT DAYS IN THE SIX-POINT CROSS-OVER ASSAY OF ACTH (AS PRINCIPLED BY SMITH, 1950)[a]

		Doses given	
Animal group	No. of animals	Day one	Day two
1	5	U_1	S_3
2	5	U_2	S_2
3	4	U_3	S_1
4	5	S_1	U_3
5	11	S_2	U_2
6	5	S_3	U_1

NOTE: On day one the left adrenals are removed and analyzed for ascorbic acid; on day two the right adrenals were thus removed and assayed.

[a] Rerup (1959).

can effect the absorption and utilization of the hormone. This latter procedure, therefore, is not an accurate measure of the hormone content per se of a preparation. The potency of a preparation, determined by subcutaneous assay, reflects more accurately the clinical efficacy to be expected after extravascular administration (S.C. or I.M.) than the potency determined by the intravenous or *in vitro* procedures.

REFERENCES

Allen, W. M. (1950). *J. Clin. Endocrinol.* **10**, 71.

Astwood, E. B., Raben, M. S., Payne, R. W., and Grady, A. B. (1951). *J. Am. Chem. Soc.* **73**, 2963.

Bates, R. W. (1953). *Endocrinology* **52**, 266.

Bell, P. H. (1954). *J. Am. Chem. Soc.* **76**, 5565.

Birmingham, M. K., and Kurlents, E. (1958). *Endocrinology* **62**, 47.

Birmingham, M. K., and Kurlents, E. (1959). *Can. J. Biochem. and Physiol.* **37**, 510.

Birmingham, M. K., Elliott, F. H., and Valere, P. H. L. (1953). *Endocrinology* **53**, 687.

Birmingham, M. K., Elliott, F. H., Schally, A. V., and Schonbaum, E. (1954). *Endocrinology* **55**, 721.

Birmingham, M. K., Kurlents, E., Rochefort, G. J., and Schally, A. V. (1956). *Endocrinology* **59**, 677.

Briggs, F. N., and Munson, P. L. (1955). *Endocrinology* **57**, 205.

Briggs, F. N., and Toepel, W. (1958). *Endocrinology* **62**, 24.

British Pharmacopeia (1953). Pharmaceutical Press, London.

Brodish, A., and Long, C. N. H. (1956). *Yale J. Biol. and Med.* **28**, 650.

Brodish, A., and Long, C. N. H. (1960). *Endocrinology* **66**, 149.

Bruce, H. M., Parkes, A. S., and Perry, W. L. M. (1952). *Lancet* **262**, 790.

Burn, J. H., Finney, D. J., and Goodwin, L. G. (1952). "Biological Standardization." Oxford Univ. Press, London and New York.

Campbell, J. (1938). *Endocrinology* **23**, 692.

Casentini, S., De Poli, A., Hukovic, S., and Martini, L. (1959). *Endocrinology* **64**, 483.

de Wied, D., and Mirsky, I. A. (1959). *Endocrinology* **64**, 955.

Elliott, F. H., Birmingham, M. K., Schally, A. V., and Schonbaum, E. (1954). *Endocrinology* **55**, 721.

Emmens, C. W., ed. (1950). "Hormone Assay." Academic Press, New York.

Finney, D. J. (1952). "Statistical Method in Biological Assay." Charles Griffin, London.

Fisher, J. D., and Thompson, R. E. (1952). *J. Clin. Endocrinol. and Metabolism* **12**, 967.

Fortier, C. (1958). *Proc. Soc. Exptl. Biol. Med.* **99**, 628.

Gass, G. H., and Umberger, E. J. (1959). *Proc. Soc. Exptl. Biol. Med.* **100**, 127.

Greenspan, F. S., Li, C. H., Simpson, M. E., and Evans, H. M. (1950). *In* "Hormone Assay" (C. W. Emmens, ed.), pp. 205–213. Academic Press, New York.

Guillemin, R., Clayton, G. W., Smith, J. D., and Lipscomb, H. S. (1957). *Compt. rend. acad. Sci.* **245**, 1834.

Guillemin, R., Clayton, G. W., Smith, J. D., and Lipscomb, H. S. (1958a). *Endocrinology* **63**, 349.

Guillemin, R., Clayton, G. W., Smith, J. D., and Lipscomb, H. S. (1958b). *Federation Proc.* **17**, 63.

Guillemin, R., Fortier, C., and Lipscomb, H. S. (1959a). *Endocrinology* **64**, 310.

Guillemin, R., Dear, W. E., and Liebelt, R. A. (1959b). *Proc. Soc. Exptl. Biol. Med.* **101**, 394.

Guillemin, R., Clayton, G. W., Lipscomb, H. S., and Smith, J. D. (1959c). *J. Lab. Clin. Med.* **53**, 830.

Halberg, F., Peterson, R. E., and Silber, R. H. (1959). *Endocrinology* **64**, 222.

Hamburger, C. (1955). *Acta Endocrinol.* **20**, 383.

Hayashida, T., and Li, C. H. (1953). *Endocrinology* **50**, 187.

Heard, R. D. H., Jacobs, R., O'Donnell, V., Peron, F. G., Saffran, J. C., Solomon, S. S., Thompson, L. M., Willoughby, H., and Yates, C. H. (1954). *Recent Progr. in Hormone Research* **9**, 383.

Holzbauer, M., and Vogt, M. (1958). *Acta Endocrinol.* **29**, 231.

"International Conference on the Standardization of Corticotropin." (1957). Ciba Foundation, London.

Jailer, J. W. (1950). *Endocrinology* **46**, 420.

Kalant, H. (1958). *Biochem. J.* **69**, 93.

Kitay, J. I., Holub, D. A., and Jailer, J. W. (1959). *Endocrinology* **65**, 548.

Koritz, S. B., and Peron, F. G. (1958). *J. Biol. Chem.* **230**, 343.

Li, C. H., Geschwind, I. I., Dixon, J. S., Levy, A. L., and Harris, J. I. (1955). *J. Biol. Chem.* **213**, 171.

Li, C. H., Fønss-Bech, P., Geschwind, I. I., Hayashida, T., Hungerford, G. F., Lostroh, A. J., Lyons, W. R., Moon, H. D., Reinhart, W. O., and Sideman, M. B. (1957). *J. Exptl. Med.* **105**, 335.

Liddle, G. W., Island, D., Cornfield, J., and Forsham, P. H. (1954). *Endocrinology* **55**, 575.

Liddle, G. W., Richard, J. E., and Peterson, R. E. (1955). *Endocrinology* **57**, 594.

Lipscomb, H. S., and Nelson, D. H. (1959). *Federation Proc.* **18**, 95.

Lipscomb, H. S., and Nelson, D. H. (1960). *Endocrinology* **66**, 144.

Loraine, J. A. (1957). *Ciba Foundation Colloq. on Endocrinol.* **11**, 19.

Lyons, W. R. (1937). *Proc. Soc. Exptl. Biol. Med.* **35**, 645.

Macchi, I. A., and Hechter, O. (1954). **55**, 434.

McKerns, K. W., and Nordstrand, E. (1955). *Can. J. Biochem. Physiol.* **33**, 209.

Mahfauz, M., and Ezz, E. A. (1958). *J. Pharmacol. Exptl. Therap.* **123**, 39.

Miles, A. A., and Perry, W. L. M. (1950). *Bull. World Health Organization* **2**, 655.

Miller, L. C. (1957). *In* "International Conference on the Standardization of Corticotropin." Ciba Foundation, London.

Moncloa, F., Peron, F. G., and Dorfman, R. I. (1959). *Endocrinology* **65**, 717.

Munson, P. L. (1946). Unpublished data.

Munson, P. L., and Toepel, W. (1958). *Endocrinology* **63**, 785.

Munson, P. L., Berry, A. G., and Koch, F. C. (1948). *J. Clin. Endocrinol.* **8**, 586.

Mussett, M. V., and Perry, W. L. M. (1956). *Bull. World Health Organization* **14**, 543.

Nelson, D. H., and Hume, D. M. (1955). *Endocrinology* **57**, 184.

Nowell, N. W. (1959). *Endocrinology* **64**, 191.

Ohler, E. A., and Sevy, R. W. (1956). *Endocrinology* **59**, 347.

Olling, C. C. J., and de Wied, D. (1956). *Acta Endocrinol.* **22**, 283.

Overbeek, G. A. (1957). *In* "International Conference on the Standardization of Corticotropin." Ciba Foundation, London.

Peron, F. G., and Dorfman, R. I. (1959). *Endocrinology* **64**, 431.

Peron, F. G., and Koritz, S. B. (1958). *J. Biol. Chem.* **233**, 256.

Perry, W. L. M. (1957). *In* "International Conference on the Standardization of Corticotropin." Ciba Foundation, London.

Peterson, R. E. (1957). *J. Biol. Chem.* **225**, 25.

"Pharmacopeia of the United States" (1960). Fifteenth and Sixteenth Revision. Mack Publ., Easton, Pennsylvania.

Porter, J. C., and Jones, J. C. (1956). *Endocrinology* **58**, 62.

Rerup, C. (1957). *Acta Endocrinol.* **25**, 17.

Rerup, C. (1958a). *Acta Endocrinol.* **29**, 70.

Rerup, C. (1958b). *Acta Endocrinol.* **29**, 83.

Rerup, C. (1958c). *Acta Endocrinol.* **29**, 93.

Rerup, C. (1959). *Acta Endocrinol.* **30**, 509.

Roberts, S. (1957). *Ciba Foundation Colloq. on Endocrinol.* **11**, 167.

Roe, J. H., and Kuether, C. A. (1943). *J. Biol. Chem.* **147**, 399.

Rosenkrantz, H. (1959). *Endocrinology* **64**, 355.

Saffran, M. (1957). *In* "International Conference on the Standardization of Corticotropin." Ciba Foundation, London.

Saffran, M., and Bayliss, M. J. (1953). *Endocrinology* **52**, 140.

Saffran, M., and Schally, A. V. (1955). *Endocrinology* **56**, 523.

Sayers, G., Sayers, M. A., Fry, E. G., White, A., and Long, C. N. H. (1944). *Yale J. Biol. and Med.* **16**, 361.

Sayers, M. A., Sayers, G., and Woodbury, L. A. (1948). *Endocrinology* **42**, 379.

Schonbaum, E., Birmingham, M. K., and Saffran, M. (1956). *Can. J. Biochem. and Physiol.* **34**, 527.

Sevy, R. W., Ohler, E. A., and Weiner, A. (1957). *Endocrinology* **61**, 45.

Shepard, R. G., Howard, K. S., Bell, P. H., Cacciola, A. R., Child, R. G., Davies, M. C., English, J. P., Tinn, B. M., Meisenhelder, J. H., Mayer, A. W., and Van Der Sheer, J. (1956). *J. Am. Chem. Soc.* **78**, 5051.

Silber, R. H., Busch, R. D., and Oslapas, R. (1958). *Clin. Chem.* **4**, 278.

Slusher, M. A. (1958). *Endocrinology* **63**, 412.

Slusher, M. A., and Roberts, S. (1957). *Endocrinology* **61**, 98.

Smith, K. L. (1950). *In* "Hormone Assay" (C. W. Emmens, ed.), p. 67. Academic Press, New York.

Smith, K. W., Marks, H. P., Fieller, E. C., and Broom, W. A. (1944). *Quart J. Pharm. and Pharmacol.* **17**, 108.

Spiers, R. S., Panzenhagen, H., and Sullivan, J. S. (1953). *Endocrinology* **52**, 300.

Stacke-Dunne, M. (1957). *In* "International Conference on the Standardization of Corticotropin." Ciba Foundation, London.

Sweat, M. L. (1954). *Anal. Chem.* **26**, 773.

Thompson, R. E., and Fisher, J. D. (1953). *Endocrinology* **52**, 496.

Thing, E. (1953). *Acta Endocrinol.* **13**, 343.

Umbreit, W. W., Burris, R. H., Stauffer, J. F. (1949). "Manometric Techniques and Tissue Metabolism." Burgess, Publ. Co., Minneapolis, Minnesota.

Van Peenen, D. P. F., and Way, E. L. (1957). *J. Pharmacol. Exptl. Therap.* **120**, 261.

Wells, H., Briggs, F. N., and Munson, P. L. (1956). *Endocrinology* **59**, 571.

White, W. F. (1953). *J. Am. Chem. Soc.* **75**, 503.

Wolfson, W. Q. (1953). *A.M.A. Arch. Internal. Med.* **92**, 108.

Chapter 21

Hypophyseal Growth Hormone

HAROLD PAPKOFF AND CHOH HAO LI

I. Introduction

By 1940, the now historic studies of Cushing (Crowe *et al.*, 1910), Smith (1930), Evans (1925) and Evans and Long (1921) had left little doubt concerning the existence in the anterior lobe of the pituitary gland of a principle intimately concerned with the processes of growth. The isolation of growth hormone from ox pituitary extracts by Li and Evans (1944) and Li *et al.* (1945) and later in 1948 by Wilhelmi *et al.* (1948) served to provide a concrete chemical basis for the previous biological studies. In addition, the isolation of this hormone provided investigators with a preparation free from other hormonal activities, and thus enabled studies to be performed the interpretations of which were not complicated by the presence of more than one biological factor.

The bioassay of a hormone is frequently nothing more than a quantitative statement or definition of its biological activity. Because growth hormone does not have a single well-defined target organ as do others of the pituitary hormones, and since its observable biological and metabolic effects are so numerous, such a definition is necessarily complex, and hence there is a diversity of methods which have been employed to measure the activity of the hormone. However, it should be kept in mind that despite the fact that we can observe the diverse biological activities exercised by this hormone, it cannot truly be said that we have any precise insight into its mechanism of action. Moreover, it is already a truism that it is misleading to think about this hormone simply in terms of growth. Yet, as far as terminology is concerned, although the term "growth" hormone is perhaps faulty or at least does not adequately define the scope of the biological action of the hormone, it has had a long history of usage and will undoubtedly continue to be used, even though the alternative designation, "somatotropin," has the advantage of eliminating some of the connotations which one rightfully or not associates with the term growth. In this discussion, the two terms shall be used interchangeably.

Prior to a consideration of the methods employed for the bioassay of growth hormone, it might be helpful to discuss briefly the chemical nature of the hormone as we understand it today, as well as to make a few specific comments on the biological effects that may be elicited by growth hormone; in addition, since it is now apparent that species specificity is an important factor in connection with the biological action of the hormone, a re-examination of the existing bioassay procedures in terms of the responses elicited by growth hormones of various species is advisable.

Since the isolation of growth hormone from ox pituitaries in the middle years of the 1940's, the major part of the subsequent biological studies has been carried out with somatotropin of bovine origin prepared either by the method of Li (1954) and of Li et al. (1945) or of Wilhelmi et al. (1948). Several excellent reviews covering the nature and action of growth hormone are available (Smith et al., 1955; De Bodo and Altszuler, 1957; Ketterer et al., 1957; Russell and Wilhelmi, 1958). It is sufficient here to say that somatotropin will elicit a body weight increase in either adult rats or hypophysectomized immature rats, and in normal and dwarf mice. It also elicits increases in the weight of such organs as the liver, kidneys, stomach, and viscera in rats. An increase in the length of the tail, as well as skeletal changes such as an increase in the width of the tibial epiphysis, are observed in the hypophysectomized rat following its administration. Growth hormone has also been found to influence those activities associated with protein, carbohydrate, and fat metabolism. Indeed, it has been suggested that perhaps this hormone might best be designated the "metabolic" hormone (Li, 1956). For example, growth hormone will produce nitrogen retention, and will elicit decreases in the level of plasma amino nitrogen, blood urea, and an increase in plasma phosphate, to mention but a few effects associated with protein metabolism. With respect to carbohydrate metabolism, the maintenance of muscle or cardiac glycogen in the fasting hypophysectomized rat is one of the effects of treatment with growth hormone, and in addition, the hormone exercises a diabetogenic action in dogs, cats, and the intact rat. That fat metabolism is affected by this hormone is demonstrated by the fact that if rats are chronically treated with growth hormone, their fat deposits are soon depleted, and, more recently, by the observation of the capacity of growth hormone to cause a rapid increase in plasma non-esterified fatty acid (NEFA) concentration in a number of species.

It was inevitable that the availability of a pure growth hormone preparation would stimulate clinicians to study the effect of this hormone in human subjects (Escamilla and Bennett, 1951). The results of such studies soon showed that growth hormone of bovine origin was inactive in the human. In 1951, Raben and Westermeyer were able to prepare, as a side fraction from the purification of ACTH, a growth hormone concentrate from swine pituitaries. This material, although active in the rat, was also found to be inactive in man (Kinsell *et al.*, 1954). In addition, the studies of Knobil and colleagues (1959) demonstrated the ineffectiveness of bovine and porcine growth hormone in the rhesus monkey.

In 1955, Wilhelmi reported on preparations of pituitary growth hormone derived from the horse, sheep, and two species of fish. Although these materials were not as highly purified as ox somatotropin, the results obtained with them provided a valuable extension of our knowledge of species specificity. The horse and sheep preparations were found to be active in the rat, but the two fish growth hormones were inactive. Even more interesting, however, was the observation of Pickford (1954) that not only the fish growth hormone preparations but bovine growth hormone as well were active in eliciting growth in the hypophysectomized killifish, *Fundulus heteroclitus*. It might also be noted that hypophysectomized tadpoles are responsive to bovine growth hormone (Smith, 1923), but the guinea pig, either normal or hypophysectomized, does not respond (Mitchell *et al.*, 1954). These and other species relationships are summarized in Table I.

Within the past five years, studies in our own laboratory have led to the isolation of highly purified somatotropin from pituitary glands of the following mammalian species: man (Li and Papkoff, 1956), rhesus

TABLE I

BIOLOGICAL RESPONSES[a] OF DIFFERENT ANIMALS TO GROWTH HORMONES
FROM VARIOUS SPECIES

Experimental animal	Pituitary growth hormone							
	Ox	Sheep	Human	Monkey	Pig	Whale	Horse	Fish
Human	−	−	+	+	?	?		
Monkey	−		+	+	−			
Sheep	+							
Goat	+							
Ox	+							
Rat	+	+	+	+	+	+	+	−
Mouse	+		+	+				
Guinea pig	−		−	−	−			
Dog]	+		+	+	+			
Cat	+							
Tadpole	+							
Fish	+							+

[a] − represents no response; +, a definitive response; ?, response doubtful or not yet established.

monkey (Li and Papkoff, 1956), sheep (Papkoff and Li, 1958a), hump-back whale (Papkoff and Li, 1958b), and pig (Papkoff *et al.*, 1960). Investigation of the chemical, physical, immunological, and biological properties of these purified preparations have given much support to the concept of a species specificity in connection with hypophyseal growth hormones.

In brief, we may divide the known somatotropins into two classes; namely, those composed of a single polypeptide chain, and those with the structural form of a branched polypeptide chain. In the latter group are beef and sheep growth hormones, proteins with molecular weights of 45,000 and 47,000, respectively, and an isoelectric point of about pH 6.85. These two ungulate somatotropins have phenylalanine and alanine as their two N-terminal amino acid residues, and phenylalanine as their C-terminal residue. Immunological studies show further similarities (Hayashida and Li, 1958b, 1959). For example, rabbit antiserum prepared against bovine growth hormone cross-reacted with the sheep hormone but not with growth hormones from the human, monkey, whale, pig, fish, or horse. Moreover, the unpublished results of experiments carried out by N. R. Moudgal in this laboratory (Moudgal and Li, 1960) have shown that antiserum to sheep growth hormone will cross-react with bovine somatotropin, but not man, monkey, whale, or pig growth hormones.

The somatotropins with a single-chain polypeptide structure can in turn be divided into two groups on the basis of molecular weights; namely, those with molecular weights of around 25,000, and those around 40,000. Human and monkey growth hormones can be paired, since molecular weights of 29,000 and 25,000, respectively, were determined for them, and isoelectric points of pH 4.9 and 5.5. N-terminal amino acid analysis of these primate hormones revealed of course only one residue, phenylalanine, which also was found at the C-terminus. In similar immunological studies (Hayashida and Li, 1958a, 1959) to those described above, antiserum to human growth hormone was found to cross-react completely with the monkey hormone, but not with any other species tested.

Pig and whale growth hormones both have molecular weights around 40,000 and isoelectric points near pH 6.3. These somatotropins are also in the form of a single peptide chain with phenylalanine at both termini. A complete summary of the physical and chemical data of these growth hormones is presented in Table II.

With this background, we can proceed to a consideration of the methods which are available for the bioassay of growth hormone. As

TABLE II

SOME PHYSICOCHEMICAL PROPERTIES OF PITUITARY GROWTH HORMONE
FROM VARIOUS SPECIES

Physicochemical characteristics[a]	Ox	Sheep	Pig	Whale (humpback)	Monkey (*Macacus*)	Man
Molecular weight, M	45,000	48,000	42,000	39,000	25,000	29,000
Isoelectric point, P_I	6.85	6.8	6.3	6.2	5.5	4.9
Number of cystine residues	4	5	3	3	4	3
Number of tyrosine residues	12	13	13	12	10	9
Number of tryptophan residues	3	3	3	3	1	1
NH₂-Terminal residues	Phe, Ala[b]	Phe, Ala	Phe	Phe	Phe	Phe
COOH-Terminal residue	Phe	Phe	Phe	Phe	Phe	Phe

[a] Cystine, tyrosine, and tryptophan, as residues per mole.
[b] Phe: phenylalanine; Ala: alanine.

TABLE III

METHODS FOR THE DETECTION OR ASSAY OF GROWTH HORMONE[a]

Test	Duration of treatment	Precision (λ)[b]
A. Body size		
Body weight increase		
Mature intact female rat	15–20 Days	0.2–0.3
Hypophysectomized rat	10–14 Days	0.3–0.4
Dwarf mouse	14 Days	0.2–0.7
Tail length, increase (hypox. rat)	7–14 Days	0.2–0.5
Tibial epiphysis, increase in width in hypox. rat	4 Days	0.3
Organ weight (e.g., liver, thymus) increase	4–14 Days	([b])
B. Metabolism of nitrogen, phosphorus, or sulfur		
Nitrogen balance, intact dog or rat	1–5 Days	([b])
Plasma amino nitrogen, decrease	2–6 Hours	0.4
Blood urea, decrease	2–6 Hours	—
Urea formation after protein hydrolyzate	1–3 Hours	0.2–0.6
Tissue constituents (e.g., amino nitrogen, amide nitrogen, glutathione)	Varied	—
Tissue enzymes (e.g., transaminases) increase or decrease	7–14 Days	—
N^{15} retention	2 Days	—
Plasma phosphate increase (hypox. rat)	15 Days	([b])
Plasma or tibial phosphatase increase (hypox. rat)	15 Days	([b])
Uptake of S^{35} methionine into muscle protein	3 Days	—
C. Carbohydrate metabolism		
Muscle or cardiac glycogen, maintenance in fasting hypox. rat	24 Hours	0.6
Cardiac glycogen, increase in intact rat	6–12 Hours	0.8
R. Q. depression in fed intact rat	2–6 Hours	([b])
Diabetogenic action, intact rat	4 Days	([b])

[a] This table was taken from Russell (1955).

[b] Significant relationship between response and dose demonstrated. Index of precision (λ = standard deviation in terms of log dose) given if estimate available.

mentioned before, a great diversity of methods have been proposed, but the number that are used routinely are few. Table III presents a summary compiled by Russell (1955) of many of these methods. We will concentrate our efforts in this discussion on the few methods which are actively employed at present and on those which appear to hold promise for the future. Thus, we will consider tests based on body weight, the "tibia" test, and the promising immunological tests that are now being developed, as well as a few procedures based upon a metabolic effect such as S^{35} uptake in cartilage, effects on the level of non-esterified fatty acids in the serum, and on the rate of urea formation in nephrectomized rats. For a discussion of hormone assay in general and the statistical treatment and design of such assay, the reader is referred to Emmens (1948) and Loraine (1958).

II. Bioassay Based on Increment of Body Weight

The simple expedient of giving injections of growth hormone to a suitable animal and measuring the hormonal effect on the basis of the increase in the body weight of the animal has long held acceptance as a suitable assay precedure for pituitary growth hormone. Four types of animals, for the most part, have been employed: normal "plateaued" rats, immature hypophysectomized rats, genetically dwarfed mice, and more recently, the hypophysectomized mouse.

A. NORMAL "PLATEAUED" RATS

Female rats six months of age, having reached maturity continue to gain weight only at a very slow pace; this slowing down of the growth rate is sometimes described as "plateauing." The use of such a plateaued animal for the assay of growth hormone was first suggested by Evans and Simpson (1931). Although such rats for all practical purposes have reached a static weight level, they can readily be induced to grow and gain weight by the administration of growth hormone. It is understood, of course, that the laboratory conditions under which these animals are maintained and the diet which they are fed must be kept as constant as possible in order for the method of bioassay to have any value.

As the assay is usually practiced in our laboratory, adult female rats (Long-Evans strain), 5–6 months old and weighing between 220 and 280 gm. are used. As a test for growth stasis, only those animals which fail to gain more than 10 gm. in a 20-day period are used. The hormone solution, in distilled water or in 0.85% saline, of pH 8–9, is injected daily, by either the intraperitoneal or the subcutaneous route, for a given period of time. The injection volume usually used in this laboratory is 0.5 ml., and an injection period of 15–20 days has been found to be adequate. It should be mentioned that groups of at least 10 animals must be used. When the assay is properly conducted, it will be found that a straight line relationship exists between the logarithm of the daily dose level and the response as measured in grams of body weight increase (Marx et al., 1942).

When statistical analysis* was applied to the results obtained by the plateaued rat weight test for the bioassay of growth hormone, Marx *et al.* (1942) calculated a value for λ of 0.198 and Fønss-Bech (1947) a value of 0.226. It should be noted that when one preparation is to be compared with another, as with the growth hormones in the test described above, the slopes of the respective log-dose-response curves must be parallel if the comparison is to have any validity.

With respect to the sensitivity of the plateaued rat test, it would appear from earlier data (Greenspan *et al.*, 1949) that the lower limit at which reliable responses can be detected are on the order of 50 μg. of bovine growth hormone per rat per day. Such a dose level elicited an average weight gain in 15 days of about 8 gm. At the other end of the scale, a daily dose of 1 mg. caused an average body weight gain of 42 gm.

In considering the specificity of the assay procedure, it must be pointed out that other factors present in the pituitary can affect the body weight gain. It is well known that thyroxine, lactogenic hormone, and testosterone will cause measurable weight increases in the normal animal. The question of synergism also enters here, for it has been demonstrated that the combination of growth hormone and thyroxine will evoke a greater response than that elicited by either substance alone. On the other hand, adrenocorticotropin, if present, will antagonize many of the growth effects of the somatotropins (Li and Evans, 1947; Evans *et al.*, 1948). Thus, when the growth hormone content in pituitary extracts is estimated, most likely what is obtained is the sum total of possible synergisms and antagonisms due to the presence of factors other than growth hormone, and one must be aware that the plateaued rat test is the most accurate when pure growth hormone is used.

The advantages of the use of the plateaued rat may be summarized as follows: no operative procedure is required, the test procedure is simple, and this assay has a very high degree of precision; furthermore, this type of animal is very hardy and is easily maintained. Limiting the method is the fact that large amounts of hormone are required, a limitation which precludes use of the test for the assay of growth hormone in body fluids and tissues other than the pituitary. Furthermore, the results cannot be evaluated without a consideration of the

---

* Of the various statistical tools for describing the precision of a biological assay, one of the most frequently used is Gaddum's index of precision (λ). This is calculated by dividing the standard deviation of the responses (s) by the slope of the line (b) relating response to the logarithm of the dose (i.e., $\lambda = s/b$). According to Loraine (1948), assays in which λ is 0.2 or less are very precise and well suited for clinical studies. Assays in which λ lies between 0.2 and 0.3 are considered less precise, but still can be used with reasonable confidence.

possibility of the presence of contaminants which may set into operation a synergism with or antagonism to the effect of the growth hormone. Finally it should be mentioned that no published data have appeared where this test has been employed for the assay of highly purified growth hormone from species other than the ox, so it is only in connection with this species that the effectiveness of the assay is known.

B. IMMATURE HYPOPHYSECTOMIZED RATS

Among the most obvious effects resulting from hypophysectomy is the cessation of growth. Smith (1930) first observed this phenomenon in the operated rat, and further found that the growth of the animal could be reinitiated by the implantation of whole pituitary glands. It has also been observed that when very young rats are hypophysectomized, growth does not immediately cease, but will continue at a slower rate until the hypophysectomized rats reach about 30 days of age (Walker et al., 1950). In recent years, female rats hypophysectomized at 28–30 days of age have been widely used as test animals for the bioassay of growth hormone in preference to the normal plateaued female rat.

It cannot be emphasized too much that the successful use of the hypophysectomized rat for bioassay presupposes some assurance of the completeness of the operation. Among the criteria for completeness of hypophysectomy are the following: failure to gain more than 7 gm. in the 10 days following hypophysectomy, deterioration of body tonus, maintenance of infantile hair, and the absence of any pituitary remnants in the sella turcica at autopsy.

The assay as performed in this laboratory is essentially that described by Marx et al. (1942) and Li et al. (1945). Immature female rats are hypophysectomized at 26–28 days of age, and after being checked for completeness of operation, groups of 10 animals each are used for the assay 12–14 days later. Solutions for injection are prepared as described for the normal rats and given intraperitoneally, daily, for the requisite injection period. The length of the injection period has been the subject of much discussion; however, the results of recent studies from this laboratory (Li et al., 1959a) would suggest that a 20-day period (vide infra) will yield the maximal amount of information about the response to a given preparation. The earlier studies (Marx et al., 1942) demonstrated that a log-dose response is obtained with bovine growth hormone, and more recent studies in this laboratory show this to hold true also with preparations of porcine growth hormone, as well as with chymotryptic digests of bovine somatotropin, designated α-core (Li et al., 1959b). In addition, we have employed highly purified sheep, human, monkey, and whale somatotropins in this test with satisfactory results.

One of the advantages of the use of the immature hypophysectomized rat is that smaller amounts of the hormone are required to elicit a response. For example, as little as 10 μg. a day of porcine growth hormone elicits an average weight gain of 10.5 gm. in 10 days and 21 gm. in 20 days (see Fig. 1). Comparable results are obtained with bovine growth

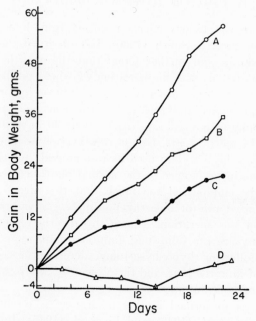

FIG. 1. Assay of porcine growth hormone in immature, hypophysectomized female rats by the body weight increment test. Animals operated at 28 days of age and used 2 weeks postoperatively; 10 animals in each group. Curve A, daily injection of 100 μg. growth hormone; Curve B, 25 μg. of hormone; Curve C, 10 μg. of hormone; Curve D, uninjected controls.

hormone. Although this would seem to suggest that the hypophysectomized rat is more sensitive to the action of growth hormone than the normal adult rat, Russell (1955) has rightly pointed out that when the dose is correlated with the body weight of the animal, there is little difference between the two in this respect.

It has also been reported (Fønss-Bech, 1947) that when the hypophysectomized rat is used, the index of precision is somewhat greater than it is with normal plateaued rats, or in other words, that this assay is not quite as precise as the other. It might be noted, however, that when the data for the porcine growth hormone curves shown in Fig. 1 were submitted to statistical analysis, the index of precision, λ, was calculated to be 0.184 for the 22-day data, lower than that previously obtained with bovine hormone (see Table III).

It has recently been reported (Lazo-Wasem and Graham, 1957, 1958; Lazo-Wasem et al., 1958) that the response of hypophysectomized rats to somatotropin will depend upon the acidity or alkalinity of the solution being injected, in the case of bovine growth hormone. We have not been able to confirm this observation in our laboratory, the only apparent difference being the strain of rat used. It does point up the need, however, for a rigid standardization of every possible aspect of the procedure.

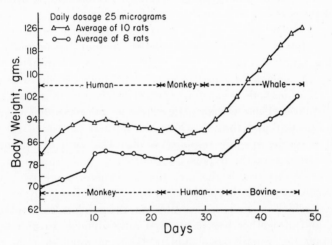

FIG. 2. Curves representing average body weight gain in hypophysectomized female rats for 47 to 48 days. Animals were hypophysectomized at 28 days of age and injections begun 14 days later with human, monkey, bovine, or whale growth hormone (Li et al., 1959a).

As previously mentioned, we have found the immature female hypophysectomized rat responsive to highly purified preparations of ox, sheep, human, monkey, whale, and pig growth hormones. We have noted, however, certain differences in response (Li et al., 1959a) which need further comment. It was found that all the rats gained weight at a comparable rate for 10 days regardless of the species of the growth hormone injected, but thereafter, as may be seen in Fig. 2, the rats given primate hormones, human and monkey, ceased to gain weight. Indeed, even when the daily dose was quadrupled, it was without effect. If, however, the human or monkey growth hormone-injected rats whose growth had ceased were then injected with either bovine or whale somatotropin, a gain in body weight was reinitiated. The explanation of this phenomena is not at all clear, but preliminary investigations carried out in collaboration with Moudgal demonstrate that the hypophysectomized rat forms antibodies to the primate growth hormone so that the growth-promoting activity is counteracted (Moudgal and Li, 1960).

It is thus evident, from the phenomena described above, that one cannot compare primate somatotropins with those of other species if the injection period is extended beyond 10 days. However, it would be useful to continue such tests for 20 days if one were assaying a somatotropin solution of doubtful animal origin, for cessation of growth after 10 days would immediately suggest a primate preparation, or one which behaves in a like manner.

Thus, it would appear that the chief advantage of the hypophysectomized rat test is that much smaller amounts of hormone are required for this test than for tests which use normal animals, although even with this increased sensitivity, it is still not possible to assay body fluids by this method, because of the extremely low hormonal levels in those substances. There is very little difference in precision and specificity between this test and that in which the normal plateaued rat is used, although a species-specific response is observed with the primate hormones in the case of the hypophysectomized animal. Limiting the widespread use of this test is the fact that a delicate operative procedure, hypophysectomy, must be performed, and that this operation produces an animal which is more susceptible to illness, less tolerant of toxic extracts, and altogether less hardy and more difficult to maintain than is the intact rat. Finally, it should be borne in mind that the cautions given above about the possibility of synergisms or antagonisms to the growth hormone effect owing to the presence of other hormonal factors are also applicable here.

C. The Hypophysectomized Mouse and the Dwarf Mouse

Perfection of an operative technique permitting the successful hypophysectomy of mice (Lostroh and Jordan, 1955) led to a study by Lostroh and Li (1958) wherein this operated animal was studied with respect to its response to bovine growth hormone as measured both by the tibia test (vide infra) and by the weight-gain method.

Female mice of the C3H strain were hypophysectomized at 35 days of age and used for assay 12 days after the operation when the weights of the animals had fallen to a constant level. The hormonal solution was injected subcutaneously once daily for periods up to 25 weeks. The data show that with an initial daily dose of 5 μg. of bovine growth hormone, a body weight gain of about 33% of the initial weight was achieved in 2 weeks. It was further noted, as has been observed with rats, that periodic increases in the daily dose of the hormone were necessary to avoid plateauing. When animals received an initial daily dose of 0.5 mg. of growth hormone, their weights doubled within 3 weeks and thereafter were maintained at a constant level as long as the hormone treatment was continued. In addition, thyroxine was demonstrated to act synergistically with the growth hormone, giving rise to weight gains greater than the sum of those elicited by either hormone alone.

Although many questions remain unanswered with respect to the use of hypophysectomized mice for the assay of growth hormone, such as specificity, dose-response relationships, and response to somatotropins of species other than bovine, because this operative technique is so new, nonetheless it seems likely that an assay procedure based on this operated animal could easily be developed.

A few words about the use of the dwarf mouse for the bioassay of growth hormone will suffice here. Although this animal was suggested as an assay animal for growth hormone as early as 1936 (Dodds and Noble) and was studied in detail in this connection by Fønss-Bech in 1947, there have been relatively few studies in which dwarf mice have actually been used. It would appear that the specificity of the response of the hereditary dwarf mouse is questionable (Kemp and Marx, 1937) since prolactin, thyrotropic hormone, and thyroxine also elicit body growth in these animals. Moreover, since the dwarf mouse originates through a hereditary defect, the supply of this animal for experimental purposes is not as plentiful as might be desired.

III. The Tibia Test

A. Historical

As was noted in the introduction, growth hormone has been found to influence profoundly skeletal changes in experimental animals; the bioassay procedure which will be discussed in this section, the tibia test, is based upon the observed effects of somatotropin on the epiphyseal cartilage plate of the tibia of the rat. It was in 1923 that Dott and Fraser reported the cessation of epiphyseal growth in dogs and cats following hypophysectomy. Later, in 1930, Handelsman and Gordon were able to show evidence of bone growth in rats injected with alkaline extracts of the anterior pituitary. Later, Lucke and Hückel in 1933 and Silberberg in 1935, employing acid pituitary extracts in the rat and guinea pig, respectively, observed stimulation of the epiphyseal cartilage plates, and in 1939, Freud *et al.*, studying the effects of growth hormone concentrates on skeletal structure in hypophysectomized rats, concluded that the hormone acts specifically upon proliferating cartilage. The following year, Ross and McLean (1940) were able to demonstrate a resumption of the growth process in the epiphyseal cartilage plates of weight-plateaued rats after the administration of growth hormone. There then followed (Ingalls, 1941; Ingalls and Hays, 1941; Ray *et al.*, 1941) studies on the development of the proximal epiphysis of the tibia and on the effect of growth hormone on this process, in both normal and hypophysectomized rats. It was shown (Ray *et al.*, 1941) that after hypophysectomy the width of the epiphyseal cartilage was markedly reduced; this finding was interpreted as reflecting an alteration of the existing equilibrium between the chondrogenic and osteogenic processes. It was also demonstrated that administration of growth hormone to the hypophysectomized animal induced a remarkable increase in the width of the epiphyseal cartilage plate.

Finally, Kibrick *et al.* (1941), studying the epiphyseal response to growth hormone of young hypophysectomized rats over a 4-day period, were able to demonstrate a straight line, log-dose response relationship. It was on the basis of these studies that Evans *et al.* (1943) proposed the tibia test for the bioassay of growth hormone. Following the isolation of bovine growth hormone (Li and Evans, 1944; Li *et al.*, 1945), the test was restandardized and has been firmly established as a standard method for the estimation of growth-promoting activity (Geschwind and Li, 1955; Greenspan *et al.*, 1949).

B. Assay Procedure

As performed in this laboratory, female Long-Evans rats 26–28 days of age are hypophysectomized and are used for the bioassay 12–14 days after the operation. The growth hormone solution (in water) is administered intraperitoneally (usually 0.5 ml.) daily for 4 days. On the fifth day, which is 24 hours after the final injection, the animals are sacrificed, a tibia is dissected free of tissue, and the bone is split at the proximal end in the mid-saggital plane. The bone halves may then either be stained immediately or fixed for future use in 10% neutral formalin. In this laboratory, the tibiae are stained immediately according to the following procedure: the bone halves are washed in water for 10 minutes, immersed in acetone for about 6 minutes, and washed again in water for 3 minutes. They are then placed in 2% silver nitrate solution for 2 minutes and rinsed with water. During the water rinse, they are exposed to a strong light which turns the calcified portions of the bone dark brown. The stained tibiae are then transferred to a microscope stage and the width of the uncalcified epiphyseal cartilage plate, which does not stain and thus remains white, is measured under low power with a calibrated micrometer eyepiece. Ten individual readings are made across the epiphysis.

C. Sensitivity and Statistical Analysis of Data

One of the great advantages of the tibia test for the bioassay of growth hormone over a test based on weight gain is a gain in sensitivity. For example, Greenspan et al. (1949) have demonstrated, and our experience in this laboratory has confirmed, that a total dose of as low as 5 μg. in 4 days is unquestionably detectable by this procedure. In addition, this test can be performed in a relatively short period of time, and, as noted above, the tibial response is a straight line function of the logarithm of the dose. On the basis of data obtained over a period of several months with highly purified bovine growth hormone, Greenspan et al. (1949) constructed a standard log-dose and response curve which has a slope of 79.4 and an index of precision, λ, of 0.300. The use, however, of such a standard curve as an absolute standard is questionable. For example, it has been shown (Geschwind and Li, 1955) that the same preparation when assayed at the same dose level repeatedly over a period of weeks gave responses which would represent variations of potency ranging from 50 to 200% of the mean.

In order to obtain data which would be amenable to statistical analysis, an assay design similar to that used by Sayers et al. (1948) for adrenocorticotropin (ACTH) has been used for the assay of growth hormone (Geschwind and Li, 1955). As practiced, three dose levels of a standard laboratory preparation as well as three levels of the unknown preparation are tested in groups of 4 or more rats. If the respective slopes can be demonstrated to be parallel, the potency of the unknown relative to the standard preparation can then be computed.

In the past five years, we have assayed growth hormone from various species in triple dose levels. Some of these results are shown in Table IV. Of interest is the approximate constancy of the slopes obtained with the hormone preparations from different species, suggesting the feasibility of comparing the potency of the various growth

TABLE IV

ASSAY OF VARIOUS PURIFIED GROWTH HORMONES BY THE TIBIA TEST

Growth hormone	Response[a]			Slope	Index of precision (λ)
	20 μg.[b]	60 μg.[b]	120 μg.[b]		
Bovine	232 + 6 (4)	250 ± 2 (4)	288 ± 6 (4)	69.6	0.152
Bovine	206 ± 3 (5)	242 ± 1 (4)	248 ± 3 (4)	56.3	0.095
Ovine	209 ± 2 (4)	231 ± 3 (5)	249 ± 4 (6)	52.6	0.157
Porcine	226 ± 4 (7)	243 ± 4 (5)[c]	279 ± 4 (6)[d]	60.8	0.168
Cetacean (humpback whale)	220 ± 4 (5)	250 ± 2 (5)	268 ± 4 (5)	62.6	0.130
Simian	230 ± 6 (5)	255 ± 7 (4)	293 ± 15 (4)	77.8	0.269
Simian	210 ± 4 (4)	242 ± 5 (6)	261 ± 3 (5)	65.7	0.147
Simian	239 ± 3 (3)	253 ± 4 (3)	276 ± 7 (5)	47.0	0.221
Human	206 ± 7 (5)	237 ± 6 (4)	254 ± 7 (5)	61.9	0.240
Human	199 ± 3 (5)	243 ± 2 (4)	248 ± 3 (4)	66.3	0.093
Human	213 ± 2 (8)	235 ± 2 (8)	256 ± 2 (6)	52.9	0.129

[a] In terms of mean tibial width ± standard error. Number of rats in parentheses.
[b] Total dose in 4 days.
[c] 40 μg. total dose.
[d] 100 μg. total dose.

hormones. However, when a single species of somatotropin was assayed at various times, fluctuations in the slope were observed. For example, the slope obtained with the monkey preparation varied from 47.0 to 77.8, emphasizing the inadvisability of relying upon an absolute standard curve. It is also of interest that the values for λ obtained in the various assays range from as low as 0.09 up to 0.269. Solomon and Greep (1959), employing triple dose assays with bovine growth hormone, obtained values for λ of 0.152 to 0.252. Thus, there seems to be a high degree of accuracy in the tibia test.

In addition to the highly purified growth hormones listed in Table IV, pituitary extracts from various other sources have been tested by means of the tibia test. Solomon and Greep (1959) found that extracts of rabbit, cat, horse, and frog pituitaries elicited significant tibial responses, and that turtle pituitary extracts induced measureable although not statistically significant responses. These authors also confirmed the finding of Wilhelmi (1955) that fish pituitary material manifested no activity by this test. Extracts of guinea pig (Knobil and Greep, 1959), cat (Li, 1960), rat (Contopoulos et al., 1958), and chicken pituitaries (Li, 1960) have all been found to exhibit activity on the basis of the tibia test.

D. Factors Influencing the Tibia Test

Insofar as hypophysectomized rats are used in the tibia test, the previously mentioned criteria for completeness of operation are applicable here as well. Not only animals whose body weight has increased more than 7 gm. in the period after operation and before injection, but also animals whose weight loss is greater than 3–4 gm., should be eliminated. The suggested postoperative period of 12–14 days appears to be adequate since the epiphyseal disc thins rapidly within the first 10–12 days after hypophysectomy and then remains essentially unchanged. Although female rats are used routinely in this laboratory, it has been found (Geschwind and Li, 1955) that the male rat may be used with comparable results.

Another factor which should be emphasized is that of diet. Indeed, the diet of experimental animals should be rigidly controlled when any assay for growth hormone is involved. Simpson *et al.* (1950) have discussed many of the dietary factors that play a role in influencing the width of the epiphysis. It is also known that many animal feeds may contain amounts of antibiotics, and experiments designed to assess the effect of these substances on the tibia test have demonstrated that they enhance growth (Geschwind and Li, 1955). For example, 2.5 mg. of Terramycin (Chas. Pfizer and Co., Brooklyn, New York) administered for 16 days following hypophysectomy produced epiphyseal cartilage plates with an average width of as much as 196 μ compared to 163 μ for the controls.

Greenspan *et al.* (1949) administered bovine growth hormone subcutaneously, intraperitoneally and intravenously and found that the route of injection made no difference in the results of the assay. Furthermore, in a study (Geschwind and Li, 1955) of the effect of various vehicles on the bioassay of growth hormone, it was found that none of the vehicles tested, including 25% polyvinylpyrrolidone, 5% beeswax-peanut oil, 16% gelatin, and 2% hesperidin phosphate (pH 8) produced any enhancement of activity over that obtained with an aqueous solution.

In restandardizing the tibia test, Greenspan *et al.* (1949) found that frequency of injection made no difference in response, i.e., a single daily injection evoked the same tibial response as the same total dose given in the form of two injections daily. We have recently repeated this experiment with human growth hormone and find indications of an enhanced response when two daily injections are given (8 A.M. and 5 P.M.) rather than a single injection. The preliminary results of this study are presented in Table V, where it can be seen that single total

TABLE V

EFFECT OF INJECTION SCHEDULE ON TIBIAL RESPONSE
OF HYPOPHYSECTOMIZED RATS TO HUMAN GROWTH
HORMONE

| Injection schedule | Average tibial width[a] | |
| | Total dose | |
	20 µg.	10 µg.
Once daily	223 ± 6 (5)	218 ± 5 (8)
Twice daily	244 ± 2 (5)	233 ± 4 (8)

[a] Values given in micra. ± Standard error; number of
rats in parentheses.

doses of 20 µg. resulted in an average tibial width of $223 \pm 6 \mu$ in contrast to a value of $244 \pm 2 \mu$ when the two daily injections were given. The difference between these two groups was highly significant statistically $(P > 0.001 < 0.01)$.

The importance of the length of the injection period has also been investigated (Kibrick *et al.*, 1941; Greenspan *et al.*, 1949; Geschwind and Li, 1955). From all these studies, it would appear that the total dose of growth hormone may be injected over a period of 3, 4, or 5 days with very little difference in response.

E. SPECIFICITY

It is the aim of this section to discuss those hormonal factors which may possibly affect the results obtained for the bioassay of growth hormone by the tibia test. It should be pointed out that the evaluation of assays of pituitary extracts and very crude preparations presents great difficulties, because in these instances we are presented with the sum total of all possible synergistic and antagonistic factors, known and unknown.

The synergism between thyroxine and growth hormone was alluded to previously in the discussion on body growth. Marx *et al.* (1944), studying the specificity of the epiphyseal response to growth hormone, demonstrated a nonspecific increase in tibial width following treatment with thyroxine. Geschwind and Li (1955) have reported that the administration of L-thyroxine in a daily dose of 2 µg. resulted in an average tibial width of 201 µ compared with a control value of 165 µ. An enhanced response was also demonstrated when thyroxine was administered together with growth hormone. A standard curve for the combined injections was obtained which had essentially the same slope as that obtained with growth hormone alone, but the entire curve was displaced to the left, i.e., in the direction of lower total doses of growth hormone.

These experiments have import not because we expect to find thyroxine as a pituitary contaminant of growth hormone, but rather because of the possibility of contamination with thyrotropic hormone (TSH) which in turn would stimulate the thyroid. When a TSH preparation of Fels *et al.* (1955) was injected in an amount of 200 µg. per day for 4 days, the width of the tibial epiphyseal cartilage plate did not differ from the control value (Geschwind and Li, 1955). A daily dose of 500 µg. of TSH increased the plate width from 163 to 192 μ and when the effect of this dose of TSH plus growth hormone was determined, no enhancement over the value obtained with the growth hormone alone was evident. After maintenance therapy with thyroxine, however, the response of the animal to growth hormone was enhanced. Moreover, in a series of experiments with thyroidectomized-hypophysectomized rats (Geschwind and Li, 1955), it was found that these test animals were quite unresponsive to growth hormone, being only about one twentieth as sensitive as the hypophysectomized animal. A maintenance dose of thyroxine, however, could partially restore the sensitivity of the doubly operated animals to growth hormone. Thus, it would appear (Geschwind and Li, 1953, 1955) that the tibia test possesses the sensitivity that it does because of the secretion of small amounts of thyroxine by the thyroid of the hypophysectomized animal, which enhance its responsiveness.

Another pituitary hormone capable of affecting the growth rate of the epiphyseal cartilage is the adrenocorticotropic hormone (ACTH). Thus, Marx *et al.* (1943) demonstrated that when hypophysectomized rats are treated with ACTH, the width of the epiphyseal cartilage is less than that observed in the controls. In addition, ACTH and growth hormone given together were found to give values lower than those obtained with growth hormone alone but higher than with ACTH alone. In a study of the effects of ACTH during the tibia test, Marx and co-workers (1944) demonstrated a slight decrease in the width of the epiphyseal cartilage plate over the controls, when daily doses of approximately 0.025–0.5 U.S.P. units of ACTH were administered for the 4-day injection period.

In a reinvestigation of the antagonism between growth hormone and ACTH, in which the pure polypeptide, α-adrenocorticotropin (Li *et al.*, 1954) was used, the response was found to be dependent upon whether the ACTH is injected in an aqueous solution or in a delaying medium

(Geschwind and Li, 1955). Thus, very high doses of α-adrenocorticotropin, on the order of 100 μg. (ca. 15 U.S.P. units), have very little effect on the tibial response, either alone or together with growth hormone, if the hormone is administered intraperitoneally in aqueous solution. On the other hand, subcutaneous injection of the α-adrenocorticotropin in beeswax-peanut oil, a vehicle which delays absorption, causes a highly significant decrease in the width of the cartilage plate and almost complete inhibition of the response to the growth hormone. For example, 100 μg. of α-adrenocorticotropin produced a tibial width of 116 μ, and the same dose of α-ACTH together with 60 μg. of bovine growth hormone produced an average tibial width of 126 μ, compared to a value of 251 μ produced by the growth hormone alone. It can be concluded that gross contamination of a somatotropin preparation with ACTH should not significantly affect the tibial response when the injections are given as they are in the tibia test, i.e., intraperitoneally in an aqueous medium.

With respect to the pituitary gonadotropins, very little work has appeared on their effect on skeletal structures. Rather, studies on these hormones have been concerned mainly with the effects of removal of the gonadal target organs or studies of the changes produced by injection of gonadal steroids. There has been a study (Geschwind and Li, 1955), however, of the effects of the administration of testosterone, estradiol, and progesterone on the tibias of hypophysectomized rats under the same conditions as those used in the tibia test for growth hormone. In the case of testosterone, it was found that whereas a daily dose of 1 mg. of this steroid alone did not affect the width of the cartilage plate, when it was given in conjunction with growth hormone a highly significant augmentation of the response could be observed, provided that no larger dose of growth hormone itself was given than would elicit a response of 250 μ. With any greater response to growth hormone, the enhancement was not detectable. With smaller doses of testosterone, an even greater enhancement was observed.

When estradiol benzoate was administered for 4 days in a dosage of 0.5 mg. daily, the widths of the cartilage plates were unaffected by the steroid alone, but the response to a given dose of growth hormone given concurrently was significantly depressed. Also, it was found that progesterone (1 mg. daily) elicited a slight increase in the cartilage plate, but had no effect when administered together with growth hormone.

In summary, testosterone enhances the tibial response to growth hormone, estradiol depresses the response, and progesterone is without effect. It might be noted that since rather large doses of estrogen are required to affect the responses, the possible contamination of growth hormone preparations with small amounts of the hormones which would stimulate estrogen production would not be expected to influence the response to the growth hormone. If the male animal is employed for the assay, however, contamination with the interstitial cell-stimulating hormone (ICSH) could well evoke an increased response to growth hormone since the growth-promoting effect is enhanced by only small amounts of testosterone.

Finally, it has been observed in studies carried out in collaboration with R. D. Cole that lactogenic hormone, depending on the method of preparation and the sex of the animal used, can also influence the tibia test (Geschwind and Li, 1955). On the basis of a number of observations, it has been suggested that there is a discrete factor that exercises tibial activity in a male animal, associated with preparations of lactogenic hormone. Whether or not the growth-promoting activity in lactogenic hormone is due to a separate factor, it differs in a number of important respects from growth hormone. A response is elicited by it in the male, but no effect is observed in the female. The maximal increase in tibial width which can be induced in the male rats by the lactogenic hormone preparations exercising this activity is about 225 μ as opposed to approximately 330 μ elicited by growth hormone. This factor is more resistant to inactivation by boiling than is growth hormone, but is completely destroyed by exposure to one-third concentrated ammonium hydroxide solution for 3 hours at room temperature. It should be reiterated that the possible presence of such a factor would not influence the tibia test if female rats are employed for the assay.

F. The Tibia Test in the Hypophysectomized Mouse

Studies by Lostroh and Li (1957) have demonstrated the feasibility of employing the hypophysectomized mouse for the tibia test. Several inbred strains of mice (BALB/c, A/He, and C3H strains) were tested, and showed comparable results. The mice were hypophysectomized at 35 days of age and used 12 days later. Bovine growth hormone was administered for periods of 4 and 17 days.

It was demonstrated that a significant increment in tibial response could be elicited with a daily dose of 0.001 mg. of growth hormone injected for 17 days. It was further shown that the response is proportional to the logarithm of the dose. The calculated index of precision for the assay was 0.17, a value comparable to that obtained with the rat as the assay animal. It was also found that subcutaneous injections were more effective when given twice daily than when given once daily by this route and much more effective than single intraperitoneal injections.

Furthermore, unpublished experiments carried out in collaboration with Lostroh (Lostroh and Li, 1960) have shown human growth hormone to possess a growth-promoting activity identical to that of bovine growth hormone as assayed by the tibia test in the hypophysectomized mouse (see Table VI).

TABLE VI

THE TIBIAL RESPONSE OF THE HYPOPHYSECTOMIZED FEMALE C3H MOUSE[a]
TO HUMAN AND BOVINE GROWTH HORMONES

Daily dose (μg.)	Human[b]		Bovine[c]	
	No. of animals	Tibial width ($\mu \pm$ S.E.)	No. of animals	Tibial width ($\mu \pm$ S.E.)
0	10	58.0 ± 1.1	10	58.0 ± 1.1
1	8	87.0 ± 3.0	15	85.6 ± 2.1
5	7	119.8 ± 3.5	15	120.1 ± 1.1
10	7	128.6 ± 3.1	5	131.0 ± 2.6

[a] All animals were hypophysectomized at 35 days of age and were sacrificed at 65 days of age; injections were begun at 47 days of age and were continued for 17 days.

[b] Taken from Lostroh and Li (1960).

[c] Taken from Lostroh and Li (1957).

When these animals were injected for the 4-day period which is standard in the rat test, the response was approximately one tenth that obtained in 17-day period. As little as 0.0003 mg. of DL-thyroxine, however, enhanced the effect of growth hormone, permitting the mice to respond about one half as effectively in 4 days as in 17. No information is available about the response of the mouse to somatotropins of other than bovine or human origin.

IV. Immunological Tests

In an effort to obtain a more sensitive assay procedure, and one not influenced by other hormonal factors, attention has turned to immunological procedures for the detection of growth hormone. Such an approach requires, of course, that the hormone be antigenic in a suitable animal, that the hormone used as the antigen be possessed of a high degree of purity in order to minimize nonspecific antibody formation, and that the antiserum produced be specific for the antigen.

In view of the physical and chemical differences described in the introduction, it is not surprising that antiserum prepared against bovine growth hormone, for example, fails to cross-react with any of the other species of somatotropin tested with the exception of the ovine hormone, which is chemically very similar to bovine growth hormone. Thus, the applicability of the immunological approach to the bioassay of various growth hormone is somewhat limited at the outset, since a single antiserum cannot be used with all species of growth hormone, and the hormones needed to produce the antiserum are more readily available from certain species than from others. The results to be described, however, are of sufficient interest and importance to warrant their discussion.

A. ANTISERUM TO BOVINE GROWTH HORMONE

Bovine growth hormone has been shown to be antigenic when injected with adjuvants into either rabbits or guinea pigs (Hayashida and Li, 1958b, 1959). For example, anaphylactic shock experiments in guinea pigs demonstrated that as little as 0.01 mg. of bovine growth hormone was effective in sensitizing the animals so that a challenge dose of 1.0 mg. produced anaphylaxis.

In rabbits immunized with bovine growth hormone, the presence of serum antibodies to the hormone were demonstrated by the precipitin ring test, the Ouchterlony procedure which involves diffusion of the antigen and antibody in an agar-gel medium, and anti-hormone assays. The antiserum, after being absorbed free of certain nonspecific antibodies, was also tested against other pituitary hormone proteins and found not to exhibit any reaction.

For the precipitin ring test, serial dilutions of various purified growth hormones were prepared and 0.1 ml. of antiserum to bovine growth hormone was carefully layered under the hormone solution in each tube. The results are shown in Table VII. Only the bovine and ovine growth hormones exhibited any degree of reaction. Thus, as little as 1.0 μg. of bovine and 2.0 μg. of ovine somatotropin gave a positive test. That this type of test could be used for a semiquantitative assay was demonstrated by estimation of the amount of growth hormone in a single bovine pituitary gland. An extract of the gland was prepared and serial dilutions were tested with the antiserum. The results indicated the presence of 10.2 mg. of growth hormone in an anterior pituitary lobe weighing 1.6 gm. (frozen weight). The same extract was assayed by means of the tibia test and calculated to contain 12.8 mg. of somatotropin.

In recent experiments carried out in collaboration with Moudgal (Moudgal and Li, 1960), the quantitative precipitin curve obtained with rabbit antiserum to bovine growth hormone was examined. These results

TABLE VII

REACTION OF GROWTH HORMONE FROM VARIOUS SPECIES WITH RABBIT ANTISERUM
TO BOVINE GROWTH HORMONE, ON THE BASIS OF PRECIPITIN RING TESTS[a]

STH	Reaction										
	500	250	125	63	32	16	8	4	2	1	0.5[b]
Bovine	+	+	+	+	+	+	+	+	+	+	0
Ovine	+	+	+	+	+	+	+	+	+	0	0
Whale	+	±	0	0	0	0	0	0	0	0	0
Porcine	0	0	0	0	0	0	0	0	0	0	0
Monkey	±	0	0	0	0	0	0	0	0	0	0
Human	0	0	0	0	0	0	0	0	0	0	0

[a] Taken from Hayashida and Li (1959).
[b] In micrograms.

show the type of curve to be expected from a single antigen-antibody system, and also demonstrate that complete cross-reaction occurs between the antiserum prepared against bovine growth hormone and ovine growth hormone.

It should also be mentioned that immunological studies (Hayashida and Li, 1958b, 1959) have demonstrated the antihormone activity of the antiserum to bovine growth hormone. Small amounts of antiserum injected at the same time as growth hormone but at different sites from the growth hormone injection were capable of inhibiting body growth in immature female rats as well as inhibiting the tibial response to a given dose of hormone.

B. ANTISERUM TO HUMAN GROWTH HORMONE

Recent years have seen an intense interest in the development of an immunological assay for human growth hormone. From the clinical point of view, there has always been a lack of an adequate bioassay for the growth hormone content of body fluids, and it would appear that an immunological approach may soon remedy this lack. Rabbit antiserum to highly purified human growth hormone, as mentioned previously, has been prepared by Hayashida and Li (1958a, 1959) and the quantitative aspects studied by Li *et al.* (1960). In addition, antisera has been prepared by Read and Stone (1958), Fishman *et al.* (1959), and Grumbach *et al.* (1960), using a human growth hormone preparation extracted by the method of Raben (1957). The precipitin reactions of the antisera have formed the basis for the studies by Hayashida and Li and their collaborators (Hayashida and Li, 1958a; Li *et al.*, 1960), whereas Read and Stone (1958) and Fishman *et al.* (1959) have employed the technique of inhibition of hemagglutination to examine their antisera; Grumbach *et al.* (1960) have used both techniques. All the workers cited above present evidence for the existence of a single antigen-antibody system in the antisera; furthermore, Hayashida and Li (1958a) have also published evidence indicating that the antiserum to human growth hormone will inhibit the biological activity of the hormone. On the basis of all this published evidence, it seems reasonable to assume that a potent, specific antiserum has been produced to the antigen, human growth hormone. It is interesting to note that human growth hormone is apparently a better antigen than bovine growth hormone insofar as good antiserum could be produced with a total of about 10 mg. of the former as opposed to approximately 80 mg. of the latter (Hayashida and Li, 1958a,b).

With respect to the problem of species specificity, it was noted earlier that the antiserum to human growth hormone will cross-react with monkey growth hormone (Hayashida and Li, 1959; Grumbach *et al.*, 1960). Studies of the quantitative precipitin curves (Li *et al.*, 1960) indicate that the cross-reaction between monkey growth hormone and human growth hormone antiserum is complete, a not surprising result in view of the chemical and physical similarities between the two (Li, 1958; Li and Papkoff, 1956).

A typical quantitative precipitin curve obtained by Li *et al.* (1960) is presented in Fig. 3. The equivalence point for the system (i.e., region in which there is neither antigen nor antibody excess) was found to be at 50 μg. Of particular importance is the fact that the portion of the curve from 0–20 μg. of growth hormone is linear, suggesting the feasibility of establishing a standard curve for an immunological assay. Human growth hormone dissolved in normal human serum did not alter the shape of the precipitin curve from that shown in Fig. 3.

The quantitative precipitin test has been applied as an immunological method for the estimation of the growth hormone content in a single human pituitary (Li *et al.*, 1960). The results of 5 assays on aliquots of pituitary extract are shown in Table VIII. The results obtained from these precipitin tests were usually slightly higher than the results of assays of the same extract by the tibia test. In view of the difficulties in assaying crude pituitary extracts by the tibia test, because of the presence of other activities which complicate the results, immunochemical results may be the more reliable.

It has also been demonstrated (Li *et al.*, 1960) that complete recovery of human growth hormone can be achieved when it is added to normal human serum in concentrations up to 20 μg. A preliminary estimate

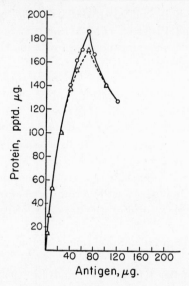

Fig. 3. Precipitin curve showing recovery of human GH added to normal human serum. △—△ — HGH added to normal human serum; ○—○ — HGH alone. 6 mg. of gamma globulin per tube (Li *et al.*, 1960).

TABLE VIII

IMMUNOCHEMICAL AND BIOLOGICAL ASSAY OF GROWTH HORMONE (GH)
IN HUMAN PITUITARY EXTRACTS[a]

Pituitary sample	Weight of pituitary (mg.)	GH content by immunochemical assay		GH content by bioassay[b]	
		in single pituitary (mg.)	per gm. of wet tissue (mg.)	in single pituitary (mg.)	per gm. of wet tissue (mg.)
A	520	4.4	8.3	—	—
B	627	6.3	10.0	4.0	6.5
C	463	3.8	8.3	2.0	4.3
D	635	5.2	8.2	3.0	4.7
E	701	8.8	12.5	6.0	8.6
Average	—	5.7	9.5	3.8	6.0

[a] Taken from Li *et al.* (1960).

[b] On the basis of increment of the width of tibial epiphyseal cartilage plate in hypophysectomized rats.

of the growth hormone content in lyophylized sera from several acromegalic subjects, made on the basis of the quantitative immunochemical method, was approximately 0.2 μg. of hormone per milliliter of serum.

The studies of Read (1959) and Read and Stone (1958), which have been primarily concerned with the estimation of growth hormone in serum, utilize the hemagglutination technique of Boyden (1951). By this method, sheep red blood cells are coated with tannic acid and are then exposed to growth hormone, absorbing it. The cells with the absorbed growth hormone are added to increasing dilutions of the antiserum. If an antibody is present to the growth hormone, the cells will agglutinate. For the assay of growth hormone, a hemagglutination-inhibition procedure is employed. After the titer of the antibody has been determined, a constant amount of antibody is added to amounts of growth hormone which are decreased until a point is reached where agglutination occurs; this is designated the end point. With a minimal amount of antibody, Read (1959) reports that he is able to detect 0.001 μg. of growth hormone by this method. For general assay purposes, conditions were selected which gave an end point of around 0.02 μg.

The serum levels obtained by this technique are very interesting. Of importance is the observation that the serum obtained from several hypophysectomized patients contained no detectable growth hormone. In normal individuals values between 0.16 and 0.64 μg. of growth hormone per milliliter of serum were reported, with no apparent difference between children and adults. In acromegalic serum, a level of 1.2 μg. per milliliter was found.

The immunological assay methods outlined in this section are necessarily in a preliminary stage at the moment, but it does appear that they hold great promise for the future. The advantage of the techniques based on precipitin reactions is greater accuracy, since the antigen-antibody precipitates are amenable to quantitative examination by the many sensitive methods now available for the analysis of proteins. On the other hand, the method involving inhibition of hemagglutination has the advantage of greater sensitivity but is limited by the fact that the end point in the test is subjectively determined. Of importance, also, is the question of the purity of the growth hormone used initially to immunize the rabbits and later as a standard. The preparation (Li and Papkoff, 1956) used in the studies described here satisfies these requirements quite adequately as gauged by the published physical and chemical data.

One final point may be introduced into the discussion here, in connection with the following question: Is the form of the hormone as it circulates in the body identical to that in which it is isolated from pituitary extracts? In order for the immunological methods to be valid in their application to the study of various body fluids, both the isolated hormone and the circulating hormone should be antigenically identical. There are no data available which would answer this question definitively, but one need only note the great discrepancy between serum growth hormone levels measured by the tibia test (Gemzell, 1959; Segaloff *et al.*, 1955) and those determined by immunological assays to consider seriously the possibility that there might be a difference between the circulating form of the hormone and the form isolated in the laboratory.

V. Miscellaneous Methods

In this section we will discuss briefly a few procedures which are concerned with effect of growth hormone on some aspect of metabolism. As indicated in Table III, numerous tests have been proposed for the bioassay of growth hormone which involve the various metabolic pathways of nitrogen, fat, and carbohydrate. Few have gained acceptance, however. In part this may be due to a lack of certain types of information about the particular test, such as specificity or time relationships. In addition, some tests require special operative and biochemical procedures which are perhaps not readily adaptable to routine laboratory use.

A. Blood Urea Decrease

It was demonstrated by Engel *et al.* (1948) that the rate of increase in blood urea in the nephrectomized rat could be used as a means of studying the rate of nitrogen metabolism in short experiments of 1–3 hours duration. Russell (1951, 1955) and Russell and Cappiello (1949) have used this method to study the effect of growth hormone on nitrogen metabolism, and has proposed a bioassay method, which has the advantage of short duration, on the basis of these studies.

It was found that growth hormone alone administered to nephrectomized rats in a basal state had little or no effect on the rate of urea formation. If, however, an amino acid mixture was given to the animal, followed by growth hormone, the rate of formation of urea was decreased, indicative of nitrogen retention. An indication of the sensitivity of the test is that a single dose of 100 μg. of the hormone per 100 gm. of body weight was sufficient to produce a significant depression in the rate of blood urea formation. In addition, the dose-response relationship was found to be linear, and an index of precision, λ, of 0.4 was calculated.

The conditions employed were as follows: young adult rats, after being fasted for 24 hours, were nephrectomized and then allowed to recover for a few hours. The test preparation (in saline) was injected intraperitoneally and measurements of blood urea were begun from 1 to 1½ hours later. For these measurements a sample of blood is taken, and a measured amount of casein hydrolyzate is injected intravenously over a period of a few minutes; a blood sample is taken again 2 hours later. In the absence of growth hormone, increase of the blood urea nitrogen averaged 22–25 mg. %; with large doses of growth hormone, the 2-hour increase in blood urea was reduced to as low as 12–14 mg. %.

Other proteins and inactivated hormone preparations had no significant effect on urea formation. Moreover, neither epinephrine nor insulin in moderately large doses altered the rate appreciably, either in the presence or absence of exogenous amino acids. Adrenocorticotropin and adrenal steroids were also without effect, no doubt because of the short duration of the test. Indeed, it would appear that the short test period required by this assay method is in itself a distinct advantage since it obviates the effects that might result from a longer, chronic hormonal treatment.

B. Plasma Fatty Acids

The role of growth hormone with respect to fat metabolism and mobilization of depot fat is well known, and need not be discussed here. We wish to mention briefly recent work in which growth hormone is shown to affect the level of fasting NEFA in the plasma. Although at the present time there are no actual assay procedures based upon the effect of growth hormone on the plasma level of NEFA, this effect would appear to be of great value in ascertaining whether or not a given growth hormone preparation may be active in man.

Raben and Hollenberg have reported on studies involving the dog and the human, in which growth hormone preparations of bovine, porcine, simian, and human origin were used (Raben, 1959; Raben and Hollenberg, 1958, 1959). It was found that in the dog, plasma fatty acid levels were increased by porcine, human, simian, and bovine growth hormone preparations. Diabetic dogs were very sensitive, responding to as little as 30 μg. growth hormone per kilogram weight. In the human, positive responses were obtained with human and monkey growth hormone, but not with the porcine or bovine hormone. Here again is a further demonstration of species specificity in connection with the biological action of growth hormone.

It should be noted that it has been found necessary to employ fasted animals or subjects in order for any adipokinetic response to growth hormone to be observed. Raben (1959) and Raben and Hollenberg (1958, 1959) find that intake of either food or glucose will abolish the ability of growth hormone to increase the level of the plasma fatty acids. On the other hand, other substances such as epinephrine and norepinephrine will raise the plasma fatty acid level.

C. Sulfate-35 Uptake in Cartilage

The skeletal effects induced by growth hormone have been previously noted, and indeed, as has been discussed above, the effect upon the tibia forms the basis of one of the most useful methods for the bioassay of this hormone. One of the components of skeletal tissue, cartilage, is chondroitin sulfate, a polysaccharide composed of repeating units of sulfate, N-acetylgalactosamine, and D-glucuronic acid. The basis of one proposed bioassay for growth hormone is the quantitative determination of the amount of radioactive sulfate taken up and incorporated into chondroitin sulfate.

It was shown by Ellis et al. (1953), Denko and Bergenstal (1955), and Murphy et al. (1956) that the extent of uptake of sulfate by cartilage in vivo in rats was greatly reduced by hypophysectomy and restored by growth hormone administration. Studies in vitro (Salman and Daughaday, 1957) showed a reduced uptake by the cartilage of hypophysectomized rats, but the addition of growth hormone to the incubation medium did not affect the sulfate uptake. However, if the animals were treated with growth hormone in vivo, then an enhanced rate of sulfate uptake could be shown in vitro. An extremely interesting observation was that although growth hormone does not have a direct effect in vitro, it induces the production of a serum "sulfation factor"; thus, incubation of cartilage in the serum of hypophysectomized rats pretreated with growth hormone augmented the uptake of sulfate.

An assay procedure based upon the uptake of radioactive sulfate by the tibial epiphysis was described by Murphy et al. (1956). The response was a linear function of the logarithm of the dose between 10 and 250 μg., and the index of precision was found to be 0.37. Thyroxine increased the incorporation of sulfate and thyrotropin augmented the action of the growth hormone. Cortisone and hydrocortisone were found to be inhibitory in this respect.

More recently, Collins and Baker (1960) have employed the uptake of radiosulfate by the costal cartilage of hypophysectomized rats as a bioassay for growth hormone. Female rats were hypophysectomized at 21 days of age and used for experimentation 3 weeks later. The animals were given intraperitoneal injections of growth hormone together with the radiosulfate once daily for 4 days. The animals were sacrificed 24 hours later and the amount of radiosulfate present in the seventh rib cartilage was determined. A linear relationship was found to exist between the uptake of radio sulfate and the logarithm of the dose of hormone given over a range of 3–20 μg. per day for 4 days. At a dose range of 3–12 μg./day, sheep and beef FSH and ICSH, lactogenic hormone, TSH, and ACTH did not increase the radiosulfate uptake.

VI. Concluding Remarks

We have attempted in this chapter to emphasize only those methods which are being actively employed for the bioassay of growth hormone. We have also sought to point out those methods which may offer promise for the future. It cannot be said that there is in current usage any assay technique which has universal applicability. Indeed, in view of the pattern of species specificity already observed, it may be expecting too much to find a biological assay procedure which will give an accurate measure of the activity of every species of pituitary growth hormone which may be encountered.

For the general laboratory assay of purified preparations of mammalian growth hormone, the tibia test stands as the best procedure, in terms of sensitivity, precision, and specificity. The tibia test, however, does not lend itself to the assay of body fluids, and here, it would appear, the use of a sensitive immunological test is indicated.

We might conclude with the thought that perhaps the fact that a biological assay for growth hormone which is entirely adequate in every respect has in truth not yet been developed, is simply a reflection of the still meager knowledge of the intimate mechanisms governing the biochemical actions of this hormone, and that it is not unreasonable to expect that as knowledge in this area is extended, better bioassay techniques will emerge.

REFERENCES

Boyden, S. V. (1951). *J. Exptl. Med.* **93**, 107.
Collins, E. J., and Baker, V. F. (1960). *Metabolism* **9**, 556.
Contopoulos, A. N., Simpson, M. E., and Koneff, A. A. (1958). *Endocrinology* **63**, 642.
Crowe, S. J., Cushing, H., and Homans, J. (1910). *Bull. Johns Hopkins Hosp.* **21**, 127.
De Bodo, R. C., and Altszuler, N. (1957). *Vitamins and Hormones* **15**, 205.
Denko, C. W., and Bergenstal, D. M. (1955). *Endocrinology* **57**, 76.
Dodds, E. C., and Noble, R. L. (1936). *Brit. Med. J.* **ii**, 824.

Dott, D. M., and Fraser, J. (1923). *Quart. J. Exptl. Physiol. Suppl.* **13**, 107.

Ellis, S., Huble, J., and Simpson, M. E. (1953). *Proc. Soc. Exptl. Biol. Med.* **84**, 603.

Emmens, C. W. (1948). "Principles of Biological Assay." Chapman and Hall, London.

Engel, F. L., Pentz, E. I., and Engel, M. G. (1948). *J. Biol. Chem.* **174**, 99.

Escamilla, R. F., and Bennett, L. (1951). *J. Clin. Endocrinol.* **11**, 221.

Evans, H. M. (1925). *Harvey Lectures* **19**, 212.

Evans, H. M., and Long, J. A. (1921). *Anat. Record* **21**, 61.

Evans, H. M., and Simpson, M. E. (1931). *Am. J. Physiol.* **98**, 511.

Evans, H. M., Simpson, M. E., Marx, W., and Kibrick, E. A. (1943). *Endocrinology* **32**, 13.

Evans, H. M., Simpson, M. E., and Li, C. H. (1948). *Growth* **12**, 15.

Fels, I. G., Simpson, M. E., and Evans, H. M. (1955). *J. Biol. Chem.* **213**, 311.

Fishman, J., McGarry, E. E., and Beck, J. C. (1959). *Proc. Soc. Exptl. Biol. Med.* **102**, 446.

Fønss-Bech, P. (1947). *Acta Pharmacol. Toxicol.* **3**, *Suppl.* **3**.

Freud, J., Levie, L. H., and Kroon, D. B. (1939). *Endocrinology* **1**, 56.

Gemzell, C. A. (1959). *J. Clin. Endocrinol. and Metabolism* **19**, 1049.

Geschwind, I. I., and Li, C. H. (1953). Cited by C. H. Li *in* "Ciba Foundation Colloquia on Endocrinology" (G. E. W. Wolstenholme, ed.), Vol. V, p. 115. Churchill, London.

Geschwind, I. I., and Li, C. H. (1955). *In* "Hypophyseal Growth Hormone, Nature and Actions" (R. W. Smith, O. H. Gaebler, and C. N. H. Long, eds.). McGraw-Hill, New York.

Greenspan, F. S., Li, C. H., Simpson, M. E., and Evans, H. M. (1949). *Endocrinology* **45**, 455 (1950). *In* "Hormone Assay" (C. W. Emmens, ed.), p. 273. Academic Press, New York.

Grumbach, M. M., Kaplan, S. L., and Solomon, S. (1960). *Nature* **185**, 170.

Handelsman, M. B., and Gordon, E. F. (1930). *J. Pharmacol. Exptl. Therap.* **38**, 349.

Hayashida, T., and Li, C. H. (1958a). *Science* **128**, 1276.

Hayashida, T., and Li, C. H. (1958b). *Endocrinology* **63**, 487.

Hayashida, T., and Li, C. H. (1959). *Endocrinology* **65**, 944.

Ingalls, T. H. (1941). *Endocrinology* **29**, 710.

Ingalls, T. H., and Hayes, D. R. (1941). *Endocrinology* **29**, 720.

Kemp, T., and Marx, L. (1937). *Acta Pathol. Microbiol. Scand.* **14**, 197.

Ketterer, B., Randle, P. J., and Young, F. G. (1957). *Ergebnisse Physiol. biol. Chem. u. exptl. Pharmakol.* **49**, 129.

Kibrick, E. A., Becks, H., Marx, W., and Evans, H. M. (1941). *Growth* **5**, 437.

Kinsell, L. W., Margen, S., Partridge, J. W., Michaels, G. D., Balch, H. E., and Jahn, J. P. (1954). *J. Clin. Endocrinol. and Metabolism* **14**, 110.

Knobil, E., and Greep, R. O. (1959). *Recent Progr. in Hormone Research* **15**, 1.

Lazo-Wasem, E. A., and Graham, C. E. (1957). *Proc. Soc. Exptl. Biol. Med.* **94**, 439.

Lazo-Wasem, E. A., and Graham, C. E. (1958). *Endocrinology* **62**, 108.

Lazo-Wasem, E. A., Michalski, J., and Graham, C. E. (1958). *Endocrinology* **63**, 831.

Li, C. H. (1954). *J. Biol. Chem.* **211**, 555.

Li, C. H. (1956). *Science* **123**, 617.

Li, C. H. (1957). *Federation Proc.* **16**, 775.

Li, C. H. (1958). *In* "Symposium on Protein Structure" (A. Neuberger, ed.), p. 302. Methuen, London.

Li, C. H. (1960). Unpublished data.

Li, C. H., and Evans, H. M. (1944). *Science* 99, 183.

Li, C. H., and Evans, H. M. (1947). *Vitamins and Hormones* 5, 197.

Li, C. H., and Papkoff, H. (1956). *Science* 124, 1293.

Li, C. H., Evans, H. M., and Simpson, M. E. (1945). *J. Biol. Chem.* 159, 353.

Li, C. H., Geschwind, I. I., Levy, A. L., Harris, J. I., Dixon, J. S., Pon, N. G., and Porath, J. O. (1954). *Nature* 173, 251.

Li, C. H., Papkoff, H., and Jordan, C. W., Jr. (1959a). *Proc. Soc. Exptl. Biol. Med.* 100, 44.

Li, C. H., Papkoff, H., and Hayashida, T. (1959b). *Arch. Biochem. Biophys.* 85, 97.

Li, C. H., Moudgal, N. R., and Papkoff, H. (1960). *J. Biol. Chem.* 235, 1038.

Loraine, J. A. (1948). "The Clinical Application of Hormone Assay." Livingstone, London.

Lostroh, A. J., and Jordan, C. W., Jr. (1955). *Proc. Soc. Exptl. Biol. Med.* 90, 267.

Lostroh, A. J., and Li, C. H. (1957). *Endocrinology* 60, 308.

Lostroh, A. J., and Li, C. H. (1958). *Endocrinology* 62, 484.

Lostroh, A. J., and Li, C. H. (1960). Unpublished data.

Lucke, H., and Hückel, R. (1933). *Arch. Exptl. Pathol. Pharmakol. Naunyn-Schmiedeberg's* 169, 290.

Marx, W., Simpson, M. E., and Evans, H. M. (1942). *Endocrinology* 30, 1.

Marx, W., Simpson, M. E., Li, C. H., and Evans, H. M. (1943). *Endocrinology* 33, 102.

Marx, W., Simpson, M. E., and Evans, H. M. (1944). *Proc. Soc. Exptl. Biol. Med.* 55, 250.

Mitchell, M. L., Guillemin, R., and Selye, H. (1954). *Endocrinology* 54, 111.

Moudgal, N. R., and Li, C. H. (1960). Unpublished data.

Murphy, W. R., Daughaday, W. H., and Hartnett, C. (1956). *J. Lab. Clin. Med.* 47, 715.

Papkoff, H., and Li, C. H. (1958a). *Biochim. et Biophys. Acta* 29, 145.

Papkoff, H., and Li, C. H. (1958b). *J. Biol. Chem.* 231, 367.

Papkoff, H., Moudgal, N. R., and Li, C. H. (1960). *Federation Proc.* 19, 157.

Pickford, G. E. (1954). *Endocrinology* 55, 274.

Raben, M. S. (1957). *Science* 125, 883.

Raben, M. S. (1959). *Recent Progr. in Hormone Research* 15, 71.

Raben, M. S., and Hollenberg, C. H. (1958). *J. Clin. Invest.* 37, 922.

Raben, M. S., and Hollenberg, C. H. (1959). *J. Clin. Invest.* 38, 484.

Raben, M. S., and Westermeyer, V. W. (1951). *Proc. Soc. Exptl. Biol. Med.* 78, 550.

Ray, R. D., Evans, H. M., and Becks, H. (1941). *Am. J. Pathol.* 17, 509.

Read, C. H. (1959). *Recent Progr. in Hormone Research* 15, 107.

Read, C. H., and Stone, D. B. (1958). *A.M.A. J. Diseases Children* 96, 538.

Ross, E. S., and McLean, F. C. (1940). *Endocrinology* 27, 329.

Russell, J. A. (1951). *Endocrinology* 49, 99.

Russell, J. A. (1955). *In* "Hypophyseal Growth Hormone, Nature and Actions" (R. W. Smith, O. H. Gaebler, and C. N. H. Long, eds.), p. 17. McGraw-Hill, New York.

Russell, J. A., and Cappiello, M. (1949). *Endocrinology* 44, 333.

Russell, J. A., and Wilhelmi, A. E. (1958). *Ann. Rev. Physiol.* 20, 43.

Salman, W. D., and Daughaday, W. H. (1957). *J. Lab. Clin. Med.* 49, 825.

Sayers, M. A., Sayers, G., and Woodbury, L. A. (1948). *Endocrinology* 42, 379.

Scow, R. D., Simpson, M. E., Asling, C. W., Li, C. H., and Evans, H. M. (1949). *Anat. Record* 104, 445.

Segaloff, A., Komrad, E. L., Flores, A., Segaloff, Ann, and Hardesty, M. (1955). *Endocrinology* **57**, 527.

Silberberg, M. (1935). *Proc. Soc. Exptl. Biol. Med.* **32**, 1423.

Simpson, M. E., Asling, C. W., and Evans, H. M. (1950). *Yale J. Biol. and Med.* **23**, 1.

Smith, P. E. (1923). *Anat. Record* **25**, 150.

Smith, P. E. (1930). *Am. J. Anat.* **45**, 205.

Smith, R. W., Gaebler, O. H., and Long, C. N. H., eds. (1955). "Hypophyseal Growth Hormone, Nature and Actions." McGraw-Hill, New York.

Solomon, J., and Greep, R. O. (1959). *Endocrinology* **65**, 334.

Walker, D. G., Simpson, M. E., Asling, C. W., and Evans, H. M. (1950). *Anat. Record* **106**, 539.

Wilhelmi, A. E. (1955). *In* "Hypophyseal Growth Hormone, Nature and Actions" (R. W. Smith, O. H. Gaebler, and C. N. H. Long, eds.) p. 59. McGraw-Hill, New York.

Wilhelmi, A. E., Fishman, J. B., and Russell, J. A. (1948). *J. Biol. Chem.* **176**, 735.

PART IV

Standard Methods

Chapter 22

Standard Methods Adopted by Official Organizations

Cancer Chemotherapy National Service Center Program[1]

RALPH I. DORFMAN

An assay program involving certain selected tests of steroid hormone activity has been developed.[2] Each assay, before adoption as an official test, either preliminary or quantitative, was modeled by at least two laboratories. The aim of the quantitative tests is to provide a method which would permit determination of activity of an unknown compared

---

[1] United States Public Health Service.

[2] The assay program was developed by a subcommittee of the Endocrinology Panel of the Cancer Chemotherapy National Service Center composed of Drs. Ralph I. Dorfman (Chairman), M. X. Zarrow, Roland Meyer, Preston Perlman, James Leathem, Milton Eisler, and Robert Stafford, and Erwin Vollmer, Nathan Mantel, and Mr. Arthur G. Hilgar of the Cancer Chemotherapy National Service Center.

to a standard with an accuracy of $\pm 20\%$ at $P = 0.01$. The concentrations of test materials in the preliminary assays were so chosen as it indicated potency ratios of unknown to standard of 5% or better.

I. General Instructions for Hormone Assay Procedures[3]

A. MINIMUM STANDARD LABORATORY REQUIREMENTS

1. Animals

Obtain only from primary breeders.

2. Animal Rooms

Maintain at temperature between 70° and 80°F. and provide adequate, draft-free ventilation preferably with air conditioning. Control of humidity between 40 and 50% is desirable.

3. Equipment and Facilities

Most types of metal cages are acceptable, solid-wall type preferred. Minimal cage area per mouse up to 60 days old will be 8 square inches; over 60 days old will be 10 square inches; and the maximal number of mice in any cage of any size will be 30. Adequate facilities for thorough cleaning of cages are necessary.

4. Cleaning

To avoid *hormone contamination,* all equipment (cages, feeders, and water bottles) exposed to test animals must be cleaned thoroughly after completing test by removing all debris, washing with an effective detergent, rinsing in hot water, and air-drying. During the course of an experiment, remove all waste, including unused food, regularly and frequently (preferably daily).

5. Animal Food

Use a commercial feed which does not deteriorate quickly and provides nutrition for adequate growth. Make food and water available for 24 hours each day, except when indicated otherwise in the specific instructions. Replace with fresh food and water at regular intervals (three times weekly). Store food in rodent-proof rooms or containers to avoid contamination by wild rodents, etc.

[3] Pertinent instruction taken from Cancer Chemotherapy Reports No. 1, January, 1959, U.S. Department of Health, Education, and Welfare, Public Health Service, pp. 67–69.

Wherever possible, limit supply of food so that it will not be held longer than one month prior to use.

A sudden and marked change in ration can influence the animal's well-being. To avoid this undesirable effect, it is wise to provide the same ration as used by the animal supplier.

B. Assay Procedures

1. Vehicles for Administration

Use sesame oil as vehicle for administering estrogens and materials tested as estrogens. Administer all other compounds and test materials in Suspending Vehicle Special Formula No. 17874 (SV No. 17874), which consists of an aqueous solution of sodium chloride (0.9%), polysorbate 80 (0.4%), carboxymethylcellulose (0.5%), and benzyl alcohol (0.9%).

2. Preparation of Materials in Aqueous Suspension

a. Material and equipment. Tenbroeck Grinders for dispersing compounds into a suspension or equivalent. Manufacturer: Macalaster-Bicknell, Boston, Massachusetts, No. 2991, 7, 15 and 40 ml.

b. Procedure. Weigh compounds and transfer to a grinder of suitable size depending on the total volume to be used. Add to the Tenbroeck grinder a suitable amount of the total final volume of suspending vehicle, usually about 10%, and reduce the material to a fine suspension by grinding for 2 minutes. Dilute the resulting suspension with an additional 50% of the total final volume of fluid and transfer to a bottle or flask using a pipet. Wash the grinder with the remaining fluid and transfer the fluid with a pipet.

3. Preparation of Animals

Before randomization, complete animal preparation which is common to all treatment groups in a given assay, i.e., castration, adrenalectomy, priming, conditioning, joining of parabionts.

4. Multiple Assays

When several assays, preliminary or quantitative, are performed simultaneously, modify the number of sets of controls as follows: For 1- or 2-test materials, use one set of controls as indicated in the specifications for each particular assay; for 3- to 6-test materials, use the equivalent of two sets of controls. However, this procedure does not apply to assays with a cross-over design.

5. Randomization

Use as an example Assay J in Section II, which requires 116 adrenalectomized rats: 20 rats for solvent controls; 12 rats at each of two levels of standard; 6 rats at each of two levels of unknown for each of the 6 unknown compounds. These 116 rats are to be distributed among 15 treatment groups.

a. Mark 116 white index cards so that each represents a rat in a control group, some level of standard, or an unknown compound. Also mark 15 colored index cards so that each represents a treatment group. No prearranged order is necessary.

b. Using a table of random numbers, list a random, four-digit number on each card. Arrange the 116 white cards in numerical order. Arrange separately the 15 colored cards in numerical order. Resolve any ties that occur by tossing a coin.

c. As the rats (preliminary preparation already accomplished consists of adrenalectomy and insertion of cotton pellets) are picked out of their holding cages, assign them to the treatment listed on the card, i.e., first rat goes to treatment on first card, etc.

d. The order of the colored index cards corresponds to the order in which the groups are to be treated each day and autopsied on the final day, i.e., the first treatment given on each of the 2 injection days is that shown on the first colored card. This will also be the first group autopsied the day after the last injection.

II. Specific Instructions for Hormone Assay Procedures[4]

A. Androgenic and Myogenic Activity
(Subcutaneous Injection)

Purpose: To compare the androgenic effect of subcutaneously administered test material with that of a reference compound on secondary sex structures and on muscle.

Test animal: Rat, single strain, male, 21-day-old, 40–55 gm.

Standard: Testosterone.

Vehicle: SV No. 17874, 0.5 ml. per injection.

Procedure: Castrate animals on 21st–24th day of life. Randomize animals. Beginning on same day, administer treatment once daily for 10 consecutive days and autopsy on 11th day.

[4] Procedures taken (with minor modifications) from Cancer Chemotherapy Reports No. 1, 1959, U.S. Department of Health, Education, and Welfare, Public Health Service, pp. 72–85.

End points: (1) Initial and (2) final body weights to nearest gram; (3) ventral prostate, (4) seminal vesicle (without coagulating gland and devoid of fluid), and (5) levator ani muscle weights to nearest 0.5 mg.

Experimental design:

PRELIMINARY

Material administered	Total dose (mg.) SV No. 17874 (S.C.)		No. of animals
	Standard	Unknown	
Vehicle	—	—	10
Standard	0.6	—	5
Standard	2.4	—	5
Unknown	—	0.6	5
Unknown	—	12.0	5
Total needed	15.0+	63.0+	30

QUANTITATIVE

Material administered	Total dose (mg.) SV. No. 17874 (S.C.)		No. of animals
	Standard	Unknown	
Vehicle	—	—	12
Standard	0.3	—	12
Standard	0.6	—	12
Standard	1.2	—	12
Standard	2.4	—	12
Unknown	—	x	12
Unknown	—	2x	12
Unknown	—	4x	12
Unknown	—	8x	12
Total needed	54.0+	180x+	108

B. ANDROGENIC AND MYOGENIC ACTIVITY (GAVAGE)

Purpose: To compare the androgenic effect of orally administered test material with that of a reference compound on secondary sex structures and on muscle.

Test animal: Rat, single strain, male, 21-day-old, 40–55 gm.

Standard: Halotestin (9α-fluoro-11β-hydroxy-17-methyltestosterone).

Vehicle: SV No. 17874, 0.5 ml. per gavage dose.

Procedure: Castrate animals on 21st–24th day of life. Randomize animals. Beginning on same day, administer treatment once daily for 10 consecutive days and autopsy on 11th day.

End points: (1) Initial and (2) final body weights to nearest gram; (3) ventral prostate, (4) seminal vesicle (without coagulating gland and devoid of fluid), and (5) levator ani muscle weights to nearest 0.5 mg.

Experimental design:

PRELIMINARY

Material administered	Total dose (mg.) SV No. 17874 (oral)		No. of animals
	Standard	Unknown	
Vehicle	—	—	10
Standard	0.6	—	5
Standard	9.6	—	5
Unknown	—	0.6	5
Unknown	—	12.0	5
Total needed	51.0+	63.0+	30

QUANTITATIVE

Material administered	Total dose (mg.) SV No. 17874 (oral)		No. of animals
	Standard	Unknown	
Vehicle	—	—	12
Standard	0.15	—	12
Standard	0.6	—	12
Standard	2.4	—	12
Standard	9.6	—	12
Unknown	—	x	12
Unknown	—	4x	12
Unknown	—	16x	12
Unknown	—	64x	12
Total needed	216.0+	1020x+	108

C. Uterotrophic Activity (Subcutaneous Injection)

Purpose: To compare the estrogenic effect of subcutaneously administered test material with that of a reference compound on secondary sex structures.

Test animal: Mouse, single strain, female, 20- to 23-day-old.

Standard: Estrone.

Vehicle: Sesame oil, 0.1 ml. per injection.

Procedure: Randomize animals. Administer treatment once daily for 3 consecutive days and autopsy on 4th day.

End points: (1) Initial and (2) final body weights to nearest gram; (3) uterus weight to nearest 0.5 mg.

Experimental design:

PRELIMINARY

| | Total dose (μg.) | | |
| | Sesame oil (S.C.) | | |
Material administered	Standard	Unknown	No. of animals
Vehicle	—	—	10
Standard	0.08	—	5
Standard	0.32	—	5
Unknown	—	0.08	5
Unknown	—	1.60	5
Total needed	2.00+	8.40+	30

QUANTITATIVE

| | Total dose (μg.) | | |
| | Sesame oil (S.C.) | | |
Material administered	Standard	Unknown	No. of animals
Vehicle	—	—	12
Standard	0.04	—	12
Standard	0.08	—	12
Standard	0.16	—	12
Standard	0.32	—	12
Unknown	—	x	12
Unknown	—	2x	12
Unknown	—	4x	12
Unknown	—	8x	12
Total needed	7.20+	180x+	108

End points: (1) Initial and (2) final body weights to nearest gram; (3) uterus weight to nearest 0.5 mg.

Experimental design:

Material administered	Total dose (µg.)		No. of animals
	Sesame oil (S.C.) standard	SV No. 17874 (oral) unknown	
Vehicle	a	a	10
Standard	0.32	a	8
Standard + unknown	0.32	50	8
Standard + unknown	0.32	1000	8
Standard + unknown	0.32	10,000	8
Unknown	a	10,000	8
Total needed	10.24+	168,400+	50

a Vehicle only.

G. PROGESTATIONAL ACTIVITY (CLAUBERG) (SUBCUTANEOUS INJECTION)

Purpose: To compare the effect of subcutaneously administered test material with that of the reference progestin on the histologic characteristics of endometrium.

Test animal: Rabbit, single strain, female, immature, 800–1000 gm.

Standard: Progesterone.

Vehicle: SV No. 17874, 0.5 ml. per injection.

Primer: Estradiol-17β, benzoate.

Procedure: Prime animals (including the vehicle controls) with 5 µg. Estradiol-17β, benzoate for 6 consecutive days. Beginning on 7th day administer treatment (standard and test material) once daily for 5 consecutive days and autopsy on 12th day. Fix midsection of each uterine horn in Bouin's fluid, section, and stain with hematoxylin and eosin.

End points: (1) Initial and (2) final body weights to nearest gram; weights of (3) uterus and (4) both ovaries (total) to nearest 0.5 mg.; and (5) degree of progestational reaction in endometrium, evaluated from 0 to +4 to nearest 0.5.

Experimental design:

PRELIMINARY

Material administered	Total dose (mg.)		No. of animals
	SV No. 17874 (S.C.)		
	Standard	Unknown	
Vehicle	—	—	2
Standard	.0.2	—	3
Standard	0.8	—	3
Unknown	—	0.2	3
Unknown	—	4.0	3
Total needed	3.0+	12.6+	14

QUANTITATIVE

Material administered	Total dose (mg.)		No. of animals
	SV No. 17874 (S.C.)		
	Standard	Unknown	
Vehicle	—	—	5
Standard	0.2	—	5
Standard	0.4	—	5
Standard	0.8	—	5
Standard	1.6	—	5
Unknown	—	x	5
Unknown	—	2x	5
Unknown	—	4x	5
Unknown	—	8x	5
Total needed	15.0+	75x+	45

H. CORTICOID ACTIVITY (GLYCOGEN DEPOSITION) (SUBCUTANEOUS INJECTION)

Purpose: To compare the effect of subcutaneously administered test material with that of a reference corticoid on glycogen deposition in the liver.

Test animal: Rat, single strain, male, 140–160 gm.

Standard: Cortisol.

Vehicle: SV No. 17874, 0.5 ml. per injection.

Procedure: Adrenalectomize, randomize, and maintain animals on a stock diet of 1% sodium chloride drink through the afternoon of the 4th postoperative day. At this time, withdraw food but leave drink in cages until assay is performed. On morning of 5th postoperative day, administer treatment. Seven hours later anesthetize animals by intraperitoneal injection of an appropriate barbiturate. Remove livers from living animals, weigh and drop into hot 30% KOH as rapidly as possible; heat until all particulate material has disappeared from digest. Determine glycogen content by a suitable anthrone procedure and express results as per cent glycogen in liver.

End points: (1) Liver weight to nearest 0.01 gm. and (2) per cent glycogen to nearest 0.01%.

Experimental design:

PRELIMINARY

| | Total dose (mg.) | | |
| | SV No. 17874 (S.C.) | | |
Material administered	Standard	Unknown	No. of animals
Vehicle	—	—	5
Standard	0.4	—	5
Standard	0.8	—	5
Standard	1.6	—	5
Unknown	—	0.8	5
Unknown	—	4.0	5
Unknown	—	16.0	5
Total needed	14.0+	104.0+	35

QUANTITATIVE

| | Total dose (mg.) | | |
| | SV No. 17874 (S.C.) | | |
Material administered	Standard	Unknown	No. of animals
Vehicle	—	—	10
Standard	0.4	—	8
Standard	0.8	—	8
Standard	1.6	—	8
Standard	3.2	—	8
Unknown	—	x	8
Unknown	—	2x	8
Unknown	—	4x	8
Unknown	—	8x	8
Total needed	36.0+	120x+	74

I. Corticoid Activity (Glycogen Deposition) (Gavage)

Purpose: To compare the effect of orally administered test material with that of a reference corticoid on glycogen deposition in the liver.

Test animal: Rat, single strain, male, 140–160 gm.

Standard: Cortisol.

Vehicle: SV No. 17874, 0.5 ml. per gavage dose.

Procedure: Adrenalectomize, randomize, and maintain animals on a stock diet of 1% sodium chloride drink through afternoon of the 4th postoperative days. At this time, withdraw food but leave drink in cages until the assay is performed. On morning of 5th postoperative day, administer treatment. Seven hours later anesthetize animals by intraperitoneal injection of an appropriate barbiturate. Remove livers from living animals, weigh and drop into hot 30% KOH as rapidly as possible; heat until all particulate material has disappeared from digest. Determine glycogen content by a suitable anthrone procedure and express results as per cent glycogen in liver.

End points: (1) Liver weight to nearest 0.01 gm. and (2) per cent glycogen to nearest 0.01%.

Experimental design:

PRELIMINARY

Material administered	Total dose (mg.)		No. of animals
	SV No. 17874 (oral)		
	Standard	Unknown	
Vehicle	—	—	5
Standard	0.8	—	5
Standard	3.2	—	5
Standard	12.8	—	5
Unknown	—	1.6	5
Unknown	—	8.0	5
Unknown	—	32.0	5
Total needed	84.0+	208.0+	35

QUANTITATIVE

| Material administered | Total dose (mg.) | | No. of animals |
| | SV No. 17874 (oral) | | |
	Standard	Unknown	
Vehicle	—	—	10
Standard	0.2	—	8
Standard	0.8	—	8
Standard	3.2	—	8
Standard	12.8	—	8
Unknown	—	x	8
Unknown	—	4x	8
Unknown	—	16x	8
Unknown	—	64x	8
Total needed	136.0+	680x	74

J. THYMOLYTIC AND ANTI-INFLAMMATORY ACTIVITY (SUBCUTANEOUS INJECTION)

Purpose: To compare the effect of subcutaneously administered test material with that of a reference corticoid on the thymus; and to determine inhibiting effect of test material on cotton pellet-induced granuloma.

Test animal: Rat, single strain, male or female (consistent within a set of tests), 21-day-old, 40–55 gm.

Standards: Cortisol.

Vehicle: SV No. 17874, 0.1 ml. per injection.

Inflammatory agent: Unrefined cotton pellet of uniform size, 5 ± 1 mg.

Procedure: Bilaterally adrenalectomize animals on the 23rd–26th day of life and insert two cotton pellets subcutaneously. Randomize animals. Beginning on same day administer treatment at separate sites once daily for 3 consecutive days and autopsy on 4th day. Remove granulomas (cotton pellets), weigh, dry for 24 hours at 100°C., and weigh again.

End points: (1) Initial and (2) final body weights to the nearest gram; (3) weights of thymus; (4) net weight wet granulomas and (5) net weight dry granulomas to nearest 0.5 mg.

Experimental design:

PRELIMINARY

Material administered	Total dose (mg.) SV No. 17874 (S.C.)		No. of animals
	Standard	Unknown	
Vehicle	—	—	10
Standard	1.2	—	6
Standard	4.8	—	6
Unknown	—	1.2	6
Unknown	—	24.0	6
Total needed	36.0+	151.2+	34

QUANTITATIVE

Material administered	Total dose (mg.) SV No. 17874 (S.C.)		No. of animals
	Standard	Unknown	
Vehicle	—	—	15
Standard	0.6	—	15
Standard	1.2	—	15
Standard	2.4	—	15
Standard	4.8	—	15
Unknown	—	x	15
Unknown	—	2x	15
Unknown	—	4x	15
Unknown	—	8x	15
Total needed	135.0+	225x	135

K. THYMOLYTIC AND ANTI-INFLAMMATORY ACTIVITY (GAVAGE)

Purpose: To compare the effect of orally administered test material with that of the reference corticoid on the thymus; and to determine inhibiting effect of test material on cotton pellet-induced granuloma.

Test animal: Rat, single strain, male or female (consistent within a set of tests), 21-day-old, 40–55 gm.

Standard: Cortisol.

Vehicle: SV No. 17874, 0.5 ml. per gavage dose.

Inflammatory agent: Unrefined cotton pellet of uniform size, 5 ± 1 mg.

Procedure: Bilaterally adrenalectomize animals on the 23rd–26th day of life and insert two cotton pellets subcutaneously. Randomize animals. Beginning on same day, administer treatment once daily for 3 consecutive days and autopsy on 4th day. Remove granulomas (cotton pellets), weigh, dry for 24 hours at 100°C., and weigh again.

End points: (1) Initial and (2) final body weights to nearest gram; (3) weights of thymus; (4) net weight wet granulomas and (5) net weight dry granulomas to nearest 0.5 mg.

Experimental design:

PRELIMINARY

Material administered	Total dose (mg.) SV No. 17874 (oral)		No. of animals
	Standard	Unknown	
Vehicle	—	—	10
Standard	4.0	—	6
Standard	32.0	—	6
Unknown	—	4.0	6
Unknown	—	80.0	6
Total needed	216.0+	504.0+	34

QUANTITATIVE

Material administered	Total dose (mg.) SV No. 17874 (oral)		No. of animals
	Standard	Unknown	
Vehicle	—	—	15
Standard	4.0	—	15
Standard	8.0	—	15
Standard	16.0	—	15
Standard	32.0	—	15
Unknown	—	x	15
Unknown	—	2x	15
Unknown	—	4x	15
Unknown	—	8x	15
Total needed	900.0+	225×+	135

L. INHIBITION OF THYMOLYTIC ACTIVITY (SUBCUTANEOUS INJECTION)

Purpose: To measure the inhibiting effect of subcutaneously administered test material on the corticoid-induced reduction of the thymus weight.

Test animal: Rat, single strain, male or female (consistent within a set of tests), 21-day-old, 40–55 gm.

Standard: Cortisol.

Vehicle: SV No. 17874, 0.1 ml. per injection.

Procedure: Bilaterally adrenalectomize animals on 23rd–26th day of life. Randomize animals. Administer treatment at separate sites on day of operation and on succeeding day. Autopsy animals on third day.

End points: (1) Initial and (2) final body weights to nearest gram; (3) weight of thymus to nearest 0.5 mg.

Experimental design:

Material administered	Total dose (mg.)		No. of animals
	SV No. 17874 (S.C.)		
	Standard	Unknown	
Vehicle	a	a	10
Standard	4.8	a	10
Standard + unknown	4.8	0.5	10
Standard + unknown	4.8	2.0	10
Standard + unknown	4.8	10.0	10
Unknown	a	10.0	10
Total needed	192.0+	225.0+	60

a Vehicle only.

M. INHIBITION OF THYMOLYTIC ACTIVITY (GAVAGE)

Purpose: To measure the inhibiting effect of orally administered material on the corticoid-induced reduction of the thymus weight.

Test animal: Rat, single strain, male or female (consistent within a set of tests), 21-day-old, 40–55 gm.

Standard: Cortisol.

Vehicle: For standard compound, SV No. 17874, 0.1 ml. per injection. For test material, SV No. 17874, 0.5 ml. per gavage dose.

Procedure: Bilaterally adrenalectomize animals on 23rd–26th day of life. Randomize animals. Administer treatment on day of operation and on succeeding day. Autopsy animals on third day.

End points: (1) Initial and (2) final body weights to nearest gram; (3) weight of thymus to nearest 0.5 mg.

Experimental design:

Material administered	Total dose (mg.)		No. of animals
	SV No. 17874		
	Standard (S.C.)	Unknown (oral)	
Vehicle	a	a	10
Standard	4.8	a	10
Standard + unknown	4.8	0.5	10
Standard + unknown	4.8	2.0	10
Standard + unknown	4.8	10.0	10
Unknown	a	10.0	10
Total needed	192.0+	225.0+	60

a Vehicle only.

N. Inhibition of Androgenic and Myogenic Activity (Subcutaneous Injection)

Purpose: To measure the inhibiting effect of subcutaneously administered test material on androgen-stimulated secondary sex structures and muscle.

Test animal: Rat, single strain, male, 21-day-old, 40–55 gm.

Standard: Testosterone.

Vehicle: SV No. 17874, 0.5 ml. per injection.

Procedure: Castrate animals on 21st–24th day of life. Randomize animals. Beginning on same day, administer treatment at separate sites once daily for 7 consecutive days and autopsy on 8th day.

End points: (1) Initial and (2) final body weights to nearest gram; (3) ventral prostate; (4) seminal vesicle (without coagulating gland and devoid of fluid); and (5) levator ani muscle weights to nearest 0.5 mg.

Experimental design:

Material administered	Total dose (mg.)		No. of animals
	SV No. 17874 (S.C.)		
	Standard	Unknown	
Vehicle	a	a	10
Standard	2.4	a	10
Standard + unknown	2.4	0.5	10
Standard + unknown	2.4	2.0	10
Standard + unknown	2.4	10.0	10
Unknown	a	10.0	10
Total needed	96.0+	225.0+	60

a Vehicle only.

O. Inhibition of Androgenic and Myogenic Activity (Gavage)

Purpose: To measure the inhibiting effect of orally administered test material on androgen-stimulated secondary sex structures and muscle.

Test animal: Rat, single strain, male, 21-day-old, 40–55 gm.

Standard: Testosterone.

Vehicle: For standard compound, SV No. 17874, 0.5 ml. per injection. For test material, SV No. 17874, 1.0 ml. per gavage dose.

Procedure: Castrate animals on the 21st–24th day of life. Randomize animals. Beginning on same day, administer treatment once daily for 7 consecutive days and autopsy on 8th day.

End points: (1) Initial and (2) final body weights to nearest gram; (3) ventral prostate; (4) seminal vesicle (without coagulating gland and devoid of fluid); and (5) levator ani muscle weights to nearest 0.5 mg.

Experimental design:

| | Total dose (mg.) | | |
| | SV No. 17874 | | |
Material administered	Standard (S.C.)	Unknown (oral)	No. of animals
Vehicle	a	a	10
Standard	2.4	a	10
Standard + unknown	2.4	0.5	10
Standard + unknown	2.4	2.0	10
Standard + unknown	2.4	10.0	10
Unknown	a	10.0	10
Total needed	96.0+	225.0+	60

a Vehicle only.

III. Interpretation of Biological Assay Data

A. PURPOSE

The assay program is designed to screen compounds for specific effects, in order to obtain profiles of their biological properties. This testing involves obtaining potency estimates for each compound by comparing its biological effects with those of standard reference compounds, or, as in the inhibition type assays, to measure the inhibiting effect of test materials on biological reactions brought about by standard compounds or occurring spontaneously.

B. TITRATION OF STANDARD

A standard reference compound for each type of biological assay is first titrated to obtain the sensitive working range (Graph I). By using this working range, two types of assays are designed: preliminary and quantitative assays for estimating potency, and assays for measuring inhibition of effects.

C. ASSAYS FOR ESTIMATING POTENCY

1. Preliminary Assay

a. Objective. To screen test materials for estimates of a minimal relative potency of 5%, with an error usually not exceeding 50% (95% confidence limits).

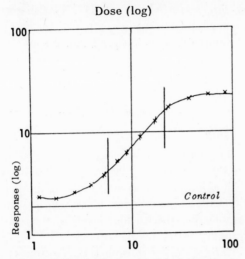

GRAPH I. Standard compound (×) titration.

b. *Design.* For standard reference compound, use two doses as far apart as possible but still within the sensitive working range. Usually give two doses of the test material. Give one dose at the same level as the low dose of the standard to detect potencies equivalent to or greater than the standard. Gear the higher dose of the test material to the lowest potency (5%) to be detected, hence 20 times the low dose of the standard.

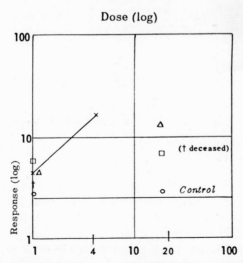

GRAPH II. Preliminary assay. KEY: × = Standard compound; O = Test material No. 1; △ = Test material No. 2; □ = Test material No. 3; † = Test material No. 4.

c. Illustrative interpretation (Graph II). Test material No. 1 shows less than 5% potency, and testing of compound for this particular activity is considered complete. Test material No. 2 shows greater than 5% potency; quantitative assay will be performed. Test material No. 3 shows greater than 5% potency but without parallelism of effect; quantitative assay will be performed. Test material No. 4 indicates probable toxicity at high dose level; preliminary assay will be repeated at new dose levels.

2. Quantitative Assay

a. Objective. To obtain more precise estimates of relative potency with an error usually not exceeding 20% (95% confidence limits) on test materials which show minimal activity in the preliminary assay.

b. Design. Typically, four doses of the standard which represent the sensitive range are compared with four levels of the test material chosen on basis of preliminary estimates of potency.

.*c. Illustrative interpretation* (Graph III). Test material No. 2: slopes

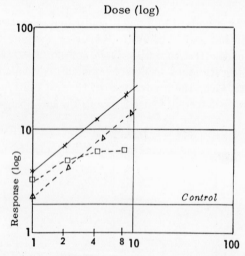

GRAPH III. Quantitative assay. KEY: $\times$ = Standard compound; $\triangle$ = Test material No. 2; $\square$ = Test material No. 3.

judged parallel indicate similar activity; test compound appears less active than preliminary assay indicated. Test material No. 3: non-parallel slopes indicate possible different activity since both materials appear to have been tested in the sensitive range.

Estimates of relative potencies will be given as per cents without reference to differences in slopes of the dose-response curves except when these differences are believed to indicate dissimilar biological activity.

An assay in which technical errors are evident is repeated unless it gives some indication of potency that could be used as an aid to getting more precise data.

In general, the assays may not yield relative potencies but rather pseudo relative potencies, since there is no guarantee that the physiological function tested is the same for the unknown as for the standard.

D. Assays for Measuring Inhibition of Effects

Although inhibition-type assays generally refer to assays in which the effect of a standard compound is inhibited, they may also be used to measure the inhibition of a spontaneous process. In neither case is there an attempt to ascertain relative potency.

Inhibition of Effects of Standard Compounds

a. Objective. To determine whether a compound can inhibit the biological effect produced by the standard compound.

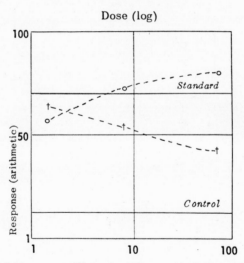

GRAPH IV. Inhibition assay. KEY: ○ = Test material No. 1; † = Test material No. 4.

b. Design. For the standard reference compound level, use a dose which produces a near maximum response in the sensitive range of the titration curve. For the test material, use three doses covering a very wide range.

c. Illustrative interpretation (Graph IV). Test material No. 1 produces 25% reduction in effect at low dose, no reduction at middle dose, and no reduction at high dose. Test material No. 4 produces 10% reduction at low dose, 25% reduction at middle dose, and 45% reduction at high dose.

AUTHOR INDEX

Numbers in italic show the page on which the complete reference is listed.

K

L

SUBJECT INDEX

A